CONTENTS

Student's Solutions Manual
for Atkins and Jones's
CHEMISTRY
Molecules, Matter, and Change

THIRD EDITION

Charles Trapp
University of Louisville
Louisville, Kentucky

W. H. FREEMAN AND COMPANY
New York

PREFACE

This manual contains solutions and answers to the odd-numbered exercises in Atkins and Jones's *Chemistry: Molecules, Matter, and Change,* Third Edition. The rules of significant figures have been rigorously adhered to in reporting the final numerical answers to the exercises, except in a small number of cases, where an extra digit has been included. This has been indicated by overlining that digit. For example, if an integral answer is called for, the numerical value would be given as say, $\overline{13}$, rather than 1×10, even though only one significant figure is warranted. In order to prevent a round-off error in the final result by someone retracing a part of the solution to an exercise, the results of intermediate calculations are often reported with more than the minimum number of significant figures—also indicated by an overline.

Procedures and results that have been fully illustrated in the solutions to the exercises of an earlier chapter may not be repeated in the solutions to the exercises of the current chapter. For example, the conversion between °C and K, or the determination of the molar mass from the formula of a compound, is not usually worked out in the solutions to exercises in later chapters.

Some abbreviations have been used to save space. These are usually defined at the start of a solution. Some that occur frequently are:

FU = formula unit
cmpd = compound referred to in the exercise
n = neutron
p = proton
e = electron

I wish to thank Peter Atkins and Loretta Jones for their support and help during the production of this manual. They, along with John Krenos and Julie Henderleiter, have carefully reviewed the solutions and have made many valuable suggestions. The staff at W. H. Freeman and Company, especially Matthew Fitzpatrick and Erica Seifert, have been patient and cooperative. I thank them all.

C. T.

CHAPTER 1
MATTER

The elements are listed in the periodic table inside the front cover and in alphabetical order inside the back cover of the main text.

EXERCISES

The Nuclear Atom and Isotopes

1.1 (a) Cathode rays are electrons; thus their charge and mass are the same as those of the electron. See Table 1.1.

$$\text{charge} = -1.602 \times 10^{-19} \text{ coulomb} = -1e$$
$$\text{mass} = 9.109 \times 10^{-28} \text{ g}$$

(b) Robert Millikan

1.3 A law summarizes observations, a theory attempts to explain the observations.

1.5 (a) As, 33 (b) S, 16 (c) Pd, 46 (d) Au, 79

1.7 See Example 1.1 for the solution strategy. In each case, the atomic number, Z, is the number of protons and electrons. Subtract the atomic number, Z, from the mass number, A, to obtain the number of neutrons, $A - Z$.

(a) 6p, 7n, 6e⁻ (b) 17p, 20n, 17e⁻ (c) 17p, 18n, 17e⁻ (d) 92p, 143n, 92e⁻

1.9 In each case, the number of protons is the atomic number and identifies the element; the sum of the number of protons and neutrons gives the mass number and identifies the isotope.

(a) $48 + 63 = 111$, hence ^{111}Cd
(b) $36 + 46 = 82$, hence ^{82}Kr
(c) $5 + 6 = 11$, hence ^{11}B

1.11 (a) Each isotope has the same number of protons and electrons, so they are chemically almost identical.
(b) Their atomic masses are all different, so the properties of these atoms that depend on mass will be different.

The Periodic Table

1.13 (a) lithium, 1 or I, metal   (b) gallium, 13 or III, metal
(c) xenon, 18 or VIII, nonmetal   (d) potassium, 1 or I, metal

1.15 (a) Cl, nonmetal   (b) Co, metal   (c) As, metalloid

1.17 tin, Sn; lead, Pb

1.19 (a) I, nonmetal   (b) Cr, metal   (c) Hg, metal   (d) Al, metal

1.21 lithium, Li, 3; sodium, Na, 11; potassium, K, 19; rubidium, Rb, 37; cesium, Cs, 55; francium, Fr, 87 (radioactive)
All react with water as follows: (M = alkali metal)

$$2M(s) + 2H_2O(l) \longrightarrow 2MOH(aq) + H_2(g).$$

Compounds

1.23 (a) An atom of an element is the smallest unit of an element that has the chemical properties of that element.
(b) A molecule is the smallest unit of elements united in chemical combination that retains the chemical properties of that combination. It is a definite and distinct electrically neutral group of bonded atoms.

1.25 Metals form cations. Main-group metals, which are elements in Groups 1, 2, and 13, form ions with a positive charge equal to their group number. Transition group metals form cations with a variety of positive charges; these must be learned (see Table 1.4). Nonmetals typically form anions; their charge can usually be determined as (18 − group number). See Example 1.2.
(a) anion, S^{2-} (b) cation, K^+ (c) cation, Sr^{2+} (d) anion, Cl^-

1.27 In each case, the number of protons is the atomic number of the element, the number of neutrons is the mass number minus the atomic number, and the number of electrons is the atomic number minus the charge (including sign) on the ion.
(a) 1p, $(2 - 1)n = 1n$, $(1 - 1)e^- = 0e^-$
(b) 4p, $(9 - 4)n = 5n$, $(4 - 2)e^- = 2e^-$
(c) 35p, $(80 - 35)n = 45n$, $[35 - (-1)]e^- = 36e^-$
(d) 16p, $(32 - 16)n = 16n$, $[16 - (-2)]e^- = 18e^-$

1.29 In each case, the symbol of the isotopic ion consists of the symbol for the element, determined by the number of protons; the mass number, which is the sum of the number of protons and neutrons; and the charge, which is the number of protons minus the number of electrons.

(a) $^{19}F^-$ (b) $^{24}Mg^{2+}$ (c) $^{128}Te^{2-}$ (d) $^{86}Rb^+$

Substances and Mixtures

1.31 In (a) and (b), only one kind of atom is present, although (b) is molecular, Cl_2. In (c), the two ions present are formed from two different atoms, Na and Cl. Hence,
(a) element (b) element (c) compound.

1.33 (a) mixture (b) element

1.35 Compounds always contain more than one element, and the majority of mixtures also do. But a compound has a fixed composition, whereas a mixture may have any composition. For example, a mixture of hydrogen and oxygen gases may contain any arbitrary ratio of hydrogen and oxygen atoms, but the compound water, formed from these two elements, always has a fixed ratio of two atoms of hydrogen for each atom of oxygen.

1.37 (a) physical (b) physical (c) chemical

1.39 (a) physical (b) physical (c) chemical (corrosion is a chemical reaction.)

1.41 (a) physical (b) physical (c) chemical (corrosion is a chemical reaction.)
(d) physical

1.43 temperature, evaporation, humidity

1.45 (a) filtration, solubility differences
(b) chromatography, differences in adsorption
(c) distillation, boiling-point differences

1.47 (a) homogeneous, distillation
(b) heterogeneous, filtration. The salt component dissolves in water; the chalk can then be filtered.
(c) homogeneous, evaporation or recrystallization

Chemical Nomenclature

1.49 (a) chloride ion (b) oxide ion (c) carbide ion (d) phosphide ion

1.51 (a) phosphate ion (b) sulfate ion (c) nitride ion (d) sulfite ion
(e) phosphite ion (f) iodide ion

1.53 See Table 1.5. (a) ClO_3^- (b) NO_3^- (c) CO_3^{2-} (d) ClO^- (e) HSO_4^-

1.55 See Table 1.4.
   (a) plumbous ion, lead(II) ion   (b) ferrous ion, iron(II) ion
   (c) cobaltic ion, cobalt(III) ion   (d) cuprous ion, copper(I) ion

1.57 (a) Cu^{2+} (b) ClO_2^- (c) P^{3-} (d) H^-

1.59 In each case, follow the strategy of Example 1.6a. First determine the charges on the positive and negative ions. Then find simple whole numbers (integers) that, after multiplying the charges on the ions, yields a net charge of 0. These simple whole numbers are the subscripts in the formula of the compound.
(a) MgO (b) $Ca_3(PO_4)_2$ (c) $Al_2(SO_4)_3$ (d) Ca_3N_2

1.61 In each case, follow the strategy of Example 1.4.
   (a) potassium phosphate
   (b) ferrous iodide or iron(II) iodide
   (c) niobium(V) oxide
   (d) cupric sulfate or copper(II) sulfate

1.63 In each case, follow the strategy of Example 1.4.
   (a) copper(II) nitrate hexahydrate
   (b) neodymium(III) chloride hexahydrate
   (c) nickel(II) fluoride tetrahydrate

1.65 In each case, follow the strategy of Example 1.6a.
(a) $Na_2CO_3 \cdot H_2O$ (b) $In(NO_3)_3 \cdot 5H_2O$ (c) $Cu(ClO_4)_2 \cdot 6H_2O$

1.67 In each case, follow the strategy of Example 1.6b.
(a) SeO_3 (b) CCl_4 (c) CS_2 (d) SF_6 (e) As_2S_3 (f) PCl_5 (g) N_2O (h) ClF_3

1.69 In each case, follow the strategy of Example 1.5.
(a) sulfur tetrafluoride   (b) dinitrogen pentoxide   (c) nitrogen triiodide
(d) xenon tetrafluoride   (e) arsenic tribromide   (f) chlorine dioxide
(g) diphosphorous pentoxide

1.71 See Table 1.5.
(a) hydrochloric acid   (b) sulfuric acid   (c) nitric acid
(d) acetic acid   (e) sulfurous acid   (f) phosphoric acid

1.73 In each case, follow the strategy of Example 1.6a and of the solution to Exercise 1.59.
(a) Na_2O (b) K_2SO_4 (c) AgF (d) $Zn(NO_3)_2$ (e) Al_2S_3

SUPPLEMENTARY EXERCISES

1.75 Chlorine exists in the form of two isotopes, ^{35}Cl and ^{37}Cl. Both of these isotopes have an atomic number of 17, but the mass numbers are 35 and 37, respectively.

1.77 (a) element   (b) homogeneous mixture   (c) compound   (d) element
(e) homogeneous mixture   (f) compound   (g) element   (h) heterogeneous mixture

1.79 (a) physical (evaporation)
(b) chemical (bonds have been broken and reformed)
(c) chemical (bonds have been broken and reformed)

1.81 Group 2 or II: Be, 4; Mg, 12; Ca, 20; Sr, 38; Ba, 56; Ra, 88

1.83 Follow the strategies of Examples 1.4 and 1.5.
(a) iron(III) chloride hexahydrate or ferric chloride hexahydrate
(b) cobalt(II) nitrate hexahydrate or cobaltous nitrate hexahydrate
(c) copper(I) chloride or cuprous chloride
(d) bromine chloride
(e) manganese(IV) oxide
(f) mercury(II) nitrate or mercuric nitrate
(g) nickel(II) nitrate
(h) dinitrogen tetraoxide
(i) vanadium(V) oxide

1.85 Follow the strategy of Example 1.6. Also use Table 1.5.

(a) $AlPO_4$ (b) $Ba(NO_3)_2 \cdot 2H_2O$ (c) SiS_2 (d) Na_3P (e) $HClO_4(aq)$ (f) CuO
(g) $HI(aq)$ (h) Ag_2SO_4

CHALLENGING EXERCISES

1.87 (a) Assume the oxygen in H_2O is ^{16}O, and that the hydrogen is ^{1}H; then

$$\text{number of protons} = \left(2H \text{ atoms} \times \frac{1p}{1H \text{ atom}} + 1O \text{ atom} \times \frac{8p}{1O \text{ atom}}\right) = 10p$$

$$\text{number of neutrons} = 1O \text{ atom} \times \frac{8n}{1O \text{ atom}} = 8n$$

$$\text{number of electrons} = \text{number of protons} = 10e^-$$

(b) $\text{mass of protons} = 10p \times \dfrac{1.673 \times 10^{-24} \text{ g}}{1p} = 1.673 \times 10^{-23} \text{ g}$

$\text{mass of neutrons} = 8n \times \dfrac{1.675 \times 10^{-24} \text{ g}}{1n} = 1.340 \times 10^{-23} \text{ g}$

$\text{mass of electrons} = 10e^- \times \dfrac{9.109 \times 10^{-28} \text{ g}}{1e^-} = 9.109 \times 10^{-27} \text{ g}$

$\text{sum} = (1.673 \times 10^{-23} + 1.340 \times 10^{-23} + 9.109 \times 10^{-27})g = 3.013\overline{9} \times 10^{-23} \text{ g}$

(c) $\text{fraction of mass due to neutrons} = \dfrac{\text{mass of neutrons in water}}{\text{total mass of water}}$

$$= \frac{1.340 \times 10^{-23} \text{ g}}{3.013\overline{9} \times 10^{-23} \text{ g}} = 0.4446$$

Or 44.46% of your body mass is due to neutrons.

Note: This calculation assumes that the protons, neutrons, and electrons in H_2O have the same masses as the free particles, as given in Table 1.1.

1.89 (a) compare to H_2SO_4, thus telluric acid (if aqueous)
(b) compare to Na_3PO_4, thus sodium arsenate
(c) compare to $CaSO_3$, thus calcium selenite
(d) compare to $Ba_3(PO_4)_2$, thus barium antimonate
(e) compare to H_3PO_4, thus arsenic acid (if aqueous)
(f) compare to $CO_2(SO_4)_3$, thus cobalt(III) tellurate

1.91 Initial observational data might include the frequency and severity of the headaches, and environmental conditions (food eaten, noise level, odors). Three hypotheses are (1) the food is the cause of the headaches, (2) the room is the cause of the headaches, (3) the homework is the cause of the headaches.

Three experiments are (1) eliminate the food (requires more than one experiment of this type if only one menu item were eliminated each time); (2) eliminate the room (do homework in another room); (3) eliminate the homework.

Other experimental variations are possible, for example, two of the three possible causes could be eliminated at a time, then if the headaches persist the remaining possible cause must be the culprit. This method would also require three experiments. No matter which approach is used, the data to be collected are (1) food eaten, (2) room used, (3) homework begun (yes or no), (4) headache (yes or no).

CHAPTER 2
MEASUREMENTS AND MOLES

EXERCISES

International System (SI) of Units

2.1 (a) This case is somewhat ambiguous. The zeros to the right of the 7 may or may not be significant. On the assumption that they are not, the answer is 2.0337×10^{14}

(b) $1.169\,811 \times 10^{6}$

(c) 6×10^{-6} g

(d) 1×10^{-7} m

2.3 (a) 4.3×10^{-1} (b) 1.492×10^{1} (c) 5.1×10^{-9} (d) 2.37×10^{14}

2.5 (a) $250 \text{ g} \times \left(\dfrac{1 \text{ kg}}{10^{3} \text{ g}} \right) = 0.250 \text{ kg}$

(b) $25.4 \text{ mm} \times \left(\dfrac{10^{-3} \text{ m}}{1 \text{ mm}} \right) \times \left(\dfrac{1 \text{ cm}}{10^{-2} \text{ m}} \right) = 2.54 \text{ cm}$

(c) $250 \text{ }\mu\text{s} \times \left(\dfrac{10^{-6} \text{ s}}{1 \text{ }\mu\text{s}} \right) \times \left(\dfrac{1 \text{ ms}}{10^{-3} \text{ s}} \right) = 0.250 \text{ ms}$

(d) $1.49 \text{ cm} \times \left(\dfrac{10^{-2} \text{ m}}{1 \text{ cm}} \right) \times \left(\dfrac{1 \text{ dm}}{10^{-1} \text{ m}} \right) = 0.149 \text{ dm}$

(e) $2.48 \text{ cg} \times \left(\dfrac{10^{-2} \text{ g}}{1 \text{ cg}} \right) = 2.48 \times 10^{-2} \text{ g}$

(f) $28.35 \text{ g} \times \left(\dfrac{1 \text{ kg}}{10^{3} \text{ g}} \right) = 2.835 \times 10^{-2} \text{ kg}$

2.7 (a) $1 \text{ }\mu\text{m} \times \left(\dfrac{10^{-6} \text{ m}}{1 \text{ }\mu\text{m}} \right) = 1 \times 10^{-6} \text{ m}$

(b) $550 \text{ nm} \times \left(\dfrac{10^{-9} \text{ m}}{1 \text{ nm}} \right) \times \left(\dfrac{1 \text{ mm}}{10^{-3} \text{ m}} \right) = 5.50 \times 10^{-4} \text{ mm}$

(c) $0.10 \text{ g} \times \left(\dfrac{1 \text{ mg}}{10^{-3} \text{ g}} \right) = 1.0 \times 10^{2} \text{ mg}$

(d) $105 \text{ pm} \times \left(\dfrac{10^{-12} \text{ m}}{1 \text{ pm}} \right) \times \left(\dfrac{1 \text{ }\mu\text{m}}{10^{-6} \text{ m}} \right) = 1.05 \times 10^{-4} \text{ }\mu\text{m}$

2.9 $\text{density} = \dfrac{\text{mass}}{\text{volume}}$

volume = volume displaced = 9.8 mL − 8.3 mL = 1.5 mL = 1.5 cm³

$\text{density} = \dfrac{3.60 \text{ g}}{1.5 \text{ cm}^3} = 2.4 \text{ g} \cdot \text{cm}^{-3}$

2.11 $\text{mass (g)} = 1 \text{ ft}^3 \times \left(\dfrac{12 \text{ in.}}{1 \text{ ft}}\right)^3 \times \left(\dfrac{2.54 \text{ cm}}{1 \text{ in.}}\right)^3 \times 0.16 \text{ g} \cdot \text{cm}^{-3} = 4.5 \times 10^3 \text{ g}$

2.13   Because density = mass/volume, volume = mass/density; hence volume = 0.300 carat × (200 mg/carat) × (10^{-3} g/1 mg) × (1 cm³/3.51 g) = 1.71×10^{-2} cm³

Conversion Factors

2.15   When units are expressed with negative exponents it is usually easier to begin the conversion by first expressing these units in the equivalent fractional form. Thus, for example, in (b) express 25 g · L^{-1} as 25 g/L.

(a) $25 \text{ L} \times \left(\dfrac{1 \text{ cm}^3}{10^{-3} \text{ L}}\right) \times \left(\dfrac{10^{-2} \text{ m}}{1 \text{ cm}}\right)^3 = 2.5 \times 10^{-2} \text{ m}^3$

(b) $\dfrac{25 \text{ g}}{1 \text{ L}} \times \left(\dfrac{1 \text{ mg}}{10^{-3} \text{ g}}\right) \times \left(\dfrac{10^{-1} \text{ L}}{1 \text{ dL}}\right) = 2.5 \times 10^3 \text{ mg} \cdot \text{dL}^{-1}$

(c) $\dfrac{1.54 \text{ mm}}{1 \text{ s}} \times \left(\dfrac{10^{-3} \text{ m}}{1 \text{ mm}}\right) \times \left(\dfrac{1 \text{ pm}}{10^{-12} \text{ m}}\right) \times \left(\dfrac{10^{-6} \text{ s}}{1 \text{ } \mu\text{s}}\right) = 1.54 \times 10^3 \text{ pm} \cdot \mu\text{s}^{-1}$

(d) $\dfrac{2.66 \text{ g}}{1 \text{ cm}^3} \times \left(\dfrac{1 \text{ } \mu\text{g}}{10^{-6} \text{ g}}\right) \times \left(\dfrac{1 \text{ cm}}{10^{-2} \text{ m}}\right)^3 \times \left(\dfrac{10^{-6} \text{ m}}{1 \text{ } \mu\text{m}}\right)^3 = 2.66 \times 10^{-6} \text{ } \mu\text{g} \cdot \mu\text{m}^{-3}$

(e) $\dfrac{4.2 \text{ L}}{\text{h}^2} \times \left(\dfrac{1 \text{ mL}}{10^{-3} \text{ L}}\right) \times \left(\dfrac{1 \text{ h}}{3600 \text{ s}}\right)^2 = 3.2 \times 10^{-4} \text{ mL} \cdot \text{s}^{-2}$

2.17   (a) $\frac{4}{5} \text{ qt} \times \left(\dfrac{0.946 \text{ L}}{1 \text{ qt}}\right) \times \left(\dfrac{1 \text{ mL}}{10^{-3} \text{ L}}\right) = 757 \text{ mL}$

(b) $450 \dfrac{\text{lb}}{\text{ft}^3} \times \left(\dfrac{454 \text{ g}}{1 \text{ lb}}\right) \times \left(\dfrac{1 \text{ kg}}{10^3 \text{ g}}\right) \times \left(\dfrac{1 \text{ ft}}{12 \text{ in}}\right)^3 \times \left(\dfrac{1 \text{ in}}{2.54 \text{ cm}}\right)^3 \times \left(\dfrac{1 \text{ cm}}{10^{-2} \text{ m}}\right)^3$
$= 7.21 \times 10^3 \text{ kg} \cdot \text{m}^{-3}$

(c) $\$1.20/\text{gallon} \times \left(\dfrac{780 \text{ peso}}{1 \text{ \$}}\right) \times \left(\dfrac{1 \text{ gallon}}{3.785 \text{ L}}\right) = 2.47 \times 10^2 \text{ peso} \cdot \text{L}^{-1}$

(d) $1.0 \dfrac{\text{g}}{\text{mL}} \times \left(\dfrac{1 \text{ lb}}{454 \text{ g}}\right) \times \left(\dfrac{1 \text{ mL}}{1 \text{ cm}^3}\right) \times \left(\dfrac{2.54 \text{ cm}}{1 \text{ in}}\right)^3 \times \left(\dfrac{12 \text{ in}}{1 \text{ ft}}\right)^3 = 62 \text{ lb} \cdot \text{ft}^{-3}$

2.19 These conversions make use of Eq. 1 on p. 46 or its inverse shown in Example 2.1.

(a) Celsius temp. $= \left[\dfrac{(\text{Fahr. temp.}/°\text{F}) - 32}{1.8}\right]°\text{C} = \left[\dfrac{98.6 - 32}{1.8}\right]°\text{C} = 37.0°\text{C}$

(b) Fahr. temp. $= \left(1.8 \times \dfrac{\text{Celsius temp.}}{°\text{C}} + 32\right)°\text{F}$

$= (1.8 \times -40 + 32)°\text{F} = -40°\text{F}$

(c) Celsius temp. $= \left(\dfrac{\text{Kelvin temp.}}{\text{K}} - 273.15\right)°\text{C}$

$= (0 - 273.15)°\text{C} = -273.15°\text{C}$

Fahr. temp. $= (1.8 \times -273.15 + 32)°\text{F} = -459.67°\text{F}$

(d) Kelvin temp. $= \left(\dfrac{\text{Celsius temp.}}{°\text{C}} + 273.15\right)\text{K}$

$= (-269 + 273.15)\text{K} = 4.15\text{ K} = 4\text{ K (2 sf)}$

2.21 (a) $1\text{ cm}^3 \times \left(\dfrac{10^{-2}\text{ m}}{1\text{ cm}}\right)^3 = 1 \times 10^{-6}\text{ m}^3$

(b) $30\text{ m}\cdot\text{s}^{-1} \times \left(\dfrac{1\text{ cm}}{10^{-2}\text{ m}}\right) \times \left(\dfrac{10^{-6}\text{ s}}{1\text{ }\mu\text{s}}\right) = 3.0 \times 10^{-3}\text{ cm}\cdot\mu\text{s}^{-1}$

$= 3.0 \times 10^{-3}\text{ cm}\cdot\mu\text{s}^{-1}$

(c) $22\text{ m}^2 \times \left(\dfrac{1\text{ cm}}{10^{-2}\text{ m}}\right)^2 = 2.2 \times 10^5\text{ cm}^2$

(d) $25\text{ cm}^3 \times \left(\dfrac{1\text{ mL}}{1\text{ cm}^3}\right) = 25\text{ mL}$

2.23 Insert the following results at the brackets in the statement of the exercise.

$1.0\text{ cm}^2 \times \left(\dfrac{10^{-2}\text{ m}}{1\text{ cm}}\right)^2 \times \left(\dfrac{1\text{ mm}}{10^{-3}\text{ m}}\right)^2 = 1.0 \times 10^2\text{ mm}^2$

$10.0\text{ cm}^3 \times \left(\dfrac{10^{-2}\text{ m}}{1\text{ cm}}\right)^3 = 1.00 \times 10^{-5}\text{ m}^3$

$100\text{ mL} \times \left(\dfrac{10^{-3}\text{ L}}{1\text{ mL}}\right) = 1.00 \times 10^{-1}\text{ L}$

$25.0\text{ mL} \times \left(\dfrac{1\text{ cm}^3}{1\text{ mL}}\right) = 25.0\text{ cm}^3$

Uncertainty of Measurements and Calculations

2.25 (a) The number of significant figures is related to the reproducibility of the measurement, which is the precision of the measurement.

(b) In addition and subtraction, the number of significant figures in the result is the same as the number of figures, counting from the first figure to the left of the decimal to the last figure to the right of the decimal. The place of this last figure is the place of the smallest number of decimals in the data set.

(c) The number of significant figures in the result of a multiplication or division is the same as the smallest number of significant figures in any of the factors (data).

2.27 (a) 3 (b) 3 (c) 3 (d) an integer, infinite (e) 2 (f) an exact number, infinite

2.29 (a) 6.60 mL (b) 26.0 mL

2.31 The sum 4.43 g rounds to 4.4 g (addition, so 1.4 g determines significant figures).

2.33 The sum 1.645 g rounds to 1.64 g (addition, so 0.21 g determines significant figures).

2.35 The factor 1.23 has the least number of significant figures, so the result should be reported to 3 significant figures. Note that (273.15 + 1.2) has 4 significant figures (not 5 and not 2).

Fun with Atoms and Moles

2.37 moles of stars $= \dfrac{10^{22} \text{ stars}}{6 \times 10^{23} \text{ stars} \cdot \text{mol}^{-1}} = 10^{-2} \text{ mol}$

2.39 (a) moles of people $= 5.7 \times 10^9 \text{ people} \times \dfrac{1 \text{ mol people}}{6.02 \times 10^{23} \text{ people}}$

$= 9.5 \times 10^{-15} \text{ mol people}$

(b) moles of peas $\cdot \text{s}^{-1} = 9.5 \times 10^{-15} \text{ mol people} \times \dfrac{1 \text{ mol peas} \cdot \text{s}^{-1}}{1 \text{ mol people}}$

$= 9.5 \times 10^{-15} \text{ mol peas} \cdot \text{s}^{-1}$

time $= 1 \text{ mol peas} \times \dfrac{1 \text{ s}}{9.5 \times 10^{-15} \text{ mol peas}} = 1.06 \times 10^{14} \text{ s}$

$$\text{time (y)} = 1.06 \times 10^{14} \text{ s} \times \left(\frac{1 \text{ min}}{60 \text{ s}}\right) \times \left(\frac{1 \text{ h}}{60 \text{ min}}\right) \times \left(\frac{1 \text{ day}}{24 \text{ h}}\right) \times \left(\frac{1 \text{ y}}{365 \text{ day}}\right)$$

$$= 3.4 \times 10^6 \text{ y}$$

3.4 million years is greater than the life span of the human species, so more than 5.7 billion people would be required.

Moles and Molar Masses of Elements

2.41 average molar mass $(\text{g} \cdot \text{mol}^{-1})$

$$= \left(\frac{98.89}{100} \times 1.9926 \times 10^{-23} \text{ g} + \frac{1.11}{100} \times 2.1593 \times 10^{-23} \text{ g}\right) \times 6.022 \times 10^{23} \text{ mol}^{-1}$$

$$= 12.01 \text{ g} \cdot \text{mol}^{-1}$$

2.43 molar mass $= \left(\frac{50.54}{100}\right) \times 78.918 \text{ g} \cdot \text{mol}^{-1} + \left(\frac{49.46}{100}\right) \times 80.916 \text{ g} \cdot \text{mol}^{-1}$

$$= 79.91 \text{ g} \cdot \text{mol}^{-1}$$

2.45 (a) number of moles of ^{35}Cl atoms $= 4.82 \times 10^{22}$ atoms ^{35}Cl

$$\times \frac{1 \text{ mol } ^{35}\text{Cl}}{6.02 \times 10^{23} \text{ atoms } ^{35}\text{Cl}} = 0.0801 \text{ mol } ^{35}\text{Cl}$$

(b) number of moles of Cu atoms $= 2.22 \text{ g Cu} \times \frac{1 \text{ mol Cu}}{63.54 \text{ g Cu}} = 0.0349 \text{ mol Cu}$

(c) number of moles of He atoms $= 1.11 \times 10^{24}$ atoms He

$$\times \frac{1 \text{ mol He}}{6.022 \times 10^{23} \text{ atoms He}} = 1.84 \text{ mol He}$$

(d) number of moles of Fe atoms $= 8.96 \text{ } \mu\text{g Fe} \times \left(\frac{10^{-6} \text{ g Fe}}{1 \text{ } \mu\text{g Fe}}\right) \times \left(\frac{1 \text{ mol Fe}}{55.85 \text{ g Fe}}\right)$

$$= 1.60 \times 10^{-7} \text{ mol Fe}$$

2.47 (a) number of atoms $= 3.97 \text{ mol Xe} \times \left(\frac{6.022 \times 10^{23} \text{ atoms}}{1 \text{ mol Xe}}\right)$

$$= 2.39 \times 10^{24} \text{ atoms}$$

(b) number of atoms $= 18.3 \text{ } \mu\text{g} \times \left(\frac{10^{-6} \text{ g}}{1 \text{ } \mu\text{g}}\right) \times \left(\frac{1 \text{ mol Sc}}{44.96 \text{ g}}\right)$

$$\times \left(\frac{6.022 \times 10^{23} \text{ atoms}}{1 \text{ mol Sc}}\right) = 2.45 \times 10^{17} \text{ atoms}$$

(c) $\text{number of atoms} = 12.8 \text{ pg} \times \left(\dfrac{10^{-12} \text{ g}}{1 \text{ pg}}\right) \times \left(\dfrac{1 \text{ mol Li}}{6.94 \text{ g}}\right)$

$$\times \left(\dfrac{6.022 \times 10^{23} \text{ atoms}}{1 \text{ mol Li}}\right) = 1.11 \times 10^{12} \text{ atoms}$$

(d) $\text{number of atoms} = 3.78 \times 10^{-4} \text{ mol Ar} \times \left(\dfrac{6.022 \times 10^{23} \text{ atoms}}{1 \text{ mol Ar}}\right)$

$$= 2.28 \times 10^{20} \text{ atoms}$$

2.49 (a) 12 g of C is one mole of C, so one mole of Ni contains the same number of atoms. One mole of Ni has a mass of 58.71 g, or 59 g (2 sf).

(b) One mole of any element contains the same number of atoms as one mole of any other element. That is, one mole of Cr atoms = one mol of Ni atoms, so the conversion factor is $\left(\dfrac{1 \text{ mol Ni atoms}}{1 \text{ mol Cr atoms}}\right)$ or, in general, $\left(\dfrac{1 \text{ mol A atoms}}{1 \text{ mol B atoms}}\right)$.

$\text{Mass of Ni atoms} = 12 \text{ g Cr} \times \left(\dfrac{1 \text{ mol Cr atoms}}{52.00 \text{ g Cr}}\right) \times \left(\dfrac{1 \text{ mol Ni atoms}}{1 \text{ mol Cr atoms}}\right)$

$$\times \left(\dfrac{58.71 \text{ g Ni}}{1 \text{ mol Ni atoms}}\right) = 13.55 \text{ g Ni} = 14 \text{ g Ni (2 sf)}$$

Molar Masses of Compounds

2.51 (a) molar mass of $CaBr_2 = 1 \times 40.08 \text{ g} \cdot \text{mol}^{-1} + 2 \times 79.91 \text{ g} \cdot \text{mol}^{-1}$
$$= 199.90 \text{ g} \cdot \text{mol}^{-1}$$

(b) molar mass of $C_8H_{18} = 8 \times 12.01 \text{ g} \cdot \text{mol}^{-1} + 18 \times 1.008 \text{ g} \cdot \text{mol}^{-1}$
$$= 114.22 \text{ g} \cdot \text{mol}^{-1}$$

(c) molar mass of $NiSO_4 \cdot 6H_2O = 58.71 \text{ g} \cdot \text{mol}^{-1} + 32.06 \text{ g} \cdot \text{mol}^{-1} + 4$
$\times 16.00 \text{ g} \cdot \text{mol}^{-1} + 6 \times (2 \times 1.008 \text{ g} \cdot \text{mol}^{-1} + 16.00 \text{ g} \cdot \text{mol}^{-1})$

$$= 262.87 \text{ g} \cdot \text{mol}^{-1}$$

(d) molar mass of $CO_2 = 12.01 \text{ g} \cdot \text{mol}^{-1} + 2 \times 16.00 \text{ g} \cdot \text{mol}^{-1} = 44.01 \text{ g} \cdot \text{mol}^{-1}$

(e) molar mass of $CH_4 = 12.01 \text{ g} \cdot \text{mol}^{-1} + 4 \times 1.008 \text{ g} \cdot \text{mol}^{-1} = 16.04 \text{ g} \cdot \text{mol}^{-1}$

2.53 (a) molar mass $CCl_4 = (12.01 + 4 \times 35.45) \text{ g} \cdot \text{mol}^{-1} = 153.81 \text{ g} \cdot \text{mol}^{-1}$

$\text{number of moles of } CCl_4 = 10 \text{ g } CCl_4 \times \left(\dfrac{1 \text{ mol } CCl_4}{153.81 \text{ g } CCl_4}\right) = 0.0650 \text{ mol } CCl_4$

$0.0650 \text{ mol } CCl_4 \times \left(\dfrac{6.02 \times 10^{23} \text{ molecules } CCl_4}{1 \text{ mol } CCl_4}\right) = 3.91$

$$\times 10^{22} \text{ molecules } CCl_4$$

(b) molar mass HI = $(1.008 + 126.90)$ g · mol^{-1} = 127.91 g · mol^{-1}

number of moles of HI = 1.65 mg HI $\times \left(\dfrac{10^{-3} \text{ g HI}}{1 \text{ mg HI}} \right) \times \left(\dfrac{1 \text{ mol HI}}{127.91 \text{ g HI}} \right)$

$= 1.29 \times 10^{-5}$ mol HI

1.29 $\times 10^{-5}$ mol HI $\times \left(\dfrac{6.02 \times 10^{23} \text{ molecules HI}}{1 \text{ mol HI}} \right) = 7.77 \times 10^{18}$ molecules HI

(c) molar mass N_2H_4 = $(2 \times 14.01 + 4 \times 1.008)$ g · mol^{-1} = 32.05 g · mol^{-1}

number of moles of N_2H_4 = 3.77 μg $N_2H_4 \times \left(\dfrac{10^{-6} \text{ g } N_2H_4}{1 \text{ } \mu\text{g } N_2H_4} \right) \times \left(\dfrac{1 \text{ mol } N_2H_4}{32.05 \text{ g } N_2H_4} \right)$

$= 1.18 \times 10^{-7}$ mol N_2H_4

1.18 $\times 10^{-7}$ mol $N_2H_4 \times \left(\dfrac{6.02 \times 10^{23} \text{ molecules } N_2H_4}{1 \text{ mol } N_2H_4} \right)$

$= 7.08 \times 10^{16}$ molecules N_2H_4

(d) molar mass sucrose = $(12 \times 12.01 + 22 \times 1.008 + 11 \times 16.00)$ g · mol^{-1}

$= 342.30$ g · mol^{-1} sucrose

number of moles of sucrose = 500 g sucrose $\times \left(\dfrac{1 \text{ mol sucrose}}{342.30 \text{ g sucrose}} \right)$

$= 1.46$ mol sucrose

1.46 mol sucrose $\times \left(\dfrac{6.02 \times 10^{23} \text{ molecules}}{1 \text{ mol sucrose}} \right) = 8.79 \times 10^{23}$ molecules sucrose

(e) number of moles of O atoms = 2.33 g O $\times \left(\dfrac{1 \text{ mol O}}{16.00 \text{ g O}} \right) = 0.146$ mol O

0.146 mol O $\times \left(\dfrac{6.02 \times 10^{23} \text{ atoms O}}{1 \text{ mol O}} \right) = 8.77 \times 10^{22}$ atoms O

8.77 $\times 10^{22}$ atoms O $\times \dfrac{1 \text{ molecule } O_2}{2 \text{ atoms O}} = 4.38 \times 10^{22}$ molecules O_2

2.55 (a) molar mass AgCl = $(107.87 + 35.45)$ g · mol^{-1} = 143.32 g · mol^{-1}

number of moles of Ag$^+$ = 2.00 g AgCl $\times \left(\dfrac{1 \text{ mol AgCl}}{143.32 \text{ g AgCl}} \right) \times \left(\dfrac{1 \text{ mol Ag}^+}{1 \text{ mol AgCl}} \right)$

$= 0.0140$ mol Ag$^+$

(b) molar mass UO_3 = $(238.03 + 3 \times 16.00)$ g · mol^{-1} = 286.03 g · mol^{-1}

number of moles of UO_3 = 600 g $UO_3 \times \left(\dfrac{1 \text{ mol } UO_3}{286.03 \text{ g } UO_3} \right) = 2.10$ mol UO_3

(c) molar mass $FeCl_3$ = $(55.85 + 3 \times 35.45)$ g · mol^{-1} = 162.20 g · mol^{-1}

number of moles of Cl$^-$ = 4.19 $\times 10^{-3}$ g $FeCl_3 \times \left(\dfrac{1 \text{ mol } FeCl_3}{162.20 \text{ g } FeCl_3} \right)$

$\times \left(\dfrac{3 \text{ mol Cl}^-}{1 \text{ mol } FeCl_3} \right) = 7.75 \times 10^{-5}$ mol Cl$^-$

(d) molar mass $AuCl_3 \cdot 2H_2O$

$$= [197.97 + 3 \times 35.45 + 2(2 \times 1.008 + 16.00)] \; g \cdot mol^{-1} = 339.36 \; g \cdot mol^{-1}$$

amount (moles) of $H_2O = 1.00 \; g \; AuCl_3 \cdot 2H_2O \times \left(\dfrac{1 \; mol \; AuCl_3 \cdot 2H_2O}{339.36 \; g \; AuCl_3 \cdot 2H_2O} \right)$

$$\times \left(\dfrac{2 \; mol \; H_2O}{1 \; mol \; AuCl_3 \cdot 2H_2O} \right) = 5.88 \times 10^{-3} \; mol \; H_2O$$

2.57 FU = formula unit, # = number sign

(a) # of FU of $AgNO_3 = 0.670 \; mol \; AgNO_3 \times \left(\dfrac{6.022 \times 10^{23} \; FU \; of \; AgNO_3}{1 \; mol \; AgNO_3} \right)$

$$= 4.03 \times 10^{23} \; FU \; of \; AgNO_3$$

(b) mass (μg) of $Rb_2SO_4 = 2.39 \times 10^{20} \; FU \; Rb_2SO_4 \times \left(\dfrac{1 \; mol \; Rb_2SO_4}{6.022 \times 10^{23} \; FU \; Rb_2SO_4} \right)$

$$\times \left(\dfrac{267.00 \; g \; Rb_2SO_4}{1 \; mol \; Rb_2SO_4} \right) \times \left(\dfrac{1 \; \mu g \; Rb_2SO_4}{10^{-6} \; g \; Rb_2SO_4} \right) = 1.06 \times 10^5 \; \mu g \; Rb_2SO_4$$

(c) # of FU of $NaHCO_2 = 6.66 \; kg \; NaHCO_2 \times \left(\dfrac{10^3 \; g \; NaHCO_2}{1 \; kg \; NaHCO_2} \right)$

$$\times \left(\dfrac{1 \; mol \; NaHCO_2}{68.01 \; g \; NaHCO_2} \right) \times \left(\dfrac{6.022 \times 10^{23} \; FU \; NaHCO_2}{1 \; mol \; NaHCO_2} \right)$$

$$= 5.90 \times 10^{25} \; FU \; of \; NaHCO_2$$

2.59 (a) molar mass testosterone $= (19 \times 12.01 + 28 \times 1.008 + 2 \times 16.00) \; g \cdot mol^{-1}$

$$= 288.41 \; g \cdot mol^{-1}$$

amount (moles) of testosterone $= 1 \; \mu g \times \left(\dfrac{10^{-6} \; g \; testosterone}{1 \; \mu g \; testosterone} \right)$

$$\times \left(\dfrac{1 \; mol \; testosterone}{288.41 \; g \; testosterone} \right) = 3.5 \times 10^{-9} \; mol \; testosterone$$

(b) mass % C $= \dfrac{19 \times 12.01 \; g \cdot mol^{-1}}{288.41 \; g \cdot mol^{-1}} \times 100\% = 79.1\% \; C$

mass % H $= \dfrac{28 \times 1.008 \; g \cdot mol^{-1}}{288.41 \; g \cdot mol^{-1}} \times 100\% = 9.8\% \; H$

mass % O $= \dfrac{2 \times 16.00 \; g \cdot mol^{-1}}{288.41 \; g \cdot mol^{-1}} \times 100\% = 11.1\% \; O$

2.61 (a) molar mass water $= 18.02 \; g \cdot mol^{-1}$

mass of 1 molecule $H_2O = 1 \; molecule \; H_2O \times \left(\dfrac{1 \; mol \; H_2O}{6.02 \times 10^{23} \; molecules \; H_2O} \right)$

$$\times \left(\dfrac{18.02 \; g \; H_2O}{1 \; mol \; H_2O} \right) = 2.99 \times 10^{-23} \; g \; H_2O$$

$$\text{number of } H_2O \text{ molecules} = 1.00 \text{ g } H_2O \times \left(\frac{1 \text{ mol } H_2O}{18.02 \text{ g } H_2O} \right)$$

$$\times \left(\frac{6.02 \times 10^{23} \text{ molecules } H_2O}{1 \text{ mol } H_2O} \right) = 3.34 \times 10^{22} \text{ molecules } H_2O$$

2.63 (a) molar mass $CuBr_2 \cdot 4H_2O$

$$= [63.54 + 2 \times 79.91 + 4(2 \times 1.008 + 16.00] \text{ g} \cdot \text{mol}^{-1} = 295.44 \text{ g} \cdot \text{mol}^{-1}$$

number of moles of $CuBr_2 \cdot 4H_2O = 5.50 \text{ g } CuBr_2 \cdot 4H_2O$

$$\times \left(\frac{1 \text{ mol } CuBr_2 \cdot 4H_2O}{295.44 \text{ g } CuBr_2 \cdot 4H_2O} \right) = 0.0186 \text{ mol } CuBr_2 \cdot 4H_2O$$

(b) number of moles of $Br^- = 0.0186 \text{ mol } CuBr_2 \cdot 4H_2O \times \left(\frac{2 \text{ mol } Br^-}{1 \text{ mol } CuBr_2 \cdot 4H_2O} \right)$

$$= 0.0372 \text{ mol } Br^-$$

(c) $0.0186 \text{ mol } CuBr_2 \cdot 4H_2O \times \left(\frac{4 \text{ mol } H_2O}{1 \text{ mol } CuBr_2 \cdot 4H_2O} \right)$

$$\times \left(\frac{6.02 \times 10^{23} \text{ molecules } H_2O}{1 \text{ mol } H_2O} \right) = 4.48 \times 10^{22} \text{ molecules } H_2O$$

(d) mass fraction of $Cu = \left(\frac{1 \text{ mol } Cu}{1 \text{ mol } CuBr_2 \cdot 4H_2O} \right) \times \left(\frac{63.54 \text{ g } Cu}{1 \text{ mol } Cu} \right)$

$$\times \left(\frac{1 \text{ mol } CuBr_2 \cdot 4H_2O}{295.44 \text{ g } CuBr_2 \cdot 4H_2O} \right) = 0.215$$

Determining Chemical Formulas

2.65 Assume 100 g of sample in each case.

(a) number of moles of $Na = 32.79 \text{ g } Na \times \left(\frac{1 \text{ mol } Na}{22.99 \text{ g } Na} \right) = 1.426 \text{ mol } Na$

number of moles of $Al = 13.02 \text{ g } Al \times \left(\frac{1 \text{ mol } Al}{26.98 \text{ g } Al} \right) = 0.482\overline{6} \text{ mol } Al$

number of moles of $F = 54.19 \text{ g } F \times \left(\frac{1 \text{ mol } F}{19.00 \text{ g } F} \right) = 2.852 \text{ mol } F$

The ratios are $Na : Al : F = 1.426 : 0.482\overline{6} : 2.852$. Dividing through by $0.482\overline{6}$ gives $2.955 : 1 : 5.910$, which is close to the ratio $3 : 1 : 6$. Therefore, the empirical formula is Na_3AlF_6.

(b) number of moles of $K = 31.91 \text{ g } K \times \left(\frac{1 \text{ mol } K}{39.10 \text{ g } K} \right) = 0.8161 \text{ mol } K$

number of moles of $Cl = 28.93 \text{ g } Cl \times \left(\frac{1 \text{ mol } Cl}{35.45 \text{ g } Cl} \right) = 0.8161 \text{ mol } Cl$

mass O $= (100 - 31.91 - 28.93)$ g $= 39.16$ g O

number of moles of O $= 39.16 \times \left(\dfrac{1 \text{ mol O}}{16.00 \text{ g O}} \right) = 2.448$ mol O

The ratios are $K:Cl:O = 0.8161:0.8161:2.448$. Dividing through by 0.8161 gives $1:1:3.00$. Therefore, the empirical formula is $KClO_3$.

(c) number of moles of N $= 12.2$ g N $\times \left(\dfrac{1 \text{ mol N}}{14.01 \text{ g N}} \right) = 0.871$ mol N

number of moles of H $= 5.26$ g H $\times \left(\dfrac{1 \text{ mol H}}{1.008 \text{ g H}} \right) = 5.21\overline{8}$ mol H

number of moles of P $= 26.9$ g P $\times \left(\dfrac{1 \text{ mol P}}{30.97 \text{ g P}} \right) = 0.869$ mol P

number of moles of O $= 55.6$ g O $\times \left(\dfrac{1 \text{ mol O}}{16.00 \text{ g O}} \right) = 3.47\overline{5}$ mol O

The ratios are $N:H:P:O = 0.871:5.21\overline{8}:0.869:3.47\overline{5}$. Dividing through by 0.869 gives $1.00:6.00:1.00:4.0$. Therefore, the empirical formula is NH_6PO_4 or $NH_4H_2PO_4$.

2.67   number of moles of P $= \dfrac{4.14 \text{ g}}{30.97 \text{ g} \cdot \text{mol}^{-1}} = 0.133\overline{6}$ mol

mass of Cl in compound $= 27.8$ g $- 4.14$ g $= 23.6\overline{6}$ g

number of moles of Cl $= \dfrac{23.6\overline{6} \text{ g}}{35.45 \text{ g} \cdot \text{mol}^{-1}} = 0.667\overline{4}$ mol

The ratio is $P:Cl = 0.133\overline{6}:0.667\overline{4}$. Dividing by $0.133\overline{6}$ gives $P:Cl = 1.00:5.00$. Therefore, the empirical formula is PCl_5.

2.69   Assume 100 g of material.

number of moles of C $= 24.78$ g C $\times \left(\dfrac{1 \text{ mol C}}{12.01 \text{ g C}} \right) = 2.063$ mol C

number of moles of H $= 2.08$ g H $\times \left(\dfrac{1 \text{ mol H}}{1.008 \text{ g H}} \right) = 2.06\overline{3}$ mol H

number of moles of Cl $= 73.14$ g Cl $\times \left(\dfrac{1 \text{ mol Cl}}{35.45 \text{ g Cl}} \right) = 2.063$ mol Cl

The ratios are $C:H:Cl = 2.063:2.06\overline{3}:2.063$, or $C:H:Cl = 1:1:1$. Therefore, the empirical formula is CHCl. The molar mass of CHCl $= (12.01 + 1.008 + 35.45)$ g $\cdot$ mol^{-1} $= 48.47$ g $\cdot$ mol^{-1}.

$$\dfrac{\text{molar mass of lindane}}{\text{molar mass of CHCl}} = \dfrac{290.85 \text{ g} \cdot \text{mol}^{-1}}{48.47 \text{ g} \cdot \text{mol}^{-1}} = 6.001 \approx 6.$$

Therefore, the molecular formula of lindane is $C_6H_6Cl_6$.

2.71   Assume 100 g of material.

$$\text{number of moles of C} = 49.48 \text{ g C} \times \frac{1 \text{ mol C}}{12.01 \text{ g C}} = 4.120 \text{ mol C}$$

$$\text{number of moles of H} = 5.19 \text{ g H} \times \frac{1 \text{ mol H}}{1.008 \text{ g H}} = 5.149 \text{ mol H}$$

$$\text{number of moles of N} = 28.85 \text{ g N} \times \frac{1 \text{ mol N}}{14.01 \text{ g N}} = 2.059 \text{ mol N}$$

$$\text{number of moles of O} = 16.48 \text{ g O} \times \frac{1 \text{ mol O}}{16.00 \text{ g O}} = 1.030 \text{ mol O}$$

Ratio is $C:H:N:O = 4.120:5.149:2.059:1.030$. Dividing by 1.030 gives $C:H:N:O = 4.000:4.999:1.999:1$, which is very close to $C:H:N:O = 4:5:2:1$. Therefore, the empirical formula $= C_4H_5N_2O$. The molar mass of $C_4H_4N_2O = (4 \times 12.01 + 5 \times 1.008 + 2 \times 14.01 + 16.00) \text{ g} \cdot \text{mol}^{-1} = 97.10 \text{ g} \cdot \text{mol}^{-1}$.

$$\frac{\text{molar mass caffeine}}{\text{molar mass } C_4H_5N_2O} = \frac{194.19 \text{ g} \cdot \text{mol}^{-1}}{97.10 \text{ g} \cdot \text{mol}^{-1}} = 2$$

Therefore, the molecular formula $= 2 \times (C_4H_5N_2O) = C_8H_{10}N_4O_2$.

Solutions

2.73   (a) $\text{molarity of AgNO}_3 = \dfrac{1.567 \text{ mol}}{0.2500 \text{ L}} = 6.268 \text{ mol} \cdot \text{L}^{-1}$

(b) $\text{molarity of NaCl} = \left(\dfrac{2.11 \text{ g NaCl}}{1.500 \text{ L}} \right) \times \left(\dfrac{1 \text{ mol}}{58.44 \text{ g NaCl}} \right) = 0.0241 \text{ mol} \cdot \text{L}^{-1}$

2.75 $\text{mass of AgNO}_3 = 0.02500 \text{ L} \times \left(\dfrac{0.155 \text{ mol AgNO}_3}{1 \text{ L}} \right) \times \left(\dfrac{169.88 \text{ g AgNO}_3}{1 \text{ mol AgNO}_3} \right)$

$$= 0.658 \text{ g AgNO}_3$$

2.77 $\text{molarity of Ba(OH)}_2 \text{ solution} = \left(\dfrac{2.577 \text{ g Ba(OH)}_2}{0.2500 \text{ L}} \right) \times \left(\dfrac{1 \text{ mol Ba(OH)}_2}{171.36 \text{ g Ba(OH)}_2} \right)$

$$= 0.06015 \text{ mol} \cdot \text{L}^{-1}$$

(a) $\text{volume} = \dfrac{n}{M}$

$$\text{volume of solution} = \frac{1.0 \times 10^{-3} \text{ mol}}{0.0602 \text{ mol} \cdot \text{L}^{-1}} = 0.017 \text{ L} = 17 \text{ mL}$$

(b) moles of $Ba(OH)_2$ = 3.5×10^{-3} mol OH^- $\times \left(\dfrac{1 \text{ mol } Ba(OH)_2}{2 \text{ mol } OH^-} \right)$

$$= 1.7\overline{5} \times 10^{-3} \text{ mol } Ba(OH)_2$$

volume of solution = $\dfrac{1.7\overline{5} \times 10^{-3} \text{ mol}}{0.0602 \text{ mol} \cdot L^{-1}}$ = 0.029 L = 29 mL

(c) volume of solution = 50.0 mg $Ba(OH)_2$ $\times \left(\dfrac{1 \text{ g } Ba(OH)_2}{1.0 \times 10^3 \text{ mg } Ba(OH)_2} \right)$

$$\times \left(\dfrac{0.2500 \text{ L}}{2.577 \text{ g } Ba(OH)_2} \right) = 0.00485 \text{ L} = 4.85 \text{ mL}$$

2.79 (a) We would determine the mass of 0.010 mole of $KMnO_4$

$\left(= 0.010 \text{ mol } KMnO_4 \times \dfrac{158.03 \text{ g } KMnO_4}{1 \text{ mol } KMnO_4} = 1.58 \text{ g } KMnO_4 \right)$ and then dissolve

that mass of $KMnO_4$ in enough water to make 1.00 liter of solution.

(b) We dilute the 0.050 M $KMnO_4$ solution by a factor of 5 $\left(= \dfrac{0.050 \text{ M}}{0.010 \text{ M}} \right)$;

for example, we could take 10 mL of 0.050 M $KMnO_4$, put it into a 50-mL volumetric flask, and add water up to the calibration mark.

2.81 In both parts, we use Eq. 2 in the form

$$V_{initial} = \frac{M_{final} \, V_{final}}{M_{initial}}$$

(a) $V_{initial} = \dfrac{0.0234 \text{ mol} \cdot L^{-1} \times 0.1500 \text{ L}}{0.778 \text{ mol} \cdot L^{-1}} = 4.51 \times 10^{-3} \text{ L} = 4.51 \text{ mL}$

(b) $V_{initial} = \dfrac{0.50 \text{ mol} \cdot L^{-1} \times 0.0600 \text{ L}}{2.5 \text{ mol} \cdot L^{-1}} = 0.012 \text{ L} = 12 \text{ mL}$

A 60-mL volumetric flask is not normally available, but a 100-mL flask can be

found. Thus, 12 mL $\times \left(\dfrac{100 \text{ mL}}{60 \text{ mL}} \right) = 20$ mL of the initial solution can be added to

a 100-mL volumetric flask and diluted with water to the mark. 60 mL of this solution can then be used.

SUPPLEMENTARY EXERCISES

2.83 (a) kg (b) pm (c) g (d) μm

2.85 $1.00 \text{ cup} \times \left(\dfrac{1 \text{ pint}}{2 \text{ cup}}\right) \times \left(\dfrac{1 \text{ qt}}{2 \text{ pint}}\right) \times \left(\dfrac{0.946 \text{ L}}{1 \text{ qt}}\right) \times \left(\dfrac{1 \text{ mL}}{10^{-3} \text{ L}}\right) = 236 \text{ mL}$

2.87 $0.1 \ \mu\text{m} \times \left(\dfrac{10^{-6} \text{ m}}{1 \ \mu\text{m}}\right) \times \left(\dfrac{1 \text{ cm}}{10^{-2} \text{ m}}\right) \times \dfrac{1 \text{ in.}}{2.54 \text{ cm}} = 4 \times 10^{-6} \text{ in.}$

2.89 $P_{\text{sn}} = \left(\dfrac{1 \text{ in.}}{2 \text{ min}}\right) \times \left(\dfrac{2.54 \text{ cm}}{1 \text{ in.}}\right) \times \left(\dfrac{1 \text{ min}}{60 \text{ s}}\right) = 2.12 \times 10^{-2} \text{ cm} \cdot \text{s}^{-1}$

2.91 Day side:
Kelvin temp. $= (127 + 273.15) \text{ K} = 400 \text{ K}$
Fahrenheit temp. $= (1.8 \times 127 + 32)°\text{F} = 261°\text{F}$
Night side:
Kelvin temp. $= (-183 + 273.15) \text{ K} = 90 \text{ K}$
Fahrenheit temp. $= [1.8 \times (-183) + 32]°\text{F} = -297°\text{F}$

2.93 precision: good, all measured values are within $0.02 \text{ g} \cdot \text{cm}^{-3}$.
accuracy: not good, relative to the precision (off by about $0.06 \text{ g} \cdot \text{cm}^{-3}$). A systematic error is probably present because the results are consistently low.

2.95 (a) number of S atoms $= 0.683 \text{ mol S} \times \dfrac{6.02 \times 10^{23} \text{ atoms S}}{1 \text{ mol S}}$
$= 4.11 \times 10^{23} \text{ atoms S}$

(b) $4.11 \times 10^{23} \text{ atoms S} \times \dfrac{1 \text{ molecule S}_8}{8 \text{ atoms S}} = 5.14 \times 10^{22} \text{ molecules S}_8$

(c) mass of S $= 0.683 \text{ mol S} \times \dfrac{32.06 \text{ g S}}{1 \text{ mol S}} = 21.9 \text{ g S} = 21.9 \text{ g S}_8$

2.97 Epsom salts $= \text{MgSO}_4 \cdot 7\text{H}_2\text{O}$; formula unit $= \text{FU}$
(a) molar mass $\text{MgSO}_4 \cdot 7\text{H}_2\text{O} = (24.31 + 32.06 + 4 \times 16.00 + 7$
$\times 18.02) \text{ g} \cdot \text{mol}^{-1} = 246.51 \text{ g} \cdot \text{mol}^{-1}$

number of Mg atoms $= 2.00 \text{ g Epsom salts} \times \left(\dfrac{1 \text{ mol Epsom salts}}{246.51 \text{ g Epsom salts}}\right)$

$\times \left(\dfrac{6.02 \times 10^{23} \text{ FU Epsom salts}}{1 \text{ mol Epsom salts}}\right) \times \left(\dfrac{1 \text{ atom Mg}}{1 \text{ FU Epsom salts}}\right) = 4.88 \times 10^{21} \text{ Mg atoms}$

(b) see (a); there is one Mg atom per FU of Epsom salts, so 4.88×10^{21} FU Epsom salts.

(c) number of moles of water = 2.00 g Epsom salts $\times \left(\dfrac{1 \text{ mol Epsom salts}}{246.51 \text{ g Epsom salts}} \right)$

$$\times \left(\dfrac{7 \text{ mol H}_2\text{O}}{1 \text{ mol Epsom salts}} \right) = 0.0568 \text{ mol H}_2\text{O}$$

2.99 (a) Assume a 100-g sample.

number of moles of C = 40.0 g C $\times \left(\dfrac{1 \text{ mol C}}{12.01 \text{ g C}} \right) = 3.33 \text{ mol C}$

number of moles of H = 6.72 g H $\times \left(\dfrac{1 \text{ mol H}}{1.008 \text{ g H}} \right) = 6.67 \text{ mol H}$

number of moles of O = 53.5 g O $\times \left(\dfrac{1 \text{ mol O}}{16.00 \text{ g O}} \right) = 3.34 \text{ mol O}$

The ratios are C:H:O = 3.33:6.67:3.34. Dividing by 3.33 gives C:H:O = 1.00:2.00:1.00. Therefore, the empirical formula is CH_2O.
(b) Molar mass of CH_2O = (12.01 + 2 × 1.008 + 16.00) g·mol^{-1} = 30.03 g·mol^{-1}
860 g mol^{-1}/30.03 g mol^{-1} = 28.6 ≈ 29
Therefore, the molecular formula is $C_{29}H_{58}O_{29}$.

2.101 mass of gold (in kg) = 3.23 × 10^{11} km^3 $\times \left(\dfrac{10^3 \text{ m}}{1 \text{ km}} \right)^3 \times \left(\dfrac{1 \text{ cm}}{10^{-2} \text{ m}} \right)^3$

$$\times \left(\dfrac{1 \text{ L}}{10^3 \text{ cm}^3} \right) \times \left(\dfrac{0.011 \text{ μg}}{1 \text{ L}} \right) \times \left(\dfrac{10^{-6} \text{ g}}{1 \text{ μg}} \right) \times \left(\dfrac{1 \text{ kg}}{10^3 \text{ g}} \right) = 3.6 \times 10^{12} \text{ kg}$$

2.103 (a) mass of $CuSO_4$ = 0.250 L $\times \left(\dfrac{0.20 \text{ mol CuSO}_4}{1 \text{ L}} \right) \times \left(\dfrac{159.6 \text{ g CuSO}_4}{1 \text{ mol CuSO}_4} \right)$

$$= 8.0 \text{ g CuSO}_4$$

(b) mass of $CuSO_4 \cdot 5H_2O$ = 0.250 L $\times \left(\dfrac{0.20 \text{ mol CuSO}_4}{1 \text{ L}} \right)$

$$\times \left(\dfrac{1 \text{ mol CuSO}_4 \cdot 5H_2O}{1 \text{ mol CuSO}_4} \right) \times \left(\dfrac{249.68 \text{ g CuSO}_4 \cdot 5H_2O}{1 \text{ mol CuSO}_4 \cdot 5H_2O} \right) = 12 \text{ g CuSO}_4 \cdot 5H_2O$$

CHALLENGING EXERCISES

2.105 Base unit = 1 Second = 1 S (capital S) = 1 s (lowercase).
Then 1 Minute = 1 M (capital M) = 100 S
   1 Hour = 1 H (capital H) = 100 M
   1 Day = 1 D (capital D) = 10 H
and so forth.

(a) Number of Seconds in 1 Hour $= 1\text{ H} \times \dfrac{100\text{ M}}{1\text{ H}} \times \dfrac{100\text{ S}}{1\text{ M}} = 10^4\text{ S}.$

There are 10 kS in one H.

(b) 1.00 Day $= 1.00\text{ D} = 10.0\text{ H} = 100\text{ kS}.$

2.107 (a) velocity $= \text{m} \cdot \text{s}^{-1}$

(b) acceleration $=$ velocity/time $= \dfrac{\text{m} \cdot \text{s}^{-1}}{\text{s}} = \text{m} \cdot \text{s}^{-2}$

(c) force $=$ mass $\times$ acceleration $= \text{kg} \cdot \text{m} \cdot \text{s}^{-2}$

(d) pressure $=$ force/area $= \dfrac{\text{kg} \cdot \text{m} \cdot \text{s}^{-2}}{\text{m}^2} = \text{kg} \cdot \text{m}^{-1} \cdot \text{s}^{-2}$

2.109 (a) density $= \dfrac{\text{mass}}{\text{volume}} = \dfrac{m}{V}$

$$m = \dfrac{12.01\text{ g} \cdot \text{mol}^{-1}}{6.022 \times 10^{23}\text{ mol}^{-1}} = 1.994 \times 10^{-23}\text{ g}$$

$$V = (\tfrac{4}{3})\pi \times \left(1.5 \times 10^{-5}\text{ pm} \times \dfrac{10^{-12}\text{ m}}{1\text{ pm}}\right)^3 = 1.4\overline{1} \times 10^{-50}\text{ m}^3$$

$$\text{density} = \dfrac{1.994 \times 10^{-23}\text{ g}}{1.4\overline{1} \times 10^{-50}\text{ m}^3} = 1.4\overline{1} \times 10^{27}\text{ g} \cdot \text{m}^{-3} = 1.4\overline{1} \times 10^{24}\text{ kg} \cdot \text{m}^{-3}$$

(b) mass $= V \times$ density

$$V = (\tfrac{4}{3})\pi r^3 = (\tfrac{4}{3})\pi \times \left(6.4 \times 10^3\text{ km} \times \dfrac{10^3\text{ m}}{1\text{ km}}\right)^3 = 1.10 \times 10^{21}\text{ m}^3$$

$$\text{density} = \left(\dfrac{5.5\text{g}}{1\text{ cm}^3}\right) \times \left(\dfrac{1\text{ kg}}{10^3\text{ g}}\right) \times \left(\dfrac{1\text{ cm}}{10^{-2}\text{ m}}\right)^3 = 5.5 \times 10^3\text{ kg} \cdot \text{m}^{-3}$$

mass of Earth $= 1.10 \times 10^{21}\text{ m}^3 \times 5.5 \times 10^3\text{ kg} \cdot \text{m}^{-3} = 6.0\overline{5} \times 10^{24}\text{ kg}$

compressed volume of Earth $= \dfrac{6.0\overline{5} \times 10^{24}\text{ kg}}{1.41 \times 10^{24}\text{ kg} \cdot \text{m}^{-3}} = 4.2\overline{9}\text{ m}^3$

$$(\tfrac{4}{3})\pi r^3 = 4.2\overline{9}\text{ m}^3$$

$$r = \sqrt[3]{\dfrac{4.2\overline{9}\text{ m}^3}{(\tfrac{4}{3})\pi}} = 1.0\text{ m}$$

2.111 1 acre $= 4840\text{ yd}^2 \times \left(\dfrac{1\text{ m}}{1.094\text{ yd}}\right)^2 = 4044\text{ m}^2$

rate $= 1\text{ acre} \cdot \text{d}^{-1} = 4044\text{ m}^2 \cdot \text{d}^{-1} \times \left(\dfrac{1.0\text{ d}}{8.0\text{ h}}\right) = 5.1 \times 10^2\text{ m}^2 \cdot \text{h}^{-1}$

2.113 molar mass $= 0.003 \times 77.92 \text{ g} \cdot \text{mol}^{-1} + 0.023 \times 79.92 \text{ g} \cdot \text{mol}^{-1} + 0.116$
$\times 81.91 \text{ g} \cdot \text{mol}^{-1} + 0.115 \times 82.92 \text{ g} \cdot \text{mol}^{-1} + 0.569 \times 83.91 \text{ g} \cdot \text{mol}^{-1}$
$$+ 0.174 \times 85.91 \text{ g} \cdot \text{mol}^{-1} = 83.8 \text{ g} \cdot \text{mol}^{-1}$$

2.115 molar mass ethanol $= (2 \times 12.01 + 6 \times 1.008 + 16.00) \text{ g} \cdot \text{mol}^{-1}$
$$= 46.07 \text{ g} \cdot \text{mol}^{-1}$$
mass of ethanol $= 0.097 \times 0.98 \text{ g} \cdot \text{mL}^{-1} \times 100 \text{ mL} = 9.5\overline{1} \text{ g}$

number of molecules of ethanol $= \dfrac{9.5\overline{1} \text{ g}}{46.07 \text{ g} \cdot \text{mol}^{-1}} \times 6.02 \times 10^{23} \text{ mol}^{-1}$
$$= 1.2 \times 10^{23} \text{ molecules}$$

2.117 (a) initial molarity of $K_2Cr_2O_7 = \left(\dfrac{0.661 \text{ g } K_2Cr_2O_7}{0.2500 \text{ L}} \right) \times \left(\dfrac{1 \text{ mol}}{294.2 \text{ g } K_2Cr_2O_7} \right)$
$$= 8.99 \times 10^{-3} \text{ mol} \cdot \text{L}^{-1}$$

final molarity $= 8.99 \times 10^{-3} \text{ mol} \cdot \text{L}^{-1} \times \left(\dfrac{1.000 \text{ mL}}{500 \text{ mL}} \right) \times \left(\dfrac{10 \text{ mL}}{250 \text{ mL}} \right)$
$$= 7.2 \times 10^{-7} \text{ mol} \cdot \text{L}^{-1}$$

(b) mass of $K_2Cr_2O_7 = 7.2 \times 10^{-7} \text{ mol} \cdot \text{L}^{-1} \times 0.250 \text{ L} \times \dfrac{294.2 \text{ g } K_2Cr_2O_7}{1 \text{ mol } K_2Cr_2O_7}$
$$= 5.3 \times 10^{-5} \text{ g } K_2Cr_2O_7$$

CHAPTER 3
CHEMICAL REACTIONS: MODIFYING MATTER

EXERCISES

Balancing Equations

3.1 (a) $P_2O_5(s) + 3H_2O(l) \longrightarrow 2H_3PO_4(l)$

(b) $Cd(NO_3)_2(aq) + Na_2S(aq) \longrightarrow CdS(s) + 2NaNO_3(aq)$

(c) $4KClO_3(s) \overset{\Delta}{\longrightarrow} 3KClO_4(s) + KCl(s)$

(d) $2HCl(aq) + Ca(OH)_2(aq) \longrightarrow CaCl_2(aq) + 2H_2O(l)$

3.3 (a) $2Na(s) + 2H_2O(l) \longrightarrow H_2(g) + 2NaOH(aq)$

(b) $Na_2O(s) + H_2O(l) \longrightarrow 2NaOH(aq)$

(c) $6Li(s) + N_2(g) \longrightarrow 2Li_3N(s)$

(d) $Ca(s) + 2H_2O(l) \longrightarrow Ca(OH)_2(aq) + H_2(g)$

3.5 1st stage: $3Fe_2O_3(l) + CO(g) \longrightarrow 2Fe_3O_4(l) + CO_2(g)$

2nd stage: $Fe_3O_4(l) + 4CO(g) \longrightarrow 3Fe(l) + 4CO_2(g)$

3.7 engine: $N_2(g) + O_2(g) \longrightarrow 2NO(g)$

atmosphere: $2NO(g) + O_2(g) \longrightarrow 2NO_2(g)$

3.9 $4HF(aq) + SiO_2(s) \longrightarrow SiF_4(g) + 2H_2O(l)$

Precipitation Reactions

3.11 First identify all soluble ionic compounds. Then write the complete ionic equation by writing all the soluble ionic compounds in ionic form. Then cancel all ions common to both sides of the reaction. What remains is the net ionic equation.

3.13 (a) nonelectrolyte (b) strong electrolyte (c) strong electrolyte

3.15 (a) soluble, all nitrates are soluble

(b) insoluble

(c) soluble, all nitrates are soluble

(d) soluble, Group 1 compounds are soluble

3.17 (a) $H_3O^+(aq)$, $Cl^-(aq)$ (b) $Cu^{2+}(aq)$, $Cl^-(aq)$ (c) $Cs^+(aq)$, $HSO_4^-(aq)$. $H_3O^+(aq)$ and $SO_4^{2-}(aq)$ are also formed, but in lesser amounts.

3.19 (a) $Na^+(aq)$, $I^-(aq)$

(b) insoluble, but very slight amounts of $Ag^+(aq)$ and $CO_3^{2-}(aq)$ form (see Chapter 15)

(c) $NH_4^+(aq)$, $PO_4^{3-}(aq)$; (d) $Na^+(aq)$, $HCO_3^-(aq)$; $H_3O^+(aq)$ and $CO_3^{2-}(aq)$ are also present, but in small amounts; (e) $Fe^{2+}(aq)$, $SO_4^{2-}(aq)$

3.21 (a) $Fe^{3+} + 3OH^- \longrightarrow Fe(OH)_3(s)$

(b) $2Ag^+ + CO_3^{2-} \longrightarrow Ag_2CO_3(s)$ (yes)

(c) No, sodium nitrate and lead acetate are soluble.

3.23 (a) $FeCl_3(aq) + 3NaOH(aq) \longrightarrow Fe(OH)_3(s) + 3NaCl(aq)$

$Fe^{3+}(aq) + 3Cl^-(aq) + 3Na^+(aq) + 3OH^-(ag) \longrightarrow$
$$Fe(OH)_3(s) + 3Na^+(aq) + 3Cl^-(aq)$$

$Fe^{3+}(aq) + 3OH^-(aq) \longrightarrow Fe(OH)_3(s)$

Na^+ and Cl^- are spectator ions.

(b) $AgNO_3(aq) + KI(aq) \longrightarrow AgI(s) + KNO_3(aq)$

$Ag^+(aq) + NO_3^-(aq) + K^+(aq) + I^-(aq) \longrightarrow AgI(s) + K^+(aq) + NO_3^-(aq)$

$Ag^+(aq) + I^-(aq) \longrightarrow AgI(s)$

K^+ and NO_3^- are spectator ions.

(c) $Pb(NO_3)_2(aq) + K_2SO_4(aq) \longrightarrow PbSO_4(s) + 2KNO_3(aq)$

$Pb^{2+}(aq) + 2NO_3^-(aq) + 2K^+(aq) + SO_4^{2-}(aq) \longrightarrow$
$$PbSO_4(s) + 2K^+(aq) + 2NO_3^-(aq)$$

$Pb^{2+}(aq) + SO_4^{2-}(aq) \longrightarrow PbSO_4(s)$

K^+ and NO_3^- are spectator ions.

(d) $Na_2CrO_4(aq) + Pb(NO_3)_2(aq) \longrightarrow PbCrO_4(s) + 2NaNO_3(aq)$

$2Na^+(aq) + CrO_4^{2-}(aq) + Pb^{2+}(aq) + 2NO_3^-(aq) \longrightarrow$
$$PbCrO_4(s) + 2Na^+(aq) + 2NO_3^-(aq)$$

$Pb^{2+}(aq) + CrO_4^{2-}(aq) \longrightarrow PbCrO_4(s)$

Na^+ and NO_3^- are spectator ions.

(e) $Hg(NO_3)_2(aq) + K_2CrO_4(aq) \longrightarrow HgCrO_4(s) + 2KNO_3(aq)$

$Hg^{2+}(aq) + 2NO_3^-(aq) + 2K^+(aq) + CrO_4^{2-}(aq) \longrightarrow$
$$HgCrO_4(s) + 2K^+(aq) + 2NO_3^-(aq)$$

$Hg^{2+}(aq) + CrO_4^{2-}(aq) \longrightarrow HgCrO_4(s)$

K^+ and NO_3^- are spectator ions.

3.25 (a) $(NH_4)_2CrO_4(aq) + BaCl_2(aq) \longrightarrow BaCrO_4(s) + 2NH_4Cl(aq)$

$2NH_4^+(aq) + CrO_4^{2-}(aq) + Ba^{2+}(aq) + 2Cl^-(aq) \longrightarrow$
$$BaCrO_4(s) + 2NH_4^+(aq) + 2Cl^-(aq)$$

$Ba^{2+}(aq) + CrO_4^{2-}(aq) \longrightarrow BaCrO_4(s)$

NH_4^+ and Cl^- are spectator ions.

(b) $CuSO_4(aq) + Na_2S(aq) \longrightarrow CuS(s) + Na_2SO_4(aq)$

$Cu^{2+}(aq) + SO_4^{2-}(aq) + 2Na^+(aq) + S^{2-}(aq) \longrightarrow CuS(s) + 2Na^+(aq) + SO_4^{2-}(aq)$

$Cu^{2+}(aq) + S^{2-}(aq) \longrightarrow CuS(s)$

Na^+ and SO_4^{2-} are spectator ions.

(c) $3FeCl_2(aq) + 2(NH_4)_3PO_4(aq) \longrightarrow Fe_3(PO_4)_2(s) + 6NH_4Cl(aq)$

$3Fe^{2+}(aq) + 6Cl^-(aq) + 6NH_4^+(aq) + 2PO_4^{3-}(aq) \longrightarrow$
$$Fe_3(PO_4)_2(s) + 6NH_4^+(aq) + 6Cl^-(aq)$$

$3Fe^{2+}(aq) + 2PO_4^{3-}(aq) \longrightarrow Fe_3(PO_4)_2(s)$

NH_4^+ and Cl^- are spectator ions.

(d) $K_2C_2O_4(aq) + Ca(NO_3)_2(aq) \longrightarrow 2KNO_3(aq) + CaC_2O_4(s)$

$2K^+(aq) + C_2O_4^{2-}(aq) + Ca^{2+}(aq) + 2NO_3^-(aq) \longrightarrow$
$$2K^+(aq) + 2NO_3^-(aq) + CaC_2O_4(s)$$

$Ca^{2+}(aq) + C_2O_4^{2-}(aq) \longrightarrow CaC_2O_4(s)$

K^+ and NO_3^- are spectator ions.

(e) $NiSO_4(aq) + Ba(NO_3)_2(aq) \longrightarrow Ni(NO_3)_2(aq) + BaSO_4(s)$

$Ni^{2+}(aq) + SO_4^{2-}(aq) + Ba^{2+}(aq) + 2NO_3^-(aq) \longrightarrow$
$$Ni^{2+}(aq) + 2NO_3^-(aq) + BaSO_4(s)$$

$Ba^{2+}(aq) + SO_4^{2-}(aq) \longrightarrow BaSO_4(s)$

Ni^{2+} and NO_3^- are spectator ions.

3.27 (a) $Pb^{2+}(aq) + 2ClO_4^-(aq) + 2Na^+(aq) + 2Br^-(aq) \longrightarrow$
$$PbBr_2(s) + 2Na^+(aq) + 2ClO_4^-(aq)$$

$Pb^{2+}(aq) + 2Br^-(aq) \longrightarrow PbBr_2(s)$

(b) $Ag^+(aq) + NO_3^-(aq) + NH_4^+(aq) + Cl^-(aq) \longrightarrow$
$$AgCl(s) + NH_4^+(aq) + NO_3^-(aq)$$

$Ag^+(aq) + Cl^-(aq) \longrightarrow AgCl(s)$

(c) $2Na^+(aq) + 2OH^-(aq) + Cu^{2+}(aq) + 2NO_3^-(aq) \longrightarrow$

$$Cu(OH)_2(s) + 2Na^+(aq) + 2NO_3^-(aq)$$

$Cu^{2+}(aq) + 2OH^-(aq) \longrightarrow Cu(OH)_2(s)$

3.29 In each case, use Table 3.1 to match the cation with an anion that results in an insoluble compound, and the anion with a cation that results in an insoluble compound. (a) $AgNO_3$, Na_2CrO_4 (b) $Ca(NO_3)_2$, Na_2CO_3 (c) $Cd(NO_3)_2$, Na_2S

3.31 (a) $Pb^{2+}(aq) + SO_4^{2-}(aq) \longrightarrow PbSO_4(s)$
(b) $Cu^{2+}(aq) + S^{2-}(aq) \longrightarrow CuS(s)$
(c) $Co^{2+}(aq) + CO_3^{2-}(aq) \longrightarrow CoCO_3(s)$
(d) In each case, use Table 3.1 to match the cation with an anion from the table that results in an insoluble compound, and the anion with a cation from the table that results in an insoluble compound. Thus, for (a), $Pb(NO_3)_2$, Na_2SO_4 [spectators Na^+, NO_3^-]; for (b), $Cu(NO_3)_2$, Na_2S [spectators Na^+, NO_3^-]; for (c), $Co(NO_3)_2$, Na_2CO_3 [spectators Na^+, NO_3^-]

Acids and Bases

3.33 See Section 3.7. Acids are molecules or ions that contain hydrogen and produce hydronium ions, H_3O^+, in water. Bases are molecules or ions that produce hydroxide ions, OH^-, in water. A base does not need to contain the hydroxide ion.

3.35 In each case, consider how the substance exists in aqueous solution; and, if it reacts with water, determine the products.
(a) $NH_3(aq) + H_2O(l) \longrightarrow NH_4^+(aq) + OH^-(aq)$
Because OH^- is produced, NH_3 is a base.
(b) $HCl(aq) + H_2O(l) \longrightarrow H_3O^+(aq) + Cl^-(aq)$
Because H_3O^+ is produced, HCl is an acid.
(c) $NaOH(aq) \longrightarrow Na^+(aq) + OH^-(aq)$; a base
(d) $H_2SO_4(aq) + H_2O(l) \longrightarrow H_3O^+(aq) + HSO_4^-(aq)$
$HSO_4^-(aq) + H_2O(l) \longrightarrow H_3O^+(aq) + SO_4^{2-}(aq)$
Because H_3O^+ is produced, H_2SO_4 is an acid.
(e) $Ba(OH)_2(aq) \longrightarrow Ba^{2+}(aq) + 2OH^-(aq)$; a base

3.37 (a) $HCl(aq) + NaOH(aq) \longrightarrow H_2O(l) + NaCl(aq)$
$H_2O^+(aq) + Cl^-(aq) + Na^+(aq) + OH^-(aq) \longrightarrow 2H_2O(l) + Na^+(aq) + Cl^-(aq)$
$H_2O^+(aq) + OH^-(aq) \longrightarrow 2H_2O(l)$

(b) $NH_3(aq) + HNO_3(aq) \longrightarrow NH_4NO_3(aq)$

$NH_3(aq) + H_3O^+(aq) + NO_3^-(aq) \longrightarrow NH_4^+(aq) + NO_3^-(aq) + H_2O(l)$

$NH_3(aq) + H_3O^+(aq) \longrightarrow NH_4^+(aq) + H_2O(l)$

(c) $CH_3NH_2(aq) + HI(aq) \longrightarrow CH_3NH_3I(aq)$

$CH_3NH_2(aq) + H_3O^+(aq) + I^-(aq) \longrightarrow CH_3NH_3^+(aq) + I^-(aq) + H_2O(l)$

$CH_3NH_2(aq) + H_3O^+(aq) \longrightarrow CH_3NH_3^+(aq) + H_2O(l)$

3.39 In each case, we need to identify a base that provides the cation of the salt and an acid that provides its anion.

(a) HBr and KOH

$HBr(aq) + KOH(aq) \longrightarrow KBr(aq) + 2H_2O(l)$

$H_3O^+(aq) + Br^-(aq) + K^+(aq) + OH^-(aq) \longrightarrow K^+(aq) + Br^-(aq) + H_2O(l)$

$H_3O^+(aq) + OH^-(aq) \longrightarrow 2H_2O(l)$

(b) HNO_2 and $Zn(OH)_2$; zinc hydroxide is barely soluble in aqueous solution.

$2HNO_2(aq) + Zn(OH)_2(s) \longrightarrow Zn(NO_2)_2(aq) + 2H_2O(l)$

$2H_3O^+(aq) + 2NO_2^-(aq) + Zn(OH)_2(s) \longrightarrow Zn^{2+}(aq) + 2NO_2^-(aq) + 4H_2O(l)$

$2H_3O^+(aq) + Zn(OH)_2(s) \longrightarrow Zn^{2+}(aq) + 4H_2O(l)$

(c) HCN and $Ca(OH)_2$

$2HCN(aq) + Ca(OH)_2(aq) \longrightarrow Ca(CN)_2(aq) + 2H_2O(l)$

$2HCN(aq) + Ca^{2+}(aq) + 2OH^-(aq) \longrightarrow Ca^{2+}(aq) + 2CN^-(aq) + 2H_2O(l)$

$HCN(aq) + OH^-(aq) \longrightarrow CN^-(aq) + H_2O(l)$

(d) H_3PO_4 and KOH

$H_3PO_4(aq) + 3KOH(aq) \longrightarrow K_3PO_4(aq) + 3H_2O(l)$

$3H_3O^+(aq) + PO_4^{3-}(aq) + 3K^+(aq) + 3OH^-(aq) \longrightarrow$
$$3K^+(aq) + PO_4^{3-}(aq) + 6H_2O(l)$$

$3H_3O^+(aq) + 3OH^-(aq) \longrightarrow 6H_2O(l)$ or $H_3O^+(aq) + OH^-(aq) \longrightarrow 2H_2O(l)$

3.41 In each case, the acid is the subtance that has donated a proton, H^+, and the base is the substance that has accepted it.

(a) $CH_3NH_2(aq)$ [base], $H_3O^+(aq)$ [acid]

(b) $C_2H_5NH_2(aq)$ [base], $HCl(aq)$ [acid]

(c) $HI(aq)$ [acid], $CaO(s)$ [base]

3.43 In each case, we use the periodic table to determine whether the element combined with oxygen is a metal or a nonmetal. Metallic oxides form bases in aqueous solution and nonmetallic oxides form acids.

(a) basic, $Ca(OH)_2$ (b) acidic, H_2SO_4 (c) acidic, HNO_2

(d) basic, TlOH

Redox Reactions

3.45   Oxidation is electron loss.

Reduction is electron gain.

3.47   In each case, first determine the oxidation numbers of all elements on both sides of the equation. Then balance, with appropriate multiplicative factors, if required, the number of electrons lost by one element against the number gained by another.

(a) $2P(s) + 3Br_2(l) \longrightarrow 2PBr_3(s)$

P: $2 \times 3 = 6$ lost; Br: $2 \times 3 \times 1 = 6$ gained

(b) $2Fe^{2+}(aq) + Sn^{4+}(aq) \longrightarrow 2Fe^{3+}(aq) + Sn^{2+}(aq)$

Fe: $2 \times 1 = 2$ lost; Sn: $1 \times 2 = 2$ gained

(c) $8H_2(g) + S_8(s) \longrightarrow 8H_2s(g)$

H: $8 \times 2 \times 1 = 16$ lost; S: $8 \times 2 = 16$ gained

(d) $2NO(g) + O_2(g) \longrightarrow 2NO_2(g)$

N: $2 \times 2 = 4$ lost; O: $2 \times 2 = 4$ gained

3.49   (a) $Mg(s) + Cu^{2+}(aq) \longrightarrow Mg^{2+}(aq) + Cu(s)$

(b) $Fe^{2+}(aq) + Ce^{4+}(aq) \longrightarrow Fe^{3+}(aq) + Ce^{3+}(aq)$

(c) $H_2(g) + Cl_2(g) \longrightarrow 2HCl(g)$

(d) $4Fe(s) + 3O_2(g) \longrightarrow 2Fe_2O_3(s)$

Fe: $4 \times 3 = 12$ lost; O: $3 \times 2 \times 2 = 12$ gained

Oxidation Numbers

3.51   The oxidation number of an element is a number assigned on the basis of a set of rules, and is used to monitor whether an element has been oxidized or reduced.

3.53   Let x represent the oxidation number of the italicized element.

(a) $x + 4 \times (-1) = 0$; therefore, $x = +4$

(b) $1 + x - 2 = 0$; therefore, $x = +1$

(c) $x - 2 = 0$; therefore, $x = +2$

(d) $1 + x + 3 \times (-2) = 0$; therefore, $x = +5$

(e) $x + 2 \times (-2) = 0$; therefore, $x = +4$

(f) $2 \times 1 + x = 0$; therefore, $x = -2$

3.55   Let x represent the oxidation number of the italicized element.

(a) $x + 4 \times (-2) = -1$; therefore, $x = +7$

(b) $2 \times x + 3 \times (-2) = -2$; therefore, $x = +2$

(c) $x + 4 \times (-2) = -2$; therefore, $x = +6$

(d) $x + 4 \times (-2) = -2$; therefore, $x = +6$

(e) $2 \times x + 7 \times (-2) = -2$; therefore, $x = +6$

3.57 (a) This is a substitution reaction; no oxidation or reduction occurs.

$$\overset{-2}{\text{(b) }BrO_3^-}(aq) + 5\overset{-1}{Br^-}(aq) + 6\overset{+1}{H^+}(aq) \longrightarrow 3\overset{0}{Br_2}(l) + 3\overset{+1\,-2}{H_2O}(l)$$

BrO_3^- is reduced and Br^- is oxidized.

$$\overset{0}{\text{(c) }2F_2}(g) + 2\overset{+1\,-2}{H_2O}(l) \longrightarrow 4\overset{+1\,-1}{HF}(aq) + \overset{0}{O_2}(g)$$

F_2 is reduced and water is oxidized.

Oxidizing and Reducing Agents

3.59 Oxidizing agents contain an element that gains electrons and decreases its oxidation number. Reducing agents lose electrons to the oxidizing agent. A loss of electrons means an increase in oxidation number for an element in the reducing agent.

3.61 The higher (in the algebraic sense) the oxidation number of an element, the stronger it is as an oxidizing agent. It has the greater ability to gain electrons.

(a) Cl_2 (0) is stronger than Cl^- (-1), because $0 > -1$

(b) N_2O_5 ($N = +5$) is stronger than N_2O ($N = +1$), because $+5 > +1$

3.63 In each case, identify the substances that contain an element that undergoes a change in oxidation number. If the change is positive, in the algebraic sense, that substance is the reducing agent. If the change is negative, in the algebraic sense, that substance is the oxidizing agent.

(a) Oxidation number changes are

Zn ($0 \longrightarrow +2$); so Zn is the reducing agent.

H ($+1 \longrightarrow 0$); so HCl is the oxidizing agent.

(b) Oxidation number changes are

S (in H_2S, $-2 \longrightarrow 0$); so H_2S is the reducing agent.

S (in SO_2, $+4 \longrightarrow 0$); so SO_2 is the oxidizing agent.

(c) Oxidation number changes are

B ($+3 \longrightarrow 0$); so B_2O_3 is the oxidizing agent.

Mg ($0 \longrightarrow +2$); so Mg is the reducing agent.

3.65 In each case, decide whether the change is oxidation or reduction. If oxidation, an oxidizing agent is required. If reduction, a reducing agent is required. Let x = oxidation number.

(a) $x(Br) = -1 \longrightarrow x(Br) = +5$; so oxidation has occurred and an oxidizing agent is required.

(b) $x(S) = +5 \longrightarrow x(S) = +6$; so oxidation has occurred and an oxidizing agent is required.

(c) $x(N) = +5 \longrightarrow x(N) = +2$; so reduction has occurred and a reducing agent is required.

(d) $x(C) = 0 \longrightarrow x(C) = -2$; so reduction has occurred and a reducing agent is required.

Rationale:

$$\left.\begin{array}{r} 2 \times x(H) + x(C) + x(O) = 0 \\ 2 + x(C) + (-2) = 0 \\ x(C) = 0 \end{array}\right\} \text{ for HCHO}$$

$$\left.\begin{array}{r} 4 \times x(H) + x(C) + x(O) = 0 \\ 4 + x(C) + (-2) = 0 \\ x(C) = -2 \end{array}\right\} \text{ for CH}_3\text{OH}$$

3.67 $2NaCl(l) \xrightarrow{\text{electrolysis at 600°C}} 2Na(l) + Cl_2(g)$

Oxidation number changes are

Na ($+1 \longrightarrow 0$); so reduction has occurred.

Cl ($-1 \longrightarrow 0$); so oxidation has occurred.

Therefore, chlorine is produced by oxidation and sodium by reduction.

SUPPLEMENTARY EXERCISES

3.69 Use Tables 3.1 and 3.2. If an acid or a base is not in Table 3.2, it is assumed to be weak.

(a) strong acid   (b) strong base   (c) weak base   (d) soluble ionic   (e) weak acid
(f) insoluble ionic   (g) insoluble ionic   (h) strong acid

3.71 (a) HNO_3, $Ba(OH)_2$ (b) H_2SO_4, NaOH   (c) $HClO_4$, KOH   (d) HCl, $Ni(OH)_2$; but $Ni(OH)_2$ is not normally thought of as a base; rather it is considered to be an insoluble salt.

3.73 (a) acid-base neutralization; HCl, acid; $Mg(OH)_2$, base

(b) acid-base neutralization; H_2SO_4, acid; $Ba(OH)_2$, base or precipitation; $Ba^{2+}(aq) + SO_4^{2-}(aq) \longrightarrow BaSO_4(s)$

(c) redox; O_2 is the oxidizing agent, because oxidation number of O is decreased $(0 \longrightarrow -2)$; SO_2 is the reducing agent, because oxidation number of S in SO_2 is increased $(+4 \longrightarrow +6)$.

3.75 (a) redox; I_2O_5 is the oxidizing agent, because oxidation number of I decreases $(+5 \longrightarrow 0)$; CO is the reducing agent, because oxidation number of C increases $(+2 \longrightarrow +4)$.

(b) redox; I_2 is the oxidizing agent, because oxidation number of I decreases $(0 \longrightarrow -1)$; $S_2O_3^{2-}(aq)$ is the reducing agent, because oxidation number of S increases $(+2 \longrightarrow 2.5)$.

(c) precipitation; $Ag^+(aq) + Br^-(aq) \longrightarrow AgBr(s)$

(d) redox; UF_4 is the oxidizing agent, because oxidation number of U decreases $(+4 \longrightarrow 0)$; Mg is the reducing agent, because oxidation number of Mg increases $(0 \longrightarrow +2)$.

CHALLENGING EXERCISES

3.77 (a) $HClO_2$, H_2O, H_3O^+, ClO_2^- ($HClO_2$ is a weak acid)

(b) NH_3, H_2O, NH_4^+, OH^- (NH_3 is a weak base)

(c) CH_3COOH, H_2O, H_3O^+, CH_3COO^- (CH_3COOH is a weak acid; its formula is usually written as $HC_2H_3O_2$, acetic acid.)

3.79 $2C_8H_{18}(l) + 25O_2(g) \longrightarrow 16CO_2(g) + 18H_2O(g)$

3.81 $4C_{10}H_{15}N(s) + 55O_2(g) \longrightarrow 40CO_2(g) + 30H_2O(l) + 2N_2(g)$

3.83 $H_2S(g) + 2NaOH(aq) \longrightarrow Na_2S(aq) + 2H_2O(l)$

$4H_2S(g) + Na_2S(alc) \longrightarrow Na_2S_5(alc) + 4H_2(g)$

$10H_2O(l) + 9O_2(g) + 2Na_2S_5(alc) \longrightarrow 2Na_2S_2O_3 \cdot 5H_2O + 6SO_2(g)$

3.85 Let x = oxidation number of H or O.

(a) K = +1, then $+1 + 2 \times x = 0$, $x(O) = -\frac{1}{2}$

(b) Li = +1, Al = +3, then $+1 + 3 + 4 \times x = 0$, $x(H) = -1$

(c) Na = −1, then $2 \times (+1) + 2 \times x = 0$, $x(O) = -1$

(d) Na = +1, then $+1 + x = 0$, $x(H) = -1$

(e) K = +1, then $+1 + 3 \times x = 0$, $x(O) = -\frac{1}{3}$

CHAPTER 4
REACTION STOICHIOMETRY: CHEMISTRY'S ACCOUNTING

EXERCISES

Mole Calculations

4.1   In each case, we first establish the stoichiometric relation. This allows us to convert from amount (in moles) of one substance to amount (in moles) of the other.

(a) $2H_2(g) + O_2(g) \longrightarrow 2H_2O(l)$; so $2 \text{ mol } H_2 \simeq 1 \text{ mol } O_2$

$$\text{number of moles of } H_2 = 5.0 \text{ mol } O_2 \times \frac{2 \text{ mol } H_2}{1 \text{ mol } O_2} = 10 \text{ mol } H_2$$

(b) $H_2(g) + O_2(g) \longrightarrow H_2O_2(l)$; so $1 \text{ mol } H_2 \simeq 1 \text{ mol } O_2$

$$\text{number of moles of } H_2 = 5.0 \text{ mol } O_2 \times \frac{1 \text{ mol } H_2}{1 \text{ mol } O_2} = 5.0 \text{ mol } H_2$$

4.3   (a) Stoichiometric relation is $1 \text{ mol } HCl \simeq 1 \text{ mol } NaOH$.

$$\text{number of moles of } NaOH = 3.7 \text{ mol } HCl \times \left(\frac{1 \text{ mol } NaOH}{1 \text{ mol } HCl} \right) = 3.7 \text{ mol } NaOH$$

(b) Stoichiometric relation $= 3 \text{ mol } NO_2 \simeq 2 \text{ mol } HNO_3$.

$$\text{number of moles of } NO_2 = 7.33 \text{ mol } HNO_3 \times \left(\frac{3 \text{ mol } NO_2}{2 \text{ mol } HNO_3} \right) = 11.0 \text{ mol } NO_2$$

(c) Stoichiometric relation $= 2 \text{ mol } MnO_4^- \simeq 10 \text{ mol } I^-$.

$$\text{number of moles of } MnO_4^- = 0.042 \text{ mol } I^- \times \left(\frac{2 \text{ mol } MnO_4^-}{10 \text{ mol } I^-} \right)$$
$$= 8.4 \times 10^{-3} \text{ mol } MnO_4^-$$

4.5   The stoichiometric relation, as determined from the chemical equation, is $12 \text{ mol } CO_2 \simeq 2 \text{ mol } C_6H_{14}$. Hexane is $C_6H_{14}(l)$.

$$\text{number of moles of } CO_2 = 1.5 \text{ mol hexane} \times \left(\frac{12 \text{ mol } CO_2}{2 \text{ mol hexane}} \right) = 9.0 \text{ mol } CO_2$$

Mass-Mole Relationships

4.7 (a) $6 \text{ mol } H_2O \simeq 4 \text{ mol } NH_3$

number of moles of H_2O = $1.0 \text{ g } NH_3 \times \left(\dfrac{1 \text{ mol } NH_3}{17.03 \text{ g } NH_3}\right) \times \left(\dfrac{6 \text{ mol } H_2O}{4 \text{ mol } NH_3}\right)$

$= 0.088 \text{ mol } H_2O$

(b) $3 \text{ mol } O_2 \simeq 4 \text{ mol } NH_3$

mass of O_2 = $13.7 \text{ mol } NH_3 \times \left(\dfrac{3 \text{ mol } O_2}{4 \text{ mol } NH_3}\right) \times \left(\dfrac{32.00 \text{ g } O_2}{1 \text{ mol } O_2}\right) = 329 \text{ g } O_2$

4.9 (a) $3 \text{ mol } CO_2 \simeq 1 \text{ mol } C_3H_8$

mass of CO_2 = $1.55 \text{ mol } C_3H_8 \times \left(\dfrac{3 \text{ mol } CO_2}{1 \text{ mol } C_3H_8}\right) \times \left(\dfrac{44.01 \text{ g } CO_2}{1 \text{ mol } CO_2}\right)$

$= 205 \text{ g } CO_2$

(b) $4 \text{ mol } H_2O \simeq 3 \text{ mol } CO_2$

number of moles of H_2O = $4.40 \text{ g } CO_2 \times \left(\dfrac{1 \text{ mol } CO_2}{44.01 \text{ g } CO_2}\right) \times \left(\dfrac{4 \text{ mol } H_2O}{3 \text{ mol } CO_2}\right)$

$= 0.133 \text{ mol } H_2O$

Mass-Mass Relationships

4.11 (a) mass of Al_2O_3 = $10.0 \text{ g } Al \times \left(\dfrac{1 \text{ mol } Al}{26.98 \text{ g } Al}\right) \times \left(\dfrac{2 \text{ mol } Al_2O_3}{4 \text{ mol } Al}\right)$

$\times \left(\dfrac{101.96 \text{ g } Al_2O_3}{1 \text{ mol } Al_2O_3}\right) = 18.9 \text{ g } Al_2O_3$

(b) mass of O_2 = $10.0 \text{ g } Al \times \left(\dfrac{1 \text{ mol } Al}{26.98 \text{ g } Al}\right) \times \left(\dfrac{3 \text{ mol } O_2}{4 \text{ mol } Al}\right) \times \left(\dfrac{32.00 \text{ g } O_2}{1 \text{ mol } O_2}\right)$

$= 8.90 \text{ g } O_2$

We see that $18.9 \text{ g } Al_2O_3 - 8.9 \text{ g } O_2 = 10.0 \text{ g } Al$.

4.13 (a) mass of Al = $1.5 \times 10^4 \text{ kg } NH_4ClO_4 \times \left(\dfrac{10^3 \text{ g } NH_4ClO_4}{1 \text{ kg } NH_4ClO_4}\right)$

$\times \left(\dfrac{1 \text{ mol } NH_4ClO_4}{117.49 \text{ g } NH_4ClO_4}\right) \times \left(\dfrac{10 \text{ mol } Al}{6 \text{ mol } NH_4ClO_4}\right) \times \left(\dfrac{26.98 \text{ g } Al}{1 \text{ mol } Al}\right)$

$= 5.7 \times 10^6 \text{ g } Al$

(b) mass of Al_2O_3 = $5000 \text{ kg } Al \times \left(\dfrac{10^3 \text{ g } Al}{1 \text{ kg } Al}\right) \times \left(\dfrac{1 \text{ mol } Al}{26.98 \text{ g } Al}\right)$

$\times \left(\dfrac{5 \text{ mol } Al_2O_3}{10 \text{ mol } Al}\right) \times \left(\dfrac{101.96 \text{ g } Al_2O_3}{1 \text{ mol } Al_2O_3}\right) = 9.448 \times 10^6 \text{ g } Al_2O_3$

$= 9.448 \times 10^3 \text{ kg } Al_2O_3$

4.15 (a) mass of H_2O = 2.5×10^3 g tristearin $\times \left(\dfrac{1 \text{ mol tristearin}}{891.51 \text{ g tristearin}}\right)$

$\times \left(\dfrac{110 \text{ mol } H_2O}{2 \text{ mol tristearin}}\right) \times \left(\dfrac{18.02 \text{ g } H_2O}{1 \text{ mol } H_2O}\right) = 2.8 \times 10^3 \text{ g } H_2O$

(b) mass of O_2 = 2.5 g tristearin $\times \left(\dfrac{1 \text{ mol tristearin}}{891.51 \text{ g tristearin}}\right) \times \left(\dfrac{163 \text{ mol } O_2}{2 \text{ mol tristearin}}\right)$

$\times \left(\dfrac{32.00 \text{ g } O_2}{1 \text{ mol } O_2}\right) = 7.3 \text{g } O_2$

4.17 There are two approaches. We can first calculate the mass of gasoline in 1.0 L of gasoline and then use that result to calculate the mass of water produced. Alternatively, we can calculate the mass of water directly from the volume of gasoline. Both approaches are illustrated below.

(1) mass of gasoline = 1.0 L gasoline $\times \left(\dfrac{1000 \text{ mL gasoline}}{1 \text{ L gasoline}}\right) \times \left(\dfrac{0.79 \text{ g gasoline}}{1 \text{ mL gasoline}}\right)$

$= 79\overline{0}$ g gasoline

mass of H_2O = $79\overline{0}$ g gasoline $\times \left(\dfrac{1 \text{ mol gasoline}}{114.22 \text{ g gasoline}}\right) \times \left(\dfrac{18 \text{ mol } H_2O}{2 \text{ mol gasoline}}\right)$

$\times \left(\dfrac{18.02 \text{ g } H_2O}{1 \text{ mol } H_2O}\right) = 1.1 \times 10^3 \text{ g } H_2O$

(2) mass of H_2O = 1.0 L gasoline $\times \left(\dfrac{1000 \text{ mL gasoline}}{1 \text{ L gasoline}}\right) \times \left(\dfrac{0.79 \text{ g gasoline}}{1 \text{ mL gasoline}}\right)$

$\times \left(\dfrac{1 \text{ mol gasoline}}{114.22 \text{ g gasoline}}\right) \times \left(\dfrac{18 \text{ mol } H_2O}{2 \text{ mol gasoline}}\right) \times \left(\dfrac{18.02 \text{ g } H_2O}{1 \text{ mol } H_2O}\right) = 1.1 \times 10^3 \text{ g } H_2O$

Titrations

4.19 The stoichiometric point is the point at which the exact amount of one reactant, the titrant, has been added to complete the reaction with the other reactant, the analyte, according to the balanced chemical equation. An example is an acid-base reaction:

$$CH_3COOH(aq) + NaOH(aq) \longrightarrow NaCH_3CO_2(aq) + H_2O(l)$$

The stoichiometric point of this reaction occurs when the number of moles of NaOH added equals the number of moles of CH_3COOH originally present.

4.21 $NaOH(aq) + HCl(aq) \longrightarrow NaCl(aq) + H_2O(l)$
Hereafter, soln means "solution."

(a) number of moles of NaOH = $0.01740 \text{ L HCl} \times \left(\dfrac{0.234 \text{ mol HCl}}{1 \text{ L HCl}} \right)$

$$\times \left(\dfrac{1 \text{ mol NaOH}}{1 \text{ mol HCl}} \right) = 4.07 \times 10^{-3} \text{ mol NaOH}$$

molarity of NaOH soln = $\left(\dfrac{4.07 \times 10^{-3} \text{ mol NaOH}}{0.01500 \text{ L NaOH}} \right) = 0.271 \text{ mol} \cdot \text{L}^{-1}$

(b) mass of NaOH = $0.015 \text{ L NaOH} \times \left(\dfrac{0.271 \text{ mol NaOH}}{1 \text{ L NaOH}} \right)$

$$\times \left(\dfrac{40.0 \text{ g NaOH}}{1 \text{ mol NaOH}} \right) = 0.163 \text{ g NaOH}$$

4.23 $2 \text{ HNO}_3(aq) + \text{Ba(OH)}_2(aq) \longrightarrow \text{Ba(NO}_3)_2(aq) + 2 \text{ H}_2\text{O}(l)$

molar concentration of Ba(OH)$_2$ soln = $\left(\dfrac{9.670 \text{ g Ba(OH)}_2}{0.2500 \text{ L}} \right) \times \left(\dfrac{1 \text{ mol Ba(OH)}_2}{171.36 \text{ g Ba(OH)}_2} \right)$

$$= 0.2257 \text{ mol} \cdot \text{L}^{-1}$$

(a) number of moles of HNO$_3$ soln = $0.01156 \text{ L Ba(OH)}_2$

$$\times \left(\dfrac{0.2257 \text{ mol Ba(OH)}_2}{1 \text{ L Ba(OH)}_2} \right) \times \left(\dfrac{2 \text{ mol HNO}_3}{1 \text{ mol Ba(OH)}_2} \right) = 5.219 \times 10^{-3} \text{ mol HNO}_3$$

molarity of HNO$_3$ soln = $\left(\dfrac{5.219 \times 10^{-3} \text{ mol HNO}_3}{0.02500 \text{ L HNO}_3} \right) = 0.2087 \text{ mol} \cdot \text{L}^{-1}$

(b) mass of HNO$_3$ = $0.02500 \text{ L HNO}_3 \times \left(\dfrac{0.2087 \text{ mol HNO}_3}{1 \text{ L HNO}_3} \right)$

$$\times \left(\dfrac{63.02 \text{ g HNO}_3}{1 \text{ mol HNO}_3} \right) = 0.3289 \text{ g HNO}_3$$

4.25 $\text{HX}(aq) + \text{NaOH}(aq) \longrightarrow \text{NaX}(aq) + \text{H}_2\text{O}(l)$

number of moles of acid = $0.0688 \text{ L NaOH} \times \left(\dfrac{0.750 \text{ mol NaOH}}{1 \text{ L NaOH}} \right)$

$$\times \left(\dfrac{1 \text{ mol acid}}{1 \text{ mol NaOH}} \right) = 0.0516 \text{ mol acid}$$

molar mass of acid = $\left(\dfrac{3.25 \text{ g acid}}{0.0516 \text{ mol acid}} \right) = 63.0 \text{ g} \cdot \text{mol}^{-1}$

Reaction Yield

4.27 percentage yield of Na$_4$XeO$_6$ = $\dfrac{1.07 \text{ mg Na}_4\text{XeO}_6}{1.25 \text{ mg Na}_4\text{XeO}_6} \times 100\% = 85.6\%$

4.29 $\text{percentage yield} = \dfrac{\text{actual yield}}{\text{theoretical yield}} \times 100\%$

$\text{theoretical yield of CO}_2 = 30.7 \text{ g CaCO}_3 \times \left(\dfrac{1 \text{ mol CaCO}_3}{100.09 \text{ g CaCO}_3}\right) \times \left(\dfrac{1 \text{ mol CO}_2}{1 \text{ mol CaCO}_3}\right)$

$\times \left(\dfrac{44.01 \text{ g CO}_2}{1 \text{ mol CO}_2}\right) = 13.5 \text{ g CO}_2$

$\text{percentage yield CO}_2 = \dfrac{11.7 \text{ g CO}_2}{13.5 \text{ g CO}_2} \times 100\% = 86.7\%$

Limiting Reactants

4.31 The limiting reactant is the reactant that governs the theoretical yield of a product in a given reaction. It is the reactant that will be depleted first in the chemical reaction. When all of the limiting reactant is consumed, the reaction is completed, regardless of how much of another reactant may be present. After the theoretical yield has been determined from the amount of the limiting reactant, the percentage yield is determined in the usual manner, namely,

$$\text{percentage yield} = \dfrac{\text{actual yield}}{\text{theoretical yield}} \times 100\%$$

In a combustion analysis, the compound that is burned in oxygen is the limiting reactant. That is, there is excess oxygen and, consequently, the amounts of the products are determined by the amount of the compound formed. The amounts of products are then related to the amounts of each element in the compound, and the smallest whole number ratio of the amounts of each element gives the empirical formula.

4.33 $\text{number of moles of C}_2\text{H}_5\text{OH supplied} = 2.00 \text{ g C}_2\text{H}_5\text{OH}$

$\times \left(\dfrac{1 \text{ mol C}_2\text{H}_5\text{OH}}{47.07 \text{ g C}_2\text{H}_5\text{OH}}\right) = 0.0425 \text{ mol C}_2\text{H}_5\text{OH}$

$\text{number of moles of O}_2 \text{ supplied} = 1.00 \text{ g O}_2 \times \left(\dfrac{1 \text{ mol O}_2}{32.00 \text{ g O}_2}\right) = 0.0313 \text{ mol O}_2$

$\text{number of moles of O}_2 \text{ required} = 0.0425 \text{ mol C}_2\text{H}_5\text{OH} \times \left(\dfrac{1 \text{ mol O}_2}{1 \text{ mol C}_2\text{H}_5\text{OH}}\right)$

$= 0.0425 \text{ mol O}_2$

Because the number of moles of O_2 supplied is less than the number required, O_2 is the limiting reactant.

4.35 Let us first establish whether an excess of O_2 remains after the first reaction.

$\text{number of moles of P}_4\text{(s) supplied} = 5.77 \text{ g P}_4 \times \left(\dfrac{1 \text{ mol P}_4}{123.90 \text{ g P}_4}\right) = 0.04656 \text{ mol P}_4$

number of moles of O_2 supplied $= 5.77$ g $O_2 \times \left(\dfrac{1 \text{ mol } O_2}{32.00 \text{ g } O_2} \right) = 0.180\overline{3}$ mol O_2

number of moles of O_2 required $= 0.0465\overline{6}$ mol $P_4 \times \left(\dfrac{3 \text{ mol } O_2}{1 \text{ mol } P_4} \right) = 0.139\overline{7}$ mol O_2

Therefore, P_4 is the limiting reactant and O_2 is present in excess in the amount $(0.180\overline{3} - 0.139\overline{7})$ mol $= 0.0406$ mol.

(a) To determine the limiting reactant in the formation of P_4O_{10} by way of the second reaction, we first calculate the number of moles of P_4O_6 formed in the first reaction.

number of moles of P_4O_6 available $= 0.04656$ mol $P_4 \times \left(\dfrac{1 \text{ mol } P_4O_6}{1 \text{ mol } P_4} \right)$

$= 0.0465\overline{6}$ mol P_4O_6

number of moles of P_4O_6 required $= 0.0406$ mol $O_2 \times \left(\dfrac{1 \text{ mol } P_4O_6}{2 \text{ mol } O_2} \right)$

$= 0.0203$ mol P_4O_6

Because this amount of P_4O_6 is less than the amount available, P_4O_6 is present in excess, and O_2 is the limiting reactant.

(b) mass of $P_4O_{10} = 0.020\overline{3}$ mol $P_4O_6 \times \left(\dfrac{1 \text{ mol } P_4O_{10}}{1 \text{ mol } P_4O_6} \right) \times \left(\dfrac{283.89 \text{ g } P_4O_{10}}{1 \text{ mol } P_4O_{10}} \right)$

$= 5.76$ g P_4O_{10}

(c) mass of P_4O_6 in excess $= (0.0465\overline{6} - 0.0203)$ mol $P_4O_6 \times \left(\dfrac{219.89 \text{ g } P_4O_6}{1 \text{ mol } P_4O_6} \right)$

$= 5.78$ g P_4O_6 remaining

4.37 (a) number of moles PCl_3 supplied $= 12.4$ g $PCl_3 \times \left(\dfrac{1 \text{ mol } PCl_3}{137.32 \text{ g } PCl_3} \right)$

$= 0.0903$ mol PCl_3

number of moles H_2O supplied $= 10.0$ g $H_2O \times \left(\dfrac{1 \text{ mol } H_2O}{18.02 \text{ g } H_2O} \right)$

$= 0.555$ mol H_2O

number of moles H_2O required $= 0.0903$ mol $PCl_3 \times \left(\dfrac{3 \text{ mol } H_2O}{1 \text{ mol } PCl_3} \right)$

$= 0.271$ mol H_2O

Because 0.555 mol H_2O is greater than 0.271 mol H_2O, PCl_3 is the limiting reactant.

(b) mass of H_3PO_3 formed $= 0.0903$ mol $PCl_3 \times \left(\dfrac{1 \text{ mol } H_3PO_3}{1 \text{ mol } PCl_3} \right)$

$\times \left(\dfrac{81.99 \text{ g } H_3PO_3}{1 \text{ mol } H_3PO_3} \right) = 7.40$ g H_3PO_3

$$\text{mass of HCl formed} = 0.0903 \text{ mol PCl}_3 \times \left(\frac{3 \text{ mol HCl}}{1 \text{ mol PCl}_3}\right) \times \left(\frac{36.46 \text{ g HCl}}{1 \text{ mol HCl}}\right)$$
$$= 9.88 \text{ g HCl}$$

4.39 (a) mass of SO_2 supplied $= 2.86 \text{ g } SO_2 \text{ L}^{-1} \times 4.0 \text{ L} = 11.\overline{4} \text{ g } SO_2$

mass of H_2S supplied $= 1.52 \text{ g } H_2S \text{ L}^{-1} \times 4.0 \text{ L} = 6.0\overline{8} \text{ g } H_2S$

$$\text{number of moles of } SO_2 \text{ supplied} = 11.\overline{4} \text{ g } SO_2 \times \left(\frac{1 \text{ mol } SO_2}{64.06 \text{ g } SO_2}\right)$$
$$= 0.17\overline{8} \text{ mol } SO_2$$

$$\text{number of moles of } H_2S \text{ supplied} = 6.0\overline{8} \text{ } H_2S \times \left(\frac{1 \text{ mol } H_2S}{34.02 \text{ g } H_2S}\right)$$
$$= 0.17\overline{8} \text{ mol } H_2S$$

$$\text{number of moles of } H_2S \text{ required} = 0.17\overline{8} \text{ mol } SO_2 \times \left(\frac{2 \text{ mol } H_2S}{1 \text{ mol } SO_2}\right)$$
$$= 0.35\overline{6} \text{ mol } H_2S$$

Because 0.356 mol of H_2S is required and there is only 0.17$\overline{8}$ mol of H_2S available, H_2S is the limiting reactant.

(b) number of moles of excess $SO_2 = \left(0.17\overline{8} \text{ mol } SO_2 - 0.017\overline{8} \text{ mol } H_2S\right.$
$$\left. \times \frac{1 \text{ mol } SO_2}{2 \text{ mol } H_2S}\right) = 0.089 \text{ mol } SO_2$$

$$\text{mass of excess } SO_2 = 0.089 \text{ mol } SO_2 \times \left(\frac{64.06 \text{ g } SO_2}{1 \text{ mol } SO_2}\right) = 5.7 \text{ g } SO_2$$

(c) mass of S $= 0.17\overline{8} \text{ mol } H_2S \times \left(\frac{3 \text{ mol S}}{2 \text{ mol } H_2S}\right) \times \left(\frac{32.06 \text{ g S}}{1 \text{ mol S}}\right) = 8.6 \text{ g S}$

$$\text{mass of } H_2O = 0.17\overline{8} \text{ mol } H_2S \times \left(\frac{2 \text{ mol } H_2O}{2 \text{ mol } H_2S}\right) \times \left(\frac{18.02 \text{ g } H_2O}{1 \text{ mol } H_2O}\right)$$
$$= 3.2 \text{ g } H_2O$$

(d) $11.\overline{4} \text{ g } SO_2 + 6.0\overline{8} \text{ g } H_2S = 17.\overline{5} \text{ g of reactants and } 5.7 \text{ g } SO_2 + 8.6 \text{ g S} +$ $3.2 \text{ g } H_2O = 17.5 \text{ g of excess reactant and products; so everything checks with the law of the conservation of mass.}$

4.41 (a) Here there are three reactants. The principles involved in determining the limiting reactant are the same as those employed for two reactants. The difference is only in the number of comparisons of moles supplied to moles required that must be considered.

$$\text{moles of } Al_2O_3 \text{ supplied} = 100 \text{ g } Al_2O_3 \times \left(\frac{1 \text{ mol } Al_2O_3}{101.95 \text{ g } Al_2O_3}\right) = 0.981 \text{ mol } Al_2O_3$$

$$\text{moles of C supplied} = 40 \text{ g C} \times \left(\frac{1 \text{ mol C}}{12.01 \text{ g C}} \right) = 3.33 \text{ mol C}$$

$$\text{moles of Cl}_2 \text{ supplied} = 160 \text{ g Cl}_2 \times \left(\frac{1 \text{ mol Cl}_2}{70.90 \text{ g Cl}_2} \right) = 2.25\overline{6} \text{ mol Cl}_2$$

Inspection of the balanced equation shows that three times as many moles of C and Cl_2 are required as of Al_2O_3. We see that

$$\frac{\text{mol C}}{\text{mol Al}_2\text{O}_3} = \frac{3.33}{0.981} = 3.39 > 3.00$$

$$\frac{\text{mol Cl}_2}{\text{mol Al}_2\text{O}_3} = \frac{2.25\overline{6}}{0.981} = 2.30 < 3.00$$

Therefore, C is present in excess relative to Al_2O_3 and Al_2O_3 is present in excess relative to Cl_2. Hence, Cl_2 is the limiting reactant.

(b) $\text{mass of AlCl}_3 = 2.25\overline{6} \text{ mol Cl}_2 \times \left(\frac{2 \text{ mol AlCl}_3}{3 \text{ mol Cl}_2} \right) \times \left(\frac{133.24 \text{ g AlCl}_3}{1 \text{ mol AlCl}_3} \right)$

$$= 200 \text{ g AlCl}_3$$

Combustion Analysis

4.43 $\text{number of moles of C} = 3.03 \text{ g C} \times \left(\frac{1 \text{ mol C}}{12.01 \text{ g C}} \right) = 0.252 \text{ mol C}$

$\text{number of moles of O} = 1.14 \text{ g O} \times \left(\frac{1 \text{ mol O}}{16.00 \text{ g O}} \right) = 0.0712 \text{ mol O}$

$\text{number of moles of H} = (4.39 - 3.03 - 1.14) \text{ g H} \times \left(\frac{1 \text{ mol H}}{1.008 \text{ mol H}} \right) = 0.218 \text{ mol H}$

The ratios are $C:O:H = 0.252:0.0712:0.218$. Dividing by 0.0712 gives $C:O:H = 3.54:1.00:3.06$. Multiplying by 2 gives $C:O:H = 7.08:2.00:6.12$, which is close to $C:O:H = 7:2:6$. Therefore, the empirical formula of benzoic acid is $C_7H_6O_2$.

4.45 $\text{number of moles of C} = 0.714 \text{ g C} \times \left(\frac{1 \text{ mol C}}{12.01 \text{ g C}} \right) = 0.0595 \text{ mol C}$

$\text{number of moles of N} = 0.138 \text{ g N} \times \left(\frac{1 \text{ mol N}}{14.01 \text{ g N}} \right) = 9.85 \times 10^{-3} \text{ mol N}$

$\text{mass of H} = (0.922 - 0.714 - 0.138) \text{ g H} = 0.070 \text{ g H}$

$\text{number of moles of H} = 0.070 \text{ g H} \times \left(\frac{1 \text{ mol H}}{1.008 \text{ g H}} \right) = 0.069 \text{ mol H}$

The ratio of amounts (in moles) is $C:N:H = 0.0595:0.00985:0.069$.
Dividing by 0.009 85 gives $C:N:H = 6.04:1:7.00$.
Therefore, the empirical formula is C_6H_7N.

4.47   number of moles of C = $0.318 \text{ g CO}_2 \times \left(\dfrac{1 \text{ mol CO}_2}{44.01 \text{ g CO}_2} \right) \times \left(\dfrac{1 \text{ mol C}}{1 \text{ mol CO}_2} \right)$

$$= 0.00723 \text{ mol C}$$

mass of C = $0.00723 \text{ mol C} \times \left(\dfrac{12.01 \text{ g C}}{1 \text{ mol C}} \right) = 0.0868 \text{ g C}$

number of moles of H = $0.084 \text{ g H}_2\text{O} \times \left(\dfrac{1 \text{ mol H}_2\text{O}}{18.02 \text{ g H}_2\text{O}} \right) \times \left(\dfrac{2 \text{ mol H}}{1 \text{ mol H}_2\text{O}} \right)$

$$= 0.0093 \text{ mol H}$$

mass of H = $0.0093 \text{ mol H} \times \left(\dfrac{1.008 \text{ g H}}{1 \text{ mol H}} \right) = 9.4 \times 10^{-3} \text{ g H}$

number of moles of N = $0.0145 \text{ g N} \times \left(\dfrac{1 \text{ mol N}}{14.01 \text{ g N}} \right) = 1.03 \times 10^{-3} \text{ mol N}$

sum of masses of C, H, and N = $(0.0868 + 0.0094 + 0.0145) \text{ g} = 0.1107 \text{ g}$

mass of O = $(0.152 - 0.111) \text{ g O} = 0.041 \text{ g O}$

number of moles of O = $0.041 \text{ g O} \times \left(\dfrac{1 \text{ mol O}}{16.00 \text{ g O}} \right) = 2.5\bar{6} \times 10^{-3} \text{ mol O}$

The ratio of amounts (in moles) is C:H:N:O = $0.00723 : 0.0093 : 0.00103 : 0.0025\bar{6}$.
Dividing by 0.00103 gives C:H:N:O = $7.02 : 9.0 : 1.00 : 2.5$.
Multiplying by 2 gives C:H:N:O = $14 : 18 : 2 : 5$.
The empirical formula is $C_{14}H_{18}N_2O_5$, which has a molar mass of $294 \text{ g} \cdot \text{mol}^{-1}$; consequently, this is also the molecular formula.

4.49   number of moles of C = $0.682 \text{ g CO}_2 \times \left(\dfrac{1 \text{ mol CO}_2}{44.01 \text{ g CO}_2} \right) \times \left(\dfrac{1 \text{ mol C}}{1 \text{ mol CO}_2} \right)$

$$= 0.0155 \text{ mol C}$$

mass of C = $0.0155 \text{ mol C} \times \left(\dfrac{12.01 \text{ g C}}{1 \text{ mol C}} \right) = 0.186 \text{ g C}$

number of moles of H = $0.174 \text{ g H}_2\text{O} \times \left(\dfrac{1 \text{ mol H}_2\text{O}}{18.02 \text{ g H}_2\text{O}} \right) \times \left(\dfrac{2 \text{ mol H}}{1 \text{ mol H}_2\text{O}} \right)$

$$= 0.0193 \text{ mol H}$$

mass of H = $0.0193 \text{ mol H} \times \left(\dfrac{1.008 \text{ g H}}{1 \text{ mol H}} \right) = 0.0195 \text{ g H}$

number of moles of N = $0.110 \text{ g N} \times \left(\dfrac{1 \text{ mol N}}{14.01 \text{ g N}} \right) = 0.00785 \text{ mol N}$

mass of O = $(0.376 - 0.186 - 0.0195 - 0.110) \text{ g O} = 0.060 \text{ g O}$

number of moles of O = $0.060 \text{ g O} \times \left(\dfrac{1 \text{ mol O}}{16.00 \text{ g O}} \right) = 0.0038 \text{ mol O}$

The ratio of amounts (in moles) is C:H:N:O = $0.0155 : 0.0193 : 0.00785 : 0.0038$.
Dividing by 0.0038 gives C:H:N:O = $4.1 : 5.1 : 2.1 : 1$, which is close to C:H:N:O =

$4:5:2:1$. Hence, the empirical formula is $C_4H_5N_2O$; its molar mass $= (4 \times 12.01 + 5 \times 1.008 + 2 \times 14.01 + 16.00)\ g \cdot mol^{-1} = 97.1\ g \cdot mol^{-1}$. We note that $194\ g \cdot mol^{-1}/97.1\ g \cdot mol^{-1} \approx 2$. Therefore, the molecular formula is $C_8N_{10}N_4O_2$.
The equation for the combustion is

$$2\ C_8H_{10}N_4O_2(s) + 19\ O_2(g) \longrightarrow 16\ CO_2(g) + 10\ H_2O(g) + 4\ N_2(g)$$

SUPPLEMENTARY EXERCISES

4.51 The theoretical yield is the maximum quantity of product(s) that can be obtained, according to the reaction stoichiometry, from a given quantity of a specified reactant (the limiting reactant).

The percentage yield of a product is the percentage of its theoretical yield that is actually achieved. It is calculated as

$$\text{percentage yield} = \frac{\text{actual yield}}{\text{theoretical yield}} \times 100\%$$

The percentage yield may be less than 100% for a specified product, because alternate reactions may take place in addition to the desired reaction, forming products other than the desired product(s).

4.53 (a) atoms of Si $= 5.00\ \mu g\ CO \times \left(\dfrac{10^{-6}\ g\ CO}{1\ \mu g\ CO}\right) \times \left(\dfrac{1\ mol\ CO}{28.01\ g\ CO}\right)$

$\times \left(\dfrac{1\ mol\ Si}{2\ mol\ CO}\right) \times \left(\dfrac{6.02 \times 10^{23}\ atoms\ Si}{1\ mol\ Si}\right) = 5.37 \times 10^{16}\ atoms\ Si$

(b) atoms of C $= 7.33 \times 10^{22}\ molecules\ SiO_2 \times \left(\dfrac{2\ atoms\ C}{1\ molecule\ SiO_2}\right)$

$= 1.47 \times 10^{23}\ atoms\ C$

4.55 In (b) and (c), the limiting reactant is H_2O_2, because N_2H_4 is present in excess.

(a) number of moles of $H_2O_2 = 0.477\ mol\ N_2H_4 \times \left(\dfrac{7\ mol\ H_2O_2}{1\ mol\ N_2H_4}\right)$

$= 3.34\ mol\ H_2O_2$

(b) number of moles of $HNO_3 = 6.77\ g\ H_2O_2 \times \left(\dfrac{1\ mol\ H_2O_2}{34.02\ g\ H_2O_2}\right)$

$\times \left(\dfrac{2\ mol\ HNO_3}{7\ mol\ H_2O_2}\right) = 5.69 \times 10^{-2}\ mol\ HNO_3$

(c) mass of H_2O = 0.0496 g H_2O_2 $\times \left(\dfrac{1 \text{ mol } H_2O_2}{34.02 \text{ g } H_2O_2} \right)$

$\times \left(\dfrac{8 \text{ mol } H_2O}{7 \text{ mol } H_2O_2} \right) \times \left(\dfrac{18.02 \text{ g } H_2O}{1 \text{ mol } H_2O} \right) = 3.00 \times 10^{-2} \text{ g } H_2O$

4.57 (a) mass of Mn = 2.935×10^{-3} g Al $\times \left(\dfrac{1 \text{ mol Al}}{26.98 \text{ g Al}} \right) \times \left(\dfrac{3 \text{ mol Mn}}{4 \text{ mol Al}} \right)$

$\times \left(\dfrac{54.94 \text{ g Mn}}{1 \text{ mol Mn}} \right) = 4.482 \times 10^{-3}$ g Mn = 4.482 mg Mn

(b) percentage yield = $\dfrac{2.386 \text{ mg}}{4.482 \text{ mg}} \times 100\% = 53.23\%$

4.59 theoretical yield of NO = 600 L O_2 $\times \left(\dfrac{1.43 \text{ g } O_2}{1 \text{ L } O_2} \right) \times \left(\dfrac{1 \text{ mol } O_2}{32.00 \text{ g } O_2} \right)$

$\times \left(\dfrac{4 \text{ mol NO}}{5 \text{ mol } O_2} \right) \times \left(\dfrac{30.01 \text{ g NO}}{1 \text{ mol NO}} \right) = 644 \text{ g NO}$

actual yield of NO = 0.90×644 g NO = 5.8×10^{2} g NO

4.61 (a) volume of O_2(g) = 2.27×10^{-3} g C_8H_{18} $\times \left(\dfrac{1 \text{ mol } C_8H_{18}}{114.22 \text{ g } C_8H_{18}} \right)$

$\times \left(\dfrac{25 \text{ mol } O_2}{2 \text{ mol } C_8H_{18}} \right) \times \left(\dfrac{32.00 \text{ g } O_2}{1 \text{ mol } O_2} \right) \times \left(\dfrac{1 \text{ L } O_2(g)}{1.43 \text{ g } O_2} \right) = 5.56 \times 10^{-3} \text{ L } O_2$

(b) volume of air = 5.56×10^{-3} L O_2 $\times \left(\dfrac{100 \text{ L air}}{21 \text{ L } O_2} \right) = 2.6 \times 10^{-2}$ L air

4.63 (a) See figure. Two molecules of ammonia can form; three molecules of N_2 remain unreacted.

(b) 3 molecules H_2 + 1 molecule N_2 $\longrightarrow$ 2 molecules NH_3

As all molecules of H_2 are used up and two molecules of N_2 remain, H_2 is the limiting reagent.

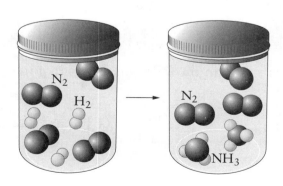

4.65 (a) number of moles of Na supplied = $10.0 \text{ g Na} \times \left(\dfrac{1 \text{ mol Na}}{22.99 \text{ g Na}} \right)$

$$= 0.435 \text{ mol Na}$$

number of moles of Al_2O_3 supplied = $10.0 \text{ g Al}_2\text{O}_3 \times \left(\dfrac{1 \text{ mol Al}_2\text{O}_3}{101.96 \text{ g Al}_2\text{O}_3} \right)$

$$= 0.0981 \text{ mol Al}_2\text{O}_3$$

number of moles of Al_2O_3 required = $0.435 \text{ mol Na} \times \left(\dfrac{1 \text{ mol Al}_2\text{O}_3}{6 \text{ mol Al}} \right)$

$$= 0.0725 \text{ mol Al}_2\text{O}_3$$

Because 0.0981 mol Al_2O_3 is greater than the 0.0725 mol Al_2O_3 required, Na is the limiting reactant.

(b) mass of Al = $0.435 \text{ mol Na} \times \left(\dfrac{2 \text{ mol Al}}{6 \text{ mol Na}} \right) \times \left(\dfrac{26.98 \text{ g Al}}{1 \text{ mol Al}} \right) = 3.91 \text{ g Al}$

(c) number of moles of Al_2O_3 in excess = 0.0981 mol Al_2O_3

$$- \left[0.435 \text{ mol Na} \times \left(\dfrac{1 \text{ mol Al}_2\text{O}_3}{6 \text{ mol Na}} \right) \right] = 0.0256 \text{ mol Al}$$

mass of Al_2O_3 in excess = $0.0256 \text{ mol Al}_2\text{O}_3 \times \left(\dfrac{101.96 \text{ g Al}_2\text{O}_3}{1 \text{ mol Al}_2\text{O}_3} \right)$

$$= 2.61 \text{ g Al}_2\text{O}_3$$

(d) percentage yield Al = $\dfrac{1.77 \text{ g Al}}{3.91 \text{ g Al}} \times 100\% = 45.3\%$

4.67 $4.94 \text{ g PH}_3 \times 0.85 = 4.24 \text{ g PH}_3$

$0.110 \text{ kg CuSO}_4 \cdot 5\text{H}_2\text{O} = 110 \text{ g CuSO}_4 \cdot 5\text{H}_2\text{O}$

number of moles of $CuSO_4 \cdot 5H_2O$ supplied = $110 \text{ g CuSO}_4 \cdot 5\text{H}_2\text{O}$

$$\times \left(\dfrac{1 \text{ mol CuSO}_4 \cdot 5\text{H}_2\text{O}}{249.68 \text{ g CuSO}_4 \cdot 5\text{H}_2\text{O}} \right) = 0.441 \text{ mol CuSO}_4 \cdot 5\text{H}_2\text{O}$$

number of moles of PH_3 supplied = $4.24 \text{ g PH}_3 \times \left(\dfrac{1 \text{ mol PH}_3}{33.99 \text{ g PH}_3} \right) = 0.1247 \text{ mol PH}_3$

number of moles of PH_3 required = 0.441 mol $CuSO_4 \cdot 5H_2O$

$$\times \left(\dfrac{2 \text{ mol PH}_3}{3 \text{ mol CuSO}_4 \cdot 5\text{H}_2\text{O}} \right) = 0.294 \text{ mol PH}_3$$

Because 0.1247 mol PH_3 is less than the 0.294 mol PH_3 required, PH_3 is the limiting reactant.

mass of Cu_3P_2 = $0.1247 \text{ mol PH}_3 \times \left(\dfrac{1 \text{ mol Cu}_3\text{P}_2}{2 \text{ mol PH}_3} \right) \times \left(\dfrac{252.56 \text{ g Cu}_3\text{P}_2}{1 \text{ mol Cu}_3\text{P}_2} \right) \times 0.0631$

$$= 0.994 \text{ g Cu}_3\text{P}_2$$

4.69 Assume 100 g of Teflon.

number of moles of C = $24 \text{ g C} \times \left(\dfrac{1 \text{ mol C}}{12.01 \text{ g C}} \right) = 2.0 \text{ mol C}$

number of moles of F = $76 \text{ g F} \times \left(\dfrac{1 \text{ mol F}}{19.00 \text{ g F}} \right) = 4.0 \text{ mol F}$

Therefore, C:F = 2.0:4.0 and the empirical formula is CF_2.

4.71 $H_2SO_4(aq) + 2\,NaOH(aq) \longrightarrow Na_2SO_4(aq) + 2\,H_2O(l)$

(a) number of moles H_2SO_4 = $0.0174 \text{ L NaOH} \times \left(\dfrac{0.100 \text{ mol NaOH}}{1 \text{ L NaOH}} \right)$

$\times \left(\dfrac{1 \text{ mol } H_2SO_4}{2 \text{ mol NaOH}} \right) = 8.70 \times 10^{-4} \text{ mol } H_2SO_4$

(b) mass percentage S = $8.70 \times 10^{-4} \text{ mol } H_2SO_4 \times \left(\dfrac{1 \text{ mol S}}{1 \text{ mol } H_2SO_4} \right)$

$\times \left(\dfrac{32.06 \text{ g S}}{1 \text{ mol S}} \right) \times \left(\dfrac{1}{6.43 \text{ g coal}} \right) \times 100\% = 0.433\%$

CHALLENGING EXERCISES

4.73 (a) $Na_2CO_3(aq) + 2\,HCl(aq) \longrightarrow 2\,NaCl(aq) + H_2CO_3(aq)$

(b) molarity of Na_2CO_3 sol = $\left(\dfrac{0.530 \text{ g } Na_2CO_3}{0.1000 \text{ L}} \right) \times \left(\dfrac{1 \text{ mol } Na_2CO_3}{105.99 \text{ g } Na_2CO_3} \right)$

$= 0.0500 \text{ M } Na_2CO_3$

number of moles of HCl = $0.02500 \text{ L } Na_2CO_3 \times \left(\dfrac{0.0500 \text{ mol } Na_2CO_3}{1 \text{ L } Na_2CO_3} \right)$

$\times \left(\dfrac{2 \text{ mol HCl}}{1 \text{ mol } Na_2CO_3} \right) = 2.5 \times 10^{-3} \text{ mol } NaCO_3$

molarity of original HCl sol = $\left(\dfrac{2.50 \times 10^{-3} \text{ mol HCl}}{0.02650 \text{ L HCl}} \right) \times \left(\dfrac{1.000 \text{ L}}{0.0100 \text{ L}} \right)$

$= 9.43 \text{ M HCl}$

4.75 mass of vitamin C = $0.0101 \text{ L } I_3^- \times \left(\dfrac{0.0521 \text{ mol } I_3^-}{1 \text{ L } I_3^-} \right) \times \left(\dfrac{1 \text{ mol vitamin C}}{1 \text{ mol } I_3^-} \right)$

$\times \left(\dfrac{176 \text{ g vitamin C}}{1 \text{ mol vitamin C}} \right) \times \left(\dfrac{100.00 \text{ mL}}{10.0 \text{ mL}} \right) = 0.926 \text{ g vitamin C}$

The manufacturer's claim is about 7% inaccurate.

CHAPTER 5
THE PROPERTIES OF GASES

EXERCISES

The Nature of a Gas

5.1 The kinetic model of a gas is described in Section 5.2. The essential features of the model are (1) Gases consist of widely separated molecular particles in ceaseless random motion. (2) Gas molecules collide with the walls of their container and with one another. The pressure of a gas is a manifestation of the collisions with the walls. (3) Collisions change the direction and speed of the molecules, resulting in a wide range of speeds, with no preferred direction for their motions. (4) The temperature of the gas is a measure of the average speed of the molecules, higher average speeds corresponding to higher temperatures.

5.3 The temperature of a gas is a measure of the average velocity of its molecules: the higher the temperature, the higher the average speed of the molecules.

Pressure

5.5 Pressure is a force exerted divided by the area of surface. Air pressure exerted on the surface of the mercury in the dish (see Figure 5.8) is transmitted through the liquid mercury and supports the mercury column. Equilibrium requires that the pressure at the base of the column of mercury is balanced by the pressure on the surface of the mercury in the dish. Thus, the height of the column is proportional to the pressure. The space above the mercury is a vacuum, so it adds no pressure. A column of mercury 760 mm high represents, by definition, one standard atmosphere. As in a thermometer, calibration makes it a true measuring device.

5.7 (a) $\left.\begin{array}{l} 1.00 \text{ bar} = 100 \text{ kPa} \\ 1 \text{ atm} = 101.3 \text{ kPa} \end{array}\right\}$ Table 5.2

$$(1.00 \text{ bar}) \times \left(\frac{100 \text{ kPa}}{1 \text{ bar}}\right) \times \left(\frac{1 \text{ atm}}{101.3 \text{ kPa}}\right) = 0.987 \text{ atm}$$

(b) $1.00 \text{ Torr} \times \dfrac{1 \text{ atm}}{760 \text{ Torr}} = 1.32 \times 10^{-3} \text{ atm}$

(c) $(1.00 \text{ mg Hg}) \times \left(\dfrac{1 \text{ Torr}}{1 \text{ mm Hg}}\right) \times \left(\dfrac{1 \text{ atm}}{760 \text{ Torr}}\right) \times \left(\dfrac{101.3 \text{ kPa}}{1 \text{ atm}}\right)$

$$\times \left(\dfrac{10^3 \text{ Pa}}{1 \text{ kPa}}\right) = 1.33 \times 10^2 \text{ Pa}$$

(d) $(1.00 \text{ kPa}) \times \left(\dfrac{1 \text{ atm}}{101.3 \text{ kPa}}\right) = 9.87 \times 10^{-3} \text{ atm}$

5.9 (a) $(8 \times 10^4 \text{ atm}) \times \left(\dfrac{101.3 \text{ kPa}}{1 \text{ atm}}\right) \times \left(\dfrac{1 \text{ bar}}{100 \text{ kPa}}\right) \times \left(\dfrac{1 \text{ kbar}}{10^3 \text{ bar}}\right) = 8 \times 10^1 \text{ kbar}$

(b) $(8 \times 10^4 \text{ atm}) \times \left(\dfrac{101.3 \text{ kPa}}{1 \text{ atm}}\right) \times \left(\dfrac{10^3 \text{ Pa}}{1 \text{ kPa}}\right) = 8 \times 10^9 \text{ Pa}$

5.11 $P = dgh$ (See sidenote on p. 147)

Because the pressure, P, is the same no matter what the measuring device, h is inversely proportional to d. That is,

$$h = \dfrac{P}{dg}, \text{ or } hd = \dfrac{P}{g} = \text{constant.}$$

Then

$$h(\text{water})\, d(\text{water}) = h(\text{Hg})\, d(\text{Hg}),$$

or

$$h(\text{water}) = \dfrac{h(\text{Hg})\, d(\text{Hg})}{d(\text{water})}$$

$$= \dfrac{77.5 \text{ cm} \times 13.6 \text{ g} \cdot \text{cm}^{-3}}{1.10 \text{ g} \cdot \text{cm}^{-3}}$$

$$= 9.58 \times 10^2 \text{ cm}$$

The Gas Laws

5.13 In each case, $V_2 = V_1 \times \dfrac{P_1}{P_2}$

(a) $V_2 = (1.00 \text{ L}) \times \left(\dfrac{2.20 \text{ kPa}}{3.00 \text{ atm}}\right) \times \left(\dfrac{1 \text{ atm}}{101.3 \text{ kPa}}\right) = 7.24 \times 10^{-3} \text{ L}$

(b) $V_2 = (25.0 \text{ mL}) \times \left(\dfrac{200 \text{ Torr}}{0.500 \text{ atm}}\right) \times \left(\dfrac{1 \text{ atm}}{760 \text{ Torr}}\right) = 13.2 \text{ mL}$

5.15 In each case, $P_2 = P_1 \times \dfrac{V_1}{V_2}$

(a) $P_2 = 105 \text{ kPa} \times \left(\dfrac{1.0 \times 10^{-3} \text{ L}}{1.0 \text{ L}}\right) = 0.10\overline{5} \text{ kPa} = 1.0 \times 10^2 \text{ Pa}$

(b) $P_2 = 600 \text{ Torr} \times \left(\dfrac{30.0 \text{ cm}^3}{5.0 \text{ cm}^3}\right) = 3.6 \times 10^3 \text{ Torr}$

5.17 (a) $P_2 = P_1 \times \dfrac{T_2}{T_1}$

$T_1 = (273 + 10) \text{ K} = 283 \text{ K}$

$T_2 = (273 + 30) \text{ K} = 303 \text{ K}$

$P_2 = 1.5 \text{ atm} \times \left(\dfrac{303 \text{ K}}{283 \text{ K}}\right) = 1.6 \text{ atm}$

(b) $V_2 = V_1 \times \dfrac{T_2}{T_1}$

$T_1 = (273 + 85) \text{ K} = 358 \text{ K}$

$T_2 = 273 \text{ K}$

$V_2 = 255 \text{ mL} \times \left(\dfrac{273 \text{ K}}{358 \text{ K}}\right) = 194 \text{ mL}$

5.19 $T_2 = T_1 \times \dfrac{P_2}{P_1}, \quad T_1 = (273 + 20) \text{ K} = 293 \text{ K}$

$P_1 = (30 + 14.7) \text{ lb} \cdot \text{in.}^{-2} = 44.\overline{7} \text{ lb} \cdot \text{in.}^{-2}, \quad P_2 = (34 + 14.7 \text{ lb} \cdot \text{in.}^{-2})$
    $= 48.\overline{7} \text{ lb} \cdot \text{in.}^{-2}$

$T_2 = 293 \text{ K} \times \dfrac{48.\overline{7} \text{ lb} \cdot \text{in.}^{-2}}{44.\overline{7} \text{ lb} \cdot \text{in.}^{-2}} = 319 \text{ K} = (319 - 273)°\text{C} = 46°\text{C}$

Note: °C = K

5.21 Because half the gas molecules have been removed, $n_2 = \frac{1}{2}n_1$. To obtain the new temperature, we rearrange the ideal gas law.

$$PV = nRT$$

$$nT = \left(\dfrac{PV}{R}\right) = \text{constant}$$

Thus, $n_1 T_1 = n_2 T_2$, or

$T_2 = T_1 \times \dfrac{n_1}{n_2}$

$T_2 = T_1 \times \dfrac{n_1}{\frac{1}{2}n_1} = 2T_1$

Therefore, the temperature must be doubled.

5.23 The ideal gas law may be rewritten as

$$\frac{PV}{T} = nR = \text{constant; therefore,}$$

$$\frac{P_1 V_1}{T_1} = \frac{P_2 V_2}{T_2}$$

Solving for P_2,

$$P_2 = P_1 \times \frac{V_1}{V_2} \times \frac{T_2}{T_1}$$

$$= 750 \text{ Torr} \times \left(\frac{150 \text{ mL}}{500 \text{ mL}}\right) \times \left[\frac{(273 + 522) \text{ K}}{(273 + 10) \text{ K}}\right]$$

$$= 632 \text{ Torr}$$

5.25 $\dfrac{P_1 V_1}{T_1} = \dfrac{P_2 V_2}{T_2}$

Solving for V_2,

$$V_2 = V_1 \times \frac{P_1}{P_2} \times \frac{T_2}{T_1}$$

$$= 350 \text{ cm}^3 \times \frac{1.08 \text{ atm}}{0.958 \text{ atm}} \times \frac{(273 + 23) \text{ K}}{(273 + 37) \text{ K}}$$

$$= 377 \text{ cm}^3$$

The Ideal Gas Law

5.27 Boyle, Charles, and Avogadro demonstrated the following proportionalities:

Boyle: $V \propto \dfrac{1}{P}$ or $P \propto \dfrac{1}{V}$ at constant n and T

Charles: $V \propto T$ at constant n and P

Avogadro: $V \propto n$ at constant p and T

These proportions can be combined into one equation by introducing a constant of proportionality, R.

$$V = R \times \left(\frac{1}{P}\right) \times T \times n$$

$$= \frac{nRT}{P}$$

or
$$PV = nRT$$

which is the ideal gas law.

5.29 (a) $PV = nRT$; therefore, amount (moles) $= n = \dfrac{PV}{RT}$

$$n = \frac{1.3 \text{ atm} \times 0.100 \text{ L}}{8.206 \times 10^{-2} \text{ L} \cdot \text{atm} \cdot \text{K}^{-1} \cdot \text{mol}^{-1} \times 350 \text{ K}} = 4.5 \times 10^{-3} \text{ mol}$$

(b) $n = \dfrac{2.7 \times 10^{-6} \text{ g}}{32.00 \text{ g} \cdot \text{mol}^{-1}} = 8.4\overline{4} \times 10^{-8} \text{ mol}$

$$P = \frac{nRT}{V} = \frac{8.4\overline{4} \times 10^{-8} \text{ mol} \times 62.36 \text{ L} \cdot \text{Torr} \cdot \text{K}^{-1} \cdot \text{mol}^{-1} \times 290 \text{ K}}{0.120 \text{ L}}$$

$$= 1.3 \times 10^{-2} \text{ Torr}$$

(c) $n = \dfrac{PV}{RT} = \dfrac{20 \text{ Torr} \times 20 \text{ L}}{62.36 \text{ L} \cdot \text{Torr} \cdot \text{K}^{-1} \cdot \text{mol}^{-1} \times 200 \text{ K}} = 0.031\overline{9} \text{ mol}$

mass $= 0.031\overline{9} \text{ mol} \times 28.02 \text{ g} \cdot \text{mol}^{-1} = 0.89 \text{ g}$

(d) $n = \dfrac{16.7 \text{ g}}{83.80 \text{ g} \cdot \text{mol}^{-1}} = 0.199\overline{3} \text{ mol}$

$$V = \frac{nRT}{P} = \frac{0.199\overline{3} \text{ mol} \times 62.36 \text{ L} \cdot \text{Torr} \cdot \text{K}^{-1} \cdot \text{mol}^{-1} \times (44 + 273) \text{ K}}{0.100 \text{ Torr}}$$

$$= 3.94 \times 10^{4} \text{ L}$$

(e) $n = \dfrac{PV}{RT} = \dfrac{2.00 \text{ Torr} \times 2.6 \times 10^{-6} \text{ L}}{62.36 \text{ L} \cdot \text{Torr} \cdot \text{K}^{-1} \cdot \text{mol}^{-1} \times 288 \text{ K}} = 2.89 \times 10^{-10} \text{ mol}$

number of Xe atoms $= 2.89 \times 10^{-10} \text{ mol} \times 6.022 \times 10^{-23} \text{ mol}^{-1} = 1.74 \times 10^{14}$

5.31 $n_{H_2S} = (12 \text{ mg H}_2\text{S}) \times \left(\dfrac{10^{-3} \text{ g}}{1 \text{ mg}}\right) \times \left(\dfrac{1 \text{ mol H}_2\text{S}}{34.0 \text{ g H}_2\text{S}}\right) = 3.5 \times 10^{-4} \text{ mol H}_2\text{S}$

According to Avogadro's law, n_{H_2S} must equal n_{NH_3}.

Therefore, $(3.5 \times 10^{-4} \text{ mol NH}_3) \times \left(\dfrac{17.0 \text{ g}}{1 \text{ mol NH}_3}\right) = 6.0 \times 10^{-3} \text{ g NH}_3$ or 6.0 mg NH_3

5.33 (a) $n = \dfrac{PV}{RT} = \dfrac{1.22 \text{ atm} \times 0.250 \text{ L}}{8.206 \times 10^{-2} \text{ L} \cdot \text{atm} \cdot \text{K}^{-1} \cdot \text{mol}^{-1} \times 298 \text{ K}} = 1.24\overline{7} \times 10^{-2} \text{ mol}$

Let M = molar mass; then mass $= n \times M = 1.24\overline{7} \times 10^{-2} \text{ mol} \times 28.97 \text{ g} \cdot \text{mol}^{-1}$

$= 0.361 \text{ g}$

(b) mass of nitrogen $= n \times M = 1.24\overline{7} \times 10^{-2} \text{ mol} \times 28.02 \text{ g} \cdot \text{mol}^{-1} = 0.349 \text{ g}$

5.35 $V = \frac{4}{3}\pi r^3 = \frac{4}{3}(3.14) \times \left(\dfrac{12.0 \text{ in.} \times \dfrac{2.54 \text{ cm}}{1 \text{ in.}}}{2}\right)^3 = 1.48 \times 10^{4} \text{ cm}^3$

$= 1.48 \times 10^{4} \text{ mL} = 14.8 \text{ L}$

$$PV = nRT$$

$$n = \frac{PV}{RT} = \frac{\left[(100 \text{ lb} \cdot \text{in.}^{-2}) \times \left(\frac{1 \text{ atm}}{14.7 \text{ lb} \cdot \text{in.}^{-2}}\right)\right] \times 14.8 \text{ L}}{8.206 \times 10^{-2} \text{ L} \cdot \text{atm} \cdot \text{K}^{-1} \cdot \text{mol}^{-1} \times 288 \text{ K}} = 4.26 \text{ mol}$$

$$\text{mass} = 4.26 \text{ mol} \times 4.00 \text{ g} \cdot \text{mol}^{-1} = 17.0 \text{ g}$$

Molar Volume

5.37 (a) $V = \dfrac{nRT}{P} = \dfrac{1.00 \text{ mol} \times 8.206 \times 10^{-2} \text{ L} \cdot \text{atm} \cdot \text{K}^{-1} \cdot \text{mol}^{-1} \times 298 \text{ K}}{1.00 \text{ atm}}$

$= 24.4\overline{5} \text{ L} = 24.5 \text{ L}$

(b) $V = \dfrac{27.0 \text{ g} \times 8.206 \times 10^{-2} \text{ L} \cdot \text{atm} \cdot \text{K}^{-1} \cdot \text{mol}^{-1} \times 298 \text{ K}}{70.91 \text{ g} \cdot \text{mol}^{-1} \times 1.00 \text{ atm}} = 9.31 \text{ L}$

(c) $V = 3 \text{ mol} \times 24.4\overline{5} \text{ L} \cdot \text{mol}^{-1} = 73.4 \text{ L}$

(d) $V = \dfrac{0.0148 \text{ g} \times 8.206 \times 10^{-2} \text{ L} \cdot \text{atm} \cdot \text{K}^{-1} \cdot \text{mol}^{-1} \times 298 \text{ K}}{64.06 \text{ g} \cdot \text{mol}^{-1} \times 1.00 \text{ atm}}$

$= 5.65 \times 10^{-3} \text{ L} = 5.65 \text{ mL}$

5.39 $n = \dfrac{PV}{RT} = V\left(\dfrac{P}{RT}\right)$

$\dfrac{P}{RT}$ is a common factor in (a) $\longrightarrow$ (d)

$\dfrac{P}{RT} = \dfrac{1.00 \text{ atm}}{8.206 \times 10^{-2} \text{ L} \cdot \text{atm} \cdot \text{K}^{-1} \cdot \text{mol}^{-1} \times 298 \text{ K}} = 0.040 \, 8\overline{9} \text{ mol} \cdot \text{L}^{-1}$

$\text{mass} = n \times M = V \times \left(\dfrac{P}{RT}\right) \times M = V \times 0.040 \, 8\overline{9} \text{ mol} \cdot \text{L}^{-1} \times M$

(a) $\text{mass} = 2.45 \text{ L} \times 0.040 \, 8\overline{9} \text{ mol} \cdot \text{L}^{-1} \times 32.00 \text{ g} \cdot \text{mol}^{-1} = 3.21 \text{ g}$

(b) $\text{mass} = 1.94 \times 10^{-3} \text{ L} \times 0.040 \, 8\overline{9} \text{ mol} \cdot \text{L}^{-1} \times 80.06 \text{ g} \cdot \text{mol}^{-1}$

$= 6.35 \times 10^{-3} \text{ g} = 6.35 \text{ mg}$

(c) $\text{mass} = 6000 \text{ L} \times 0.040 \, 8\overline{9} \text{ mol} \cdot \text{L}^{-1} \times 16.04 \text{ g} \cdot \text{mol}^{-1}$

$= 3.94 \times 10^{3} \text{ g} = 3.94 \text{ kg}$

(d) $\text{mass} = 1.44 \times 10^{-3} \text{ L} \times 0.040 \, 8\overline{9} \text{ mol} \cdot \text{L}^{-1} \times 44.01$

$= 2.59 \times 10^{-3} \text{ g} = 2.59 \text{ mg}$

Stoichiometry of Reacting Gases

5.41 $n_{O_2} = 1.00 \text{ g KClO}_3 \times \left(\dfrac{1 \text{ mol KClO}_3}{122.6 \text{ g KClO}_3}\right) \times \left(\dfrac{3 \text{ mol O}_2}{2 \text{ mol KClO}_3}\right)$

$= 1.22 \times 10^{-2} \text{ mol O}_2$

$$V_{O_2} = \frac{n_{O_2} RT}{P} = \frac{1.22 \times 10^{-2} \text{ mol } O_2 \times 8.206 \times 10^{-2} \text{ L} \cdot \text{atm} \cdot \text{K}^{-1} \cdot \text{mol}^{-1} \times 298 \text{ K}}{1.00 \text{ atm}}$$

$$= 0.298 \text{ L}$$

5.43 $n_{CO_2} = 10.0 \text{ g } CaCO_3 \times \left(\frac{1 \text{ mol } CaCO_3}{100.09 \text{ g } CaCO_3} \right) \times \left(\frac{1 \text{ mol } CO_2}{1 \text{ mol } CaCO_3} \right)$

$$= 0.100 \text{ mol } CO_2$$

$$V_{CO_2} = \frac{n_{CO_2} RT}{P} = \frac{0.100 \text{ mol } CO_2 \times 0.082\,06 \text{ L} \cdot \text{atm} \cdot \text{K}^{-1} \cdot \text{mol}^{-1} \times 298 \text{ K}}{1.00 \text{ atm}} = 2.44 \text{ L}$$

5.45 Haber process: $N_2(g) \times 3H_2(g) \longrightarrow 2NH_3(g)$

(a) $n_{H_2} = 1.0 \times 10^3 \text{ kg } NH_3 \times \left(\frac{10^3 \text{ g } NH_3}{1 \text{ kg } NH_3} \right) \times \left(\frac{1 \text{ mol } NH_3}{17.03 \text{ g } NH_3} \right)$

$$\times \left(\frac{3 \text{ mol } H_2}{2 \text{ mol } NH_3} \right) = 8.8\overline{1} \times 10^4 \text{ mol } H_2$$

$$V_{H_2} = \frac{n_{H_2} RT}{P} = \frac{8.8\overline{1} \times 10^4 \text{ mol } H_2 \times 0.082\,06 \text{ L} \cdot \text{atm} \cdot \text{K}^{-1} \cdot \text{mol}^{-1} \times 298 \text{ K}}{1.00 \text{ atm}}$$

$$= 2.15 \times 10^6 \text{ L}$$

(b) $V_{H_2} = 2.15 \times 10^6 \text{ L} \times \left(\frac{1.00 \text{ atm}}{200 \text{ atm}} \right) \times \left(\frac{(273 + 400) \text{ K}}{298 \text{ K}} \right) = 2.43 \times 10^4 \text{ L}$

5.47 $n_{CO_2} = (2.50 \text{ kg urea}) \times \left(\frac{10^3 \text{ g}}{1 \text{ kg}} \right) \times \left(\frac{1 \text{ mol urea}}{60.0 \text{ g urea}} \right) \times \left(\frac{1 \text{ mol } CO_2}{1 \text{ mol urea}} \right)$

$$= 41.7 \text{ mol } CO_2$$

$n_{NH_3} = (2.50 \text{ kg urea}) \times \left(\frac{10^3 \text{ g}}{1 \text{ kg}} \right) \times \left(\frac{1 \text{ mol urea}}{60.0 \text{ g urea}} \right) \times \left(\frac{2 \text{ mol } NH_3}{1 \text{ mol urea}} \right) = 83.3 \text{ mol } NH_3$

$V_{CO_2} = \frac{nRT}{P} = (41.7 \text{ mol } CO_2) \times \left(\frac{0.082\,06 \text{ L} \cdot \text{atm}}{\text{K} \cdot \text{mol}} \right) \times (450 + 273) \text{ K}$

$$\times \left(\frac{1}{200 \text{ atm}} \right) = 12.4 \text{ L}$$

Because $V \propto n$ at constant T and P, $V_{NH_3} = 24.8$ L.

5.49 (b) $n_{CH_4} = 2.00 \text{ g } CH_4 \times \left(\frac{1 \text{ mol } CH_4}{16.04 \text{ g } CH_4} \right) = 0.125 \text{ mol } CH_4$

$$V_{CH_4} = \frac{n_{CH_4} RT}{p} = \frac{0.125 \text{ mol} \times 0.082\,06 \text{ L} \cdot \text{atm} \cdot \text{K}^{-1} \cdot \text{mol}^{-1} \times 348 \text{ K}}{1.00 \text{ atm}} = 3.56 \text{ L}$$

Because 3.56 L > 2.00 L, starting condition (b) would produce the larger volume of CO_2 by combustion.

Density

5.51 Let M = molar mass, then $n = \dfrac{\text{mass}}{M}$.

Assume gases are ideal, then $PV = nRT = \dfrac{\text{mass}}{V} RT$.

Rearranging, density $= d = \dfrac{\text{mass}}{V} = \dfrac{PM}{RT}$, or $d = \left(\dfrac{P}{RT}\right) M$ = constant $\times$ M (at constant T and P). Therefore, at constant T and P, the most dense gas is the one with the largest molar mass.

      (a) $M_{N_2} = 28.02$ g $\cdot$ mol^{-1}
      (b) $M_{NH_3} = 17.03$ g $\cdot$ mol^{-1}
      (c) $M_{NO_2} = 46.01$ g $\cdot$ mol^{-1}
      Therefore, NO_2 is the most dense.

5.53 density $= \dfrac{\text{molar mass}}{\text{molar volume}} = \dfrac{M}{\left(\dfrac{RT}{P}\right)} = \left(\dfrac{P}{RT}\right) M$

See Exercise 5.51 for a derivation of this relation from the ideal gas law.

      (a) density $= d = \left(\dfrac{1.00 \text{ atm}}{0.082\,06 \text{ L} \cdot \text{atm} \cdot \text{K}^{-1} \cdot \text{mol}^{-1} \times 298 \text{ K}}\right) \times 119.37$ g $\cdot$ mol^{-1}

            $= 4.88$ g $\cdot$ L^{-1}

      (b) $d = 4.88$ g $\cdot$ L$^{-1} \times \left(\dfrac{298 \text{ K}}{373 \text{ K}}\right) = 3.90$ g $\cdot$ L^{-1}

5.55 It is convenient to work part (b) first. Rearrange $d = \left(\dfrac{P}{RT}\right) M$ to give

$M = \left(\dfrac{RT}{P}\right) \times d = \left(\dfrac{RT}{P}\right)\left(\dfrac{\text{mass}}{V}\right).$

      (b) molar mass $= M = \left(\dfrac{0.082\,06 \text{ L} \cdot \text{atm} \cdot \text{K}^{-1} \cdot \text{mol}^{-1} \times 303 \text{ K}}{0.880 \text{ atm}}\right) \times \left(\dfrac{21.3 \text{ g}}{7.73 \text{ L}}\right)$

            $= 77.9$ g $\cdot$ mol^{-1}

      (a) $d = \left(\dfrac{1.00 \text{ atm}}{0.082\,06 \text{ L} \cdot \text{atm} \cdot \text{K}^{-1} \cdot \text{mol}^{-1} \times 298 \text{ K}}\right) \times 77.9$ g $\cdot$ mol$^{-1} = 3.18$ g $\cdot$ L^{-1}

5.57 (a) M-molar mass $= \left(\dfrac{RT}{P}\right) \times d$ [see Exercise 5.55]

         $= \left(\dfrac{62.36 \text{ L} \cdot \text{Torr} \cdot \text{K}^{-1} \cdot \text{mol}^{-1} \times 420 \text{ K}}{727 \text{ Torr}}\right) \times 3.60$ g $\cdot$ L$^{-1} = 130$ g $\cdot$ mol^{-1}

      (b) $d = 3.60$ g $\cdot$ L$^{-1} \times \left(\dfrac{760 \text{ Torr}}{727 \text{ Torr}}\right) \times \left(\dfrac{420 \text{ K}}{298 \text{ K}}\right) = 5.30$ g $\cdot$ L^{-1}

5.59 $(1.77 \text{ g}) \times \left(\dfrac{85.7 \text{ g C}}{100 \text{ g gas}}\right) = 1.52 \text{ g C}; \ n_C = (1.52 \text{ g C}) = \left(\dfrac{1 \text{ mol C}}{12.0 \text{ g C}}\right)$

$$= 0.127 \text{ mol C}$$

$(1.77 \text{ g}) \times \left(\dfrac{14.3 \text{ g H}}{100 \text{ g gas}}\right) = 0.253 \text{ g H}; \ n_H = (0.253 \text{ g H}) \times \left(\dfrac{1 \text{ mol H}}{1.00 \text{ g H}}\right) = 0.253 \text{ mol H}$

Because H : C ratio is 2 $\left(\text{that is, } \dfrac{0.253}{0.127} = 2\right)$, the empirical formula is CH_2 and the empirical molar mass is $14.0 \text{ g} \cdot \text{mol}^{-1}$.

$$n = \frac{PV}{RT}$$

$$n = \left(508 \text{ Torr} \times \frac{1 \text{ atm}}{760 \text{ Torr}}\right) \times (1.500 \text{ L}) \times \left(\frac{K \cdot \text{mol}}{0.082\,06 \text{ L} \cdot \text{atm}}\right) \times \left(\frac{1}{(273 + 17) \text{ K}}\right)$$

$$= 0.0421 \text{ mol}$$

Then, molar mass $= \dfrac{1.77 \text{ g}}{0.0421 \text{ mol}} = 42 \text{ g} \cdot \text{mol}^{-1}$ and $\dfrac{42 \text{ g} \cdot \text{mol}^{-1}}{14 \text{ g} \cdot \text{mol}^{-1}} \approx 3.$

Therefore, C_3H_6.

Gaseous Mixtures

5.61 (a) $n_{N_2} = 0.020 \text{ mol N}_2; \ n_{O_2}(2.33 \text{ g O}_2) \times \left(\dfrac{1 \text{ mol O}_2}{32.0 \text{ g O}_2}\right) = 0.0728 \text{ mol O}_2$

Then, $P = \dfrac{nRT}{V}$

$$P_{N_2} = (0.020 \text{ mol N}_2) \times \left(\frac{0.082\,06 \text{ L} \cdot \text{atm}}{K \cdot \text{mol}}\right) \times (273 \text{ K}) \times \left(\frac{1}{500 \text{ mL}} \times \frac{1 \text{ mL}}{10^{-3} \text{ L}}\right)$$

$$= 0.90 \text{ atm}$$

$$P_{O_2} = (0.0728 \text{ mol O}_2) \times \left(\frac{0.082\,06 \text{ L} \cdot \text{atm}}{K \cdot \text{mol}}\right) \times (273 \text{ K}) \times \left(\frac{1}{500 \text{ mL}} \times \frac{1 \text{ mL}}{10^{-3} \text{ L}}\right)$$

$$= 3.26 \text{ atm}$$

$P_{\text{total}} = P_{N_2} + P_{O_2} = 0.90 \text{ atm} + 3.26 \text{ atm} = 4.16 \text{ atm (3 sf)}$

(b) $n_{H_2} = 0.015 \text{ mol H}_2; \ n_{NH_3} = 0.030 \text{ mol NH}_3; \ n_{He} = (4.22 \text{ mg})$

$$\times \left(\frac{10^{-3} \text{ g}}{1 \text{ mg}}\right) \times \left(\frac{1 \text{ mol He}}{4.00 \text{ g He}}\right) = 1.06 \times 10^{-3} \text{ mol He}$$

Then, $P = \dfrac{nRT}{V}$

$$P_{H_2} = (0.015 \text{ mol H}_2) \times \left(\frac{0.082\,06 \text{ L} \cdot \text{atm}}{K \cdot \text{mol}}\right) \times (273 \text{ K}) \times \left(\frac{1}{500 \text{ mL}} \times \frac{1 \text{ mL}}{10^{-3} \text{ L}}\right)$$

$$= 0.67 \text{ atm}$$

$$P_{NH_3} = (0.030 \text{ mol NH}_3) \times \left(\frac{0.082\,06 \text{ L} \cdot \text{atm}}{\text{K} \cdot \text{mol}} \right) \times (273 \text{ K})$$

$$\times \left(\frac{1}{500 \text{ mL}} \times \frac{1 \text{ mL}}{10^{-3} \text{ L}} \right) = 1.34 \text{ atm}$$

$$P_{HE} = (1.06 \times 10^{-3} \text{ mol He}) \times \left(\frac{0.082\,06 \text{ L} \cdot \text{atm}}{\text{K} \cdot \text{mol}} \right) \times (273 \text{ K})$$

$$\times \left(\frac{1}{500 \text{ mL}} \times \frac{1 \text{ mL}}{10^{-3} \text{ L}} \right) = 0.047 \text{ atm}$$

$$P_{total} = P_{H_2} + P_{NH_3} + P_{He} = 0.67 \text{ atm} + 1.34 \text{ atm} + 0.047 \text{ atm}$$
$$= 2.06 \text{ atm} = 2.1 \text{ atm (2 sf)}$$

5.63 At $-10.0°C$, all water vapor is condensed, 607.1 Torr $= P_{air}$ at $-10.0°C$, and,

$$P_{air \text{ at } 20°C} = (607.1 \text{ Torr}) \times \left(\frac{(273 + 20) \text{ K}}{(273 - 10) \text{ K}} \right) = 676.1 \text{ Torr, and, } P_{total} = P_{air} + P_{H_2O}.$$

$$P_{H_2O} = P_{total} - P_{air} = 762.0 \text{ Torr} - 676.4 \text{ Torr} = 85.6 \text{ Torr}$$

$$n_{H_2O} = \frac{P_{H_2O}V}{RT} = \frac{85.6 \text{ Torr} \times 1.00 \text{ L}}{62.36 \text{ L} \cdot \text{Torr} \cdot \text{K}^{-1} \cdot \text{mol}^{-1} \times 293 \text{ K}} = 4.69 \times 10^{-3} \text{ mol}$$

$$\text{mass} = 4.69 \times 10^{-3} \text{ mol} \times 18.02 \text{ g} \cdot \text{mol}^{-1} = 8.45 \times 10^{-2} \text{ g H}_2O$$

5.65 (a) $P_{N_2} = (803 \text{ kPa}) \times \left(\frac{4.0 \text{ L}}{14.0 \text{ L}} \right) = 22\overline{9} \text{ kPa} = 2.3 \times 10^2 \text{ kPa}$

$$P_{Ar} = (47.2 \text{ kPa}) \times \left(\frac{10.0 \text{ L}}{14.0 \text{ L}} \right) = 33.7 \text{ kPa}$$

(b) $P_T = P_{N_2} + P_{Ar} = 229 \text{ kPa} + 33.7 \text{ kPa} = 26\overline{3} \text{ kPa} = 2.6 \times 10^2 \text{ kPa}$

5.67 (a) $P_{H_2} + P_{H_2O} = P_T$

$P_{H_2} = P_T - P_{H_2O} = 756.7 \text{ Torr} - 17.5 \text{ Torr (from Table 5.4)} = 739.2 \text{ Torr}$

(b) Electrolysis of H_2O: $2H_2O \longrightarrow 2H_2 + O_2$

Pressures of H_2 and O_2 are directly proportional to number of moles of products.

Therefore, $P_{O_2} = \frac{1}{2}P_{H_2} = (\frac{1}{2})(739.2 \text{ Torr}) = 369.6 \text{ Torr and,}$

$$n = \frac{PV}{RT} = \left(369.6 \text{ Torr} \times \frac{1 \text{ atm}}{760 \text{ Torr}} \right) \times \left(220 \text{ mL} \times \frac{10^{-3} \text{ L}}{1 \text{ mL}} \right)$$

$$\times \left(\frac{\text{K} \cdot \text{mol}}{0.08206 \text{ L} \cdot \text{atm}} \right) \times \left(\frac{1}{(273 + 20) \text{ K}} \right) = 4.45 \times 10^{-3} \text{ mol O}_2, \text{ and,}$$

$$\text{mass of O}_2 = 4.45 \times 10^{-3} \text{ mol O}_2 \times \left(\frac{32.0 \text{ g O}_2}{1 \text{ mol O}_2} \right) = 0.142 \text{ g O}_2$$

5.69 $P_{total} = (107 \text{ kPa}) \times \left(\dfrac{1 \text{ atm}}{101.3 \text{ kPa}}\right) = 1.05\overline{6} \text{ atm}$

$P_{H_2O} = (22.38 \text{ Torr}) \times \left(\dfrac{1 \text{ atm}}{760 \text{ Torr}}\right) = 0.029 \text{ atm}$

$P_{total} = P_{H_2} + P_{H_2O} = 1.05\overline{6} \text{ atm}$

$P_{H_2} = P_{total} - P_{H_2O} = (1.05\overline{6} - 0.029) \text{ atm} = 1.02\overline{7} \text{ atm}$

$V = 37.6 \text{ mL} \times \left(\dfrac{1.05\overline{6} \text{ atm}}{1.02\overline{7} \text{ atm}}\right) = 38.7 \text{ mL } H_2 \text{ collected over water}$

Molecular Motion

5.71 The assumptions of the kinetic theory of gases are (1) a gas consists of a collection of molecules in continuous random motion; (2) gas molecules are infinitely small; (3) gas molecules move in straight lines until they collide; and (4) gas molecules do not influence one another except during collisions.

5.73 As the temperature increases, the average speed of the gas molecules increases; this change increases the number of collisions with the container walls per unit time. Because pressure is the result of the force generated by these collisions, it should, therefore, increase with increasing temperature.

5.75 Rate of effusion $\propto \dfrac{1}{\sqrt{M}}$; M = molar mass,

Therefore, $\dfrac{\text{rate (A)}}{\text{rate (B)}} = \sqrt{\dfrac{M_B}{M_A}}$

(a) $\dfrac{\text{rate (Ar)}}{\text{rate (SO}_2)} = \sqrt{\dfrac{64.06 \text{ g} \cdot \text{mol}^{-1}}{39.95 \text{ g} \cdot \text{mol}^{-1}}} = 1.266 > 1$, Ar is faster

(b) $\dfrac{\text{rate (D}_2)}{\text{rate (H}_2)} = \sqrt{\dfrac{2.016 \text{ g} \cdot \text{mol}^{-1}}{4.018 \text{ g} \cdot \text{mol}^{-1}}} = 0.7083 < 1$, H_2 is faster

5.77 We use Eq. 5 of Section 5.15. M = molar mass.

$$\dfrac{t(A)}{t(B)} = \sqrt{\dfrac{M_A}{M_B}} \text{ and } \dfrac{M_A}{M_B} = \left(\dfrac{t(A)}{t(B)}\right)^2$$

Let $M_B = M_{XeF_2}$.

$$M_A = \left(\dfrac{t(A)}{t(XeF_2)}\right)^2 M_{XeF_2} = (2.7)^2 \times 169.3 \text{ g} \cdot \text{mol}^{-1} = 1.2 \times 10^3 \text{ g} \cdot \text{mol}^{-1}$$

Real Gases

5.79   Gases behave most ideally at high temperatures and low pressures. These conditions minimize the oportunity for interactions between molecules, that is, attractive and repulsive forces, which are the cause of deviations from ideality. The farther apart molecules are, the less interaction there will be.

5.81   Figure 5.31 shows this relationship. As two molecules approach, the strength of attraction increases until they are close enough to touch, then they repel each other strongly. An energy of interaction curve shows this effect as a decrease to a minimum value followed by a sharp increase in intermolecular energy.

5.83   (a) Intermolecular attractions in C_2H_4 result in its having a lower pressure than that of an ideal gas. Thus the ideal gas vessel has the greater pressure.
(b) The free space is almost equal. Although the molecules of C_2H_4 do take up some space, this space is a small percentage of the total volume.

SUPPLEMENTARY EXERCISES

5.85   The ideal gas equation, $PV = nRT$, can be rewritten as $\dfrac{PV}{T} = nR = $ constant (at constant amount of gas, n).

Hence, $\dfrac{P_1 V_1}{T_1} = \dfrac{P_2 V_2}{T_2}$

Solving for V_2, $V_2 = \left(\dfrac{T_2}{T_1}\right)\left(\dfrac{P_1}{P_2}\right) V_1$.

For $T_1 = 273$ K and $P_1 = 1.00$ atm, this becomes $V_2 = \left(\dfrac{T_2}{273}\right)\left(\dfrac{1.00 \text{ atm}}{P_2}\right) V_1$.

5.87   The Joule-Thomson effect is the cooling of a gas that occurs as it expands. Pulling the molecules apart results in a lowering of their average energy, as they expend energy to free themselves from each other. Lower average energy corresponds to lower average speed, which in turn corresponds to lower temperature. After repeated expansions, followed by compressions in which heat is abstracted from the gas, the temperature will fall below the boiling point, and the gas will liquefy.

5.89   (a) The number of molecules is the same, but Cl_2 is diatomic.
(c) average speed $\propto \sqrt{\dfrac{\text{temperature}}{\text{molar mass}}}$ $M_{Cl_2} > M_{He}$; therefore, average speed of He > average speed of Cl_2

(e) $d = \left(\dfrac{P}{RT}\right) M$ [See Exercise 5.51, M = molar mass] $M_{Cl_2} > M_{He}$; therefore, $d_{Cl_2} > d_{He}$.

5.91 $(1.5 \text{ in } H_2O) \times \left(\dfrac{1.0 \text{ g} \cdot \text{cm}^{-3}}{13.6 \text{ g} \cdot \text{cm}^{-3}}\right) = 0.11 \text{ in Hg}$

$P = (0.11 \text{ in Hg}) \times \left(\dfrac{2.54 \text{ cm}}{1 \text{ in.}}\right) \times \left(\dfrac{10 \text{ mm}}{1 \text{ cm}}\right) \times \left(\dfrac{1 \text{ Torr}}{1 \text{ mm Hg}}\right) = 2.8 \text{ Torr}$

5.93 $P_2 = \left(\dfrac{V_1}{V_2}\right) P_1 = \left(\dfrac{500 \text{ cm}^3}{58.8 \text{ cm}^3}\right) \times 764 \text{ Torr} = 6.50 \times 10^3 \text{ Torr}$

5.95 $P_{final} = (765 \text{ Torr}) \times \left(\dfrac{555 \text{ mL}}{125 \text{ mL}}\right) = 3.40 \times 10^3 \text{ Torr}$

Additional pressure $= P_{final} - P_{initial} = 3.40 \times 10^3 \text{ Torr} - 765 \text{ Torr}$

Additional pressure $= 2.63 \times 10^3 \text{ Torr}$

5.97 (a) $V_2 = \left(\dfrac{P_1}{P_2}\right)\left(\dfrac{T_2}{T_1}\right) V_1 = \left(\dfrac{2.00 \text{ atm}}{1.55 \text{ atm}}\right) \times \left(\dfrac{(273 + 175) \text{ K}}{273 \text{ K}}\right) \times 100.0 \text{ L}$

$= 212 \text{ L}$

Note that the intermediate temperature of 100°C is of no significance in the solution of this exercise.

(b) $n = \dfrac{PV}{RT} = \dfrac{2.00 \text{ atm} \times 100.0 \text{ L}}{0.082\,06 \text{ L} \cdot \text{atm} \cdot \text{K}^{-1} \cdot \text{mol}^{-1} \times 273 \text{ K}} = 8.93 \text{ mol}$

mass $= n \times$ molar mass $= 8.93 \text{ mol} \times 28.97 \text{ g} \cdot \text{mol}^{-1} = 259 \text{ g}$

5.99 $V = (2.10 \text{ mL}) \times \left(\dfrac{6.4 \text{ atm}}{1.0 \text{ atm}}\right) \times \left(\dfrac{(273 + 25) \text{ K}}{(273 + 8.1) \text{ K}}\right) = 14.2 \text{ mL}$

5.101 (a) $PV = nRT$; $n = \dfrac{PV}{RT}$

$n = (5.00 \text{ atm}) \times \left(425 \text{ mL} \times \dfrac{10^{-3} \text{ L}}{1 \text{ mL}}\right) \times \left(\dfrac{\text{K} \cdot \text{mol}}{0.082\,06 \text{ L} \cdot \text{atm}}\right)$

$\times \left(\dfrac{1}{(273 + 23) \text{ K}}\right) = 8.75 \times 10^{-2} \text{ mol}$

mass $= (8.75 \times 10^{-2} \text{ mol}) \times \left(\dfrac{28.0 \text{ g}}{1 \text{ mol CO}}\right) = 2.45 \text{ g CO}$

(b) density = $\dfrac{\text{mass}}{\text{volume}} = \dfrac{2.45 \text{ g}}{425 \text{ mL} \times \left(\dfrac{10^{-3} \text{ L}}{1 \text{ mL}}\right)} = 5.76 \text{ g} \cdot \text{L}^{-1}$

(c) Because the mass and volume are fixed quantities in this experiment, the density does not change.

5.103 number of moles = $n = \dfrac{PV}{RT}$

$n = \dfrac{0.84 \text{ atm} \times 22.1 \text{ L}}{0.082\,06 \text{ L} \cdot \text{atm} \cdot \text{K}^{-1} \cdot \text{mol}^{-1} \times (273 + 26) \text{ K}} = 0.75\overline{7} \text{ mol}$

mass = $n \times$ molar mass = $0.75\overline{7} \text{ mol} \times 33.8 \text{ g} \cdot \text{mol}^{-1} = 26 \text{ g}$

5.105 (a) $PV = nRT$; $\quad n = \dfrac{PV}{RT}$

$n_{TiO_2} = n_{TiCl_4} = \left(500 \text{ kPa} \times \dfrac{1 \text{ atm}}{101.3 \text{ kPa}}\right) \times (200 \text{ L}) \times \left(\dfrac{K \cdot \text{mol}}{0.082\,06 \text{ L} \cdot \text{atm}}\right)$

$\times \left(\dfrac{1}{(273 + 30) \text{ K}}\right) = 39.7 \text{ mol TiCl}_4$ and so, 39.7 mol TiO$_2$

mass = $(39.7 \text{ mol TiO}_2) \times \left(\dfrac{79.9 \text{ g}}{1 \text{ mol TiO}_2}\right) = 3.17 \times 10^3 \text{ g TiO}_2$

(b) $n_{HCl} = 39.7 \text{ mol TiO}_2 \times \left(\dfrac{4 \text{ mol HCl}}{1 \text{ mol TiO}_2}\right) = 159 \text{ mol HCl}$

$V_{HCl} = \dfrac{n_{HCl} RT}{P} = \dfrac{159 \text{ mol} \times 0.082\,06 \text{ L} \cdot \text{atm} \cdot \text{K}^{-1} \cdot \text{mol}^{-1} \times 298 \text{ K}}{1.00 \text{ atm}}$

$= 3.89 \times 10^3 \text{ L HCl(g)}$

5.107 (a) $n = \dfrac{PV}{RT}$

$n_{\text{butane}} = \dfrac{2.33 \text{ atm} \times 250 \text{ L}}{0.082\,06 \text{ L} \cdot \text{atm} \cdot \text{K}^{-1} \cdot \text{mol}^{-1} \times (273 + 150) \text{ K}} = 16.7\overline{8} \text{ mol}$

mass of CO$_2$ = $16.7\overline{8} \text{ mol butane} \times \left(\dfrac{8 \text{ mol CO}_2}{2 \text{ mol butane}}\right) \times \left(\dfrac{44.01 \text{ g CO}_2}{\text{mol CO}_2}\right)$

$= 2.95 \times 10^3 \text{ g CO}_2 = 2.95 \text{ kg CO}_2$

(b) $n_{CO_2} = 16.7\overline{8} \text{ mol butane} \times \left(\dfrac{8 \text{ mol CO}_2}{2 \text{ mol butane}}\right) = 67.1\overline{2} \text{ mol CO}_2$

$P = \dfrac{n_{CO_2} RT}{V} = \dfrac{67.1\overline{2} \text{ mol} \times 0.082\,06 \text{ L} \cdot \text{atm} \cdot \text{K}^{-1} \cdot \text{mol}^{-1} \times 289 \text{ K}}{4.000 \times 10^3 \text{ L}}$

$= 0.398 \text{ atm}$

5.109 $n_{CO_2} = (10.0 \text{ g } C_6H_{12}O_6) \times \left(\dfrac{1 \text{ mol } C_6H_{12}O_6}{180 \text{ g } C_6H_{12}O_6}\right) \times \left(\dfrac{6 \text{ mol } CO_2}{1 \text{ mol } C_6H_{12}O_6}\right)$

$= 0.333 \text{ mol } CO_2$

$PV = nRT; \quad V = \dfrac{nRT}{P}$

$V_{CO_2} = (0.333 \text{ mol } CO_2) \times \left(\dfrac{0.082\ 06 \text{ L} \cdot \text{atm}}{\text{K} \cdot \text{mol}}\right) \times [(273 + 25) \text{ K}]$

$\times \left(\dfrac{1}{0.26 \text{ Torr} \times \dfrac{1 \text{ atm}}{760 \text{ Torr}}}\right)$

$V_{CO_2} = 2.38 \times 10^4 \text{ L} = $ volume of air required

5.111 number of moles of N $= 0.414 \text{ g N} \times \left(\dfrac{1 \text{ mol N}}{14.01 \text{ g N}}\right) = 0.029\ 5\overline{5} \text{ mol N}$

number of moles of H $= 0.0591 \text{ g H} \times \left(\dfrac{1 \text{ mol H}}{1.0079 \text{ g H}}\right)$

$= 0.058\ 6\overline{4} \text{ mol H} \quad \dfrac{0.058\ 6\overline{4} \text{ mol H}}{0.029\ 5\overline{5} \text{ mol N}} = 1.98 \approx 2$

Therefore, the empirical formula is NH_2.

The molar mass is calculated from $M = d\left(\dfrac{RT}{P}\right) = \left(\dfrac{m}{V}\right)\left(\dfrac{RT}{P}\right)$

$M = \left(\dfrac{0.473 \text{ g}}{0.200 \text{ L}}\right) \times \left(\dfrac{0.082\ 06 \text{ L} \cdot \text{atm} \cdot \text{K}^{-1} \cdot \text{mol}^{-1} \times 298 \text{ K}}{1.81 \text{ atm}}\right) = 32.0 \text{ g} \cdot \text{mol}^{-1}$

Then, $\dfrac{\text{molar mass of compound}}{\text{molor mass of empirical formula}} = \dfrac{32.0 \text{ g} \cdot \text{mol}^{-1}}{16.0 \text{ g} \cdot \text{mol}^{-1}} = 2$

Therefore, N_2H_4.

5.113 We use Eq. 5 of Section 5.15.

General expression: $\dfrac{t_{Ar}}{t_x} = \sqrt{\dfrac{\text{molar mass Ar}}{\text{molar mass } x}}$ and, $t_x = t_{Ar}\sqrt{\dfrac{\text{molar mass } x}{\text{molar mass Ar}}}$

Then,

(a) $t_{CO_2} = (147 \text{ s})\sqrt{\dfrac{44.0 \text{ g} \cdot \text{mol}^{-1}}{40.0 \text{ g} \cdot \text{mol}^{-1}}} = 154 \text{ s}$

(b) $t_{C_2H_4} = (147 \text{ s})\sqrt{\dfrac{28.0 \text{ g} \cdot \text{mol}^{-1}}{40.0 \text{ g} \cdot \text{mol}^{-1}}} = 123 \text{ s}$

(c) $t_{H_2} = (147 \text{ s})\sqrt{\dfrac{2.02 \text{ g} \cdot \text{mol}^{-1}}{40.0 \text{ g} \cdot \text{mol}^{-1}}} = 33.0 \text{ s}$

(d) $t_{SO_2} = (147 \text{ s})\sqrt{\dfrac{64.0 \text{ g} \cdot \text{mol}^{-1}}{40.0 \text{ g} \cdot \text{mol}^{-1}}} = 186 \text{ s}$

5.115 We use Eq. 5 with HC = hydrocarbon, M = molar mass.

$$\frac{t(\text{Ar})}{t(\text{HC})} = \sqrt{\frac{M_{\text{Ar}}}{M_{\text{HC}}}}$$

Solve for M_{HC}.

$$M_{\text{HC}} = \left(\frac{t(\text{HC})}{t(\text{Ar})}\right)^2 M_{\text{Ar}} = \left(\frac{349\ \text{s}}{210\ \text{s}}\right)^2 \times 39.95\ \text{g}\cdot\text{mol}^{-1} = 110\ \text{g}\cdot\text{mol}^{-1}$$

$$\frac{M_{\text{HC}}}{\text{molar mass } C_2H_3} = \frac{110\ \text{g}\cdot\text{mol}^{-1}}{27\ \text{g}\cdot\text{mol}^{-1}} \approx 4$$

So the molecular formula would be C_8H_{12}.

5.117 The partial pressure of a component of a gaseous mixture is proportional to its fractional composition.

$P_{CO_2} = 0.0400 \times 640\ \text{Torr} = 25.6\ \text{Torr}$

CHALLENGING EXERCISES

5.119 The overly high pressure obtained when S_8 is vaporized is an indication that S_8 units have decomposed to lighter units, S_6, S_4, S_2, etc. In other words, the number of moles of gas increased (remember, $P \propto n$).

5.121 $PV = nRT$; $n = \dfrac{PV}{RT}$

$$n = \left(745\ \text{Torr} \times \frac{1\ \text{atm}}{760\ \text{Torr}}\right) \times \left(235\ \text{mL} \times \frac{10^{-3}\ \text{L}}{1\ \text{mL}}\right) \times \left(\frac{\text{K}\cdot\text{mol}}{0.082\,06\ \text{L}\cdot\text{atm}}\right)$$

$$\times \left(\frac{1}{(273 + 200)\ \text{K}}\right)$$

$n = 5.94 \times 10^{-3}\ \text{mol}$ and, $\dfrac{1.509\ \text{g}}{5.94 \times 10^{-3}\ \text{mol}} = 254\ \text{g}\cdot\text{mol}^{-1}$ = molar mass of oxide

molar mass (Os) = $190\ \text{g}\cdot\text{mol}^{-1}$

mass of O per mole of OsO_x = $254\ \text{g}\cdot\text{mol}^{-1} - 190\ \text{g}\cdot\text{mol}^{-1} = 64\ \text{g}\cdot\text{mol}^{-1}$

$\dfrac{64\ \text{g}\cdot\text{mol}^{-1}}{16\ \text{g}\cdot\text{mol}^{-1}} = 4 = x$

Therefore, the molecular formula is OsO_4.

5.123 (a) $PV = nRT$; $n = \dfrac{PV}{RT}$

$$n_{NH_3} = \left(100\ \text{Torr} \times \frac{1\ \text{atm}}{760\ \text{Torr}}\right) \times \left(15\ \text{mL} \times \frac{10^{-3}\ \text{L}}{1\ \text{mL}}\right)$$

$$\times \left(\frac{\text{K}\cdot\text{mol}}{0.082\,06\ \text{L}\cdot\text{atm}}\right) \times \left(\frac{1}{(273 + 30)\ \text{K}}\right)$$

$n_{NH_3} = 7.9 \times 10^{-5}$ mol NH_3

$$n_{HCl} = \left(150 \text{ Torr} \times \frac{1 \text{ atm}}{760 \text{ Torr}}\right) \times \left(25 \text{ mL} \times \frac{10^{-3} \text{ L}}{1 \text{ mL}}\right)$$

$$\times \left(\frac{K \cdot mol}{0.082\ 06 \text{ L} \cdot atm}\right) \times \left(\frac{1}{(273 + 25) \text{ K}}\right)$$

$n_{HCl} = 2.0 \times 10^{-4}$ mol HCl

Clearly, NH_3 is the limiting reagent.

Then, mass of $NH_4Cl = (7.9 \times 10^{-5} \text{ mol } NH_3) \times \left(\frac{1 \text{ mol } NH_4Cl}{1 \text{ mol } NH_3}\right)$

$$\times \left(\frac{53.5 \text{ g } NH_4Cl}{1 \text{ mol } NH_4Cl}\right) = 4.2 \times 10^{-3} \text{ g } NH_4Cl$$

(b) From part (a), the gas in excess is HCl. The number of moles in excess is $2.0 \times 10^{-4} - 7.9 \times 10^{-5} = 1.2 \times 10^{-4}$ mol HCl excess.

$$PV = nRT; \quad P = \frac{nRT}{V}$$

$$P = (1.2 \times 10^{-4} \text{ mol}) \times \left(\frac{0.082\ 06 \text{ L} \cdot atm}{K \cdot mol}\right) \times [(273 + 27) \text{ K}]$$

$$\times \left(\frac{1}{[15 \text{ mL} + 25 \text{ mL}] \times \frac{10^{-3} \text{ L}}{1 \text{ mL}}}\right)$$

$P = 7.4 \times 10^{-2}$ atm

5.125 Under conditions of constant volume and pressure, n, and hence mass, is inversely proportional to T.

$$n = \left(\frac{PV}{R}\right)\left(\frac{1}{T}\right) = \text{constant} \times \left(\frac{1}{T}\right)$$

$$\text{mass} = n \times \text{molar mass} \quad (\text{molar mass} = \text{constant})$$

Therefore, mass $\propto \left(\frac{1}{T}\right)$ or $\dfrac{\text{final mass}}{\text{initial mass}} = \dfrac{\text{initial } T}{\text{final } T}$

final mass $= 32.5 \text{ g} \times \left(\dfrac{295 \text{ K}}{485 \text{ K}}\right) = 19.8$ g

mass released $= 32.5 \text{ g} - 19.8 \text{ g} = 12.7$ g

CHAPTER 6
THERMOCHEMISTRY: THE FIRE WITHIN

EXERCISES

Energy and Heat

6.1 *System:* that part of the universe which we are investigating. An example is a reaction vessel and its contents: the reactants and products of a chemical reaction in which we are interested.
Surroundings: everything outside the system. The environment of a reaction flask is an example.

6.3 4.184 J = 1 cal, hence 4.184 kJ = 1 kcal

$$\text{energy content (kJ)} = 16 \text{ kcal} \times \left(\frac{4.184 \text{ kJ}}{1 \text{ kcal}} \right) = 67 \text{ kJ}$$

6.5 As the temperature of a system increases, the average velocity of the molecules in a system also increases.

6.7 Enthalpy is that property of a system that changes when heat is released or absorbed by a system at constant pressure. When we say that the enthalpy of a system is a state property, we mean that its value is determined only by the state of the system, not by how that state was achieved; that is, the enthalpy of a system is not dependent on how the sample was prepared.

6.9 (a) heat needed = temperature change × mass × specific heat capacity
$$= (37.2 - 25.3) \, ^\circ\text{C} \times 50.0 \text{ g} \times 1.05 \text{ J} \cdot \text{g}^{-1} \cdot (^\circ\text{C})^{-1} = 625 \text{ J}$$
(b) ΔT = temperature change
heat supplied = mass × specific heat capacity × ΔT
Solving for ΔT,

$$\Delta T = \frac{\text{heat supplied}}{\text{mass} \times \text{specific heat capacity}}$$

$$= \frac{4.90 \times 10^5 \text{ J}}{1.0 \text{ kg} \times \left(\dfrac{10^3 \text{ g}}{1 \text{ kg}}\right) \times 0.90 \text{ J} \cdot \text{g}^{-1} \cdot (^\circ\text{C})^{-1}} = 5.4 \times 10^2 \text{ }^\circ\text{C}$$

6.11 ss = stainless steel

heat = temperature change × mass × specific heat capacity

total heat needed = heat(ss) + heat(H_2O)

heat(ss) = $(100 - 25)\,^\circ\text{C} \times 500 \text{ g} \times 0.51 \text{ J} \cdot \text{g}^{-1} \cdot (^\circ\text{C})^{-1} = 1.9 \times 10^4 \text{ J}$

heat(H_2O) = $75\,^\circ\text{C} \times 450.0 \text{ g} \times 4.18 \text{ J} \cdot \text{g}^{-1} \cdot (^\circ\text{C})^{-1} = 1.4\overline{1} \times 10^5 \text{ J}$

total heat needed = $1.9 \times 10^4 + 1.4\overline{1} \times 10^5 \text{ J} = 1.6\overline{0} \times 10^5 \text{ J}$

% heat(H_2O) = $\dfrac{\text{heat}(H_2O)}{\text{total heat}} \times 100\% = \dfrac{1.4\overline{1} \times 10^5 \text{ J}}{1.6\overline{0} \times 10^5 \text{ J}} \times 100\% = 88\%$

6.13 (a) heat energy needed = temperature change × mass × specific heat capacity

heat energy needed = $(500 - 25)\,^\circ\text{C} \times 10.0 \text{ g} \times 0.45 \text{ J} \cdot \text{g}^{-1} \cdot (^\circ\text{C})^{-1} = 2.1 \times 10^3 \text{ J}$

(b) Solving the equation in part (a) for mass yields

$$\text{mass} = \frac{\text{heat energy}}{\text{specific heat capacity} \times \text{temperature change}}$$

$$\text{mass}_{\text{Au}} = \frac{2.1 \times 10^3 \text{ J}}{0.13 \text{ J} \cdot \text{g}^{-1} \cdot (^\circ\text{C})^{-1} \times 475 \text{ K}} = 34 \text{ g}$$

6.15 Let ΔT = temperature change = T(final) − T(initial), c = specific heat capacity.
Because all the energy lost by the metal is gained by the water, we can write

heat(metal) = −heat(H_2O)

heat(metal) = ΔT(metal) × mass(metal) × c(metal)

heat(H_2O) = ΔT(H_2O) × mass(H_2O) × c(H_2O)

Note that ΔT(metal) is negative and ΔT(H_2O) is positive. Then

ΔT(metal) × mass(metal) × c(metal) = $-\Delta T$(H_2O) × mass(H_2O) × c(H_2O)

Solving for c(metal):

$$c(\text{metal}) = \frac{-\Delta T(H_2O) \times \text{mass}(H_2O) \times c(H_2O)}{\Delta T(\text{metal}) \times \text{mass(metal)}}$$

$$= \frac{-(25.7 - 22.0)\,^\circ\text{C} \times 50.7 \text{ g } H_2O \times 4.18 \text{ J} \cdot \text{g}^{-1} \cdot (^\circ\text{C})^{-1}}{(25.7 - 100)\,^\circ\text{C} \times 20.0 \text{ g metal}} = 0.53 \text{ J} \cdot \text{g}^{-1} \cdot (^\circ\text{C})^{-1}$$

6.17 (a) endothermic ($\Delta H > 0$)

     (b) exothermic ($\Delta H < 0$)

6.19 ΔH = heat lost by water

       = mass $\times$ specific heat capacity $\times$ temperature change

       = $20.0\text{g} \times 4.184 \text{ J} \cdot \text{g}^{-1} \cdot (°\text{C})^{-1} \times (4.00°\text{C} - 20.0°\text{C})$

       = $-1.3\overline{4} \times 10^3$ J

       = -1.3 kJ, exothermic, $\Delta H < 0$

6.21 Let us first calculate the heat lost by the 100 g of water originally at 62.5°C. Let this quantity be q.

$$q = \text{mass} \times \text{specific heat} \times \text{temperature change}$$
$$= 100 \text{ g} \times 4.184 \text{ J} \cdot \text{g}^{-1} \cdot (°\text{C})^{-1} \times (62.5 - 40.1) \,°\text{C}$$
$$= 9.37\overline{2} \times 10^3 \text{ J}$$

Then calculate the heat gained by the 100 g of water originally at 19.8°C. Let this be q'.

$$q' = 100 \text{ g} \times 4.184 \text{ J} \cdot \text{g}^{-1} \cdot (°\text{C})^{-1} \times (40.1 - 19.8) \,°\text{C} = 8.49\overline{4} \times 10^3 \text{ J}$$

The difference between these two quantities is the heat leaked to the surroundings.

$$q - q' = 9.37\overline{2} \times 10^3 \text{ J} - 8.49\overline{4} \times 10^3 \text{ J} = 8.8 \times 10^2 \text{ J}$$

6.23 $\Delta H_c = -3227 \text{ kJ} \cdot \text{mol}^{-1}$. Because heat is given off by the reaction (exothermic), heat is absorbed by the calorimeter. And we can write (rxn means "reaction")

$$\Delta H_{cal} = -\Delta H_{rxn}$$

Let C_{cal} = heat capacity of the calorimeter and n = amount (moles) of benzoic acid:

$$n = 1.236 \text{ g} \times \left(\frac{1 \text{ mol}}{122.12 \text{ g}}\right) = 0.010 \ 12 \text{ mol}$$

Then $\Delta H_{cal} = C_{cal} \times \Delta T$, $\Delta T = 2.345°\text{C}$

$\Delta H_{rxn} = n \times \Delta H_c = 0.010 \ 12 \text{ mol} \times (-3227 \text{ kJ} \cdot \text{mol}^{-1}) = -32.66 \text{ kJ}$

Then $\Delta H_{cal} = -\Delta H_{rxn}$, $C_{cal} \times 2.345°\text{C} = +32.66 \text{ kJ}$

$$C_{cal} = \frac{32.66 \text{ kJ}}{2.345°\text{C}} = 13.93 \text{ kJ} \cdot (°\text{C})^{-1}$$

6.25 Let C_{cal} = heat capacity of calorimeter. (comb means "combustion")

$\Delta H_{comb} = -\Delta H_{cal}$

$\Delta H_{cal} = C_{cal} \times \Delta T = 5.24 \text{ kJ} \cdot (°C)^{-1} \times (23.17 - 22.45) °C = 3.8 \text{ kJ}$

$\Delta H_{comb} = -3.8 \text{ kJ}$

6.27 Let C_{cal} = heat capacity of calorimeter. (neut means "neutralization")

(a) $\Delta H_{neut} = -\Delta H_{cal} = -C_{cal} \times \Delta T$

$\qquad = -525.0 \text{ J} \cdot (°C)^{-1} \times (21.3 - 18.6)°C = -1.4\overline{2} \times 10^3 \text{ J}$

(b) number of moles $HNO_3 = 0.0500 \text{ L} \times 0.500 \text{ mol} \cdot \text{L}^{-1} = 0.0250 \text{ mol}$

$\Delta H = \dfrac{\Delta H_{neut}}{n_{HNO_3}} = \dfrac{-1.4\overline{2} \times 10^3 \text{ J}}{0.0250 \text{ mol}} = -57 \text{ kJ} \cdot \text{mol}^{-1}$

Enthalpy of Physical Change

6.29 Under constant pressure conditions, ΔH is the heat associated with the process. Therefore, if ΔH is negative, heat is given off, and the process is exothermic. Conversely, if ΔH is positive, heat is absorbed, and the process is endothermic.

6.31 ΔH = heat required, n = number of moles

(a) $\Delta H_{vap} = \dfrac{\Delta H}{n} = \dfrac{1.93 \text{ kJ}}{0.235 \text{ mol}} = 8.21 \text{ kJ} \cdot \text{mol}^{-1}$

(b) $\Delta H_{vap} = \dfrac{\Delta H}{n} = \left(\dfrac{21.2 \text{ kJ}}{22.45 \text{ g } C_2H_5OH}\right) \times \left(\dfrac{46.07 \text{ g } C_2H_5OH}{1 \text{ mol } C_2H_5OH}\right)$

$\qquad = 43.5 \text{ kJ} \cdot \text{mol}^{-1}$

6.33 (a) number of moles of $H_2O = 100 \text{ g } H_2O \times \left(\dfrac{1 \text{ mol } H_2O}{18.02 \text{ g } H_2O}\right) = 5.55 \text{ mol } H_2O$

$\Delta H° = 5.55 \text{ mol } H_2O \times 40.7 \text{ kJ} \cdot \text{mol}^{-1} \text{ } H_2O = +226 \text{ kJ}$

(b) number of moles of $NH_3 = 600 \text{ g } NH_3 \times \left(\dfrac{1 \text{ mol } NH_3}{17.03 \text{ g } NH_3}\right) = 35.2 \text{ mol } NH_3$

$\Delta H° = 35.2 \text{ mol } NH_3 \times 5.65 \text{ kJ} \cdot \text{mol}^{-1} \text{ } NH_3 = +199 \text{ kJ}$

6.35 heat needed $= 6.01 \times 10^3 \text{ J} \cdot \text{mol}^{-1} \times \left(\dfrac{1 \text{ mol}}{18.02 \text{ g } H_2O}\right) \times 50.0 \text{ g } H_2O$

$+ 4.18 \text{ J} \cdot \text{g}^{-1} \cdot (°C)^{-1} \times 50.0 \text{ g} \times 25°C = 16.\overline{7} \times 10^3 \text{ J} + 5.2\overline{2} \times 10^3 \text{ J}$

$\qquad = 21.\overline{9} \times 10^3 \text{ J} = 22 \text{ kJ}$

Enthalpy of Chemical Change

6.37 The standard state of a substance is its pure form at 1 atmosphere pressure. Standard state data are usually reported at 25°C, but can be reported for any temperature.

6.39 (a) heat absorbed = $0.20 \text{ mol } S_8 \times \left(\dfrac{+358.8 \text{ kJ}}{1 \text{ mol } S_8} \right) = +72 \text{ kJ}$

(b) heat absorbed = $20.0 \text{ g C} \times \left(\dfrac{1 \text{ mol C}}{12.01 \text{ g C}} \right) \times \left(\dfrac{+358.8 \text{ kJ}}{4 \text{ mol C}} \right) = +149 \text{ kJ}$

(c) mass of CS_2 produced = $217 \text{ kJ} \times \left(\dfrac{0.20 \text{ mol } S_8}{72 \text{ kJ}} \right) \times \left(\dfrac{4 \text{ mol } CS_2}{1 \text{ mol } S_8} \right)$

$$\times \left(\dfrac{76.14 \text{ g } CS_2}{1 \text{ mol } CS_2} \right) = 1.8 \times 10^2 \text{ g}$$

6.41 (a) mass of octane = $-12 \times 10^6 \text{ J} \times \left(\dfrac{2 \text{ mol octane}}{-10.942 \times 10^6 \text{ J}} \right) \times \left(\dfrac{114.22 \text{ g octane}}{1 \text{ mol octane}} \right)$

$$= 2.5 \times 10^2 \text{ g octane}$$

(b) 1 gal = 3.785 L

heat evolved = $1.0 \text{ gal} \times \left(\dfrac{3.785 \text{ L}}{1 \text{ gal}} \right) \times \left(\dfrac{1 \text{ mL}}{10^{-3} \text{ L}} \right) \times \left(\dfrac{0.70 \text{ g octane}}{1 \text{ mL}} \right)$

$$\times \left(\dfrac{1 \text{ mol octane}}{114.22 \text{ g octane}} \right) \times \left(\dfrac{-10.942 \times 10^6 \text{ J}}{2 \text{ mol octane}} \right) = -1.3 \times 10^8 \text{ J}$$

6.43 $Fe_2O_3(s) + 2 \text{ Al}(s) \longrightarrow Al_2O_3(s) + 2 \text{ Fe}(s) \quad \Delta H° = -851.5 \text{ kJ}$

number of moles of Fe_2O_3 supplied = $50.0 \text{ g } Fe_2O_3 \times \left(\dfrac{1 \text{ mol } Fe_2O_3}{159.70 \text{ g } Fe_2O_3} \right)$

$$= 0.313 \text{ mol } Fe_2O_3$$

number of moles of Al supplied = $25.0 \text{ g Al} \times \left(\dfrac{1 \text{ mol Al}}{26.98 \text{ g Al}} \right) = 0.927 \text{ mol Al}$

number of moles of Al required = $0.313 \text{ mol } Fe_2O_3 \times \left(\dfrac{2 \text{ mol Al}}{1 \text{ mol } Fe_2O_3} \right) = 0.626 \text{ mol Al}$

Because 0.626 mol Al required is less than 0.927 mol Al supplied, Fe_2O_3 is the limiting reactant.

heat produced = $0.313 \text{ mol } Fe_2O_3 \times \left(\dfrac{-851.5 \text{ kJ}}{1 \text{ mol } Fe_2O_3} \right) = -266 \text{ kJ}$

Hess's Law

6.45 The fact that enthalpy is a state function means that the enthalpy change for a sequence of reactions that yield a specific set of products from a specific set of reactants is the same as that for the direct single reaction yielding those same products. Changes in state functions depend only on the initial (reactants) and final (products) states for the process, not on how the change was achieved.

6.47 (1) $C(graphite) + O_2(g) \longrightarrow CO_2(g)$ $\Delta H° = -393.51 \text{ kJ} \cdot \text{mol}^{-1}$
(2) $C(diamond) + O_2(g) \longrightarrow CO_2(g)$ $\Delta H° = -395.41 \text{ kJ} \cdot \text{mol}^{-1}$
Reverse (2) and then add to (1); thus

$$C(graphite) + O_2(g) \longrightarrow CO_2(g) \qquad \Delta H° = -393.51 \text{ kJ} \cdot \text{mol}^{-1}$$
$$CO_2(g) \longrightarrow C(diamond) + O_2(g) \qquad \Delta H° = -(-395.41 \text{ kJ} \cdot \text{mol}^{-1})$$
$$= 395.41 \text{ kJ} \cdot \text{mol}^{-1}$$

$$\overline{C(graphite) \longrightarrow C(diamond) \qquad \Delta H° = (-393.51 + 395.41) \text{ kJ} \cdot \text{mol}^{-1}}$$
$$= +1.90 \text{ kJ} \cdot \text{mol}^{-1}$$

6.49 (1) $S(s) + O_2(g) \longrightarrow SO_2(g)$ $\Delta H° = -296.83 \text{ kJ}$
(2) $2S(s) + 3O_2(g) \longrightarrow 2 SO_3(g)$ $\Delta H° = -791.44 \text{ kJ}$
Reverse (1) and multiply by 2, then add to (2); thus

$$2SO_2(g) \longrightarrow 2S(s) + 2O_2(g) \qquad \Delta H° = -2(-296.83 \text{ kJ}) = 593.66 \text{ kJ}$$
$$2S(s) + 3O_2(g) \longrightarrow 2SO_3(g) \qquad \Delta H° = -791.44 \text{ kJ}$$
$$\overline{2SO_2(g) + O_2(g) \longrightarrow 2SO_3(g) \qquad \Delta H° = (593.66 - 791.44) \text{ kJ} = -197.78 \text{ kJ}}$$

6.51 (1) $P_4(s) + 6Cl_2(g) \longrightarrow 4PCl_3(l)$ $\Delta H° = -1278.8 \text{ kJ}$
(2) $PCl_3(l) + Cl_2(g) \longrightarrow PCl_5(s)$ $\Delta H° = -124 \text{ kJ}$
Multiply (2) by 4, then add to (1); thus

$$P_4(s) + 6Cl_2(g) \longrightarrow 4PCl_3(l) \qquad \Delta H° = -1278.8 \text{ kJ}$$
$$4PCl_3(l) + 4Cl_2(g) \longrightarrow 4PCl_5(s) \qquad \Delta H° = 4(-124 \text{ kJ}) = -496 \text{ kJ}$$
$$\overline{P_4(s) + 10Cl_2(g) \longrightarrow 4PCl_5(s) \qquad \Delta H° = (-1278.8 - 496) \text{ kJ}}$$
$$= -1.775 \times 10^3 \text{ kJ}$$
$$= -1.775 \text{ MJ}$$

6.53 (1) $2C_2H_2(g) + 5O_2(g) \longrightarrow 4CO_2(g) + 2H_2O(l)$ $\Delta H° = -2600 \text{ kJ}$
(2) $2C_2H_6(g) + 7O_2(g) \longrightarrow 4CO_2(g) + 6H_2O(l)$ $\Delta H° = -3120 \text{ kJ}$
(3) $H_2(g) + \frac{1}{2}O_2(g) \longrightarrow H_2O(l)$ $\Delta H° = -286 \text{ kJ}$
Multiply (1) by $\frac{1}{2}$, reverse (2) and multiply by $\frac{1}{2}$, multiply (3) by 2, and then add all together.

$$C_2H_2(g) + \tfrac{5}{2}O_2(g) \longrightarrow 2CO_2(g) + H_2O(l) \qquad \Delta H° = \tfrac{1}{2} \times (-2600 \text{ kJ}) = -1300 \text{ kJ}$$
$$2CO_2(g) + 3H_2O(l) \longrightarrow C_2H_6(g) + \tfrac{7}{2}O_2(g) \qquad \Delta H° = -\tfrac{1}{2} \times (-3120 \text{ kJ}) = 1560 \text{ kJ}$$
$$2H_2(g) + O_2(g) \longrightarrow 2H_2O(l) \qquad \Delta H° = 2 \times (-286 \text{ kJ}) = -572 \text{ kJ}$$
$$\overline{C_2H_2(g) + 2H_2(g) \longrightarrow C_2H_6(g) \qquad \Delta H° = (-1300 + 1560 - 572) \text{ kJ}}$$
$$= -312 \text{ kJ}$$

6.55 (1) $NH_3(g) + HCl(g) \longrightarrow NH_4Cl(s)$ $\qquad \Delta H° = -176.0$ kJ

(2) $N_2(g) + 3H_2(g) \longrightarrow 2NH_3(g)$ $\qquad \Delta H° = -92.22$ kJ

(3) $N_2(g) + 4H_2(g) + Cl_2(g) \longrightarrow 2NH_4Cl(s)$ $\quad \Delta H° = -628.86$ kJ

Reverse (1) and multiply by 2, reverse (2), then add to (3).

$2NH_4Cl(s) \longrightarrow 2NH_3(g) + 2HCl(g)$ $\qquad \Delta H° = -2(-176.0 \text{ kJ}) = 352.0$ kJ

$2NH_3(g) \longrightarrow N_2(g) + 3H_2(g)$ $\qquad \Delta H° = -(-92.22 \text{ kJ}) = 92.22$ kJ

$\underline{N_2(g) + 4H_2(g) + Cl_2(g) \longrightarrow 2NH_4Cl(s) \quad \Delta H° = -628.86 \text{ kJ}}$

$H_2(g) + Cl_2(g) \longrightarrow 2HCl(g)$ $\qquad \Delta H° = (352.0 + 92.22 - 628.86)$ kJ

$\qquad\qquad\qquad\qquad\qquad\qquad\qquad = -184.7$ kJ

Enthalpy of Formation

6.57 (a) $K(s) + \frac{1}{2}Cl_2(g) + \frac{3}{2}O_2(g) \longrightarrow KClO_3(s) \quad \Delta H_f° = -397.73$ kJ·mol^{-1}

(b) $\frac{5}{2}H_2(g) + \frac{1}{2}N_2(g) + 2C(\text{graphite}) + O_2(g) \longrightarrow H_2NCH_2COOH(s)$

$\Delta H_f° = -532.9$ kJ·mol^{-1}

(c) $2Al(s) + \frac{3}{2}O_2(g) \longrightarrow Al_2O_3(s) \quad \Delta H_f° = -1675.7$ kJ·mol^{-1}

6.59 $\Delta H_f°(NO)$ is available in Appendix 2A and is 90.25 kJ·mol^{-1}.

(1) $2NO(g) + O_2(g) \longrightarrow 2NO_2(g)$ $\qquad \Delta H° = -114.1$ kJ

(2) $4NO_2(g) + O_2(g) \longrightarrow 2N_2O_5(g)$ $\qquad \Delta H° = -110.2$ kJ

(3) $\frac{1}{2}N_2(g) + \frac{1}{2}O_2(g) \longrightarrow NO(g)$ $\qquad \Delta H° = +90.25$ kJ

Multiply (1) by 2, (3) by 4, and add to (2).

$4NO(g) + 2O_2(g) \longrightarrow 4NO_2(g) \quad \Delta H° = 2 \times (-114.1 \text{ kJ}) = -228.2$ kJ

$4NO_2(g) + O_2(g) \longrightarrow 2N_2O(g) \quad \Delta H° = -110.2$ kJ

$\underline{2N_2(g) + 2O_2(g) \longrightarrow 4NO(g) \qquad \Delta H° = 4 \times (90.25 \text{ kJ}) = 361.0 \text{ kJ}}$

$2N_2(g) + 5O_2(g) \longrightarrow 2N_2O_5(g) \quad \Delta H° = (-228.2 - 110.2 + 361.0)$ kJ

$\qquad\qquad\qquad\qquad\qquad\qquad\qquad = +22.6$ kJ

$\qquad\qquad\qquad\qquad \Delta H_f° = \dfrac{+22.6 \text{ kJ}}{2 \text{ mol}} = +11.3$ kJ·mol^{-1}

6.61 (1) $P(s) + \frac{3}{2}Cl_2(g) \longrightarrow PCl_3(l)$ $\qquad \Delta H° = -319.7$ kJ

$\underline{(2) \ PCl_3(l) + Cl_2(g) \longrightarrow PCl_5(s) \quad \Delta H° = -124 \text{ kJ}}$

$(1) + (2) = P(s) + \frac{5}{2}Cl_2(g) \longrightarrow PCl_5(s)$

$\Delta H° = (-319.7 \text{ kJ}) + (-124 \text{ kJ}) = -444$ kJ

$\Delta H_f° = -444$ kJ·mol^{-1}

6.63 rxn means "reaction."

(a) $\Delta H° = 2 \text{ mol} \times \Delta H_f°[SO_3(g)] - 2 \text{ mol} \times \Delta H_f°[SO_2(g)]$

$\Delta H° = 2 \text{ mol} \times (-395.72 \text{ kJ} \cdot \text{mol}^{-1}) - 2 \text{ mol} \times (-296.83 \text{ kJ} \cdot \text{mol}^{-1})$

$\qquad = -197.78 \text{ kJ}$

$\Delta H_{rxn}°(10.0 \text{ g } SO_2) = 10.0 \text{ g } SO_2 \times \left(\dfrac{1 \text{ mol } SO_2}{64.06 \text{ g } SO_2}\right) \times \left(\dfrac{-197.78 \text{ kJ}}{2 \text{ mol } SO_2}\right)$

$\qquad\qquad = -15.4 \text{ kJ}$

(b) $\Delta H° = 1 \text{ mol} \times \Delta H_f°[H_2O(l)] - 1 \text{ mol} \times \Delta H_f°[CuO(s)]$

$\Delta H° = -285.83 \text{ kJ} - (-157.3 \text{ kJ}) = -128.5 \text{ kJ}$

6.65 (a) $\Delta H° = 1 \text{ mol} \times \Delta H_f°[H_2O(l)] - 1 \text{ mol} \times \Delta H_f°[D_2O(l)]$

$\Delta H° = 1 \text{ mol} \times (-285.83 \text{ kJ} \cdot \text{mol}^{-1}) - 1 \text{ mol} \times (-294.60 \text{ kJ} \cdot \text{mol}^{-1})$

$\qquad = +8.77 \text{ kJ}$

(b) $\Delta H° = 2 \text{ mol} \times \Delta H_f°(H_2O, l) - 2 \text{ mol} \times \Delta H_f°(H_2S, g) - 1 \text{ mol}$
$\qquad\qquad\qquad\qquad\qquad\qquad\qquad\qquad\qquad\qquad\times \Delta H_f°(SO_2, g)$

$\Delta H° = 2 \text{ mol} \times (-285.83 \text{ kJ} \cdot \text{mol}^{-1}) - 2 \text{ mol} \times (-20.63 \text{ kJ} \cdot \text{mol}^{-1}) - 1 \text{ mol}$
$\qquad\qquad\qquad\qquad\qquad \times (-296.83 \text{ kJ} \cdot \text{mol}^{-1}) = -233.57 \text{ kJ}$

(c) $\Delta H° = 4 \text{ mol} \times \Delta H_f°[NO(g)] + 6 \text{ mol} \times \Delta H_f°[H_2O(g)] - 4 \text{ mol}$
$\qquad\qquad\qquad\qquad\qquad\qquad\qquad\qquad\qquad\qquad\times \Delta H_f°[NH_3(g)]$

$\Delta H° = 4 \text{ mol} \times (90.25 \text{ kJ} \cdot \text{mol}^{-1}) + 6 \text{ mol} \times (-241.82 \text{ kJ} \cdot \text{mol}^{-1}) - 4 \text{ mol}$
$\qquad\qquad\qquad\qquad\qquad\qquad\qquad\qquad \times (-46.11 \text{ kJ} \cdot \text{mol}^{-1})$

$\Delta H° = -905.48 \text{ kJ}$

Fuels

6.67 specific enthalpy $= 4854 \text{ kJ} \cdot \text{mol}^{-1} \times \left(\dfrac{1 \text{ mol}}{100.20 \text{ g}}\right) = 48.44 \text{ kJ} \cdot \text{g}^{-1}$

enthalpy density $= 48.44 \text{ kJ} \cdot \text{g}^{-1} \times 0.68 \text{ g} \cdot \text{mL}^{-1} \times \left(\dfrac{1 \text{ mL}}{10^{-3} \text{ L}}\right) = 3.3 \times 10^4 \text{ kJ} \cdot \text{L}^{-1}$

6.69 The reactions are

$$Mg(s) + \tfrac{1}{2}O_2(g) \longrightarrow MgO(s)$$
$$2A(s) + \tfrac{3}{2}O_2(g) \longrightarrow Al_2O_3(s)$$

For Mg: $\dfrac{601.7 \text{ kJ} \cdot \text{mol}^{-1}}{24.31 \text{ g} \cdot \text{mol}^{-1}} = 24.76 \text{ kJ} \cdot \text{g}^{-1}$

For Al: $\dfrac{837.8 \text{ kJ} \cdot \text{mol}^{-1}}{26.9 \text{ g} \cdot \text{mol}^{-1}} = 31.05 \text{ kJ} \cdot \text{g}^{-1}$; hence, Al is better.

6.71 See Tables 6.3 and 6.4.

(a) $CH_4(g) + 2O_2(g) \longrightarrow CO_2(g) + 2H_2O(l)$ $\Delta H_c^\circ = -890$ kJ

$$\frac{890 \text{ kJ}}{1 \text{ mol } CO_2} = 890 \text{ kJ} \cdot \text{mol}^{-1} \text{ } CO_2$$

$C_8H_{18}(l) + \frac{25}{2}O_2(g) \longrightarrow 8CO_2(g) + 9H_2O(l)$ $\Delta H_c^\circ = -5471$ kJ

$$\frac{5471 \text{ kJ}}{8 \text{ mol } CO_2} = 683.9 \text{ kJ} \cdot \text{mol}^{-1} \text{ } CO_2$$

(b) $C_6H_{12}O_6(s) + 6O_2(g) \longrightarrow 6CO_2(g) + 6H_2O(l)$ $\Delta H_c^\circ = -2808$ kJ

$$\frac{2808 \text{ kJ}}{6 \text{ mol } CO_2} = 468.0 \text{ kJ} \cdot \text{mol}^{-1} \text{ } CO_2$$

(c) Take reciprocals of the above figures.

octane: 1.462×10^{-3} mol $CO_2 \cdot$ kJ^{-1}

glucose: 2.137×10^{-3} mol $CO_2 \cdot$ kJ^{-1} (eating glucose produces more CO_2)

SUPPLEMENTARY EXERCISES

6.73 The standard enthalpy of formation of a compound is the enthalpy change associated with the formation of one mole of the compound in its standard state at a specified temperature (usually 25°C) from the elements in their most stable form at 1 atmosphere pressure and the specified temperature.

6.75 For the calorimeter, heat = heat capacity × temperature rise, so ΔH_{cal}

$$= C_{cal} \times \Delta T$$

For the reaction, $\Delta H = -\Delta H_{cal} = -C_{cal} \times \Delta T = -8.92 \text{ kJ} \cdot (°C)^{-1} \times 2.37°C$

$$= -21.1\overline{4} \text{ kJ}$$

$$\text{mass} = -21.1\overline{4} \text{ kJ} \times \left(\frac{30 \text{ g}}{-460 \text{ kJ}} \right) = 1.4 \text{ g}$$

6.77 energy = $(24 \text{ slices}) \times \left(\frac{85 \text{ kcal}}{1 \text{ slice}} \right) \times \left(\frac{4.18 \text{ kJ}}{1 \text{ kcal}} \right) = 8.5 \times 10^3 \text{ kJ}$

6.79 $\Delta H_{vap} = 43.5 \text{ kJ} \cdot \text{mol}^{-1}$ (Table 6.2)

$$\text{area} = 50 \text{ cm}^2 \times \left(\frac{10^{-2} \text{ m}}{1 \text{ cm}} \right)^2 = 5.0 \times 10^{-3} \text{ m}^2$$

heat added = $1 \text{ kJ} \cdot \text{m}^{-2} \cdot \text{s}^{-1} \times 5.0 \times 10^{-3} \text{ m}^2 \times 10 \text{ min} \times \left(\frac{60 \text{ s}}{1 \text{ min}} \right) = 3 \text{ kJ}$

$$= \text{mass} \times \left(\frac{1 \text{ mol}}{46.07 \text{ g}} \right) \times \left(\frac{43.5 \text{ kJ}}{1 \text{ mol}} \right)$$

Solving for mass, mass = 3 g

6.81 (a) heat required $= 10 \text{ g} \times \left(\dfrac{1 \text{ mol}}{46.07 \text{ g}}\right) \times 4.60 \text{ kJ} \cdot \text{mol}^{-1} = 1 \text{ kJ}$

(b) heat required $= 10 \text{ g} \times \left(\dfrac{1 \text{ mol}}{46.07 \text{ g}}\right) \times 43.5 \text{ kJ} \cdot \text{mol}^{-1} = 9.4 \text{ kJ}$

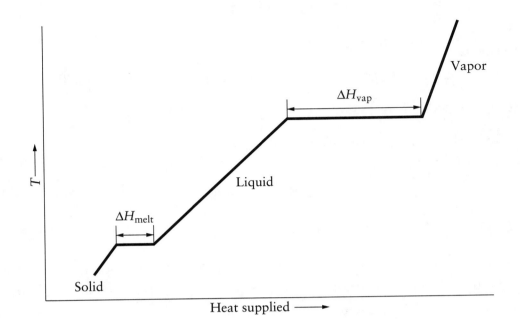

6.83 (a) $\Delta H° = 2 \text{ mol} \times \Delta H_f°[\text{Al}_2\text{O}_3(\text{s})] - 3 \text{ mol} \times \Delta H_f°[\text{MnO}_2(\text{s})]$

$\Delta H° = 2 \text{ mol} \times (-1675.7 \text{ kJ} \cdot \text{mol}^{-1}) - 3 \text{ mol} \times (-521 \text{ kJ} \cdot \text{mol}^{-1})$

$= -1.79 \times 10^3 \text{ kJ}$

(b) $\Delta H° (10.0 \text{ g Mn}) = 10.0 \text{ g Mn} \times \left(\dfrac{1 \text{ mol Mn}}{54.94 \text{ g Mn}}\right) \times \left(\dfrac{-1.79 \times 10^3 \text{ kJ}}{3 \text{ mol Mn}}\right)$

$= -109 \text{ kJ}$

6.85 $\text{CH}_3\text{OH}(\text{l}) + \tfrac{3}{2}\text{O}_2(\text{g}) \longrightarrow \text{CO}_2(\text{g}) + 2\text{H}_2\text{O}(\text{l}) \quad \Delta H_c = -726 \text{ kJ}$

$\Delta H_c = 1 \text{ mol} \times \Delta H_f°[\text{CO}_2(\text{g})] + 2 \text{ mol} \times \Delta H_f°[\text{H}_2\text{O}(\text{l})] - 1 \text{ mol} \times \Delta H_f°[\text{CH}_3\text{OH}(\text{l})]$

$-726 \text{ kJ} = 1 \text{ mol} \times (-393.51 \text{ kJ} \cdot \text{mol}^{-1}) + 2 \text{ mol} \times (-285.83 \text{ kJ} \cdot \text{mol}^{-1}) - 1 \text{ mol}$
$\times \Delta H_f°[\text{CH}_3\text{OH}(\text{l})]$

Solving for $\Delta H_f°[\text{CH}_3\text{OH}(\text{l})]$, $\Delta H_f°[\text{CH}_3\text{OH}(\text{l})] = -239 \text{ kJ} \cdot \text{mol}^{-1}$

6.87 $\Delta H° = 1 \text{ mol} \times \Delta H_f°[\text{H}_2\text{O}(\text{g})] + 1 \text{ mol} \times \Delta H_f°[\text{CO}(\text{NH}_2)_2(\text{s})] - \{1 \text{ mol}$
$\times \Delta H_f°[\text{CO}_2(\text{g})] + 2 \text{ mol} \times \Delta H_f°[\text{NH}_3(\text{g})]\}$

$\Delta H° = 1 \text{ mol} \times (-241.82 \text{ kJ} \cdot \text{mol}^{-1}) + 1 \text{ mol} \times (-333.51 \text{ kJ} \cdot \text{mol}^{-1}) - [1 \text{ mol}$
$\times (-393.51 \text{ kJ} \cdot \text{mol}^{-1}) + 2 \text{ mol} \times (-46.11 \text{ kJ} \cdot \text{mol}^{-1})] = -89.60 \text{ kJ}$, exothermic.

Therefore, heat would have to be removed.

6.89 $S_8(s) + 8O_2(g) \longrightarrow 8SO_2(g)$ $\Delta H_c^\circ = -2374.4 \text{ kJ} \cdot \text{mol}^{-1}$

$$\Delta H_f^\circ = \left(\frac{1 \text{ mol } S_8}{8 \text{ mol } SO_2}\right) \times (-2374.4 \text{ kJ} \cdot \text{mol}^{-1} \text{ } S_8) = -296.80 \text{ kJ} \cdot \text{mol}^{-1}$$

6.91

(1) $2C_2H_2(g) + 5O_2(g) \longrightarrow 4CO_2(g) + 2H_2O(l)$ $\Delta H^\circ = -2600 \text{ kJ}$

(2) $C(s) + O_2(g) \longrightarrow CO_2(g)$ $\Delta H^\circ = -394 \text{ kJ}$

(3) $2H_2(g) + O_2(g) \longrightarrow 2H_2O(g)$ $\Delta H^\circ = -483.6 \text{ kJ}$

(4) $H_2O(l) \longrightarrow H_2O(g)$ $\Delta H^\circ = +44 \text{ kJ}$

Reverse (1) and multiply by $\frac{1}{2}$, multiply (2) by 2, multiply (3) by $\frac{1}{2}$, reverse (4), and then add.

$2CO_2(g) + H_2O(l) \longrightarrow C_2H_2(g) + \frac{5}{2}O_2(g)$ $\Delta H^\circ = -\frac{1}{2} \times (-2600 \text{ kJ}) = +1300 \text{ kJ}$

$2C(s) + 2O_2(g) \longrightarrow 2CO_2(g)$ $\Delta H^\circ = 2 \times (-394 \text{ kJ}) = -788 \text{ kJ}$

$H_2(g) + \frac{1}{2}O_2(g) \longrightarrow H_2O(g)$ $\Delta H^\circ = \frac{1}{2} \times (-483.6 \text{ kJ}) = -241.8 \text{ kJ}$

$\underline{H_2O(g) \longrightarrow H_2O(l) \hspace{3.5cm} \Delta H^\circ = -44 \text{ kJ}}$

$2C(s) + H_2(g) \longrightarrow C_2H_2(g)$ $\Delta H^\circ = (1300 - 788 - 241.8 - 44) \text{ kJ}$

$= +226 \text{ kJ} \cdot \text{mol}^{-1} \text{ } C_2H_2$

6.93 (a) $\Delta H^\circ = 1 \text{ mol} \times \Delta H_f^\circ[CO(g)] - 1 \text{ mol} \times \Delta H_f^\circ[H_2O(g)]$

$\Delta H^\circ = 1 \text{ mol} \times (-110.53 \text{ kJ} \cdot \text{mol}^{-1}) - 1 \text{ mol} \times (-241.82 \text{ kJ} \cdot \text{mol}^{-1})$

$= +131.29 \text{ kJ}$

Therefore, endothermic.

(b) $pV = nRT$

$$n_{H_2} = \frac{pV}{RT} = \frac{500 \text{ Torr} \times \left(\dfrac{1 \text{ atm}}{760 \text{ Torr}}\right) \times 200 \text{ L}}{0.0821 \text{ L} \cdot \text{atm} \cdot \text{K}^{-1} \cdot \text{mol}^{-1} \times (273 + 65) \text{ K}} = 4.74 \text{ mol } H_2$$

$$\Delta H^\circ = 4.74 \text{ mol } H_2 \times \left(\frac{131.29 \text{ kJ}}{1 \text{ mol } H_2}\right) = 623 \text{ kJ}$$

6.95 Consider

$H_2(g) + \frac{1}{2}O_2(g) \longrightarrow H_2O(g)$ $\Delta H_f^\circ[H_2O(g)]$

$\underline{H_2O(g) \longrightarrow H_2O(l) \hspace{3.1cm} \Delta H^\circ = -\Delta H_{vap}^\circ}$

$H_2(g) + \frac{1}{2}O_2(g) \longrightarrow H_2O(l)$ $\Delta H_f^\circ[H_2O(l)]$

So $\Delta H_f^\circ[H_2O(l)] = \Delta H_f^\circ[H_2O(g)] - \Delta H_{vap}^\circ = \Delta H_f^\circ[H_2O(g)] - 40.7 \text{ kJ} \cdot \text{mol}^{-1}$
and $\Delta H_f^\circ[H_2O(g)] = \Delta H_f^\circ[H_2O(l)] + 40.7 \text{ kJ} \cdot \text{mol}^{-1}$.

Therefore, $\Delta H_f^\circ[H_2O(g)]$ is less negative than $\Delta H_f^\circ[H_2O(l)]$, because additional enthalpy is released when gaseous water condenses.

6.97 The heat evolved is ΔH°_{sol}, see Chapter 12.

$\Delta H^\circ_{sol} = 1 \text{ mol} \times \Delta H^\circ_f[Na^+(aq)] + 1 \text{ mol} \times \Delta H^\circ_f[OH^-(aq)] - 1 \text{ mol} \times \Delta H^\circ_f[NaOH(s)]$

$\Delta H^\circ_{sol} = 1 \text{ mol} \times (-240.12 \text{ kJ} \cdot \text{mol}^{-1}) + 1 \text{ mol} \times (-229.99 \text{ kJ} \cdot \text{mol}^{-1}) - 1 \text{ mol}$
$$\times (-425.61 \text{ kJ} \cdot \text{mol}^{-1}) = -44.50 \text{ kJ}$$

$$\Delta H^\circ_{rxn} = 20.0 \text{ g NaOH} \times \left(\frac{1 \text{ mol NaOH}}{40.00 \text{ g NaOH}} \right) \times \left(\frac{-44.50 \text{ kJ}}{1 \text{ mol NaOH}} \right) = -22.2\overline{5} \text{ kJ}$$

6.99 $\Delta H^\circ = 1 \text{ mol} \times \Delta H^\circ_f[Fe^{2+}(aq)] + 1 \text{ mol} \times \Delta H^\circ_f[H_2S(g)] - 1 \text{ mol}$
$$\times \Delta H^\circ_f[FeS(s)] - 2 \text{ mol} \times \Delta H^\circ_f[H^+(aq)]$$

$\Delta H^\circ = 1 \text{ mol} \times (-89.1 \text{ kJ} \cdot \text{mol}^{-1}) + 1 \text{ mol} \times (-20.63 \text{ kJ} \cdot \text{mol}^{-1}) - 1 \text{ mol}$
$$\times (-100.0 \text{ kJ} \cdot \text{mol}^{-1}) - 2 \text{ mol} \times 0 = -9.7 \text{ kJ}$$

$$n = \frac{PV}{RT} = \frac{1.00 \text{ atm} \times 30.0 \text{ L}}{0.082\,06 \text{ L} \cdot \text{atm} \cdot \text{K}^{-1} \cdot \text{mol}^{-1} \times 298 \text{ K}} = 1.23 \text{ mol H}_2\text{S}$$

$$\Delta H^\circ_{rxn} = 1.23 \text{ mol H}_2\text{S} \times \left(\frac{-9.7 \text{ kJ}}{1 \text{ mol H}_2\text{S}} \right) = -11.\overline{9} \text{ kJ} = -12 \text{ kJ (2 sf)}$$

6.101 There may be many different considerations related to the manner in which the fuel is to be used. Among them are (1) cost, (2) ease of combustion, (3) environmental considerations, such as air and water pollution, (4) transportability, and (5) the specific enthalpy and enthalpy density. Large values of these latter quantities are generally desired.

6.103 $\Delta H^\circ_c(C_8H_{18}) = -5471 \text{ kJ} \cdot \text{mol}^{-1}$

$$\text{heat produced} = 0.70 \times 0.100 \text{ g C}_8\text{H}_{18} \times \left(\frac{1 \text{ mol C}_8\text{H}_{18}}{114.23 \text{ g C}_8\text{H}_{18}} \right) \times \left(\frac{-5471 \text{ kJ}}{1 \text{ mol C}_8\text{H}_{18}} \right)$$
$$= -3.3\overline{5} \text{ kJ}$$

$\text{heat added} = +3.3\overline{5} \text{ kJ}$

$$\Delta T = \frac{+3.3\overline{5} \times 10^3 \text{ J}}{2.42 \text{ J} \cdot \text{g}^{-1} \cdot (°\text{C})^{-1} \times 250.0 \text{ g}} = 5.5°\text{C}$$

CHALLENGING EXERCISES

6.105 $\text{total heat supplied} = +20.0 \text{ g} \times 2.03 \text{ J} \cdot (°\text{C})^{-1} \cdot \text{g}^{-1} \times (0 + 14) \, °\text{C}$
$$+ 20.0 \text{ g} \times \left(\frac{1 \text{ mol}}{18.02 \text{ g}} \right) \times 6.01 \times 10^3 \text{ J} \cdot \text{mol}^{-1}$$
$$+ 20.0 \text{ g} \times 4.18 \text{ J} \cdot (°\text{C})^{-1} \cdot \text{g}^{-1} \times 100 \, °\text{C}$$
$$+ 20.0 \text{ g} \times \left(\frac{1 \text{ mol}}{18.02 \text{ g}} \right) \times 4.07 \times 10^4 \text{ J} \cdot \text{mol}^{-1}$$
$$+ 20.0 \text{ g} \times 2.01 \text{ J} \cdot (°\text{C})^{-1} \cdot \text{g}^{-1} \times (110 - 100) \, °\text{C}$$
$$= 6.12 \times 10^4 \text{ J}$$

6.107 $\Delta H° = 28\ \text{mol} \times \Delta H_f°[CO_2(g)] + 10\ \text{mol} \times \Delta H_f°[H_2O(g)] - 4\ \text{mol}$
$$\times\ \Delta H_f°[C_7H_5N_3O_6(s)]$$
$\Delta H° = 28\ \text{mol} \times (-393.51\ \text{kJ} \cdot \text{mol}^{-1}) + 10\ \text{mol} \times (-241.82\ \text{kJ} \cdot \text{mol}^{-1}) - 4\ \text{mol}$
$$\times\ (-67\ \text{kJ} \cdot \text{mol}^{-1}) = -13\ 168\ \text{kJ}$$

$$\text{enthalpy density} = \left(\frac{+13\ 168\ \text{kJ}}{4\ \text{mol TNT}}\right) \times \left(\frac{1\ \text{mol TNT}}{227.14\ \text{g TNT}}\right) \times \left(\frac{1.65\ \text{g TNT}}{1\ \text{cm}^3\ \text{TNT}}\right)$$
$$= +23.9\ \text{kJ} \cdot \text{cm}^{-3} = +23.9 \times 10^3\ \text{kJ} \cdot \text{L}^{-1}$$

6.109   (1) $Na(s) \longrightarrow Na(g)$ $\qquad\qquad \Delta H° = +108.4\ \text{kJ}$
(2) $Na(g) \longrightarrow Na^+(g) + e^-(g)$ $\qquad \Delta H° = +495.8\ \text{kJ}$
(3) $Cl_2(g) \longrightarrow 2Cl(g)$ $\qquad\qquad \Delta H° = +242\ \text{kJ}$
(4) $Cl(g) + e^-(g) \longrightarrow Cl^-(g)$ $\qquad \Delta H° = -348.6\ \text{kJ}$
(5) $Na(s) + \frac{1}{2}Cl_2(g) \longrightarrow NaCl(s)$ $\quad \Delta H° = -411.15\ \text{kJ}$
Multiply (3) by $\frac{1}{2}$, reverse (5), and then add.

$Na(s) \longrightarrow Na(g)$ $\qquad\qquad \Delta H° = +108.4\ \text{kJ}$

$Na(g) \longrightarrow Na^+(g) + e^-(g)$ $\qquad \Delta H° = +495.8\ \text{kJ}$

$\frac{1}{2}Cl_2(g) \longrightarrow Cl(g)$ $\qquad\qquad \Delta H° = \dfrac{+242\ \text{kJ}}{2} = 121\ \text{kJ}$

$Cl(g) + e^-(g) \longrightarrow Cl^-(g)$ $\qquad \Delta H° = -348.6\ \text{kJ}$

$NaCl(s) \longrightarrow Na(s) + \frac{1}{2}Cl_2(g)$ $\quad \Delta H° = +411.15\ \text{kJ}$
_____
$NaCl(s) \longrightarrow Na^+(g) + Cl^-(g)$ $\quad \Delta H° = 788\ \text{kJ} \cdot \text{mol}^{-1}$

6.111   Multiply (a) and (b) by $\frac{3}{4}$, reverse (c) and multiply it by $\frac{1}{2}$, then add.
$\frac{3}{4}CH_4(g) + \frac{3}{2}O_2(g) \longrightarrow \frac{3}{4}CO_2(g) + \frac{3}{2}H_2O(g)$ $\quad \Delta H = \frac{3}{4} \times (-802\ \text{kJ}) = -601.\overline{5}\ \text{kJ}$
$\frac{3}{4}CH_4(g) + \frac{3}{4}CO_2(g) \longrightarrow \frac{3}{2}CO_2(g) + \frac{3}{2}H_2(g)$ $\quad \Delta H = \frac{3}{4} \times (+206\ \text{kJ}) = 154.\overline{5}\ \text{kJ}$
$\frac{1}{2}CO(g) + \frac{3}{2}H_2(g) \longrightarrow \frac{1}{2}CH_4(g) + \frac{1}{2}H_2O(g)$ $\quad \Delta H = -\frac{1}{2} \times (+247\ \text{kJ}) = -123.\overline{5}\ \text{kJ}$
$\Delta H = (-601.\overline{5} + 154.\overline{5} - 123.\overline{5})\ \text{kJ} = -570\ \text{kJ}$

CHAPTER 7
INSIDE THE ATOM

EXERCISES

Frequency and Wavelength

7.1 (a) $400 \text{ nm} \times \left(\dfrac{10^{-9} \text{ m}}{1 \text{ nm}}\right) = 4.00 \times 10^{-7} \text{ m}$ and $\nu = \dfrac{c}{\lambda} = \dfrac{3.00 \times 10^8 \text{ m} \cdot \text{s}^{-1}}{4.00 \times 10^{-7} \text{ m}}$

$$= 7.50 \times 10^{14} \text{ s}^{-1}$$

Because $1 \text{ s}^{-1} = 1 \text{ Hz}$, the frequency is $7.50 \times 10^{14} \text{ Hz}$.

$700 \text{ nm} \times \left(\dfrac{10^{-9} \text{ m}}{1 \text{ nm}}\right) = 7.00 \times 10^{-7} \text{ m}$ and $\nu = \dfrac{c}{\lambda} = \dfrac{3.00 \times 10^8 \text{ m} \cdot \text{s}^{-1}}{7.00 \times 10^{-7} \text{ m}}$

$$= 4.28 \times 10^{14} \text{ s}^{-1}$$

Because $1 \text{ s}^{-1} = 1 \text{ Hz}$, the frequency is $4.28 \times 10^{14} \text{ Hz}$. Thus the wavelength range is $4.28 \times 10^{14} \text{ Hz}$ to $7.50 \times 10^{14} \text{ Hz}$.

(b) $\nu = \dfrac{c}{\lambda} = \dfrac{3.00 \times 10^8 \text{ m} \cdot \text{s}^{-1}}{250 \text{ m}} = 1.2 \times 10^6 \text{ s}^{-1} = 1.2 \times 10^6 \text{ Hz}$

7.3 (a) $\lambda = \dfrac{c}{\nu} = \left(\dfrac{3.00 \times 10^8 \text{ m} \cdot \text{s}^{-1}}{7.1 \times 10^{14} \text{ s}^{-1}}\right) \times \left(\dfrac{1 \text{ nm}}{10^{-9} \text{ m}}\right) = 420 \text{ nm}$

(b) $\lambda = \dfrac{c}{\nu} = \left(\dfrac{3.00 \times 10^8 \text{ m} \cdot \text{s}^{-1}}{2.0 \times 10^{18} \text{ s}^{-1}}\right) \times \left(\dfrac{1 \text{ pm}}{10^{-12} \text{ m}}\right) = 150 \text{ pm}$

Quanta and Photons

7.5 (a) $589 \text{ nm} \times \left(\dfrac{10^{-9} \text{ m}}{1 \text{ nm}}\right) = 5.89 \times 10^{-7} \text{ m}$

$E = \dfrac{hc}{\lambda} = \dfrac{(6.63 \times 10^{-34} \text{ J} \cdot \text{s}) \times (3.00 \times 10^8 \text{ m} \cdot \text{s}^{-1})}{5.89 \times 10^{-7} \text{ m}} = 3.37 \times 10^{-19} \text{ J}$

(b) $3.37 \times 10^{-19} \text{ J} \cdot \text{photon}^{-1} \times \left(\dfrac{1 \text{ photon}}{1 \text{ Na atom}}\right)$

$$\times \left(\dfrac{6.022 \times 10^{23} \text{ Na atoms}}{1.00 \text{ mol Na atoms}}\right) = 2.03 \times 10^5 \text{ J} \cdot \text{mol}^{-1}$$

7.7 (a) $86 \text{ pm} \times \left(\dfrac{10^{-12} \text{ m}}{1 \text{ pm}}\right) = 8.6 \times 10^{-11} \text{ m}$

$$E = \frac{hc}{\lambda} = \frac{(6.63 \times 10^{-34} \text{ J} \cdot \text{s}) \times (3.00 \times 10^8 \text{ m} \cdot \text{s}^{-1})}{8.6 \times 10^{-11} \text{ m}} = 2.3 \times 10^{-15} \text{ J}$$

(b) $470 \text{ nm} \times \left(\dfrac{10^{-9} \text{ m}}{1 \text{ nm}}\right) = 4.70 \times 10^{-7} \text{ m}$

$$E = \frac{hc}{\lambda} = \frac{(6.63 \times 10^{-34} \text{ J} \cdot \text{s}) \times (3.00 \times 10^8 \text{ m} \cdot \text{s}^{-1})}{4.70 \times 10^{-7} \text{ m}} = 4.23 \times 10^{-19} \text{ J}$$

and $4.23 \times 10^{-19} \text{ J} \cdot \text{photon}^{-1} \times \left(\dfrac{6.022 \times 10^{23} \text{ photons}}{1.0 \text{ mol photons}}\right)$

$$= 2.5 \times 10^5 \text{ J} \cdot (\text{mol photons})^{-1}$$

Atomic Spectra

7.9 $(589 \text{ nm}) \times \left(\dfrac{10^{-9} \text{ m}}{1 \text{ nm}}\right) = 5.89 \times 10^{-7} \text{ m}$

$$\Delta E = \frac{hc}{\lambda} = (6.63 \times 10^{-34} \text{ J} \cdot \text{s}) \times \left(\frac{3.00 \times 10^8 \text{ m} \cdot \text{s}^{-1}}{5.89 \times 10^{-7} \text{ m}}\right) = 3.38 \times 10^{-19} \text{ J}$$

7.11 (a) Let $n_1 = 2$, $n_u = 6$, then $E(\text{photon}) = -\Delta E(\text{atom}) = h\,\mathcal{R} \times \left(\dfrac{1}{n_1^2} - \dfrac{1}{n_u^2}\right)$

and because $E(\text{photon}) = h\nu$

$$\nu = \mathcal{R} \times \left[\frac{1}{n_1^2} - \frac{1}{n_u^2}\right] = 3.29 \times 10^{15} \text{ Hz} \times \left(\frac{1}{2^2} - \frac{1}{6^2}\right) = 3.29 \times 10^{15} \text{ Hz}\left(\frac{2}{9}\right)$$

$\nu = 7.31 \times 10^{14} \text{ Hz}$

and $\lambda = \dfrac{c}{\nu} = \dfrac{3.00 \times 10^8 \text{ m} \cdot \text{s}^{-1}}{7.31 \times 10^{14} \text{ Hz}} = 4.10 \times 10^{-7} \text{ m}$ (or 410 nm)

(b) violet

7.13 (a) See the solution to Exercise 7.11(a).

$$\nu = \mathcal{R} \times \left(\frac{1}{n_1^2} - \frac{1}{n_u^2}\right)$$

The highest frequency photon corresponds to the largest value of $\left(\dfrac{1}{n_1^2} - \dfrac{1}{n_u^2}\right)$. This frequency occurs when $n_1 = 1$ and $n_u = \infty$.

$$\nu = \mathcal{R} \times \left(\frac{1}{1^2} - \frac{1}{\infty^2}\right) = \mathcal{R} = 3.29 \times 10^{15} \text{ Hz}$$

(b) $\lambda = \dfrac{c}{\nu} = \dfrac{3.00 \times 10^8 \text{ m} \cdot \text{s}^{-1}}{3.29 \times 10^{15} \text{ s}^{-1}} = 9.12 \times 10^{-8} \text{ m}$; x-ray or gamma ray.

Particles and Waves

7.15 (a) electron mass $= 9.11 \times 10^{-31}$ kg

$h = 6.63 \times 10^{-34}$ J·s $\equiv 6.63 \times 10^{-34}$ kg·m^2·s^{-1}

$$\lambda = \frac{h}{mv} = \frac{6.63 \times 10^{-34} \text{ kg} \cdot \text{m}^2 \cdot \text{s}^{-1}}{(9.11 \times 10^{-31} \text{ kg}) \times (1.5 \times 10^7 \text{ m} \cdot \text{s})} = 4.9 \times 10^{-11} \text{ m}$$

(b) neutron mass $= 1.67 \times 10^{-27}$ kg

$h = 6.63 \times 10^{-34}$ kg·m^2·s^{-1}

$$\lambda = \frac{h}{mv} = \frac{6.63 \times 10^{-34} \text{ kg} \cdot \text{m}^2 \cdot \text{s}^{-1}}{(1.67 \times 10^{-27} \text{ kg}) \times (1.5 \times 10^7 \text{ m} \cdot \text{s}^{-1})} = 2.6 \times 10^{-14} \text{ m}$$

Atomic Orbitals and Quantum Numbers

7.17 (a) An atomic orbital is a region of space in which the electron is most likely to be found in an atom. It is a description of the wave characteristics of electrons in atoms in terms of three quantum numbers n, l, and m_l. Each orbital is characterized by its own unique set of these quantum numbers.

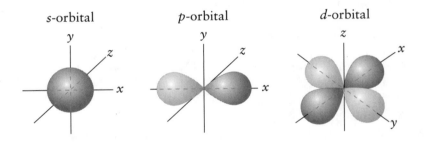

7.19 Subshells are characterized by the allowed l values, which range from 0 up to $l_{max} = n - 1$. Hence, the number of subshells is simply given by n.

(a) $n = 2$; therefore, $l_{max} = 1$ and subshells with $l = 0$ and 1 [2]

(b) $n = 3$; therefore, $l_{max} = 2$ and subshells with $l = 0, 1, 2$ [3]

(c) $n = 3$; therefore, l can be 0, 1, and 2

7.21 In each case, determine $2l + 1$.

(a) $l = 0$, $2l + 1 = 2 \times 0 + 1 = 1$

(b) $l = 2$, $2l + 1 = 2 \times 2 + 1 = 5$

(c) $l = 1$, $2l + 1 = 2 \times 1 + 1 = 3$

(d) $l = 3$, $2l + 1 = 2 \times 3 + 1 = 7$

7.23 (a) number of subshells = $n = 2$; $l = 0$ and $l = 1$

(b) number of orbitals = $2l + 1 = 2 \times 2 + 1 = 5$

(c) number of orbitals = $n^2 = 2^2 = 4$; they are one s- and three p-orbitals.

(d) for $3d$, $l = 2$; number of orbitals = $2l + 1 = 2 \times 2 + 1 = 5$

7.25 In each case, calculate $2l + 1 = $ number of orbitals.

(a) $3d, 5$ (b) $1s, 1$ (c) $6f, 7$ (d) $2p, 3$

7.27 In each case, determine the number of orbitals and multiply by 2.

(a) $2 \times (2l + 1) = 2 \times (2 + 1) = 6$ electrons

(b) $2 \times 1 = 2$ electrons

(c) $2 \times n^2 = 2 \times 2^2 = 8$ electrons

(d) $2 \times 1 = 2$ electrons

7.29 For each n value, the maximum l value is $n - 1$.

(a) $n = 2$, $l = 0, 1$; s and p only, so $2d$ not allowed

(b) $n = 4$, $l = 0, 1, 2, 3$; s, p, d, f allowed, so $4d$ allowed

(c) $n = 4$, $l = 0, 1, 2, 3$; s, p, d, f only, so $4g$ not allowed

(d) $n = 6$, $l = 0, 1, 2, 3, 4, 5$; s, p, d, f, g, h allowed, so $6f$ allowed

7.31 (a) allowed

(b) not allowed; if $l = 0$, then m_l can only be 0. n and l cannot be equal: $l = 0 \ldots, n - 1$.

(c) not allowed

7.33 (a) $n = 2$, $l = 1$, $m_l = 0$, $m_s = -\frac{1}{2}$

(b) $n = 5$, $l = 2$, $m_l = +1$, $m_s = +\frac{1}{2}$

Orbital Energies

7.35 The average distance from the nucleus for a $2s$-electron is much less than for a $3s$-electron; consequently, the electrostatic force of attraction between the nucleus and the $2s$-electron is much greater than that for a $3s$-electron. The electron cloud of the $2s$-electron is bunched more densely around the nucleus than is the $3s$-electron cloud.

7.37 (a) $n = 1, 2, 3, 4$; energy increases from 1 to 4

(b) $l = 0, 1, 2, 3$; energy increases from 1 to 3

7.39 $1s, 2p, 3s, 3d, 5d$; energy increases left to right

7.41 In each case, arrange the orbitals in order of increasing energy and then add electrons (no more than 2 to an orbital) starting from the lowest energy orbital. Note: m_l values are not assigned in any particular order.

(a) $\dfrac{\uparrow}{1s}$ $n = 1, l = 0, m_l = 0, m_s = +\frac{1}{2}$

(b) $\dfrac{\uparrow\downarrow}{1s}\ \dfrac{\uparrow\downarrow}{2s}\ \dfrac{\uparrow\downarrow}{2p_x}\ \dfrac{\uparrow\downarrow}{2p_y}\ \dfrac{\uparrow}{2p_z}$; $n = 2, l = 1, m_l = 0, m_s = +\frac{1}{2}$

(c) $\dfrac{\uparrow\downarrow}{1s}\ \dfrac{\uparrow\downarrow}{2s}\ \dfrac{\uparrow\downarrow}{2p}\ \dfrac{\uparrow\downarrow}{2p}\ \dfrac{\uparrow\downarrow}{2p}\ \dfrac{\uparrow\downarrow}{3s}\ \dfrac{\uparrow\downarrow}{3p}\ \dfrac{\uparrow\downarrow}{3p}\ \dfrac{\uparrow\downarrow}{3p}\ \dfrac{\uparrow\downarrow}{4s}$; $n = 4, l = 0, m_l = 0, m_s = -\frac{1}{2}$

7.43 (a) Ca; $[Ar]4s^2$
(b) N; $1s^2 2s^2 2p^3$
(c) Br; $[Ar]3d^{10}4s^2 4p^5$
(d) U; $[Rn]5f^3 6d^1 7s^2$. For U, the *Aufbau* rules would give $[Rn]5f^4 7s^2$. Uranium is an exception to these rules.

7.45 (a) Ni; $[Ar]3d^8 4s^2$
(b) Cd; $[Kr]4d^{10}5s^2$
(c) Pb; $[Xe]4f^{14}5d^{10}6s^2 6p^2$
(d) Ag; $[Kr]4d^{10}5s^1$

7.47 (a) Group 2: ns^2
(b) Group 18: $ns^2 np^6$

7.49 (a) Fe^{2+}; $[Ar]3d^6$
(b) Cl^-; $[Ne]3s^2 3p^6$
(c) Tl^+; $[Xe]4f^{14}5d^{10}6s^2$

7.51 (a) Si; $[Ne]3s^2 3p^2$
(b) Ne; $[He]2s^2 2p^6$
(c) Cs; $[Xe]6s^1$
(d) S; $[Ne]3s^2 3p^4$

7.53 (a) Si; s^2, p^2; 4 electrons
(b) Cl; s^2, p^5; 7 electrons

(c) Mn; s^2, d^5; 7 electrons

(d) Co; s^2, d^7; 9 electrons

Atomic and Ionic Radius

7.55 The outermost electrons of an atom determine the atomic radius. Proceeding down a group, the outermost electrons occupy shells that lie farther and farther from the nucleus, so the size (radius) increases down a group.

7.57 (a) Group 1 (alkali metals)

(b) The radius of the cation is less than the radius of the neutral atom.

(c) Cations with the largest number of protons (among a set of cations with the same number of electrons) will have the smallest radius.

7.59 (a) S (size decreases from left to right)

(b) S^{2-} (same number of electrons; Cl has more protons, hence, it is smaller)

(c) Na (size decreases from left to right)

(d) Mg^{2+} (same number of electrons; Al has more protons, hence, it is smaller)

Ionization Energy

7.61 First ionization energies decrease down a group because the outermost electron occupies a shell that is farther from the nucleus and is therefore less tightly bound. Ionization energies increase across a period because the effective nuclear charge increases as we go from left to right across a given period. As a result, the outermost electron is gripped more tightly and the ionization energies increase.

7.63 (a) Mg; consistent with the trend

(b) N; consistent with the trend

(c) P; inconsistent with the trend; S might have been predicted.

7.65 The ionizations energies for Group 16 elements are less than those for Group 15 elements. The group configurations are Group 16, ns^2np^4, and Group 15, ns^2np^3. The half-filled subshell of Group 15 is more stable than simple theory suggests. This stability makes removal of the electron more difficult; therefore, it has a higher ionization energy. In Group 16, the fourth p-electron pairs with another electron, thereby producing stronger electron repulsion, which makes it easier to remove this electron. Although there is the competing effect of increasing effective nuclear charge, the electron repulsion effect predominates.

7.67   Both the first and second electrons lost from Mg are 3s. The second electron for sodium must be removed from a 2p level that not only is filled but also is considerably lower in energy than the 3s level. Thus the second ionization energy of sodium is very high and sodium exists only as Na^+, not Na^{2+}.

Electron Affinity

7.69   (a) Group 17 (halogens)   (b) Electron affinities generally increase (left to right) across a period. However, anomalies are common.

7.71   (a) Cl   (b) O   (c) Cl

7.73   Atomic radii increase and ionization energies decrease from top to bottom within a group. Atomic radii decrease and ionization energies increase (left to right) across a period. In both cases, there is an inverse correlation.

Trends in Chemical Properties

7.75   A diagonal relationship is a similarity between diagonal neighbors in the periodic table, especially for elements at the left of the table. Two examples are (1) Li and Mg, which both burn in nitrogen to form the nitride; (2) Be and Al, which both are amphoteric, reacting with both acids and bases. Other examples are the metalloids, which fall in a diagonal band across the periodic table.

7.77   (a) Metals react with acids and form ionic compounds with nonmetals; many of them (transition metals) exhibit a variety of positive oxidation states.
(b) Nonmetals form acidic oxides, react with other nonmetals to form molecular compounds, and react with metals to form ionic compounds in which they exhibit negative oxidation states.

7.79   The ionization energies of the p-block metals are quite high, so they are less reactive than the s-block metals, which have low ionization energies.

7.81   (a) aluminum, metal   (b) carbon, nonmetal   (c) germanium, metalloid
(d) arsenic, metalloid

7.83 See Fig. 7.39 and 7.42.

(a) do (Fig. 7.39)   (b) do (Fig. 7.39)   (c) do, but not strongly (Fig. 7.42)   (d) do, but not strongly (Fig. 7.42)

SUPPLEMENTARY EXERCISES

7.85   (a) high energy, ultraviolet   (b) low energy, infrared

7.87 $\lambda = (3 \text{ cm}) \times \left(\dfrac{10^{-2} \text{ m}}{1 \text{ cm}}\right) = 3 \times 10^{-2}$ m

$\nu = \dfrac{c}{\lambda} = \dfrac{3.00 \times 10^8 \text{ m} \cdot \text{s}^{-1}}{3 \times 10^{-2} \text{ m}} = 1 \times 10^{10} \text{ s}^{-1} = 1 \times 10^{10}$ Hz

7.89   mass of one H_2 molecule $= \left(\dfrac{2.016 \text{ g } H_2}{1 \text{ mol } H_2}\right) \times \left(\dfrac{1 \text{ mol } H_2}{6.023 \times 10^{23} \text{ molecules}}\right)$

$\times \left(\dfrac{1 \text{ kg}}{10^3 \text{ g}}\right) = 3.347 \times 10^{-27}$ kg per H_2 molecule

and $h = 6.63 \times 10^{-34}$ J $\cdot$ s $\equiv 6.63 \times 10^{-34}$ kg $\cdot$ m^2 $\cdot$ s^{-1}

$\lambda = \dfrac{h}{m\nu} = \dfrac{6.63 \times 10^{-34} \text{ kg} \cdot \text{m}^2 \cdot \text{s}^{-1}}{(3.347 \times 10^{-27} \text{ kg per } H_2 \text{ molecule})(1930 \text{ m} \cdot \text{s}^{-1})} = 1.026 \times 10^{-10}$ m

7.91 $\lambda = (420 \text{ nm}) \times \left(\dfrac{10^{-9} \text{ m}}{1 \text{ nm}}\right) = 4.20 \times 10^{-7}$ m

$E = \dfrac{hc}{\lambda} = (6.63 \times 10^{-34} \text{ J} \cdot \text{s}) \times \left(\dfrac{3.00 \times 10^8 \text{ m} \cdot \text{s}^{-1}}{4.20 \times 10^{-7} \text{ m}}\right) = 4.73 \times 10^{-19}$ J

and $(4.73 \times 10^{-19} \text{ J}) \times (6.023 \times 10^{23} \text{ mol}^{-1}) \times \left(\dfrac{1 \text{ kJ}}{10^3 \text{ J}}\right) = 284$ kJ mol^{-1}

Because 284 kJ $\cdot$ mol^{-1} < 348 kJ $\cdot$ mol^{-1}, insufficient energy is available.

7.93   The number of l values for a given n is always equal to n, as can be seen from the series $l = 0, 1, 2, \ldots, n - 1$.

The number of m_l values for a given l is always equal to $2l + 1$, as can be seen from the series $-l, -l + 1, \ldots, +l$.

    (a) 6

    (b) $l = 2$, $2l + 1 = 5$

(c) $l = 1, 2l + 1 = 3$

(d) The number of l values is equal to the number of subshells; hence, for $n = 4$, there are 4 subshells.

7.95 (a) Fe; $[Ar]3d^6 4s^2$; the d-sublevel fills according to Hund's rule as

$$\underline{\uparrow\downarrow} \quad \underline{\uparrow} \quad \underline{\uparrow} \quad \underline{\uparrow} \quad \underline{\uparrow}$$
$$3d \quad 3d \quad 3d \quad 3d \quad 3d$$

Therefore, there are 4 unpaired electrons.

(b) P; $1s^2 2s^2 2p^6 3s^2 3p^3$; 9 p-electrons

(c) maximum number of electrons $= 2n^2 = 2(3)^2 = 18$

(d) [noble gas]ns^2; Group 2 (alkaline earth)

7.97 (a) Negative values of l are not acceptable.

(b) l values greater than $n - 1$ are not acceptable.

(c) and (d) are acceptable.

7.99 (a) Zr; $[Kr]4d^2 5s^2$

(b) Se; $[Ar]3d^{10} 4s^2 4p^4$

(c) Rb; $[Kr]5s^1$

(d) Cl; $[Ne]3s^2 3p^5$

(e) Sb; $[Kr]4d^{10} 5s^2 5p^3$

(f) Pu; $[Rn]5f^6 7s^2$

(g) Si; $[Ne]3s^2 3p^2$

(h) Ar; $[Ne]3s^2 3p^6$

7.101 (a) $n = 3; l = 1; m_l = +1; m_s = +\frac{1}{2}$

(b) $n = 3; l = 0; m_l = 0; m_s = -\frac{1}{2}$

7.103
(a) S (e) Ca (i) N (m) 4g
(b) F^- (f) Fe (j) Cl (n) 4
(c) Cs (g) Ba^{2+} (k) I (o) 7
(d) F (h) S^{2-} (l) K

7.105 (a) d-block (b) s-block (c) p-block (d) d-block (e) p-block (f) d-block

CHALLENGING EXERCISES

7.107 (a)

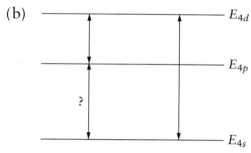

$$\Delta E(4p \longrightarrow 3s) = \frac{hc}{\lambda} = \frac{(6.63 \times 10^{-34} \text{ J} \cdot \text{s}) \times (3.00 \times 10^8 \text{ m} \cdot \text{s}^{-1})}{3.00 \times 10^{-7} \text{ m}}$$
$$= 6.63 \times 10^{-19} \text{ J}$$

$$\Delta E(4s \longrightarrow 3s) = \frac{hc}{\lambda} = \frac{(6.63 \times 10^{-34} \text{ J} \cdot \text{s}) \times (3.00 \times 10^8 \text{ m} \cdot \text{s}^{-1})}{3.89 \times 10^{-7} \text{ m}}$$
$$= 5.11 \times 10^{-19} \text{ J}$$

Therefore, $\Delta E(4p \longrightarrow 4s) = (6.63 - 5.11) \times 10^{-19} \text{ J} = 1.52 \times 10^{-19} \text{ J}$
$$= 1.52 \times 10^{-19} \text{ J} \cdot \text{atom}^{-1} \times 6.022 \times 10^{23} \text{ atoms} \cdot \text{mol}^{-1} = 9.15 \times 10^4 \text{ J} \cdot \text{mol}^{-1}$$
$$= 91.5 \text{ kJ} \cdot \text{mol}^{-1}$$

(b)

$$\Delta E(4d \longrightarrow 4s) = \frac{hc}{\lambda} = \frac{(6.63 \times 10^{-34} \text{ J} \cdot \text{s}) \times (3.00 \times 10^8 \text{ m} \cdot \text{s}^{-1})}{3.65 \times 10^{-7} \text{ m}}$$
$$= 5.45 \times 10^{-19} \text{ J}$$

$$\Delta E(4d \longrightarrow 4p) = \frac{hc}{\lambda} = \frac{(6.63 \times 10^{-34} \text{ J} \cdot \text{s}) \times (3.00 \times 10^8 \text{ m} \cdot \text{s}^{-1})}{6.89 \times 10^{-7} \text{ m}}$$
$$= 2.89 \times 10^{-19} \text{ J}$$

$$\Delta E(4p \longrightarrow 4s) = (5.45 - 2.89) \times 10^{-19} \text{ J} = 2.56 \times 10^{-19} \text{ J}$$
$$= 2.56 \times 10^{-19} \text{ J} \cdot \text{atom}^{-1} \times 6.022 \times 10^{23} \text{ atoms} \cdot \text{mol}^{-1}$$
$$= 1.54 \times 10^5 \text{ J} \cdot \text{mol}^{-1} = 154 \text{ kJ} \cdot \text{mol}^{-1}$$

(c) The separation is larger in potassium because of its greater nuclear charge and the fact that the differences in shielding between 4s and 4p are greater in K than in Na. Note: The $4s \longrightarrow 3s$ and $4d \longrightarrow 4s$ transitions belong to a class normally referred to as forbidden transitions. The intensities of these transitions are consequently very weak.

7.109 (a) It would be at the position of Na, which also has 11 protons.

(b) The element NH$_4$ should react with H$_2$O to form a basic hydroxide, NH$_4$OH. It should react with the halogens to form ionic compounds such as NH$_4$Cl. It should have a low ionization energy and be a low-melting-point solid with good electrical conductivity. Some of these predictions by analogy seem more reasonable than others. NH$_4$Cl(s) and NH$_4$OH (aq) indeed exist, and the predicted low ionization energy would be most likely, but the values for the other physical properties are more difficult to speculate about.

(c) Na$^+$ has a radius of 102 pm, considerably smaller than NH$_4^+$. The difference is a result of the much bigger "nucleus" of NH$_4^+$; the protons are spread out farther from the center, and consequently, the electrons that are attracted to them are also more spread out.

7.111 (a) Answered in the question: some of the energy of the incoming radiation, $h\nu$, is required to ionize the atom (free the electron); the remainder is the kinetic energy for the electron.

(b) $h\nu = I + \frac{1}{2} m_e \nu^2$

$$\frac{(6.63 \times 10^{-34} \text{ J} \cdot \text{s}) \times (3.00 \times 10^8 \text{ m} \cdot \text{s}^{-1})}{5.84 \times 10^{-8} \text{ m}}$$

$$= I + \frac{1}{2}(9.11 \times 10^{-31} \text{ kg}) \times (2.450 \times 10^6 \text{ m} \cdot \text{s}^{-1})^2$$

$I = 6.72 \times 10^{-19} \text{ J} \cdot \text{atom}^{-1}$ (404 kJ $\cdot$ mol^{-1})

CHAPTER 8
INSIDE MATERIALS:
CHEMICAL BONDS

EXERCISES

Ionic Bonds

8.1 Refer to Section 1.10 and Example 1.2 for the rules of assigning charges to monatomic ions formed from main-group elements.
(a) $+1$ (b) -2 (c) $+2$ (d) $+3$

8.3 Na^{2+} has the configuration $1s^2 2s^2 2p^6$, which is a very stable electronic configuration, identical to that of Ne, which has an octet of electrons in the $n = 2$ shell. These electrons are all core electrons, with high ionization energies. To lose one, as required to form Na^{2+}, would take a great deal of energy, because these core electrons are so tightly held. Detailed consideration of the energetics of all the processes resulting in the formation of ionic compounds of Na^{2+} shows that the existence of such compounds is energetically unfavorable. See the discussion of the Born-Haber cycle in Section 8.2. The ΔH_f° of ionic compounds of Na^{2+} would be predicted to be positive and is not consistent with the existence of stable ionic compounds.

8.5 (a) Ca: (b) $\cdot \ddot{S} \cdot$ (c) $\left[:\ddot{O}: \right]^{2-}$ (d) $\left[:\ddot{N}: \right]^{3-}$

8.7 (a) $K^+ \left[:\ddot{F}: \right]^-$

(b) $\left[:\ddot{S}: \right]^{2-} Al^{3+} \left[:\ddot{S}: \right]^{2-} Al^{3+} \left[:\ddot{S}: \right]^{2-}$

(c) $Ca^{2+} \left[:\ddot{N}: \right]^{3-} Ca^{2+} \left[:\ddot{N}: \right]^{3-} Ca^{2+}$

Lattice Enthalpies

8.9 This difference is a result of the difference in ionic radii between Mg^{2+} and Ba^{2+}. See Fig. 7.28. The radius of Mg^{2+} (72 pm) is smaller than the radius of Ba^{2+} (136 pm), so the distance between Mg^{2+} and O^{2-} ions is less than that between Ba^{2+} and O^{2-} ions in the crystal lattice. Thus, the lattice enthalpy of MgO exceeds that of BaO. In MgO, O^{2-} is so much bigger than Mg^{2+} that O^{2-} almost touches other O^{2-} anions. This is not the case in BaO. In other words, O^{2-}—O^{2-} repulsions are greater in MgO than in BaO because of the shorter distance between them.

8.11 The lattice enthalpy corresponds to the $\Delta H°$ of the process:

$$AgF(s) \longrightarrow Ag^+(g) + F^-(g)$$

This process can be broken down into the following steps:

	$\Delta H°$, $kJ \cdot mol^{-1}$
(1) $Ag(s) \longrightarrow Ag(g)$	$+284$
(2) $Ag(g) \longrightarrow Ag^+(g) + e^-$	$+731$
(3) $\frac{1}{2}F_2(g) \longrightarrow F(g)$	$+79$
(4) $F(g) + e^- \longrightarrow F^-(g)$	$-(+328)$ [Figure 7.40]
(5) $AgF(s) \longrightarrow Ag(s) + \frac{1}{2}F_2(g)$	$-(-205)$
$AgF(s) \longrightarrow Ag^+(g) + F^-(g)$	$+971 = \Delta H°_L$

Note that the enthalpy change of step 4 is the negative of the electron affinity of Fig. 7.40 and that step 5 is the reverse of the formation of AgF(s) from the elements.

8.13 (a) endothermic; all ionization energies of the elements correspond to positive ΔH values. See Section 7.16.

(b) exothermic.

(c) endothermic; sublimation always corresponds to a positive ΔH value.

(d) exothermic; the ΔH for this process is negative, because it is the negative of the lattice enthalpy, which is always positive.

(e) exothermic; Appendix 2A shows that the enthalpy of formation of CuO(s) is -157.3 $kJ \cdot mol^{-1}$.

Lewis Structures

8.15 (a) H—F̈: (b) H—N̈—H (c) see structure
                          |
                          H

(c)
```
      H
      |
  H—C—H
      |
      H
```

8.17 (a) $\left[\begin{array}{c} H \\ | \\ H-N-H \\ | \\ H \end{array} \right]^{+}$ (b) $\left[:\ddot{\underset{..}{C}}l-\ddot{\underset{..}{O}}: \right]^{-}$ (c) $\left[\begin{array}{c} :\ddot{F}: \\ | \\ :\ddot{F}-B-\ddot{F}: \\ | \\ :\ddot{F}: \end{array} \right]^{-}$

8.19 (a) $\left[\begin{array}{c} H \\ | \\ H-N-H \\ | \\ H \end{array} \right]^{+} \left[:\ddot{\underset{..}{C}}l: \right]^{-}$ (b) $K^{+} \; K^{+} \left[\begin{array}{c} :\ddot{O}: \\ | \\ :\ddot{O}-P-\ddot{O}: \\ | \\ :\ddot{O}: \end{array} \right]^{3-}$ (c) $Na^{+} \left[:\ddot{\underset{..}{C}}l-\ddot{\underset{..}{O}}: \right]^{-}$

8.21 (a) $H-C\begin{array}{c} \nearrow \ddot{O}: \\ \searrow H \end{array}$ (b) $H-\underset{\underset{H}{|}}{\overset{\overset{H}{|}}{C}}-\ddot{\underset{..}{O}}-H$ (c) $H-\underset{\underset{H-N:}{\underset{|}{\underset{H}{|}}}}{\overset{\overset{H}{|}}{C}}-C\begin{array}{c} \nearrow \ddot{O}: \\ \searrow \ddot{O} \diagdown H \end{array}$

Resonance

8.23 An example is the benzene molecule, which can be represented as a resonance hybrid of two principal Lewis structures, although other structures contribute slightly.

Resonance is a blending of Lewis structures, none of which by themselves are capable of adequately describing the properties of the molecule. Two consequences of resonance are that (1) the blended structure, or resonance hybrid, has a significantly lower energy than any of the individual structures. Thus, resonance plays a significant role in the chemical properties of the compound. The compound is less reactive than would have been predicted for a molecule existing in the form of just one of the structures. (2) Bond lengths are significantly different from what would be expected without resonance. In benzene, the C—C bond distance is intermediate between that expected for a C—C (single) bond and a C=C (double) bond, but the distance is not merely an average of the two.

8.25 (a) $\left[:\ddot{\underset{..}{O}}-\ddot{N}=\ddot{O}: \right]^{-} \longleftrightarrow \left[:\ddot{O}=\ddot{N}-\ddot{\underset{..}{O}}: \right]^{-}$

(b) $:\ddot{\underset{..}{O}}-\underset{\underset{..}{|}}{\overset{\overset{:\ddot{C}l:}{|}}{N}}=\ddot{\underset{..}{O}} \longleftrightarrow \ddot{\underset{..}{O}}=\underset{\underset{..}{|}}{\overset{\overset{:\ddot{C}l:}{|}}{N}}-\ddot{\underset{..}{O}}:$

8.27 (a)

$$\left[\text{H}-\ddot{\text{O}}-\overset{\displaystyle :\overset{..}{\text{O}}:}{\underset{\displaystyle :\overset{..}{\text{O}}:}{\text{P}}}-\ddot{\text{O}}-\text{H}\right]^{-} \longleftrightarrow \left[\text{H}-\ddot{\text{O}}-\overset{\displaystyle :\text{O}:}{\underset{\displaystyle :\overset{..}{\text{O}}:}{\text{P}}}-\ddot{\text{O}}-\text{H}\right]^{-} \longleftrightarrow$$

2 ways

$$\left[\text{H}-\ddot{\text{O}}-\overset{\displaystyle :\text{O}:}{\underset{\displaystyle :\text{O}:}{\text{P}}}-\ddot{\text{O}}-\text{H}\right]^{-}$$

(b)

$$\left[:\ddot{\text{O}}-\overset{\displaystyle :\ddot{\text{O}}:}{\underset{\displaystyle :\overset{..}{\text{O}}:}{\text{S}}}\right]^{2-} \longleftrightarrow \left[:\text{O}=\overset{\displaystyle :\ddot{\text{O}}:}{\underset{\displaystyle :\overset{..}{\text{O}}:}{\text{S}}}:\right]^{2-} \longleftrightarrow \left[:\text{O}=\overset{\displaystyle \cdot\overset{..}{\text{O}}\cdot}{\underset{\displaystyle :\overset{..}{\text{O}}:}{\text{S}}}:\right]^{2-}$$

3 ways   3 ways

(c)

$$\left[:\ddot{\text{O}}-\overset{\displaystyle :\ddot{\text{O}}:}{\underset{\displaystyle :\overset{..}{\text{O}}:}{\text{Cl}}}\right]^{2-} \longleftrightarrow \left[:\ddot{\text{O}}-\overset{\displaystyle \cdot\text{O}\cdot}{\underset{\displaystyle :\overset{..}{\text{O}}:}{\text{Cl}}}:\right]^{2-} \longleftrightarrow \left[:\ddot{\text{O}}-\overset{\displaystyle \cdot\text{O}\cdot}{\underset{\displaystyle \cdot\overset{..}{\text{O}}\cdot}{\text{Cl}}}:\right]^{2-}$$

3 ways   3 ways

(d)

$$\left[:\text{O}=\text{N}\overset{\displaystyle \cdot\ddot{\text{O}}:}{\underset{\displaystyle \cdot\overset{..}{\text{O}}:}{}}\right]^{-} \longleftrightarrow \left[:\ddot{\text{O}}-\text{N}\overset{\displaystyle \ddot{\text{O}}:}{\underset{\displaystyle \cdot\overset{..}{\text{O}}:}{}}\right]^{-} \longleftrightarrow \left[:\ddot{\text{O}}-\text{N}\overset{\displaystyle \cdot\ddot{\text{O}}:}{\underset{\displaystyle \text{O}:}{}}\right]^{-}$$

Note: Further expansion of the octet, although conceivable, would place unrealistic formal charges on the central atoms.

Formal Charge

8.29 Formal charge is a good "bookkeeping" system for electrons and is based on the assumption that the molecule is "perfectly covalent." However, as with any model, we must be careful not to follow it too rigorously. Molecules do not have such a clearly defined distribution of charge. Formal charge is determined by dividing the electrons in a bond equally between the atoms connected by the bond. The concept is used primarily for deciding between otherwise equally plausible Lewis structures.

8.31 We use the general expression $FC = V - (L + \frac{1}{2}S)$. See Section 8.8 for the meaning of these symbols.

90

(a)

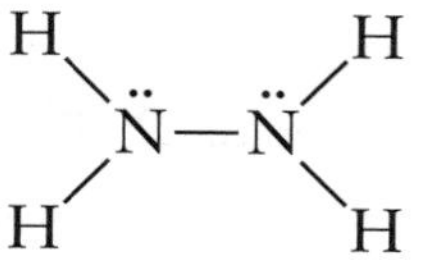

$$FC(N) = 5 - 2 - \tfrac{1}{2}(6) = 0$$
$$FC(H) = 1 - 0 - \tfrac{1}{2}(2) = 0$$

(b) 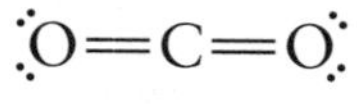 $\ddot{O}=C=\ddot{O}$

$$FC(C) = 4 - 0 - \tfrac{1}{2}(8) = 0$$
$$FC(O) = 6 - 4 - \tfrac{1}{2}(4) = 0$$

8.33 In each case, we use the formula $FC = V - (L + \tfrac{1}{2}S)$. The best structure is the one with formal charges closest to 0.

(a) First structure   Second structure

FC: +1   0

FC: 0   0

FC: −1   0

The second structure has formal charges closest to 0; hence, it is the more plausible structure.

(b) First structure   Second structure

FC: 0   +1

FC: 0   0

FC: 0   −1

The first structure is more plausible.

8.35 The structures differ only about the S—O bond. Therefore, look at the formal charge for these two atoms.

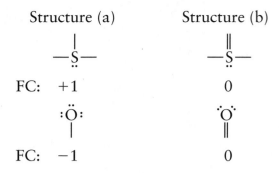

Structure (a)   Structure (b)

FC: +1   0

FC: −1   0

Structure (b) has formal charges closest to 0; hence it is the more plausible.

8.37 (a) First structure   Second structure

FC: 0   +1

FC: 0   −2

FC: 0   +1

The first structure is dominant.

(b) First structure   Second structure

FC: 0   −1

FC: 0   0

FC: 0   +1

The first structure is dominant.

Ionic and Covalent Bonding

8.39 A compound is likely to be ionic if it is a binary compound of a metal and non-metal between which there is a large difference in electronegativity. Binary compounds of nonmetals are likely to be nonionic.

(a) ionic, metal and nonmetal

(b) nonionic, nonmetal and nonmetal

(c) ionic, metal and nonmetal

8.41 We use the rule of thumb that an electronegativity difference of $\Delta\chi > 2.0$ corresponds to an ionic bond; $\Delta\chi < 1.5$ corresponds to a covalent bond; and $1.5 \leq \Delta\chi \leq 2.0$ corresponds to a significant mix of both ionic and covalent bonding.

(a) Ba—Cl, $\Delta\chi = 3.0 - 0.9 = 2.1$; therefore, ionic

(b) Bi—T, $\Delta\chi = 2.7 - 2.0 = 0.7$; therefore, covalent

(c) Si—H, $\Delta\chi = 2.2 - 1.9 = 0.3$; therefore, covalent

8.43 The order is most likely $Rb^+ < Sr^{2+} < Be^{2+}$, which corresponds to the order of ionic size in reverse. Higher charge predominates over lower charge, and for the same charge, smaller size predominates over larger size.

8.45 $O^{2-} < N^{3-} < Cl^- < Br^-$. The order parallels the ionic size, Br^- is largest, O^{2-} is smallest. The bigger the ion, the more electrons present, and the more spread out the charge, thus making the ion more susceptible to charge distortion by another charge.

8.47 In each case, calculate the difference in electronegativity, $\Delta\chi$, between the atoms in the bonds. Larger $\Delta\chi$ corresponds to greater ionic character in the bond. Use Fig. 8.15.

(a) $\Delta\chi$ (H—Cl) $= 3.2 - 2.2 = 1.0$; HCl is more ionic.

$\Delta\chi$(H—I) $= 2.7 - 2.2 = 0.5$

(b) $\Delta\chi$(C—H) $= 2.6 - 2.2 = 0.4$

$\Delta\chi$(C—F) $= 4.0 - 2.6 = 1.4$; CF_4 is more ionic.

(c) $\Delta\chi$(C—O) $= 3.4 - 2.6 = 0.8$; CO_2 is more ionic.

$\Delta\chi$(C—S) $= 2.6 - 2.6 = 0$

8.49 In each case, calculate the electronegativity difference of the bond, $\Delta\chi$, and then use the rule of thumb given in the last paragraph of Section 8.13. See also Exercise 8.41.

(a) $\Delta\chi$ (Ag—F) $= 4.0 - 1.9 = 2.1$; $\Delta\chi > 2.0$, therefore ionic

(b) $\Delta\chi$ (Ag—I) $= 2.7 - 1.9 = 0.9$; $\Delta\chi < 1.5$, therefore mainly covalent

(c) $\Delta\chi$ (Al—Cl) $= 3.2 - 1.6 = 1.6$; $\Delta\chi > 1.5$, therefore mixed ionic and covalent

(d) $\Delta\chi$ (Al—F) $= 4.0 - 1.6 = 2.4$; $\Delta\chi > 2.0$, therefore ionic

Exceptions to the Octet Rule

8.51 A radical is any species with an unpaired electron. Examples are

$$(1)\ \cdot CH_3 \quad or \quad \cdot \overset{\displaystyle H}{\underset{\displaystyle H}{C}}-H$$

(2) NO or $:\dot{N}{=}\ddot{O}:$

(3) NO_2 or $\ddot{O}{=}\dot{N}{-}\ddot{O}: \longleftrightarrow :\ddot{O}{-}\dot{N}{=}\ddot{O}$

8.53 (a)

$$\begin{array}{c} :\!\ddot{C}l\!: \\ | \\ :\!\ddot{C}l\!-\!\overset{..}{S}\!: \\ \diagup\;\;\diagdown \\ :\!\ddot{C}l\;\;\;:\!\ddot{C}l\!: \end{array}$$

1 lone pair on S

(b)

$$\begin{array}{c} :\!\ddot{C}l\!: \\ | \\ :\!\ddot{C}l\!-\!\ddot{I}\!: \\ | \\ :\!\ddot{C}l\!: \end{array}$$

2 lone pairs on I

(c)

$$\left[\begin{array}{cc} :\!\ddot{F} & \ddot{F}\!: \\ \diagdown & \diagup \\ & I \\ \diagup & \diagdown \\ :\!\ddot{F} & \ddot{F}\!: \end{array}\right]^{-}$$

2 lone pairs on I

8.55 (a)

$$\left[\begin{array}{cc} :\!\ddot{C}l & \ddot{C}l\!: \\ \diagdown & \diagup \\ & \cdot\ddot{I}\cdot \end{array}\right]^{+}$$

4 electron pairs on I
2 bonding pairs
2 lone pairs

(b)

$$\left[\begin{array}{cc} :\!\ddot{C}l & \ddot{C}l\!: \\ \diagdown & \diagup \\ & I \\ \diagup & \diagdown \\ :\!\ddot{C}l & \ddot{C}l\!: \end{array}\right]^{-}$$

6 electron pairs on I
4 bonding pairs
2 lone pairs

(c)

$$\begin{array}{c} :\!\ddot{C}l\!-\!\ddot{I}\!-\!\ddot{C}l\!: \\ | \\ :\!\ddot{C}l\!: \end{array}$$

5 electron pairs on I
3 bonding pairs
2 lone pairs

(d)

$$\begin{array}{c} :\!\ddot{C}l\;\;\;\;\ddot{C}l\!: \\ \diagdown\;\;\;\diagup \\ I \\ \diagup\;|\;\diagdown \\ :\!\ddot{C}l\;:\!\ddot{C}l\!:\;\ddot{C}l\!: \end{array}$$

6 electron pairs on I
5 bonding pairs
1 lone pair

8.57 (a) $:\!\ddot{C}l\!-\!\dot{\ddot{O}}\!:$ (b) $:\!\ddot{C}l\!-\!\ddot{O}\!-\!\ddot{O}\!-\!\ddot{C}l\!:$

FC: 0   0   FC: 0   0   0   0

a radical   not a radical

(c)

$$:\!\ddot{C}l\!-\!\ddot{O}\!-\!N\!\!\begin{array}{c}\nearrow \dot{\ddot{O}}\!: \\ \searrow \\ \overset{..}{O}\!\cdot \end{array} \quad\longleftrightarrow\quad :\!\ddot{C}l\!-\!\ddot{O}\!-\!N\!\!\begin{array}{c}\nearrow \dot{\ddot{O}}\!\cdot \\ \searrow \\ \ddot{O}\!: \end{array} \quad \text{(resonance)}$$

FC: 0   0   +1   0, −1   not a radical

(d) $:\!\ddot{C}l\!-\!\ddot{O}\!-\!\ddot{O}\!\cdot$

FC: 0   0   −1

a radical

8.59 (a) $:\ddot{F}\!-\!\dot{X}\dot{e}\!-\!\ddot{F}:$ 2 lone pairs on Xe

$\quad\quad\quad\quad\quad\overset{|}{:\!\ddot{O}\!:}$

(b) $:\ddot{F}\!-\!\dot{X}\dot{e}\!-\!\ddot{F}:$ 3 lone pairs on Xe

(c) $\left[\begin{array}{c} \quad\quad\overset{H}{\nearrow} \\ :\ddot{O}: \\ | \\ :\ddot{O}\!=\!\ddot{X}\dot{e}\!=\!\ddot{O}: \\ | \\ :\ddot{O}: \end{array}\right]^{-}$ 1 lone pair on Xe

3 ways

Lewis Acids and Bases

8.61 A *Lewis acid* is an electron pair acceptor, therefore its electronic structure must allow an additional electron pair to become attached to it. A *Lewis base* is an electron pair donor, therefore it must contain a lone pair of electrons that it can donate.

Lewis acids: H^+, Al^{3+}, BF_3

Lewis bases: OH^-, NH_3, H_2O

8.63 The net ionic reaction for an acid-base neutralization is

$$H^+ \quad + \quad \left[:\ddot{O}\!-\!H\right]^- \longrightarrow \quad \overset{\textstyle \cdot\ddot{O}\cdot}{\underset{H\quad\quad H}{\diagup\quad\diagdown}}$$

Lewis acid +   Lewis base $\longrightarrow$ Lewis complex

8.65 (a) $\overset{\textstyle \ddot{N}}{\underset{H\quad H\quad H}{\diagup\,|\,\diagdown}}$ There is a lone pair, which can be donated, hence, NH_3 is a Lewis base.

(b) $F\!-\!\overset{\textstyle F}{\underset{\textstyle F}{\overset{|}{\underset{|}{B}}}}$ There is an incomplete octet on B; hence, there is room to accept a pair. BF_3 is, therefore, a Lewis acid.

(c) Ag^+ There are a number of empty orbitals close in energy to the highest occupied orbital that could accept an electron pair; hence, Ag^+ is a Lewis acid.

(d) $\left[:\ddot{F}:\right]^-$ There are four lone pairs; hence, F^- is a Lewis base.

8.67 $\left[\begin{array}{c} \quad H \\ | \\ H\!-\!C\!-\!\ddot{O}: \\ | \\ H \end{array}\right]^{-}$ There are available electron pairs on the O; thus CH_3O^- would be expected to be a Lewis base.

8.69 (a)

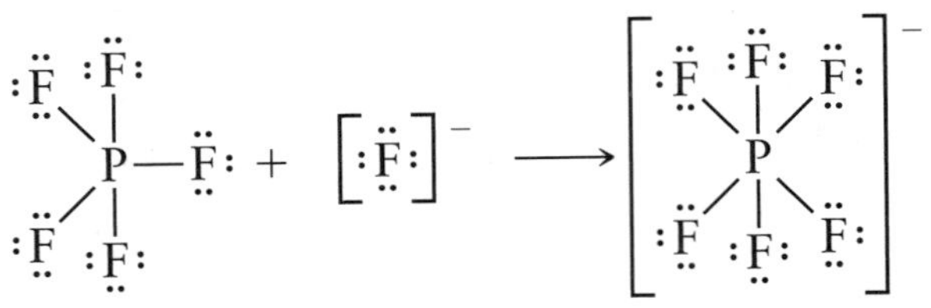

Lewis acid   Lewis base   Product

(b)

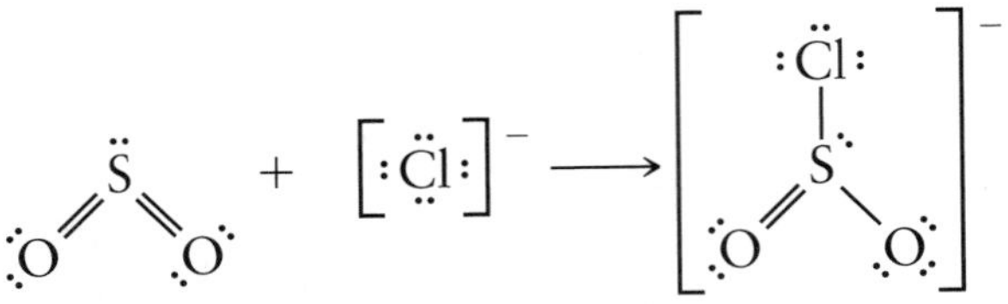

Lewis acid   Lewis base   Product

(c) Cu^{2+} + 4 :N—H ⟶

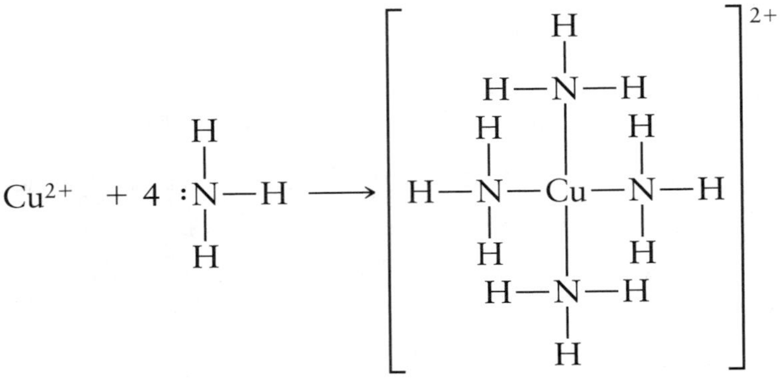

Lewis acid   Lewis base   Product

SUPPLEMENTARY EXERCISES

8.71 Boron is in Group 13 and Period 2 of the periodic table and has only 3 valence electrons. In order to have an octet of electrons, boron would have to add 5 electrons by sharing with other atoms. That is improbable, especially because the other atoms involved are likely to be highly electronegative nonmetals. Other elements in Period 2, or later periods, that form covalent bonds have to acquire no more than 4 additional electrons to complete their octet and hence are not likely to form electron-deficient compounds.

8.73 In each case, we calculate the electronegativity difference, $\Delta\chi$. The greater $\Delta\chi$, the greater the ionic character.

$\Delta\chi$ (Na—Cl) = 3.2 − 0.9 = 2.3, most ionic
$\Delta\chi$ (Al—Cl) = 3.2 − 1.6 = 1.6
$\Delta\chi$ (C—Cl) = 3.2 − 2.6 = 0.6
$\Delta\chi$ (Br—Cl) = 3.2 − 3.0 = 0.2, least ionic

8.75 (a) Li^+ $\left[:H \right]^-$

(b) $\left[:\ddot{Cl}: \right]^-$ Cu^{2+} $\left[:\ddot{Cl}: \right]^-$

96

(c) $Ba^{2+} \left[:\ddot{\underset{..}{N}}: \right]^{3-} Ba^{2+} \left[:\ddot{\underset{..}{N}}: \right]^{3-} Ba^{2+}$

(d) $\left[:\ddot{\underset{..}{O}}: \right]^{2-} Ga^{3+} \left[:\ddot{\underset{..}{O}}: \right]^{2-} Ga^{3+} \left[:\ddot{\underset{..}{O}}: \right]^{2-}$

8.77 (a) The lattice enthalpy corresponds to the $\Delta H°$ of the following process:

$$Na_2O(s) \longrightarrow 2Na^+(g) + O^{2-}(g)$$

This process can be broken down into the following steps:

Step	$\Delta H°$, kJ·mol^{-1}
(1) $2Na(s) \longrightarrow 2Na(g)$	$2 \times (+108)$
(2) $2Na(g) \longrightarrow 2Na^+(g) + 2e^-$	$2 \times (+494)$
(3) $\frac{1}{2}O_2(g) \longrightarrow O(g)$	249
(4) $O(g) + 2e^- \longrightarrow O^{2-}(g)$	703
(5) $Na_2O(s) \longrightarrow 2Na(s) + \frac{1}{2}O_2(g)$	$-(-409)$
$Na_2O(s) \longrightarrow 2Na^+(g) + O^{2-}(g)$	$+2565 \; = \Delta H_L°$

The numerical value for $\Delta H°$ in step 4 is obtained from the data of Fig. 7.40 as follows:

$\Delta H°$ (electron gain enthalpy) $= [-(-844) + 141] \; kJ·mol^{-1} = 703 \; kJ·mol^{-1}$

(b) The lattice enthalpy corresponds to the $\Delta H°$ of the following process:

$$AlCl_3(s) \longrightarrow Al^{3+}(g) + 3 \, Cl^-(g)$$

This process can be broken down into the following steps:

Step	$\Delta H°$, kJ·mol^{-1}
(1) $Al(s) \longrightarrow Al(g)$	$+326$
(2) $Al(g) \longrightarrow Al^+(g) + e^-$	$+577$
$Al^+(g) \longrightarrow Al^{2+}(g) + e^-$	$+1820$
$Al^{2+}(g) \longrightarrow Al^{3+}(g) + e^-$	$+2740$
(3) $\frac{3}{2}Cl_2(g) \longrightarrow 3Cl(g)$	$3 \times (+121)$
(4) $3Cl(g) + 3e^- \longrightarrow 3Cl^-(g)$	$3 \times (-349)$
(5) $AlCl_3(s) \longrightarrow Al(s) + \frac{3}{2}Cl_2(g)$	$-(-704)$
$AlCl_3(s) \longrightarrow Al^{3+}(g) + 3Cl^-(g)$	$+5483 \; = \Delta H_L°$

8.79 (a) Lewis acid (b) Lewis acid (c) either Lewis acid (at Ga) or a Lewis base (at I)

8.81

Lewis acid   Lewis base   Product

Note: Pure sulfurous acid has never been isolated. The structure shown above is one of two possibilities for the complex of SO_2 and water.

8.83 (a) CH_3^-, because the Lewis structure of CH_3^- shows a lone pair on the C atom; there is no lone pair in CH_4. So CH_3^- is a better lone pair donor and a stronger Lewis base.

(b) H_2O, because O is more electronegative than S and thus has a stronger partial negative charge.

8.85 (a)   First structure   Second structure

$:\!\overset{..}{O}\!=$ $:\!\overset{..}{\underset{..}{O}}\!-$

FC: 0 -1

$:\!\overset{..}{O}\!:$ $:\!\overset{..}{\underset{..}{O}}\!:$
$\|$ $|$

FC: 0 -1

$-H$ $-H$

FC: 0   0

$-\overset{..}{\underset{..}{O}}-$ $-\overset{..}{\underset{..}{O}}-$

FC: 0   0

$\|$ $|$
$=\!\overset{}{\underset{..}{Cl}}\!-$ $-\!\overset{}{\underset{..}{Cl}}\!-$

FC: 0 $+2$

The first structure has the lower energy.

(b) $:\!\overset{..}{O}\!=$ $=\!C\!=$ $=\!\overset{..}{\underset{.}{S}}$

FC: 0   FC: 0   FC: 0

(c) $H-$ $-C\!\equiv$ $\equiv\!N\!:$

FC: 0   FC: 0   FC: 0

(d) First structure   Second structure

$\overset{.}{\underset{..}{N}}\!=$ $:\!N\!\equiv$

FC: -1 0

$=\!C\!=$ $\equiv\!C\!-$

FC: 0   0

$=\!\overset{.}{\underset{..}{N}}$ $-\overset{..}{\underset{..}{N}}\!:$

FC: -1 -2

The first structure has the lower energy.

(e) First structure   Second structure

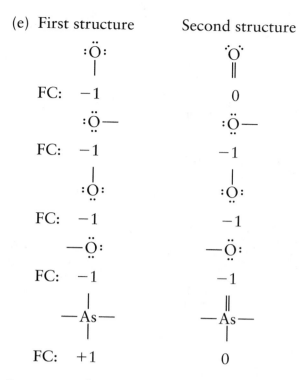

FC: −1   0

FC: −1   −1

FC: −1   −1

FC: −1   −1

FC: +1   0

Structure 2 has the lower energy.

CHALLENGING EXERCISES

8.87 In a very broad sense, yes. All bonds involve a pair of electrons influenced by two nuclear centers. It becomes simply a question of the degree (or probability) to which the electron pair resides closer to one rather than the other of the bonded nuclei. Covalent bonds share the electron pair equally; polar bonds less so, and ionic bonds hardly at all. The octet rule is useful in the understanding of all the bonding situations mentioned to the extent that it applies. Recall that there are exceptions. The coordinate covalent bond that results from complex formation is like any other covalent bond once it has formed.

8.89 The ΔH°_f for $Cl(g)$ is obtained from the data in Exercise 8.76.
The overall process can be broken down into the following steps:

Step	ΔH°, kJ·mol^{-1}
(1) $Na(s) \longrightarrow Na(g)$	+107
(2) $Na(g) \longrightarrow Na^+(g) + e^-$	+494
(3) $Na^+(g) \longrightarrow Na^{2+}(g) + e^-$	+4560
(4) $Cl_2(g) \longrightarrow 2Cl(g)$	+242
(5) $2Cl(g) + 2e^- \longrightarrow 2Cl^-(g)$	$2 \times (-349)$
(6) $Na^{2+}(g) + 2Cl^-(g) \longrightarrow NaCl_2(s)$	−2524 (same as $MgCl_2$)
$Na(s) + Cl_2(g) \longrightarrow NaCl_2(s)$	2181 $= \Delta H^\circ_f$

A compound with such a large positive $\Delta H°_f$ is not likely to form under any conditions.

8.91   Assume 100 g of sample.

$$\text{number of moles of C} = 12.1 \text{ g C} \times \left(\frac{1 \text{ mol C}}{12.01 \text{ g C}}\right) = 1.008 \text{ mol C}$$

$$\text{number of moles of O} = 16.2 \text{ g O} \times \left(\frac{1 \text{ mol O}}{16.00 \text{ g O}}\right) = 1.012 \text{ mol O}$$

$$\text{number of moles of Cl} = 71.7 \text{ g Cl} \times \left(\frac{1 \text{ mol Cl}}{35.45 \text{ g Cl}}\right) = 2.023 \text{ mol Cl}$$

The ratios are $C:O:Cl = 1.008:1.012:2.023$ or $C:O:Cl = 1:1:2$. The empirical formula is $COCl_2$. This is also the molecular formula, as can be seen by comparing the molar mass of the empirical formula to 98.9 g mol^{-1}. They are the same.

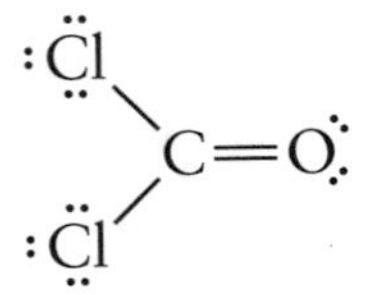

8.93   (a)

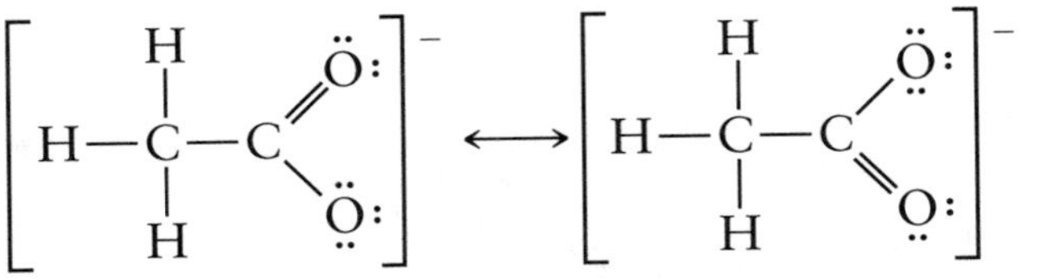

(b)

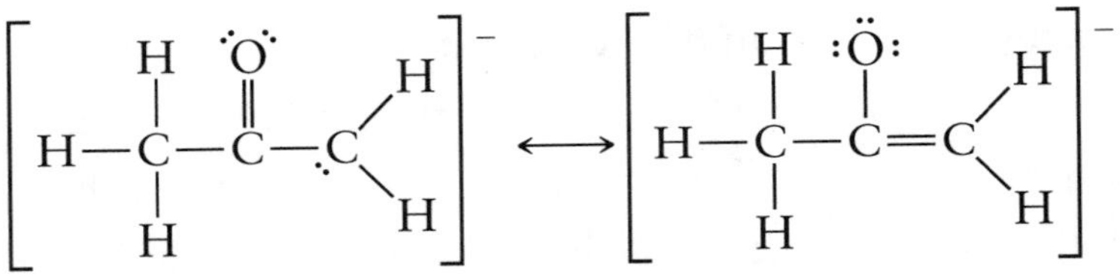

(c)

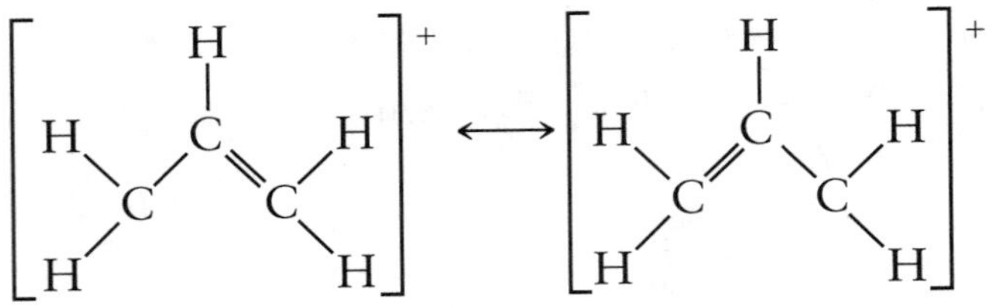

(d)

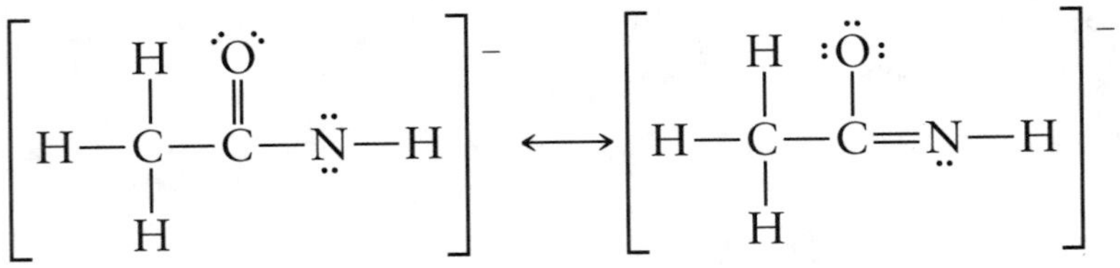

CHAPTER 9
MOLECULES: SHAPE, SIZE, AND BOND STRENGTH

EXERCISE

The Shapes of Molecules and Ions

9.1 (a) trigonal bipyramidal, 120° bond angles in equatorial plane, 90° between axial bonds and equatorial plane

(b) linear, 180°

(c) trigonal pyramidal, slightly less than 109°

(d) angular, slightly less than 109°

(e) tetrahedral, 109.5°

9.3 (a) 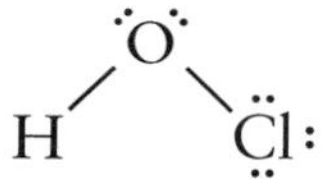 AX_2E_2, angular

(b) 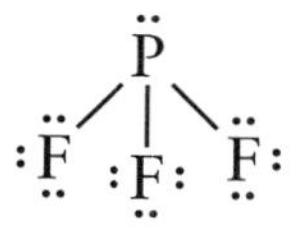 AX_3E, trigonal pyramidal

(c) $:N= N =O:$ AX_2, linear

(d) 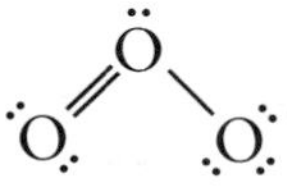 two resonance forms AX_2E, angular

9.5 (a) 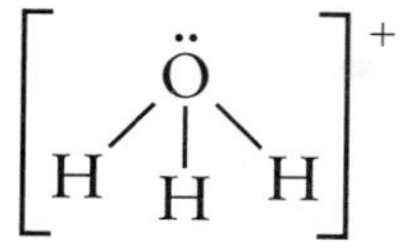 AX_3E, trigonal pyramidal

(b) 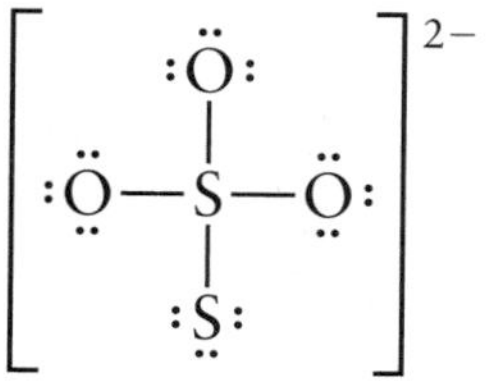 AX_4, tetrahedral

Lewis structures with one and two S=O double bonds also contribute to the overall resonance hybrid that represents SO_4^{2-}. All structures are AX_4 and have a tetrahedral shape.

(c) $\left[\begin{array}{c}:\ddot{F} \quad \ddot{F}: \\ \diagdown I \diagup \\ \diagup \quad \diagdown \\ :\ddot{F} \quad \ddot{F}:\end{array}\right]^{+}$ AX$_4$E, seesaw

(d) $\left[:\ddot{O}=N\diagup\overset{\displaystyle :\ddot{O}:}{}_{\diagdown\ddot{O}:}\right]^{-}$ 3 resonance forms, AX$_3$, trigonal planar

9.7 (a) $:\overset{\textstyle :\ddot{Cl}:}{\underset{:\ddot{Cl}\diagup \diagdown :\ddot{Cl}:}{\overset{}{\diagup}}}\overset{}{}$ AX$_4$E, seesaw

(b) $:\ddot{Cl}-\overset{\textstyle :\ddot{Cl}:}{\underset{:\ddot{Cl}:}{\overset{|}{\underset{|}{\ddot{I}:}}}}$ AX$_3$E$_2$, T-shaped

(c) $\left[\begin{array}{c}:\ddot{F} \quad \ddot{F}: \\ \diagdown I \diagup \\ \diagup \quad \diagdown \\ :\ddot{F} \quad \ddot{F}:\end{array}\right]^{-}$ AX$_4$E$_2$, square planar

(d) $:\ddot{O}\diagup\overset{\textstyle \ddot{Xe}}{\underset{:\ddot{O}:}{|}}\diagdown\ddot{O}:$ AX$_3$E, trigonal pyramidal

Resonance forms with Xe=O double bonds also contribute to the overall structure. All are AX$_3$E and have the trigonal-pyramidal shape.

9.9 (a) $:\ddot{I}-\dot{\ddot{I}}-\ddot{I}:$ central I is AX$_2$E$_3$, linear, 180°

(b) $:\ddot{F}-\dot{\ddot{I}}-\ddot{F}:$ AX$_3$E$_2$, T-shaped, slightly less than 90°

(c) $\left[\overset{\textstyle :\ddot{O} \quad \ddot{O}:}{\underset{:\ddot{O}. \quad .\ddot{O}:}{\diagdown I \diagup}}\right]^{-}$ AX$_4$, tetrahedral, 109.5°

(d) $\overset{\textstyle :\ddot{F}:}{\underset{:\ddot{F}:}{\dot{F}\diagdown \overset{|}{Te} \diagup \dot{F}}}$ AX$_6$, octahedral, 90°

9.11 (a)

$$\begin{array}{c} :\ddot{C}l: \\ | \\ :\ddot{F}-C-\ddot{F}: \\ | \\ :\ddot{F}: \end{array}$$

AX$_4$, tetrahedral, 109.5°

(b)

$$:\ddot{I}-Ga\begin{array}{c} \ddot{I}: \\ \\ \ddot{I}: \end{array}$$

AX$_3$, trigonal planar, 120°

(c)

$$\left[\begin{array}{c} \ddot{C} \\ / \, | \, \backslash \\ H \quad H \quad H \end{array}\right]^{-}$$

AX$_3$E, trigonal pyramidal, slightly less than 109°

(d)

$$\begin{array}{c} :\ddot{F}: \\ .\dot{F} \, | \, \dot{F}. \\ \backslash \, | \, / \\ S \\ / \, | \, \backslash \\ .\dot{F}. \, | \, \dot{F}. \\ :\ddot{F}: \end{array}$$

AX$_6$, octahedral, 90°

(e)

$$\begin{array}{c} :\ddot{F} \qquad \ddot{F}: \\ \backslash \qquad / \\ \ddot{X}e \\ / \quad \| \quad \backslash \\ :\ddot{F} \quad \ddot{O}. \quad \ddot{F}: \end{array}$$

AX$_5$E, square pyramidal, 90°

9.13

$$\begin{array}{c} H \qquad H \\ \backslash \qquad / \\ C=C \,)\, a \\ / \qquad \backslash \\ H \qquad C=C \\ \qquad / \\ \qquad H \quad)\, b \end{array}$$

All C atoms can be considered as the central A atom of AX$_3$ structures; therefore, angles a and b are approximately 120°.

9.15

$$\begin{array}{c} :\ddot{F}: \\ | \\ B \\ / \quad \backslash \\ :\ddot{F}: \quad :\ddot{F}: \end{array} \quad + \quad \begin{array}{c} \ddot{N} \\ / \, | \, \backslash \\ H \quad H \quad H \end{array} \quad \longrightarrow \quad \begin{array}{c} :\dot{F}. \qquad H \\ \backslash \qquad / \\ :\ddot{F}-B\!-\!\!-\!\!-\!N-H \\ / \qquad \backslash \\ :\dot{F}. \qquad H \end{array}$$

AX$_3$ AX$_3$E   AX$_4$ AX$_4$
trigonal   trigonal   tetrahedral   tetrahedral
planar   pyramidal

all angles 120°   all angles <109°   all angles ≈ 109°

Charge Distribution in Molecules

9.17 An electric dipole ("two poles") is a positive charge next to an equal but opposite negative charge. An electric dipole moment is a measure of the magnitude of the electric dipole in debye (D) units.

9.19 The direction of the dipole moment is toward the element in the bond with the larger electronegativity, χ.

(a) O—H; $\chi_O = 3.4$, $\chi_H = 2.2$; therefore, toward O

(b) O—F; $\chi_O = 3.4$, $\chi_F = 4.0$; therefore, toward F

(c) F—Cl; $\chi_F = 4.0$, $\chi_{Cl} = 3.2$; therefore, toward F

(d) O—S; $\chi_O = 3.4$, $\chi_S = 2.6$; therefore, toward O

9.21 (a) Br_2; one nonpolar bond

(b) H_2NNH_2; 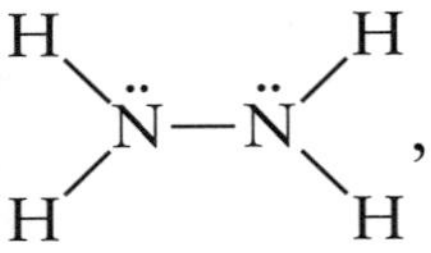 , four polar N—H bonds, one nonpolar N—N bond

(c) CH_4; all C—H bonds are slightly polar

(d) O_3; 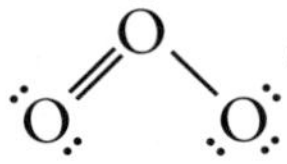 , AX_2E, both bonds are polar

9.23 See Fig. 9.10 in the text.

(a) AX_3, trigonal planar, nonpolar

(b) AX_4E_2, square planar, nonpolar

(c) AX_3E, trigonal pyramidal, polar

(d) AX_2E_2, angular, polar

9.25 See Fig. 9.10 in the text.

(a) 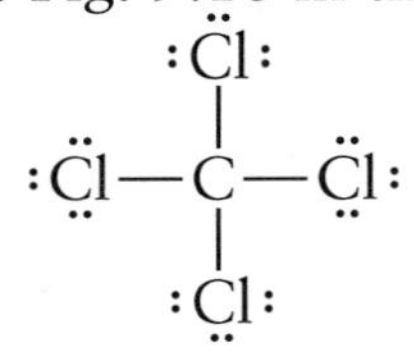 AX_4, tetrahedral, nonpolar

(b) 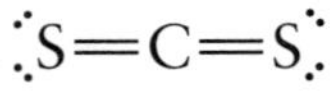 AX_2, linear, nonpolar

(c) 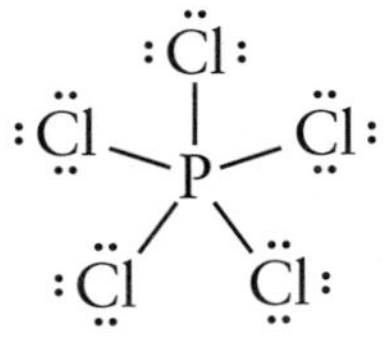 AX_5, trigonal bipyramidal, nonpolar

(d) 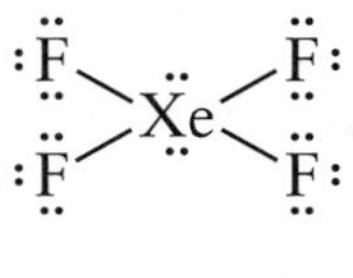 AX_4E_2, square planar, nonpolar

9.27 (a) C_6H_6 nonpolar (symmetrical molecule)

(b) $H-\overset{\displaystyle H}{\underset{\displaystyle H}{\overset{|}{\underset{|}{C}}}}-\ddot{O}-H$ polar (nonsymmetrical molecule)

(c) $\overset{\displaystyle H}{\underset{\displaystyle H}{\diagdown\diagup}}C=O$ polar (nonsymmetrical molecule)

9.29 (a)

1	2	3
polar	polar	nonpolar

(b) Structure **1** is the most unsymmetrical and has the largest separation of charge; hence, it is the most polar and has the largest dipole moment.

Bond Strengths and Bond Lengths

9.31 (a) $H_2O \longrightarrow 2H + O$

$\Delta H = 2 \times \Delta H_B \text{ (O—H)} = (2 \times 463) \text{ kJ} \cdot \text{mol}^{-1} = +926 \text{ kJ} \cdot \text{mol}^{-1}$

(b) $CO_2 \longrightarrow C + 2O \qquad O{=}C{=}O$

$\Delta H = 2 \times \Delta H_B(C{=}O) = (2 \times 743) \text{ kJ} \cdot \text{mol}^{-1} = +1486 \text{ kJ} \cdot \text{mol}^{-1}$

(c) $CH_3COOH \longrightarrow 2C + 4H + 2O$

$\Delta H = 3 \times \Delta H_B(C{-}H) + 1 \times \Delta H_B(C{-}C) + 1 \times \Delta H_B(C{=}O)$
$\qquad\qquad\qquad\qquad + 1 \times \Delta H_B(C{-}O) + 1 \times \Delta H_B(O{-}H)$

$\quad = (3 \times 412 + 1 \times 348 + 1 \times 743 + 1 \times 360 + 1 \times 463) \text{ kJ} \cdot \text{mol}^{-1}$
$\quad = +3150 \text{ kJ} \cdot \text{mol}^{-1}$

(d) $CH_3NH_2 \longrightarrow C + 5H + N$

$\Delta H = 3 \times \Delta H_B(C{-}H) + 1 \times \Delta H_B(C{-}N) + 2 \times \Delta H_B(N{-}H)$
$\quad = (3 \times 412 + 1 \times 305 + 2 \times 388) \text{ kJ} \cdot \text{mol}^{-1} = +2317 \text{ kJ} \cdot \text{mol}^{-1}$

9.33 Use Tables 9.2 and 9.3.

(a) $\frac{1}{2}H_2 + \frac{1}{2}Cl_2 \longrightarrow HCl$

$$\begin{aligned}
\Delta H_f^\circ &= -\Delta H_B(H{-}Cl) + \frac{1}{2}\Delta H_B(H{-}H) + \frac{1}{2}\Delta H_B(Cl{-}Cl) \\
&= (-431 + \frac{1}{2} \times 436 + \frac{1}{2} \times 242)\ kJ \cdot mol^{-1} \\
&= -92\ kJ \cdot mol^{-1} \quad (\text{exptl. value} = -92.31\ kJ \cdot mol^{-1})
\end{aligned}$$

(b) $H_2 + O_2 \longrightarrow H_2O_2 \qquad H{-}O{-}O{-}H$

$$\begin{aligned}
\Delta H_f^\circ &= -\Delta H_B(O{-}O) - 2 \times \Delta H_B(O{-}H) + \Delta H_B(O{=}O) + \Delta H_B(H{-}H) \\
&= (-157 - 2 \times 463 + 496 + 436)\ kJ \cdot mol^{-1} \\
&= -151\ kJ \cdot mol^{-1} \quad (\text{exptl. value} = -187.78\ kJ \cdot mol^{-1})
\end{aligned}$$

(c) $C + 2Cl_2 \longrightarrow CCl_4$

$$\begin{aligned}
\Delta H_f^\circ &= -4 \times \Delta H_B(C{-}Cl) + 2 \times \Delta H_B(Cl{-}Cl) \\
&= (-4 \times 338 + 2 \times 242)\ kJ \cdot mol^{-1} = -868\ kJ \cdot mol^{-1}
\end{aligned}$$

(d) $\frac{1}{2}N_2 + \frac{3}{2}H_2 \longrightarrow NH_3$

$$\begin{aligned}
\Delta H_f^\circ &= -3 \times \Delta H_B(N{-}H) + \frac{1}{2} \times \Delta H_B(N{\equiv}N) + \frac{3}{2} \times \Delta H_B(H{-}H) \\
&= (-3 \times 388 + \frac{1}{2} \times 944 + \frac{3}{2} \times 436)\ kJ \cdot mol^{-1} \\
&= -38\ kJ \cdot mol^{-1} \quad (\text{exptl. value} = -46.11\ kJ \cdot mol^{-1})
\end{aligned}$$

Note that the accuracy of the estimated values of ΔH_f°, as determined from bond enthalpies, varies somewhat from one compound to another, because ΔH_B, for the same bond, can vary substantially from one compound to another.

9.35 (a) $H_2 + \frac{1}{2}O_2 \longrightarrow H_2O(l)$

$$\begin{aligned}
\Delta H_f^\circ &= -2 \times \Delta H_B(O{-}H) + \Delta H_B(H{-}H) + \frac{1}{2} \times \Delta H_B(O{=}O) - \Delta H_{vap}^\circ(H_2O) \\
&= (-2 \times 463 + 436 + \frac{1}{2} \times 496 - 40.7)\ kJ \cdot mol^{-1} \\
&= -283\ kJ \cdot mol^{-1} \quad (\text{exptl. value} = -285.83\ kJ \cdot mol^{-1})
\end{aligned}$$

(b) $C + 2H_2 + \frac{1}{2}O_2 \longrightarrow CH_3OH \qquad$ (structural formula: $H{-}C{-}O{-}H$ with two H atoms on C)

$$\begin{aligned}
\Delta H_f^\circ &= -3 \times \Delta H_B(C{-}H) - 1 \times \Delta H_B(C{-}O) - 1 \times \Delta H_B(O{-}H) \\
&\quad + \Delta H_{sub}(C) + 2 \times \Delta H_B(H{-}H) + \frac{1}{2} \times \Delta H_B(O{-}O) - \Delta H_{vap}^\circ(CH_3OH) \\
&= [-3 \times 412 - 1 \times 360 - 1 \times 463 + 1 \times 717 + 2 \times 436 + \frac{1}{2} \times 496 \\
&\quad - 25]\ kJ \cdot mol^{-1} = -247\ kJ \cdot mol^{-1} \quad (\text{exptl. value} = -238.86\ kJ \cdot mol^{-1})
\end{aligned}$$

(c) $6C + 3H_2 \longrightarrow C_6H_6$ (assume no resonance)

106

$$\Delta H_f^\circ = -3 \times \Delta H_B(C{=}C) - 3 \times \Delta H_B(C{-}C) - 6 \times \Delta H_B(C{-}H) + 6 \times \Delta H_{sub}(C)$$
$$+ 3 \times \Delta H_B(H{-}H) - \Delta H_{vap}^\circ(C_6H_6)$$
$$= [-3 \times 612 - 3 \times 348 - 6 \times 412 + 6 \times 717 + 3 \times 436 - 31]\ kJ \cdot mol^{-1}$$
$$= +227\ kJ \cdot mol^{-1}\ (\text{exptl. value for benzene} = +49.0\ kJ \cdot mol^{-1})$$

(d) $6C + 3H_2 \longrightarrow C_6H_6$ (assume resonance)

$$\Delta H_f^\circ = -6 \times \Delta H_B(C{\cdots}C) - 6 \times \Delta H_B(C{-}H) + 6 \times \Delta H_{sub}(C)$$
$$+ 3 \times \Delta H_B(H{-}H) - \Delta H_{vap}^\circ(C_6H_6)$$
$$= [-6 \times 518 - 6 \times 412 + 6 \times 717 + 3 \times 436 - 31]\ kJ \cdot mol^{-1}$$
$$= -1\ kJ \cdot mol^{-1}$$

This latter value is closer to the experimental value, but neither one is quite close enough.

9.37 (a) $HCl(g) + F_2(g) \longrightarrow HF(g) + ClF(g)$ or $H{-}Cl + F{-}F \longrightarrow H{-}F + Cl{-}F$

The enthalpy required to break the bonds in the reactants is

$$\Delta H^\circ = 1 \times \Delta H_B(H{-}Cl) + 1 \times \Delta H_B(F{-}F) = [1(431) + 1(158)]\ kJ = 589\ kJ$$

The enthalpy released when the products form is

$$\Delta H^\circ = -[1 \times \Delta H_B(H{-}F) + 1 \times \Delta H_B(Cl{-}F)] = -[1(565) + 1(256)]\ kJ$$
$$= -821\ kJ$$

The sum of these two enthalpy changes is the reaction enthalpy:

$$\Delta H^\circ = 589\ kJ - 821\ kJ = -232\ kJ$$

(b) $C_2H_4(g) + HCl(g) \longrightarrow CH_3CH_2Cl(g)$ or

The enthalpy required to atomize reactants is

$$\Delta H^\circ = 1 \times \Delta H_B(C{=}C) + 4 \times \Delta H_B(C{-}H) + 1 \times \Delta H_B(H{-}Cl)$$
$$= (1 \times 612 + 4 \times 412 + 1 \times 431)\ kJ = 2691\ kJ$$

The enthalpy released when the products form is

$$\Delta H^\circ = -[1 \times \Delta H_B(C{-}C) + 1 \times \Delta H_B(C{-}Cl) + 5 \times \Delta H_B(C{-}H)]$$
$$= -(1 \times 348 + 1 \times 327 + 5 \times 412)\ kJ = -2735\ kJ$$

The sum of these two enthalpy changes is the reaction enthalpy: $\Delta H^\circ = 2691\ kJ - 2735\ kJ = -44\ kJ$

(c) $C_2H_2(g) + 2\ H_2(g) \longrightarrow CH_3CH_3$ or

The enthalpy required to atomize reactants is

$$\Delta H° = 1 \times \Delta H_B(C\equiv C) + 2 \times \Delta H_B(C—H) + 2 \times \Delta H_B(H—H)$$
$$= (1 \times 837 + 2 \times 412 + 2 \times 436)\text{ kJ} = 2533\text{ kJ}$$

The enthalpy released when the products form is

$$\Delta H° = -[1 \times \Delta H_B(C—C) + 6 \times \Delta H_B(C—H)]$$
$$= -(1 \times 348 + 6 \times 412)\text{ kJ} = -2820\text{ kJ}$$

The sum is the reaction enthalpy: $\Delta H° = 2533\text{ kJ} - 2820\text{ kJ} = -287\text{ kJ}$

9.39 (a)

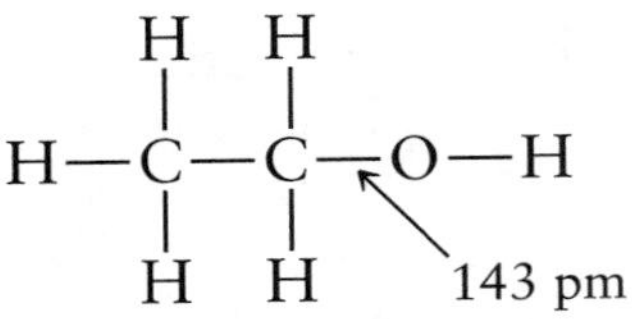

H—C—C—O—H
(with H H on top, H H on bottom, 143 pm)

(b) 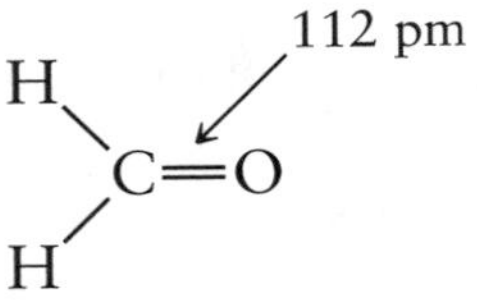 C=O (with H, H and 112 pm)

(c) C≡O

Data are not available for C≡O in Table 9.4, but it is expected to be the shortest of the three, because largest bond order corresponds to shortest bond length. Therefore, (c) < (b) < (a).

9.41 (a)

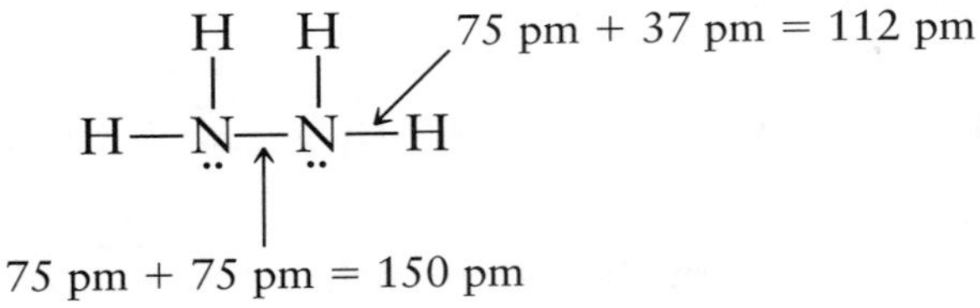

H—N—N—H
(75 pm + 37 pm = 112 pm; 75 pm + 75 pm = 150 pm)

(b)

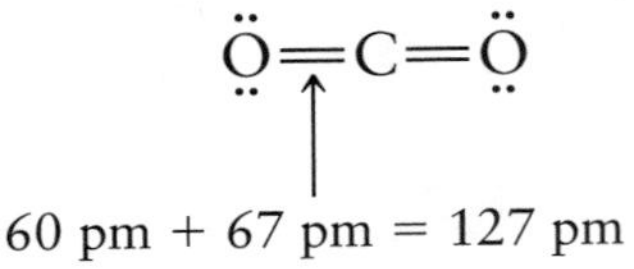

Ö=C=Ö
(60 pm + 67 pm = 127 pm)

(c)

N—C—N (with O on top)
(60 pm + 67 pm = 127 pm; 75 pm + 37 pm = 112 pm; 75 pm + 77 pm = 152 pm)

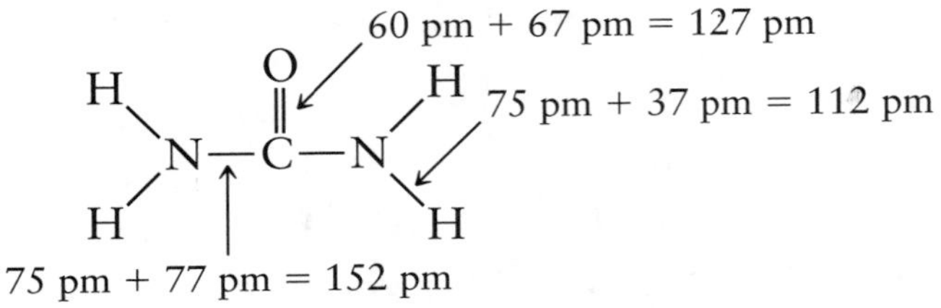

(d)

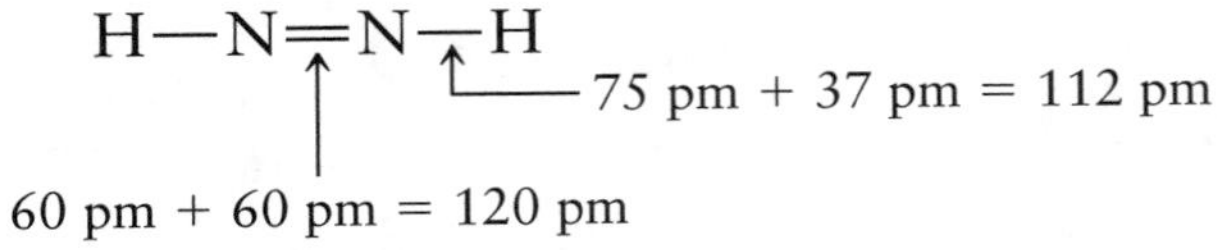

H—N=N—H
(75 pm + 37 pm = 112 pm; 60 pm + 60 pm = 120 pm)

Orbitals and Bonds

9.43 (a) $1s—1s$, σ (b) $2p_x—2p_x$, π (c) $2s—2p_y$, neither (d) $2p_z—2p_z$, σ
No bond forms in case (c) because there is no net positive overlap between the spherically symmetric $2s$-orbital and the two opposite lobes of the $2p_y$-orbital. The overlap of $2s$ with

the negative lobe of the $2p_y$-orbital exactly cancels the overlap with the positive lobe of $2p_y$; so overall the overlap is 0.

9.45   Cl: $[Ne]3s^2 3p_x^2\, 3p_y^2\, 3p_z^1$; hence, in the diatomic molecule, $3p_z$—$3p_z$ overlap occurs to form the bond, which is a σ bond.

9.47   See Table 9.5.
  (a) tetrahedral   (b) linear   (c) octahedral   (d) trigonal planar

9.49   (a) SF_4 is AX_4E; therefore, the electron pairs adopt a trigonal bipyramidal arrangement that corresponds to dsp^3 hybridization on S.
  (b) BCl_3 is AX_3; trigonal planar electron pairs; sp^2 hybridization on B
  (c) NH_3 is AX_3E; tetrahedral electron pairs; sp^3 hybridization on N
  (d) $(CH_3)_2\, Be$ is AX_2; linear electron pairs; sp hybridization on Be

9.51   (a)

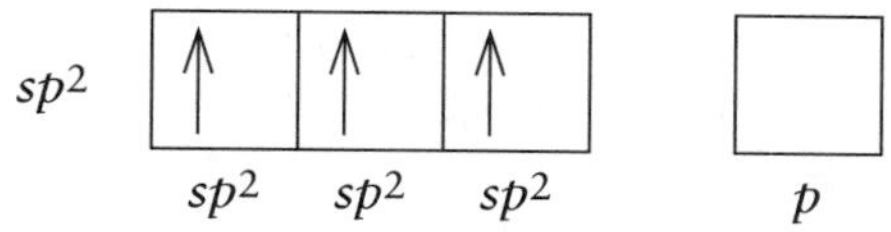

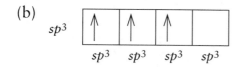

  (b)
  (c) 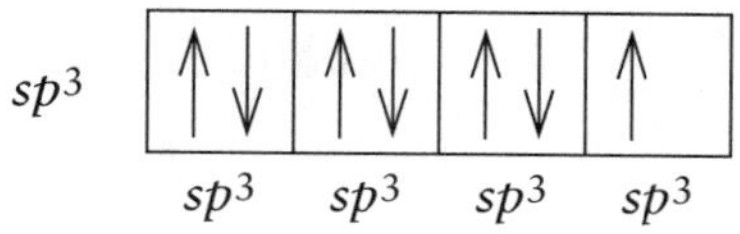
  (d)

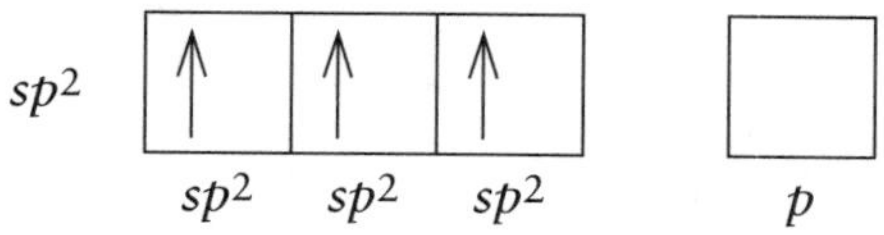

9.53   (a) each C is A of AX_4; tetrahedral electron pairs; sp^3 hybrid orbitals
  (b) each C is A of AX_2; linear electron pairs; sp orbitals
  (c) PCl_5 is AX_5; trigonal bipyramidal pairs; dsp^3 hybrid orbitals
  (d) HOCl is AX_2E_2; tetrahedral pairs; sp^3 hybrid orbitals

SUPPLEMENTARY EXERCISES

9.55 (a) [Lewis structure of SO_2Cl_2]   distorted tetahedron, polar   (b) [Lewis structure]   seesaw, polar

(c) [Lewis structure of $AsCl_5$]   trigonal bipyramidal, nonpolar   (d) [Lewis structure of SiF_4] tetrahedral, nonpolar

(e) [Lewis structure of SF_4]   seesaw, polar   (f) [Lewis structure of H_2O]   angular, polar

(g) $H-C\equiv N\!:$ linear, polar   (h) $:\!\ddot{C}l-\overset{..}{I}-\ddot{C}l\!:$ T-shaped, polar

9.57 (a) [Lewis structure of $CH_3CH_2NH_2$]   C—N (single bond) is longest

(b) [Lewis structure $H-CH_2-C\equiv N\!:$]   C≡N (triple bond) is shortest

(c) [Lewis structure $H-CH_2-CH=NH$]   C=N (double bond) is midlength

Therefore, (b) < (c) < (a).

9.59 (a) $\left[:\!\ddot{O}-\overset{\overset{\textstyle :\ddot{O}:}{|}}{\underset{\underset{\textstyle :\ddot{S}:}{|}}{S}}-\ddot{O}\!: \right]^{2-}$ tetrahedral, approximately 109°

Lewis structures with one or two S=O double bonds are also possible; all structures have the tetrahedral shape.

(b) $H_3C-Be-CH_3$ linear, 180°

(c) $\left[\begin{array}{c} H \diagdown \overset{\displaystyle ..}{B} \diagup H \\ H \end{array} \right]^{-}$ angular, slightly less than 120°

(d) $:\overset{..}{\underset{..}{Cl}} \diagdown \overset{\displaystyle ..}{Sn} \diagdown \overset{..}{\underset{..}{Cl}}:$ angular, slightly less than 120°

9.61 (a) $\overset{H}{\underset{H}{\diagup}} C = C \overset{H}{\underset{H}{\diagdown}}$

Each C is A of AX_3; therefore, the molecule is trigonal planar, with bond angles of about 120°.

(b) $:\overset{..}{\underset{..}{Cl}} - C \equiv N:$ 180° (c) $\overset{:\overset{..}{O}}{\underset{:\overset{..}{\underset{..}{Cl}}}{}} P \overset{\overset{..}{\underset{..}{Cl}}:}{\underset{\overset{..}{\underset{..}{Cl}}:}{}}$ 109° (d) $\overset{H}{\underset{H}{\diagup}} \overset{..}{N} - \overset{..}{N} \overset{H}{\underset{H}{\diagdown}}$ 109°

9.63 $CCl_4(g) + 2HF(g) \longrightarrow CCl_2F_2(g) + 2HCl(g)$ or

$$Cl - \overset{\overset{\displaystyle Cl}{|}}{\underset{\underset{\displaystyle Cl}{|}}{C}} - Cl + 2H - F \longrightarrow F - \overset{\overset{\displaystyle Cl}{|}}{\underset{\underset{\displaystyle F}{|}}{C}} - Cl + 2H - Cl$$

$$\Delta H° = -2 \times \Delta H_B(H-Cl) - 2 \times \Delta H_B(C-Cl) - 2 \times \Delta H_B(C-F)$$
$$+ 2 \times \Delta H_B(H-F) + 4 \times \Delta H_B(C-Cl)$$
$$= (-2 \times 431 - 2 \times 327 - 2 \times 485 + 2 \times 565 + 4 \times 327) \text{ kJ} = -48 \text{ kJ}$$

9.65 (a) CF_4, 77 pm (for C) + 72 pm (for F) = 149 pm
(b) SiF_4, 111 pm (for Si) + 72 pm (for F) = 183 pm
(c) SnF_4, 141 pm (for Sn) + 72 pm (for F) = 213 pm
The bond length is proportional to the increasing size of the atom attached to the fluorine atom; and size increases down a group in the periodic table.

9.67 XX' $:\overset{..}{X} - \overset{..}{X}:$ AX, linear, polar, 180°

XX_3' $X' - \overset{..}{\underset{\underset{\displaystyle X'}{|}}{X}} - X'$ AX_3E_2, T-shaped, polar;

$X' - X - X'$ angle is slightly less than 90°

XX_5' $\overset{X' \overset{\displaystyle X'}{|} X'}{\underset{X' \quad X'}{\diagup X \diagdown}}$ AX_5E, square pyramidal, polar;

$X'_{base} - X - X'_{apex}$ angle is a little less than 90°; $X'_{base} - X - X'_{base}$ angle is a little less than 90°

9.69 $:\ddot{O}-\ddot{F}:$ sp^3 hybridization (two sp^3—p bonds), AX_2E_2, angular; the bond angle is
       |
    $:\ddot{F}:$

somewhat less than 109°

9.71 (a)

$$
\begin{array}{ccc}
& \text{H} & \text{\.{O}:} \\
& | & \hspace{-0.3em}\parallel \\
\text{H}- & \text{C}_1- & \text{C}_2 \\
& | & \hspace{0.8em}\diagdown \\
& \text{H} & \hspace{1.2em}\text{H}
\end{array}
$$

C_1 is A of AX_4; therefore, it is part of a tetrahedral structure with 109.5° bond angles and sp^3 hybrid orbitals. C_2 is A of AX_3; therefore, it is part of a trigonal-planar structure with 120° bond angles and sp^2 hybrid orbitals.

(b)

$$
\begin{array}{ccc}
& \text{H} & \text{\.{O}:} \\
& | & \hspace{-0.3em}\parallel \\
\text{H}- & \text{C}_1- & \text{C}_2 \\
& | & \hspace{0.8em}\diagdown \\
& \text{H} & \hspace{1.2em}\text{\.{O}}-\text{H}
\end{array}
$$

For C_1 and C_2, everything is the same as in acetaldehyde, part (a).

9.73

$$
\begin{array}{c}
:\ddot{F}: \\
| \\
\cdot\text{Cl}\cdot \\
\diagup \quad \diagdown \\
\cdot\text{F}\cdot \quad \cdot\ddot{F}:
\end{array}
$$

F uses p-orbitals (no hybridization); Cl uses sp^3d hybrid orbitals (Cl is A of AX_3E_2). The molecule is T-shaped, with lone pairs above and below the plane. The F—Cl—F bond angles are ≤90° and ≤180°.

9.75 The formula of the compound can be determined by the standard techniques fully described in the examples and exercises of Chapter 2. Here it can be done more directly by noting that there must be at least one C atom and one O atom in the compound. Then the number of H atoms is

$$
\frac{(32.04 - 12.01 - 16.00)\ \text{g}\cdot\text{mol}^{-1}}{1.008\ \text{g}\cdot\text{mol}^{-1}} = 4
$$

The formula is then CH_4O.

(a) The only possible atomic arrangement is

$$
\begin{array}{c}
\hspace{2em}\text{H} \\
\hspace{2em}| \\
\text{H}-\text{C}-\ddot{O}-\text{H} \\
\hspace{2em}| \\
\hspace{2em}\text{H}
\end{array}
$$

C is A of AX_4; thus, the bond angles are 109.5°. O is A of AX_2E_2; thus, the bond angles are slightly less than 109°.

(b) The electron-pair geometry about both C and O is tetrahedral; hence, both have sp^3 hybridization.

(c) O is A of AX_2E_2; hence, the molecule is polar.

9.77 (a) Step 1: $Cl(g) + O_3(g) \longrightarrow ClO(g) + O_2(g)$ or

$$Cl + \underset{\ddot{\underset{\cdot\cdot}{O}}}{\diagup}\ddot{O}=\ddot{O} \longrightarrow :\ddot{C}l-\ddot{O}\cdot + \ddot{O}=\ddot{O}$$

$\Delta H = -\Delta H_B(O{=}O) - \Delta H_B(Cl{-}O) + \Delta H_B(O{-}O) + \Delta H_B(O{=}O)$

$= [-496 - 270 + 157 + 496]$ kJ $= -113$ kJ for step 1

Step 2: $ClO(g) + O(g) \longrightarrow Cl(g) + O_2(g)$ or $Cl{-}O + O \longrightarrow Cl + O{=}O$

$\Delta H = -\Delta H_B(O{=}O) + \Delta H_B(Cl{-}O) = [-496 + 270]$ kJ $= -226$ kJ for step 2

(b) ΔH(overall) $= -113$ kJ $+ (-226$ kJ$) = -339$ kJ $\quad O_3(g) + O(g) \longrightarrow 2O_2(g)$

(c) The average ΔH_B for the two O—O bonds in O_3 is probably closer to the double bond value (496 kJ$\cdot$mol^{-1}) than to the single bond value (157 kJ$\cdot$mol^{-1}). This would make ΔH (overall) $>$ (less negative than) -339 kJ, which would compare even less favorably to the experimental value. These results indicate that mean values of bond enthalpies should be used with caution.

9.79 The Kekulé structures are

Each has 6 C—H single bonds, 3 C=C double bonds, and 3 C—C single bonds. The resonance structure can be written

This structure has 6 C—H single bonds and 6 C⋯C resonance bonds. The difference between the resonance structure and the Kekulé structure is in the C—C bonds, not in the C—H bonds.

For the Kekulé structure,

total bond enthalpy $= 3 \times \Delta H_B(\text{C}{=}\text{C}) + 3 \times \Delta H_B(\text{C}{-}\text{C})$
$$= 3 \times 612 \text{ kJ} \cdot \text{mol}^{-1} + 3 \times 348 \text{ kJ} \cdot \text{mol}^{-1}$$
$$= 2880 \text{ kJ} \cdot \text{mol}^{-1}$$

For the resonance structure,

total bond enthalpy $= 6 \times \Delta H_B(\text{C}{\cdots}\text{C}) = 6 \times 518 \text{ kJ} \cdot \text{mol}^{-1} = 3108 \text{ kJ} \cdot \text{mol}^{-1}$

The lowering in energy (enthalpy) is then $2880 \text{ kJ} \cdot \text{mol}^{-1} - 3108 \text{ kJ} \cdot \text{mol}^{-1} = -228$ $\text{kJ} \cdot \text{mol}^{-1}$, which is very close to the accepted value of $-206 \text{ kJ} \cdot \text{mol}^{-1}$.

9.81 P_4, sp^3 (other P_n molecules exist); S_8, sp^3 (other S_n molecules exist). N and O have small atoms that can easily form multiple bonds with each other and so can achieve octets by forming diatomic molecules. Period 3 atoms, such as those of P and S, are simply too large to get close enough to form π bonds, so they have to form a lot of single bonds to more than one atom at a time.

9.83 (a, b)

1 allene   2 cyclopropene   3 propyne

(c) Structure **1**: C_1 and C_3 have sp^2 hybridization; C_2 has sp.
Structure **2**: C_1 and C_2 have approximate sp^2 hybridization; C_3 has approximate sp^3 hybridization. The great strain imposed by the ~60° interior angles is such that the usual carbon atom hybridization scheme is hardly an adequate description.
Structure **3**: C_1 and C_2 have sp hybridization; C_3 has sp^3 hybridization.
(d) Structure **1** does not have alternating single and double bonds, so resonance would not occur. Structures **2** and **3** have fixed bonding arrangements. For resonance to occur, bonds would have to be broken and remade. This is exceedingly unlikely, so resonance does not occur.

CHAPTER 10
LIQUID AND SOLID MATERIALS

EXERCISES

Intermolecular Forces

10.1 (a) London forces

(b) dipole-dipole, London forces

(c) London forces

(d) dipole-dipole, London forces

10.3 (a) $:C\equiv O:$ London forces are dominant, but very weak dipole-dipole forces also exist.

(b)

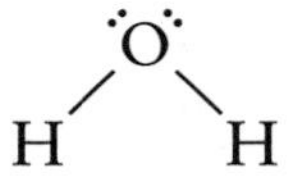

$\ddot{O}$
/ \
H   H

Hydrogen bonding is dominant, but London forces also occur.

(c)

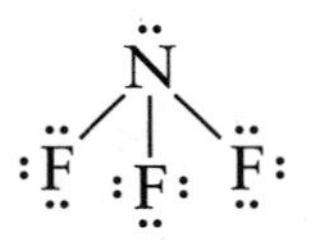

$\ddot{N}$
/ | \
$:\ddot{F}$ $:\ddot{F}:$ $\ddot{F}:$

London forces are dominant, but very weak dipole-dipole forces also exist.

(d)

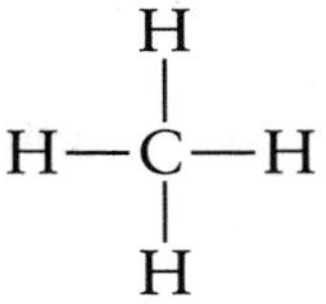

H
|
H—C—H
|
H

London forces.

10.5 A hydrogen bond may be described as A—H···B with the dotted bond, ···, representing the hydrogen bond. A must be N, O, or F. They are the only elements sufficiently electronegative to produce the strongly polar A—H bond necessary to attract the lone pair of electrons on the neighboring B atoms. Likewise, the B atoms should also be N, O, or F, because they are the smallest of the highly electronegative elements. Their small size results in the strongest interaction with the positive side of the polar A—H bond.

10.7 (a) HF, (c) NH_3, and (d) CH_3OH can form hydrogen bonds. Hydrogen bonding is especially strong in HF. All three have higher normal boiling points, enthalpies of vaporization, and surface tension, and lower vapor pressures at a given temperature than similar compounds of their congeners.

10.9 (a) HCl has strong dipole-dipole interactions, but these forces are not nearly as strong as the ion-ion interactions in NaCl; thus NaCl has the higher melting point. It is a general rule that ionic compounds have higher melting and boiling points than molecular compounds.

(b) These compounds have the same structure, but SiH_4 has the greater molar mass; hence, we expect that it has the higher normal boiling point, and, in fact, it does: $-112°C$ for SiH_4 versus $-162°C$ for CH_4.

(c) HF, because of stronger hydrogen bonding

(d) H_2O, because of stronger hydrogen bonding; there are two O—H bonds

10.11 (a) The attraction between atoms in both Xe and Ar is a result of London forces, but, because Xe has more electrons, it is bigger and therefore more polarizable; hence, it has stronger London forces and a higher melting point.

(b) HI and HCl have both London forces and dipole-dipole attractions, but the dominant attraction is the London force, which is greater in HI.

(c) There is strong hydrogen bonding in water, but none in $C_2H_5OC_2H_5$, so water has the lower vapor pressure at the same temperature.

10.13 (a)

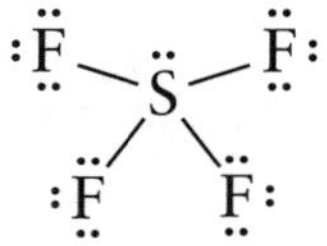

SF₄
bp = −40°C

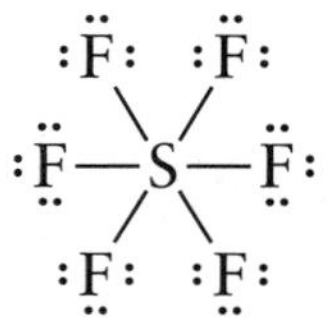

SF₆
bp = −64°C (sublimation point)

VSEPR predicts that SF_4 has the seesaw shape; whereas SF_6 is octahedral; so SF_4 is polar and SF_6 is not. Hence, SF_4 has the higher boiling point.

(b)

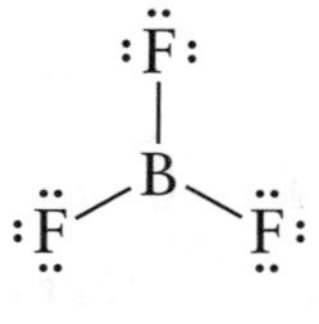

BF₃
bp = −99.9°C

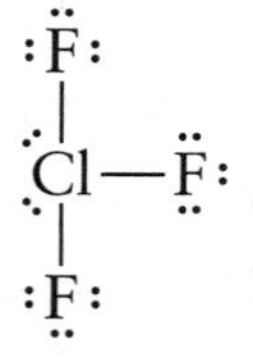

ClF₃
bp = 11.3°C

VSEPR predicts that BF_3 is trigonal planar and nonpolar, whereas ClF_3 is T-shaped and polar. Therefore, ClF_3 has the higher boiling point.

(c)

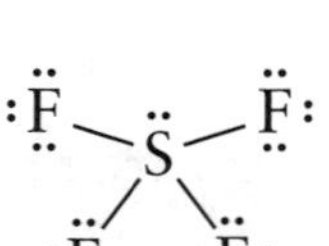

SF₄
bp = −40°C

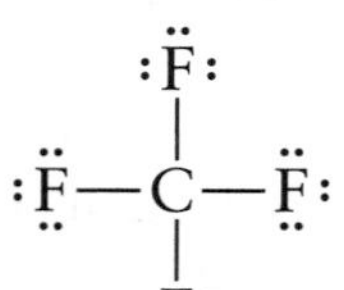

CF₄
bp = −128°C

CF_4 is tetrahedral; SF_4 is seesaw. SF_4 has the higher boiling point; it has a small dipole moment; CF_4 has none.

(d)

$$\begin{array}{ccc} \text{H} & \text{H} & \text{H} & \text{Cl} \\ \diagdown & \diagup & \diagdown & \diagup \\ \text{C}=\text{C} & & \text{C}=\text{C} \\ \diagup & \diagdown & \diagup & \diagdown \\ \text{Cl} & \text{Cl} & \text{Cl} & \text{H} \end{array}$$

cis-CHCl=CHCl   trans-CHCl=CHCl
bp = 60°C   bp = 48°C

Both molecules have the same shape, but the atomic arrangement in the cis compound produces a dipole moment and, hence, a higher boiling point.

Liquid Structure

10.15 The intermolecular forces are stronger between water molecules in water than between water molecules and the hydrocarbon molecules in wax. Water molecules hydrogen bond to one another, but not to hydrocarbon molecules. These intermolecular forces in water are manifested in the physical property called surface tension.

10.17 (a) Ethanol has the greater viscosity, as a result of its stronger intermolecular forces due to hydrogen bonding, than dimethyl ether, which cannot engage in hydrogen bonding.
(b) Propanone has the greater viscosity; it has stronger intermolecular forces, due to dipole-dipole interactions than does butane, which is nonpolar. Butane is, in fact, a gas at 0°C. It boils at −0.5°C.

Classification of Solids

10.19 (a) ionic (b) molecular (c) molecular (d) metallic

10.21 Use Table 10.3. A, ionic; B, metallic; C, molecular

Close-Packed Structures

10.23 Refer to Fig. 10.24 and 10.27b, also Example 10.3.
(a) number of atoms per unit cell = 1 center atom × 1 atom per center = 1 atom
8 corner atoms × $\frac{1}{8}$ atom per corner = 1 atom
total = 2 atoms per unit cell
(b) Each atom is surrounded by 8 others; hence, the coordination number is 8.

10.25 (a) See Example 10.4. The length of a side in a ccp structure is side = $\sqrt{8}\ r$ = 2.828 × 125 pm = 354 pm = 3.54 × 10⁻⁸ cm

(b) volume of unit cell = side^3 = $(3.54 \times 10^{-8}$ cm$)^3$ = 4.42×10^{-23} cm^3

number of unit cells in 1.00 cm^3 = $\dfrac{1.00 \text{ cm}^3}{4.42 \times 10^{-23} \text{ cm}^3/\text{unit cell}}$ = 2.26 $\times$ 10^{22}/unit cells

10.27

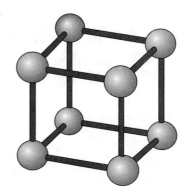

(a) There are 8 corners, so the number of atoms per unit cell = 8 corners $\times$ $\frac{1}{8}$ atom/corner = 1 atom.

(b) There are 6 nearest neighbors; hence the coordination number is 6. This is best seen by imagining the cell above with its neighboring unit cells stacked around it.

(c)

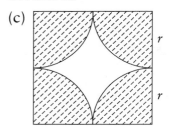

Let a = length of side of unit cell; then $a = 2r = 2 \times 190$ pm = 380 pm.

10.29 (a) See Example 10.4 and the solutions to Exercises 10.25 and 10.26. Let a = length of a side of the unit cell.

$a = \sqrt{8}r = 2.828 \times 125$ pm = 354 pm

volume of cell = $(354 \times 10^{-12}$ m$)^3$ = 4.42×10^{-29} m^3 = 4.42×10^{-23} cm^3

mass of one cell = 4 Ni atoms $\times \dfrac{58.71 \text{ g} \cdot \text{mol}^{-1}}{6.022 \times 10^{23} \text{ Ni atoms} \cdot \text{mol}^{-1}}$

$= 3.900 \times 10^{-22}$ g

density = $\dfrac{\text{mass}}{\text{volume}}$ = $\dfrac{3.900 \times 10^{-22} \text{ g}}{4.42 \times 10^{-23} \text{ cm}^3}$ = 8.82 g $\cdot$ cm^{-3}

(b) a = length of side = $\dfrac{4r}{\sqrt{3}}$ = $\dfrac{4 \times 250 \text{ pm}}{\sqrt{3}}$ = 577 pm

volume of cell = $(577 \times 10^{-12}$ m$)^3$ = $1.92\overline{5} \times 10^{-28}$ m^3 = $1.92\overline{5} \times 10^{-22}$ cm^3

$$\text{mass of one cell} = 2 \text{ Rb atoms} \times \frac{85.47 \text{ g} \cdot \text{mol}^{-1}}{6.022 \times 10^{23} \text{ Rb atoms} \cdot \text{mol}^{-1}}$$

$$= 2.839 \times 10^{-22} \text{ g}$$

$$\text{density} = \frac{\text{mass}}{\text{volume}} = \frac{2.839 \times 10^{-22} \text{ g}}{1.92\overline{5} \times 10^{-22} \text{ cm}^3} = 1.48 \text{ g} \cdot \text{cm}^{-3}$$

10.31 (a) mass of one unit cell $= (1 \text{ unit cell}) \times \left(\dfrac{4 \text{ atoms}}{1 \text{ unit cell}}\right)$

$$\times \left(\frac{1 \text{ mol Au}}{6.02 \times 10^{23} \text{ atoms Au}}\right) \times \left(\frac{197 \text{ g Au}}{1 \text{ mol Au}}\right) = 1.30\overline{9} \times 10^{-21} \text{ g}$$

$$V = \text{volume of unit cell} = \frac{\text{mass of unit cell}}{\text{density}} = \frac{1.30\overline{9} \times 10^{-21} \text{ g}}{19.3 \text{ g} \cdot \text{cm}^{-3}}$$

$$= 6.78 \times 10^{-23} \text{ cm}^3$$

$$a = \text{length of side} = \sqrt[3]{V} = 4.08 \times 10^{-8} \text{ cm}$$

$$\text{radius} = r = \frac{\sqrt{2}a}{4} = \frac{\sqrt{2}(4.08 \times 10^{-8} \text{ cm})}{4} = 1.44 \times 10^{-8} \text{ cm} = 144 \text{ pm}$$

(b) volume of unit cell $= \dfrac{\text{mass of unit cell}}{\text{density}}$

$V = \text{volume}$

$$= \frac{(1 \text{ unit cell}) \times \left(\dfrac{2 \text{ atoms}}{1 \text{ unit cell}}\right) \times \left(\dfrac{1 \text{ mol V}}{6.02 \times 10^{23} \text{ atoms V}}\right) \times \left(\dfrac{50.94 \text{ g V}}{1 \text{ mol V}}\right)}{6.11 \text{ g} \cdot \text{cm}^{-3}}$$

$$= 2.77 \times 10^{-23} \text{ cm}^3$$

$$a = \sqrt[3]{V} = 3.03 \times 10^{-8} \text{ cm}$$

$$\text{radius} = r = \frac{\sqrt{3}a}{4} = \frac{\sqrt{3} \times 3.03 \times 10^{-8} \text{ cm}}{4} = 1.31 \times 10^{-8} \text{ cm} = 131 \text{ pm}$$

Metals and Alloys

10.33 The fundamental difference is that the charge is carried by electrons in electronic conduction and by ions in ionic conduction. This difference is apparent from their names.

10.35 (a) Doping is a substitutional process in which silicon atoms are replaced with atoms of another element from a neighboring group in the periodic table. It is substitutional because Si and P atoms are similar in size.
(b) Doping either adds an electron or a "hole." In the former case (*n*-type), as in phosphorus-doped silicon, the additional electron is free to move in the normally

empty conduction band, thus increasing the conductivity of the silicon relative to the pure material.

10.37 Heating in a vacuum, where the partial pressure of oxygen is below its equilibrium value, causes partial loss of oxygen by way of the reaction

$$ZnO(s) \longrightarrow ZnO_{1-x} + \tfrac{x}{2}O_2$$

Thus, the zinc oxide is left nonstoichiometric, for example, $ZnO_{0.95}$. For every oxygen atom formed, two conducting electrons are left in the zinc oxide lattice, and its conductivity increases. This trend is reversed when the ZnO is heated in oxygen.

Ionic Solids

10.39 (a)

Cl^-	Na^+
8 corners $\times \tfrac{1}{8}$ ion/corner = 1 ion	1 center $\times$ 1 ion/center = 1 ion
6 faces $\times \tfrac{1}{2}$ ion/face = 3 ions	12 edges $\times \tfrac{1}{4}$ ion/edge = 3 ions
total = 4 Cl^- ions	total = 4 Na^+ ions

Thus, there are 4 formula units of NaCl per unit cell.

(b)

Ca^{2+}	F^-
8 corners $\times \tfrac{1}{8}$ ion/corner = 1 ion	8 sites $\times$ 1 ion/site = 8 ions
6 faces $\times \tfrac{1}{2}$ ion/face = 3 ions	
total = 4 Ca^{2+} ions	total = 8 F^- ions

Thus, there are 4 formula units of CaF_2 per unit cell. The Ca^{2+} and F^- ions have coordination number of 8 and 4, respectively.

10.41 Ca^{2+}: 8 corners $\times \tfrac{1}{8}$ ion per corner = 1 ion
Ti^{4+}: 1 center $\times$ 1 ion per center = 1 ion
O^{2-}: 12 edges $\times \tfrac{1}{4}$ ion per edge = 3 ions
Therefore, the formula is $CaTiO_3$.

10.43 FU = formula unit.

$$\text{number of unit cells} = (1 \text{ mm}^3) \times \left(\frac{0.1 \text{ cm}}{1 \text{ mm}}\right)^3 \times \left(\frac{2.16 \text{ g}}{1 \text{ cm}^3}\right) \times \left(\frac{1 \text{ mol}}{58.44 \text{ g}}\right)$$

$$\times \left(\frac{6.02 \times 10^{23} \text{ FU}}{1 \text{ mol}}\right) \times \left(\frac{1 \text{ unit cell}}{4 \text{ FU}}\right) = 5.56 \times 10^{18} \text{ unit cells}$$

10.45   radius ratio $= \dfrac{\text{radius of cation}}{\text{radius of anion}}$

(a) radius ratio $= \dfrac{138 \text{ pm}}{196 \text{ pm}} = 0.704 > 0.7$

We predict the cesium chloride structure, but this is a close call. The cation is predicted to have a coordination number of 8 by the rules, but the actual structure is the rock-salt structure with a coordination number of 6.

(b) radius ratio $= \dfrac{58 \text{ pm}}{196 \text{ pm}} = 0.296 < 0.7$

We predict the rock-salt structure, with a coordination number of 6 for the cations.

(c) radius ratio $= \dfrac{136 \text{ pm}}{140 \text{ pm}} = 0.971 > 0.7$

Cesium chloride structure, coordination number 8.

10.47   (a) Referring to Fig. 10.36, we see that the side of the unit cell is defined by two I^- ions at the corners in contact with one Na^+ ion between them. So the side length is equal to one I^- radius, plus one Na^+ diameter, plus another I^- radius.

$$\text{side} = 2 \times r_{I^-} + 2 \times r_{Na^+}$$
$$= 2 \times 220 \text{ pm} + 2 \times 102 \text{ pm} = 644 \text{ pm}$$
$$= 6.44 \times 10^{-10} \text{ m} = 6.44 \times 10^{-8} \text{ cm}$$

$$\text{volume of unit cell} = (\text{side})^3 = (6.44 \times 10^{-8} \text{ cm})^3 = 2.67 \times 10^{-22} \text{ cm}^3$$

$$\text{mass of unit cell} = 4 \text{ FU} \times \left(\frac{1 \text{ mol NaI}}{6.022 \times 10^{23} \text{ FU}} \right) \times \left(\frac{149.89 \text{ g NaI}}{1 \text{ mol NaI}} \right)$$
$$= 9.96 \times 10^{-22} \text{ g NaCl}$$

$$\text{density} = \frac{9.96 \times 10^{-22} \text{ g}}{2.67 \times 10^{-22} \text{ cm}^3} = 3.73 \text{ g} \cdot \text{cm}^{-3}$$

This value compares well with the actual density of NaI, which is $3.67 \text{ g} \cdot \text{cm}^{-3}$.

(b) Referring to Fig. 10.38, we see that the dimension of the unit cell is defined by two I^- ions at the corners of a body diagonal in contact with one Cs^+ ion in the body center. Thus the body diagonal has length given by

$$l = 2 \times r_{I^-} + 2 \times r_{Cs^+}$$
$$= 2 \times 220 \text{ pm} + 2 \times 170 \text{ pm} = 780 \text{ pm}$$
$$= 7.80 \times 10^{-10} \text{ m} = 7.80 \times 10^{-8} \text{ cm}$$

For a cube, $l = \sqrt{3} \times \text{side}$, so side $= \dfrac{7.80 \times 10^{-8} \text{ cm}}{\sqrt{3}} = 4.50 \times 10^{-8} \text{ cm}$

volume of unit cell $= (\text{side})^3 = (4.50 \times 10^{-8} \text{ cm})^3 = 9.11 \times 10^{-23} \text{ cm}^3$

$$\text{mass of unit cell} = 1 \text{ FU} \times \frac{1 \text{ mol CsI}}{6.022 \times 10^{23} \text{ FU}} \times \frac{259.81 \text{ g CsI}}{1 \text{ mol CsI}} = 4.31 \times 10^{-22} \text{ g}$$

$$\text{density} = \frac{4.31 \times 10^{-22} \text{ g}}{9.11 \times 10^{-23} \text{ cm}^3} = 4.74 \text{ g} \cdot \text{cm}^{-3}$$

Network Solids

10.49   B, C, Si, Ge, P, As

10.51   See Fig. 10.45. Each carbon atom is bonded to four other carbon atoms, but the average number of C—C bonds per carbon atom is obtained by dividing four by two, in order to avoid counting the same bond twice. Thus,

$$\left(\frac{713 \text{ kJ}}{1 \text{ mol C}}\right) \times \left(\frac{1 \text{ mol C}}{2 \text{ mol bonds}}\right) = 356 \text{ kJ} \cdot \text{mol}^{-1} \text{ bonds}$$

Molecular Solids

10.53   (a) London forces   (b) dipole-dipole, London forces, and hydrogen bonding
(c) dipole-dipole and London forces

10.55 $A_2B_2C_4$

Vapor Pressure

10.57   Dynamic equilibrium is a condition in which a forward process and its reverse are occurring simultaneously at equal rates. Thus, in a dynamic equilibrium, processes (at the molecular level) are occurring; it is only the net effect that is unchanging. In a static equilibrium, no process is occurring at any level. Static equilibrium is rare or nonexistent at the atomic or molecular level.

10.59 $PV = nRT$

$$\text{amount (moles) of } H_2O = n = \frac{PV}{RT} = \frac{17.5 \text{ Torr} \times \left(\dfrac{1 \text{ atm}}{760 \text{ Torr}}\right) \times 1.0 \text{ L}}{0.08206 \text{ L} \cdot \text{atm} \cdot \text{K}^{-1} \cdot \text{mol}^{-1} \times 293 \text{ K}}$$

$$= 9.5\overline{8} \times 10^{-4} \text{ mol}$$

$$\text{mass of } H_2O = 9.5\overline{8} \times 10^{-4} \text{ mol} \times 18.02 \text{ g} \cdot \text{mol}^{-1} = 0.017 \text{ g } H_2O$$

10.61 $PV = nRT$

amount (moles) of water $= n = \dfrac{PV}{RT} = \dfrac{7.4 \text{ kPa} \times \dfrac{10^3 \text{ Pa}}{1 \text{ kPa}} \times (4 \times 3 \times 3) \text{ m}^3}{8.314 \text{ J} \cdot \text{K}^{-1} \cdot \text{mol}^{-1} \times 313 \text{ K}} = 10\overline{2} \text{ mol}$

mass of $H_2O = 10\overline{2} \text{ mol} \times 18.02 \text{ g} \cdot \text{mol}^{-1} = 1.8 \times 10^3 \text{ g}$

10.63 (a) 99.2°C (b) 99.7°C

Phase Diagrams

10.65 (a) vapor (b) liquid (c) vapor (d) vapor

10.67 (a) ~2.4 k (b) 10 atm (c) from figure, about 5 K, actual value is 4.2 K
(d) No, there is no phase equilibrium line between solid and gas.

10.69 (a) At the lower pressure triple point, liquid helium I and II are in equilibrium
with helium gas; at the higher pressure triple point, liquid helium I and II are in
equilibrium with solid helium.
(b) The negative slope of the helium II/helium I phase boundary line suggests
that—as in the case of the solid/liquid water phase boundary—helium II is the
less dense, despite the fact that it is the lower temperature phase. Recall that solid
water is less dense than liquid water. See the phase diagram of water, Fig. 10.51.

10.71 Its triple point temperature is higher than room temperature. From this information alone, no firm conclusion can be drawn about its triple point pressure, because some
sublimation will occur even if its sublimation vapor pressure is less than 1 atm.

SUPPLEMENTARY EXERCISES

10.73 The equilibrium vapor pressure corresponds to the situation at a given temperature where the molecules in a liquid in a closed container are leaving the surface at the
same rate that the molecules in the vapor phase above the liquid are returning to the
surface.

10.75 As pressure increases, the melting point of water decreases; whereas, the melting
point increases for carbon dioxide. The behavior of carbon dioxide is the more normal.
The reason for the anomalous behavior of water is that liquid water is denser than solid
water, so that as pressure increases, the denser (smaller molar volume) phase is favored.

The most important practical consequence of the anomalous behavior of water is that as the water in rivers, lakes, oceanfronts, etc., freezes it floats to the top. The water below remains at higher temperatures, allowing the living creatures in the body of water to survive.

10.77 (a) H_2O; it has two O—H bonds, both of which are capable of strong hydrogen bonding. Each H_2O molecule is involved in about 4 hydrogen bonds.

(b) The surface tension of all of these liquids is about the same. They are all capable of hydrogen bonding to about the same extent. However, London forces increase with increasing molar mass, so C_3H_7OH will have the greatest surface tension.

(c) CO_2; this is a nonpolar compound; SO_2 is polar and SiO_2 is a network solid.

(d) Very likely HI; it has the strongest London forces, although it has the weakest dipole-dipole forces. The London forces probably predominate.

(e) H_2S; its hydrogen bonding forces are much less than in H_2O, and its London forces are much less than in H_2Te.

(f) H_2; it has the weakest London forces.

(g) NH_3, due to relatively strong hydrogen bonding forces.

(h) Na_2O; ion-ion forces are stronger than all other forces.

(i) All have the same shape, but the electronegativity difference is greatest in SF_2; hence it probably has the strongest dipole-dipole forces.

(j) GeF_4, because it has the largest atoms with the most electrons.

10.79 (a, b) Viscosity and surface tension decrease with increasing temperature. At high temperatures, the molecules can move away from their neighbors more readily because of increased kinetic energy.

(c, d) Evaporation rate and vapor pressure increase with increasing temperature. The kinetic energy of the molecules increases with temperature and the probability of the molecules escaping into the gas phase increases.

10.81 If the external pressure is lowered, as in a cyclonic region, water will boil at a lower temperature. The boiling temperature is the temperature at which vapor pressure is equal to external pressure. Because vapor pressure and temperature are related—a lower temperature results in a lower vapor pressure, and vice versa—lowering the external pressure lowers the boiling temperature.

10.83 Figure 10.52 is a schematic representation of an accurate phase diagram for CO_2, but from it we can predict the likely results of these processes. The sudden increase in pressure from 1 atm to 73 atm at $-50°C$ would bring CO_2 into the solid region.

10.85 (a) relative humidity $= \dfrac{25.0 \text{ Torr}}{31.82 \text{ Torr}} \times 100\% = 78.6\%$

(b) At 25°C, the vapor pressure of water is 23.76 Torr; therefore, some of the water vapor in the air would condense as dew or fog.

10.87 Assume 100 g of alloy in each case.

(a) number of moles of Ni $= (25 \text{ g Ni}) \times \left(\dfrac{1 \text{ mol Ni}}{58.7 \text{ g Ni}}\right) = 0.43 \text{ mol Ni}$

number of moles of Cu $= (75 \text{ g Cu}) \times \left(\dfrac{1 \text{ mol Cu}}{63.5 \text{ g Cu}}\right) = 1.1\overline{8} \text{ mol Cu}$

$\dfrac{0.43 \text{ mol Ni}}{1.18 \text{ mol Cu}} = \dfrac{0.43 \text{ atoms Ni}}{1.18 \text{ atoms Cu}} = 0.36 \text{ atoms Ni/1 atom Cu}$

or about 1 nickel atom to 3 copper atoms.

(b) number of moles of Sb $= (7 \text{ g Sb}) \times \left(\dfrac{1 \text{ mol Sb}}{121.8 \text{ g Sb}}\right) = 0.05\overline{7} \text{ mol Sb}$

number of moles of Cu $= (3 \text{ g Cu}) \times \left(\dfrac{1 \text{ mol Cu}}{63.5 \text{ g Cu}}\right) = 0.04\overline{7} \text{ mol Cu}$

number of moles of Sn $= (90 \text{ g Sn}) \times \left(\dfrac{1 \text{ mol Sn}}{118.7 \text{ g Sn}}\right) = 0.75\overline{8} \text{ mol Sn}$

The ratios are $0.05\overline{7}$ mol Sb : $0.04\overline{7}$ mol Cu : $0.75\overline{8}$ mol Sn or approximately 12 mol Sb : 10 mol Cu : 161 mol Sn or approximately 12 atoms Sb : 10 atoms Cu : 161 atoms Sn.

(c) number of moles of Sn $= (12.5 \text{ g Sn}) \times \left(\dfrac{1 \text{ mol Sn}}{118.7 \text{ g Sn}}\right) = 0.105 \text{ mol Sn}$

number of moles of Cd $= (12.5 \text{ g Cd}) \times \left(\dfrac{1 \text{ mol Cd}}{112.4 \text{ g Cd}}\right) = 0.111 \text{ mol Cd}$

number of moles of Pb $= (25 \text{ g Pb}) \times \left(\dfrac{1 \text{ mol Pb}}{207.2 \text{ g Pb}}\right) = 0.12\overline{1} \text{ mol Pb}$

number of moles of Bi $= (50 \text{ g Bi}) \times \left(\dfrac{1 \text{ mol Bi}}{209 \text{ g Bi}}\right) = 0.23\overline{9} \text{ mol Bi}$

The ratios are 0.105 mol Sn : 0.111 mol Cd : $0.12\overline{1}$ mol Pb : $0.23\overline{9}$ mol Bi. Multiplying by 20 gives approximately 21 mol Sn : 22 mol Cd : 24 mol Pb : 48 mol Bi or approximately 21 atoms Sn : 22 atoms Cd : 24 atoms Pb : 48 atoms Bi.

10.89 (a) a = length of side of unit cell

volume of unit cell $= a^3 = (1 \text{ unit cell}) \times \left(\dfrac{1 \text{ cm}^3}{0.97 \text{ g}}\right) \times \left(\dfrac{22.99 \text{ g}}{1 \text{ mol}}\right)$

$\times \left(\dfrac{1 \text{ mol}}{6.02 \times 10^{23} \text{ atoms}}\right) \times \left(\dfrac{2 \text{ atoms}}{1 \text{ unit cell}}\right) = 7.8\overline{7} \times 10^{-23} \text{ cm}^3$

$$a = \sqrt[3]{7.8\overline{7} \times 10^{-23} \text{ cm}^3} \times \left(\frac{10^{-2} \text{ m}}{1 \text{ cm}}\right) \times \left(\frac{1 \text{ pm}}{10^{-12} \text{ m}}\right) = 42\overline{9} \text{ pm}$$

(b) The relationship between radius (r) and side length (a) in a bcc lattice is

$$r = \frac{\sqrt{3}a}{4} = \frac{\sqrt{3}}{4} \times 42\overline{9} \text{ pm} = 18\overline{6} \text{ pm}$$

(c) mass $= \left(\frac{0.97 \text{ g}}{1 \text{ cm}^3}\right) \times (7.8\overline{7} \times 10^{-23} \text{ cm}^3) = 7.6 \times 10^{-23} \text{ g}$

10.91 (a) density $= \left(\dfrac{1 \text{ unit cell}}{(559 \times 10^{-12} \text{ m})^3}\right) \times \left(\dfrac{4 \text{ atoms}}{1 \text{ unit cell}}\right) \times \left(\dfrac{1 \text{ mol}}{6.02 \times 10^{23} \text{ atoms}}\right)$

$$\times \left(\frac{83.80 \text{ g}}{1 \text{ mol}}\right) \times \left(\frac{10^{-2} \text{ m}}{1 \text{ cm}}\right)^3 = 3.19 \text{ g} \cdot \text{cm}^{-3}$$

(b) for an fcc lattice

$$r = \frac{\sqrt{2}a}{4} \quad a = 559 \text{ pm} \quad r = \frac{\sqrt{2}(559 \text{ pm})}{4} = 198 \text{ pm}$$

(c) $V_{\text{atom}} = \frac{4}{3}\pi r^3 = \frac{4}{3}\pi(198 \text{ pm})^3 = 3.25 \times 10^7 \text{ pm}^3$

(d) volume of unit cell $= (559 \text{ pm})^3 = 17.4\overline{7} \times 10^7 \text{ pm}^3$

percentage of empty space $= \dfrac{(17.4\overline{7} - 4 \times 3.25) \times 10^7 \text{ pm}^3}{17.4\overline{7} \times 10^7 \text{ pm}^3} \times 100\% = 25.6\%$

10.93 The spacing between the carbon layers increases, resulting in decreased perpendicular conductivity. The parallel conductivity increases, although the effect may not be dramatic, because the band is already half-filled.

10.95 r = atomic radius, a = length of side of unit cell, M = molar mass, d = density

for an fcc lattice, $a = \dfrac{4r}{\sqrt{2}}, \quad V = a^3 = \left(\dfrac{4r}{\sqrt{2}}\right)^3,$

mass (g) $= 4 \text{ atoms} \times \left(\dfrac{1 \text{ mol atoms}}{6.022 \times 10^{23} \text{ atoms}}\right) \times \left(\dfrac{M \text{ g}}{1 \text{ mol atoms}}\right)$

$d = \dfrac{\text{mass}}{V} = \dfrac{4M}{(6.022 \times 10^{23}) \times \left(\dfrac{4r}{\sqrt{2}}\right)^3} = \dfrac{2.94 \times 10^{-25} M}{r^3}$

solving for r,

$$r = (6.65 \times 10^{-9}) \sqrt[3]{\frac{M}{d}} \quad [M \text{ in g}, d \text{ in g} \cdot \text{cm}^{-3}]$$

$$r_{\text{Ne}} = (6.65 \times 10^{-9}) \sqrt[3]{\frac{20.18}{1.20}} = 1.70 \times 10^{-8} \text{ cm} = 170 \text{ pm}$$

$$r_{Ar} = (6.65 \times 10^{-9}) \sqrt[3]{\frac{39.95}{1.40}} = 2.03 \times 10^{-8} \text{ cm} = 203 \text{ pm}$$

$$r_{Kr} = (6.65 \times 10^{-9}) \sqrt[3]{\frac{83.8}{2.16}} = 2.25 \times 10^{-8} \text{ cm} = 225 \text{ pm}$$

$$r_{Xe} = (6.65 \times 10^{-9}) \sqrt[3]{\frac{131.3}{2.83}} = 2.39 \times 10^{-8} \text{ cm} = 239 \text{ pm}$$

$$r_{Rn} = (6.65 \times 10^{-9}) \sqrt[3]{\frac{222}{4.4}} = 2.4\overline{6} \times 10^{-8} \text{ cm} = 24\overline{6} \text{ pm}$$

10.97   The relationship between the densities of a bcc structure and a ccp structure was derived in the solution to Exercise 10.96. It is

$$d_{ccp} = 1.089 d_{bcc}$$

Therefore, $d_{ccp}(W) = 1.089 d_{bcc}(W) = 1.089 \times 19.3 \text{ g} \cdot \text{cm}^{-3} = 21.0 \text{ g} \cdot \text{cm}^{-3}$
Alternatively, we can rework the conversion as follows:
The mass of an atom of W is fixed; hence

$$\text{mass per atom} = \frac{(19.3 \text{ g} \cdot \text{cm}^{-3})\left(\frac{4r}{\sqrt{3}}\right)\frac{\text{cm}^3}{\text{unit cell}}}{2 \text{ atoms/unit cell}} = \frac{d_{ccp} \times \left(\frac{4r}{\sqrt{2}}\right)\frac{\text{cm}^3}{\text{unit cell}}}{4 \text{ atoms/unit cell}}$$

where d_{ccp} = density in the ccp structure. Solving for d_{ccp},

$$d_{ccp} = (19.3 \text{ g} \cdot \text{cm}^{-3})(2)\left(\sqrt{\frac{2}{3}}\right)^3 = 21.0 \text{ g} \cdot \text{cm}^{-3}$$

10.99   (a) Assuming that the air at 25°C is originally saturated with ethanol, the partial pressure of ethanol is still 58.9 Torr. The vapor pressure above a liquid is determined, for all practical purposes, by the temperature alone. So condensation of some of the gaseous ethanol occurs.

(b) $P_{\text{total}} = P_{\text{air}} + P_{\text{ethanol}} = P_{\text{air, initial}} + 58.9 \text{ Torr}$
750 Torr $= P_{\text{air, initial}} + 58.9 \text{ Torr}$

$$P_{\text{air, final}} = P_{\text{air, initial}} \times \frac{V_{\text{initial}}}{V_{\text{final}}} = (750 - 58.9) \text{ Torr} \times \frac{10 \text{ L}}{5 \text{ L}} = 1382 \text{ Torr}$$

$P_{\text{total}} = (1382 + 58.9) \text{ Torr} = 1441 \text{ Torr}$

CHAPTER 11
CARBON-BASED MATERIALS

EXERCISES

Structures and Reactions of Aliphatic Compounds

11.1 The difference can be traced to the weaker London forces that exist between branched molecules. Atoms in neighboring branched molecules cannot lie as close together as they do in the unbranched isomers. As a result of the molecules' irregular shape, the atoms in neighboring branched molecules are more effectively shielded from one another than they are in neighboring unbranched molecules.

11.3 (a) four σ-type single bonds   (b) two σ-type single bonds and one double bond, consisting of one σ bond and one π bond   (c) one σ-type single bond, and one triple bond, consisting of one σ bond and two π bonds

11.5 (a) $CH_4 + Cl_2 \xrightarrow{light} CH_3Cl + HCl$, substitution
(b) $CH_2{=}CH_2 + Br_2 \longrightarrow CH_2Br{-}CH_2Br$, addition

11.7 (a) $CH_3CH_3 + 2Cl_2 \xrightarrow{light} CH_2ClCH_2Cl + 2HCl$, substitution ($CH_2ClCH_3$ may also be produced)
(b) $CH_2CH_2 + Cl_2 \longrightarrow CH_2ClCH_2Cl$, addition
(c) $HC{\equiv}CH + 2Cl_2 \longrightarrow CHCl_2CHCl_2$, addition

Nomenclature of Aliphatic Compounds

11.9 (a) ethane (b) hexane (c) octane (d) methane

11.11 (a) methyl (b) pentyl (c) propyl

11.13 (a) propane (b) ethane (c) pentane (d) 2,3-dimethylbutane

11.15 (a) 4-methyl-2-pentene (b) 2,3-dimethyl-2-phenylpentane

11.17 (a) propene (no geometrical isomers)   (b) *cis*-2-hexene, *trans*-2-hexene

(c) 1-butyne (no geometrical isomers)   (d) 2-butyne (no geometrical isomers)

11.19 (a) $CH_2{=}CHCH(CH_3)CH_2CH_3$ (b) $CH_3CH_2C(CH_3)_2CH(CH_2CH_3)(CH_2)_2CH_3$

(c) $CH{\equiv}C(CH_2)_2C(CH_3)_3$ (d) $CH_3CH(CH_3)CH(CH_2CH_3)CH(CH_3)_2$

11.21 (a)

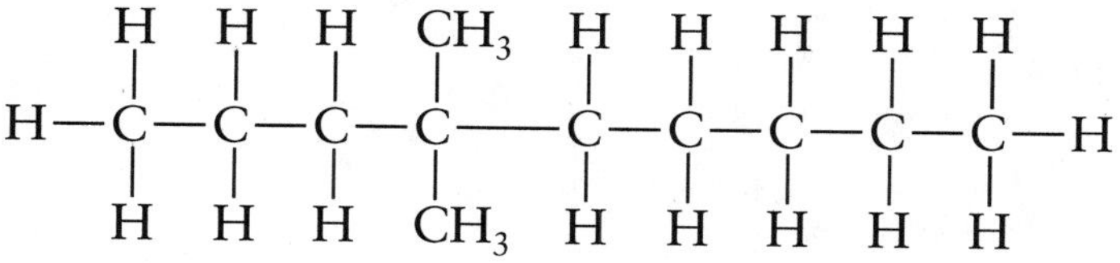

(b)

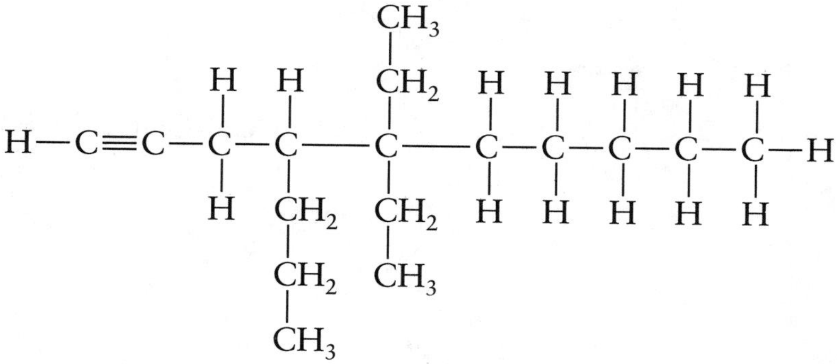

(c)

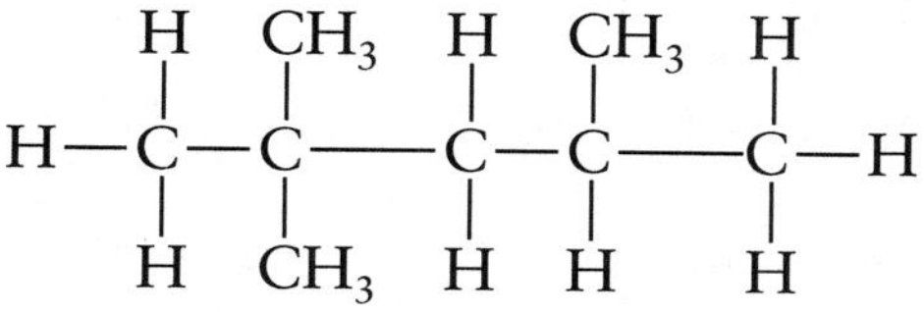

(d)

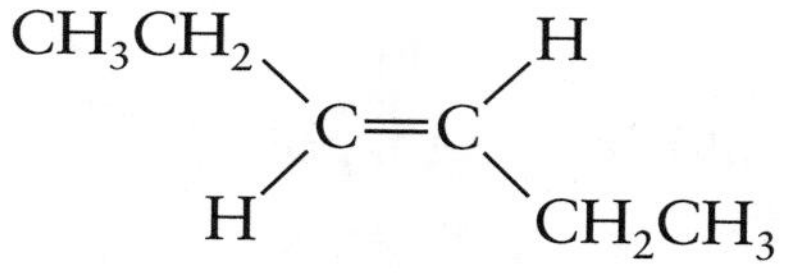

Aromatic Compounds

11.23 (a) 1-ethyl-3-methylbenzene   (b) 1,2,3,4,5-pentamethylbenzene (or, because there is only one possible structure, pentamethylbenzene)

11.25 (a)   (b) 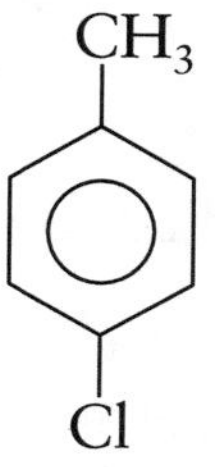   (c) 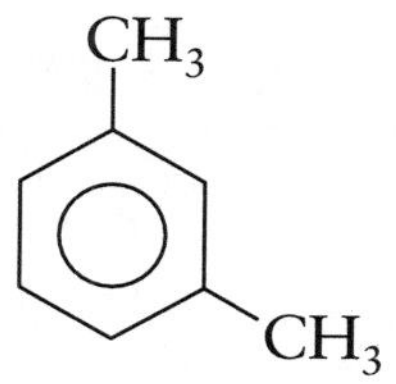   (d)

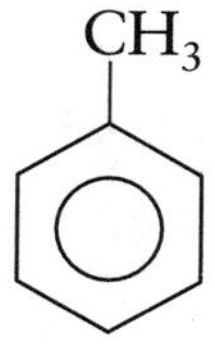

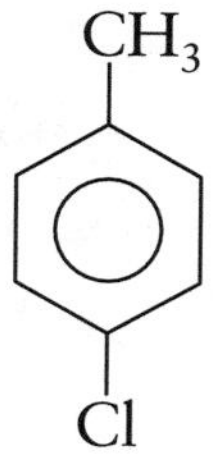

11.27

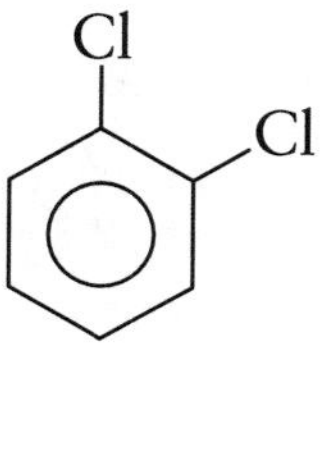

ortho-Dichlorobenzene   *meta*-Dichlorobenzene   *para*-Dichlorobenzene
(polar)   (polar)   (nonpolar)

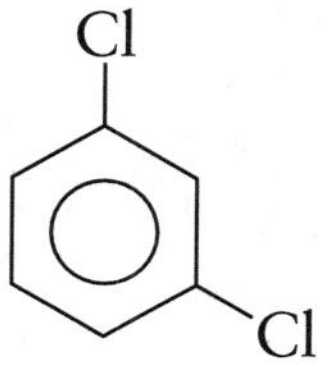

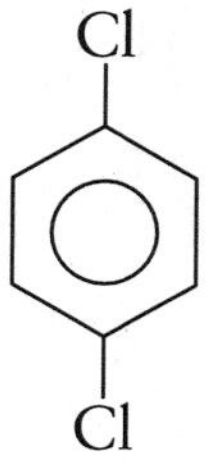

11.29 (a) RNH_2, R_2NH, R_3N (b) ROH   (c) 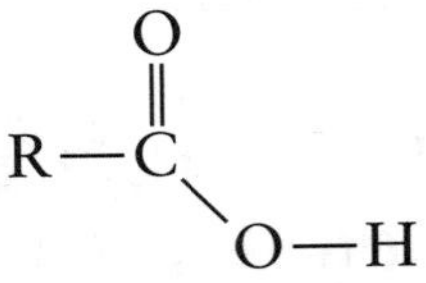 R—C(=O)—O—H or RCOOH

(d) 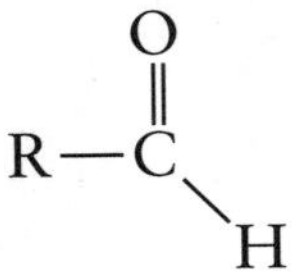 R—C(=O)—H or RCHO

11.31 (a) ether (b) ketone (c) primary amine (d) ester

11.33 (a) $CH_3CH_2CH_2CH_2OH$, primary alcohol (b) $CH_3CH_2CH(OH)CH_3$, secondary alcohol (c) 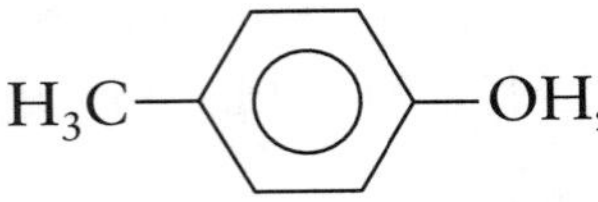 H_3C—⟨◯⟩—OH, phenol

11.35 (a) diethyl ether (b) $CH_3OCH_2CH_3$

11.37 (a) aldehyde, ethanol
(b) ketone, propanone
(c) ketone, 3-pentanone

11.39 (a) 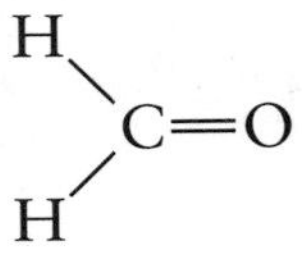 $\overset{H}{\underset{H}{}}$C=O (b) $\overset{CH_3}{\underset{CH_3}{}}$C=O (c) $\overset{CH_3}{\underset{CH_3(CH_2)_3CH_2}{}}$C=O

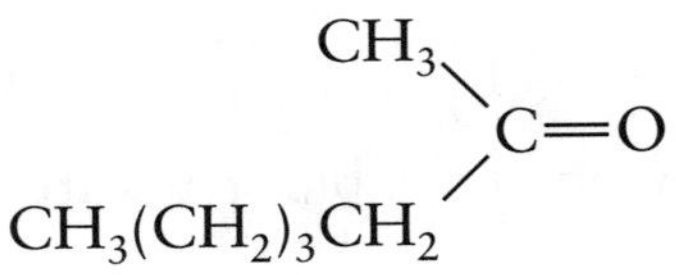

11.41 (a) ethanol (b) 2-octanol (c) 5-methyl-1-octanol   These reactions can be accomplished with an oxidizing agent such as acidified sodium dichromate, $Na_2Cr_2O_7$.

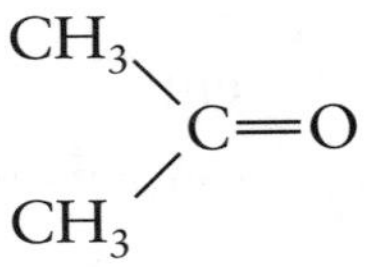

11.43 (a) ethanoic acid (b) butanoic acid (c) 2-aminoethanoic acid

11.45 (a) 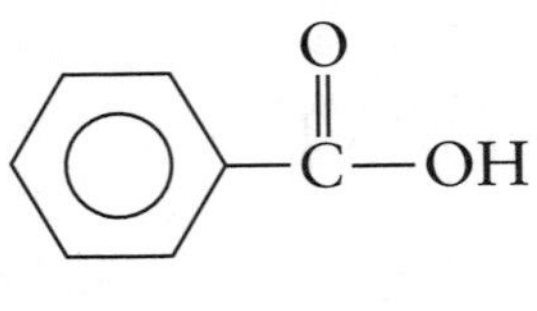 ⟨◯⟩—C(=O)—OH (b) CH_3—CH_2—CH(CH$_3$)—C(=O)—OH

(c) CH_3—CH_2—C(=O)—OH

130

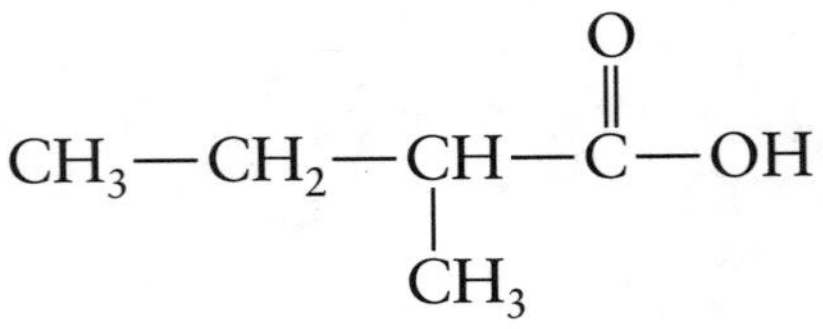

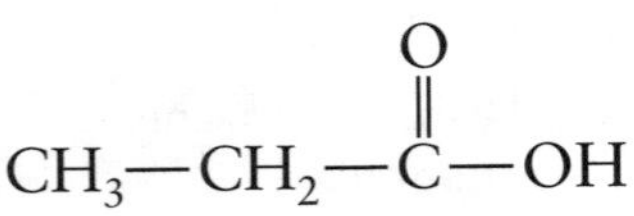

11.47 (a) methylamine (b) diethylamine (c) *o*-methylaniline or 2-methylaniline or *o*-methylphenylamine

11.49 (a)

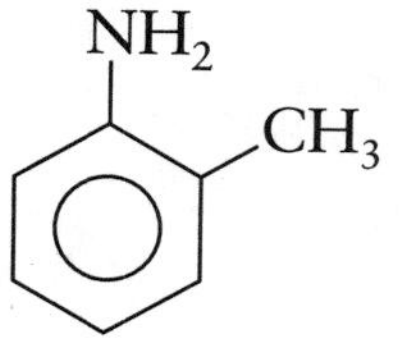

(b)

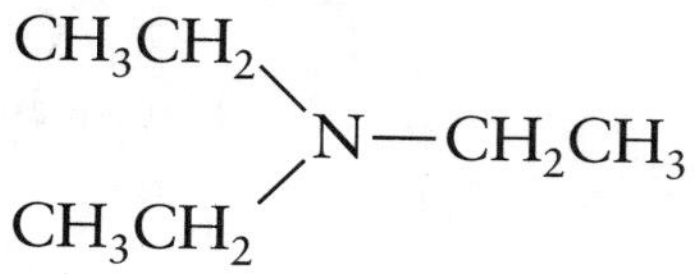

(c)

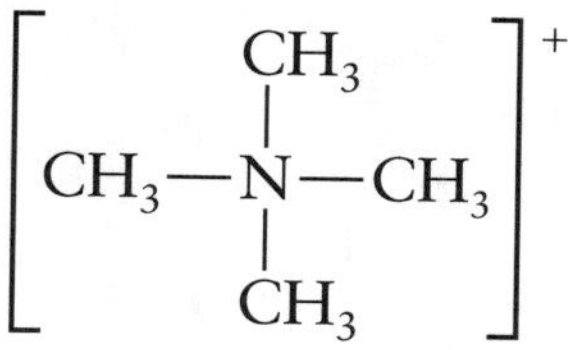

11.51 (a) 2-propanol (b) dimethyl ether (c) methanol or formaldehyde
(d) 3-pentanone (e) methylamine

11.53 (a) alcohol (—OH), ether (—OCH$_3$), aldehyde (—CHO)

(b) ketone $\left(\begin{array}{c} \diagdown \\ \diagup \end{array} C=O \right)$

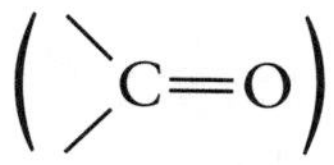

(c) tertiary amine $\left(\begin{array}{c} \diagdown \\ \diagup \end{array} N-CH_3 \right)$, amide $\left(\begin{array}{c} \diagdown \\ \diagup \end{array} N-C \begin{array}{c} \diagup O \\ \diagdown \end{array} \right)$, ketone $\left(-C \begin{array}{c} \diagup O \\ \diagdown \end{array} \right)$

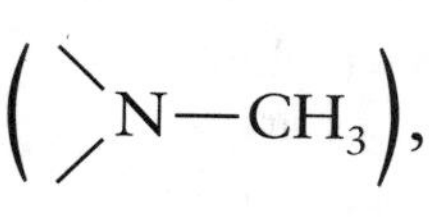

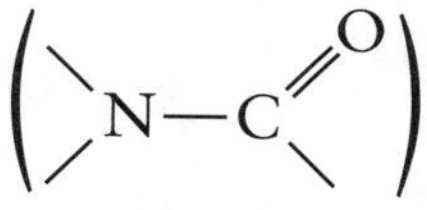

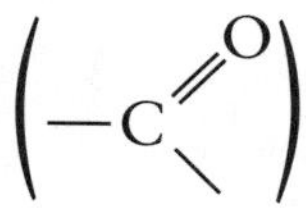

11.55 (a)

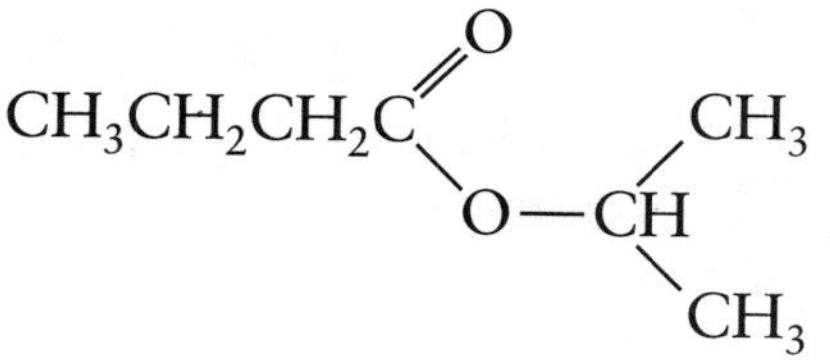

(b)

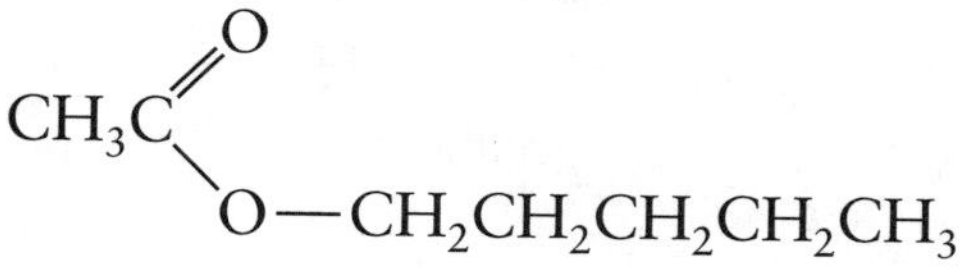

(c)

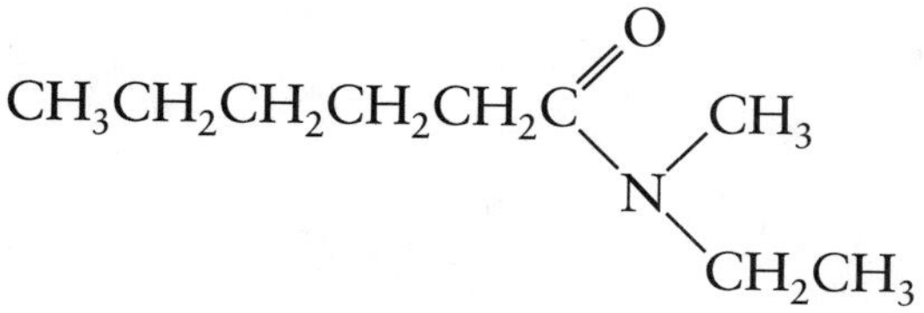

(d)

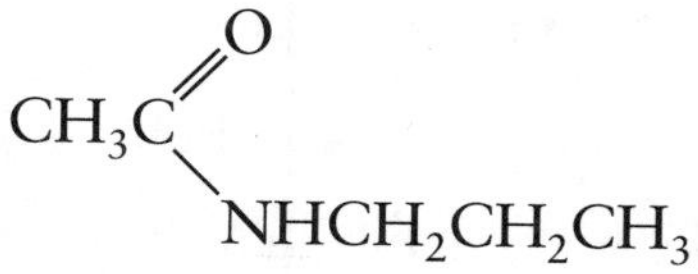

11.57 The following procedures may be used:
(1) Use an acid-base indicator and look for a color change.

(2) $CH_3CH_2CHO \xrightarrow{\text{Tollens reagent}} CH_3CH_2COOH + Ag(s)$

(3) $CH_3COCH_3 \xrightarrow{\text{Tollens reagent}}$ no reaction

Procedure (1) distinguishes ethanoic acid from propanal and 2-propanone.
(2) and (3) distinguish propanal from 2-propanone.

Isomerism

11.59 C_4H_8

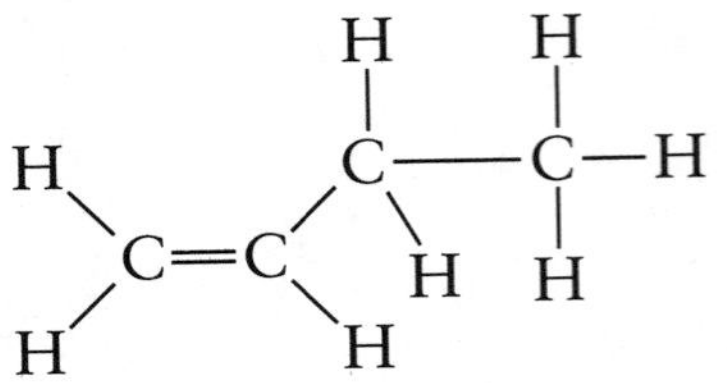

1-Butene

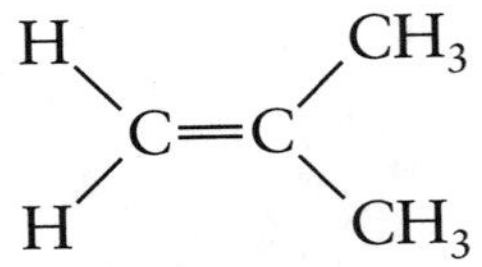

2-Methylpropene

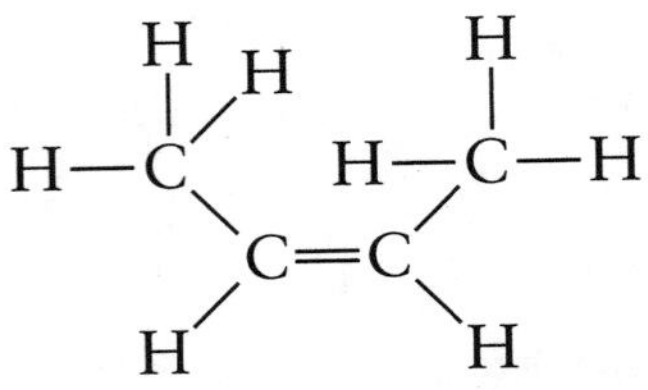

cis-2-Butene

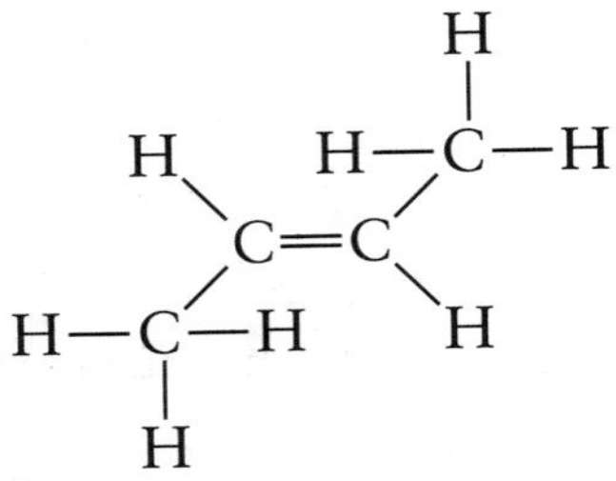

trans-2-Butene

11.61 (a)

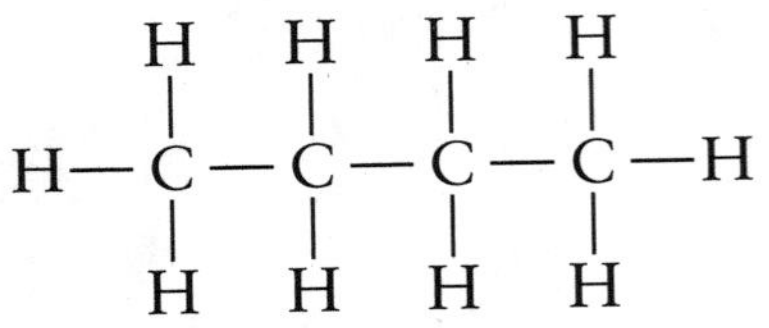

Butane

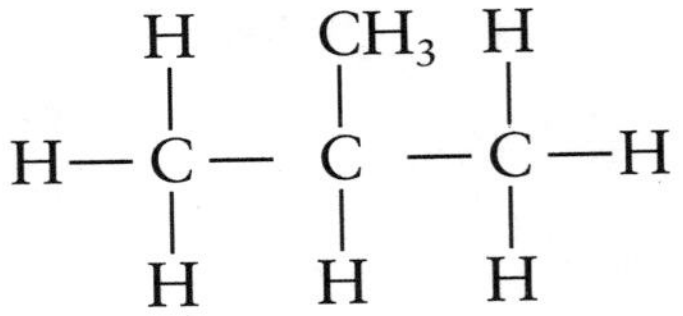

2-Methylpropane
(Isobutane)

(b)

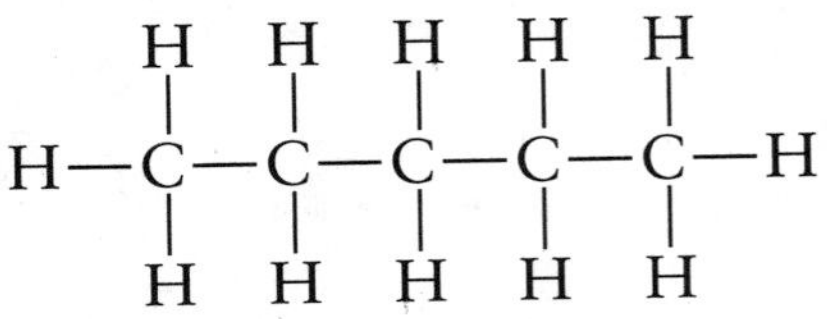

Pentane

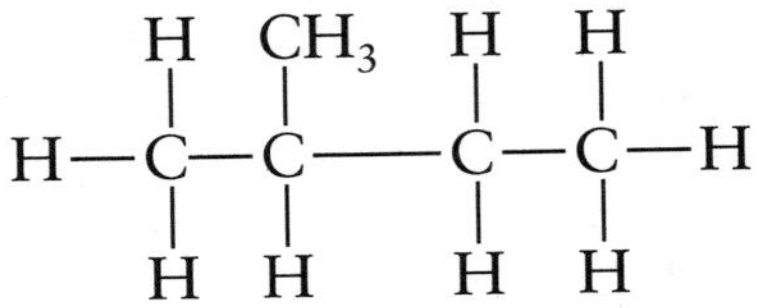

2-Methylbutane
(Isopentane)

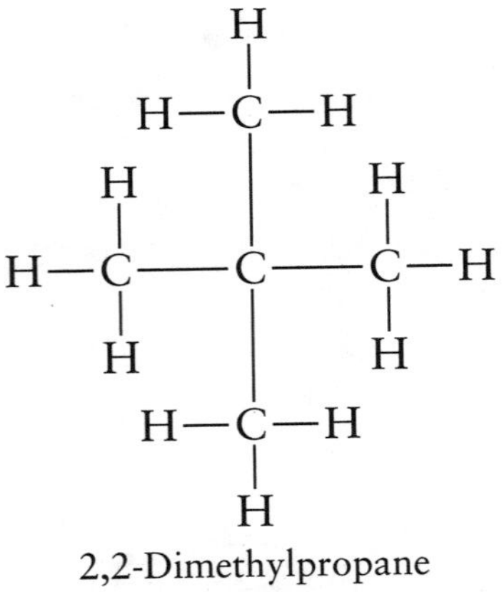

2,2-Dimethylpropane
(Neopentane)

11.63 (a) Butane is C_4H_{10}, cyclobutane is C_4H_8. Because they have different formulas, they are not isomers.

(b) $CH_3CH_2CH_2CH_2CH_3$

$$CH_3-\overset{\overset{\displaystyle CH_3}{|}}{\underset{\underset{\displaystyle CH_3}{|}}{C}}-CH_3$$

Pentane (C_5H_{12}) 2,2-Dimethylpropane (C_5H_{12})

Same formula, but different structures; therefore, they are structural isomers.

(c)

Cyclopentane (C_5H_{10}) Pentene (C_5H_{10})

Same formula, but different structures; therefore, they are structural isomers.

(d) Same formula (C_5H_{10}), same structure (bonding arrangement is the same), but different geometry; therefore, they are geometrical isomers.

(e) Not isomers, because only their positions in space are different and these positions can be interchanged. Same molecule.

11.65 If only two isomeric products are formed, and they are both branched, then the only possibilities are

(a) $CH_3-\overset{\overset{\displaystyle H}{|}}{\underset{\underset{\displaystyle CH_3}{|}}{C}}-CH_3$ (b) $CH_3-\overset{\overset{\displaystyle Cl}{|}}{\underset{\underset{\displaystyle CH_3}{|}}{C}}-CH_3$ $Cl-\overset{\overset{\displaystyle H}{|}}{\underset{\underset{\displaystyle H}{|}}{C}}-\overset{\overset{\displaystyle H}{|}}{\underset{\underset{\displaystyle CH_3}{|}}{C}}-CH_3$

Note: All methyl groups are equivalent.

11.67 (a) , (c), and (d) are optically active.

(a) $CH_3-\overset{\overset{\displaystyle H}{|}}{\underset{\underset{\displaystyle Br}{|}}{C^*}}-CH_2CH_3$ (c) $H-\overset{\overset{\displaystyle Br}{|}}{\underset{\underset{\displaystyle H}{|}}{C}}-\overset{\overset{\displaystyle Cl}{|}}{\underset{\underset{\displaystyle H}{|}}{C^*}}-CH_3$

(d) $H-\overset{\overset{\displaystyle Cl}{|}}{\underset{\underset{\displaystyle H}{|}}{C}}-\overset{\overset{\displaystyle Cl}{|}}{\underset{\underset{\displaystyle H}{|}}{C^*}}-\overset{\overset{\displaystyle H}{|}}{\underset{\underset{\displaystyle H}{|}}{C}}-\overset{\overset{\displaystyle H}{|}}{\underset{\underset{\displaystyle H}{|}}{C}}-\overset{\overset{\displaystyle H}{|}}{\underset{\underset{\displaystyle H}{|}}{C}}-H$

*Indicates the chiral carbon atoms.

11.69 (a) (b)

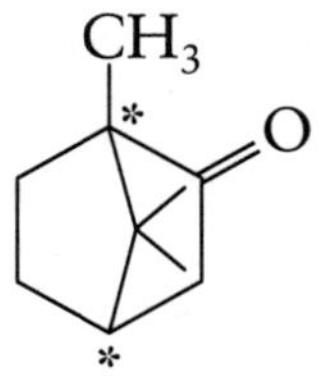

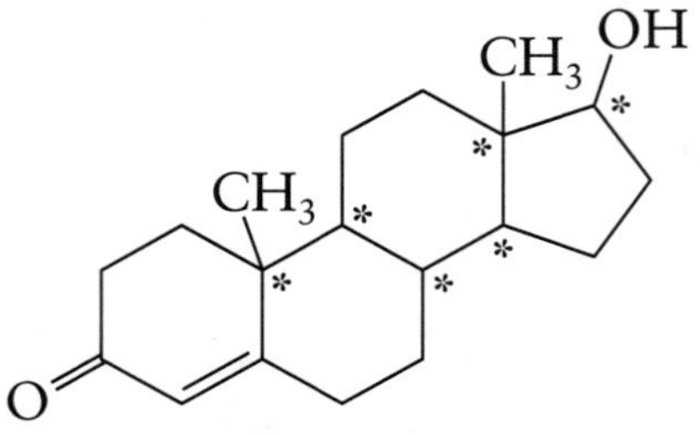

*Indicates the chiral carbon atoms.

Polymers

11.71 (a) $-CH_2-C(CH_3)_2-CH_2-C(CH_3)_2-CH_2-C(CH_3)_2-$

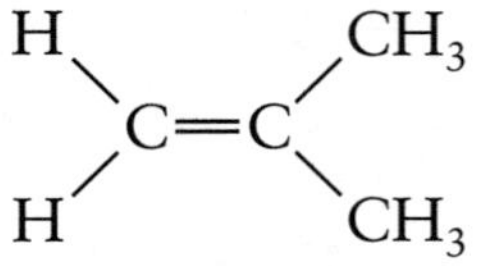

(b) acrylonitrile: $CH_2=CH-CN$

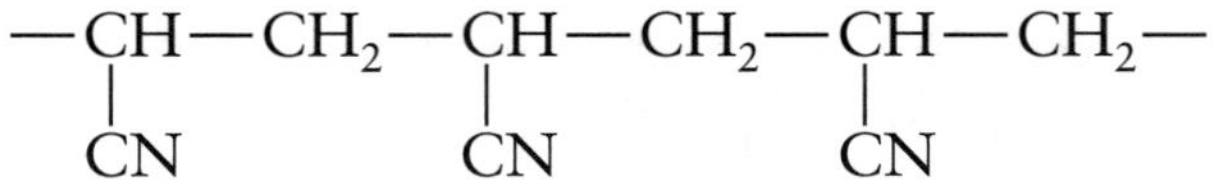

$$-\underset{\underset{CN}{|}}{CH}-CH_2-\underset{\underset{CN}{|}}{CH}-CH_2-\underset{\underset{CN}{|}}{CH}-CH_2-$$

(c) 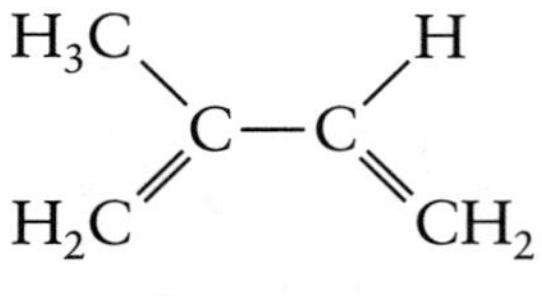
Isoprene

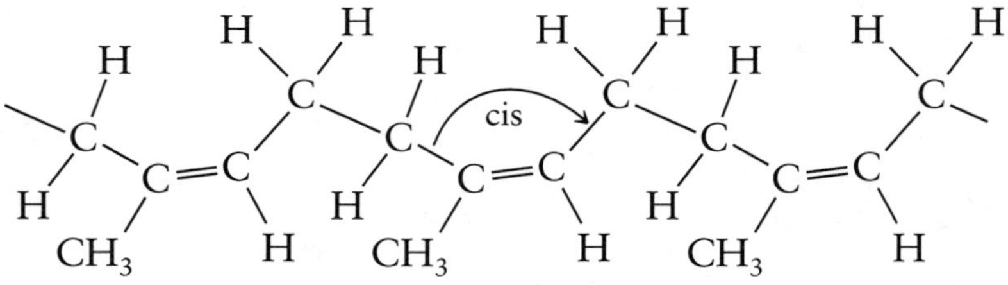

cis version

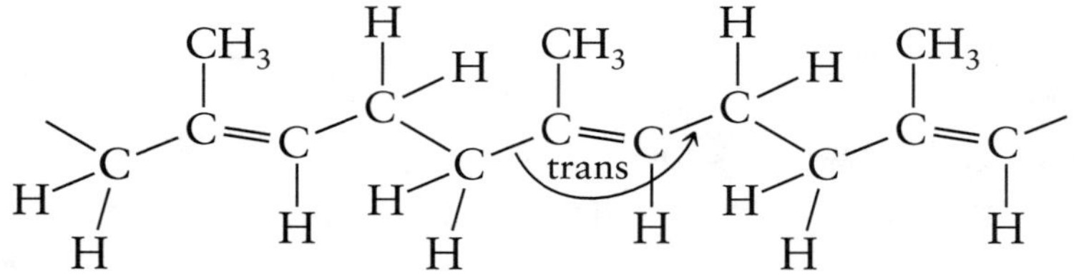

trans version

11.73 (a) $\underset{\underset{Cl}{|}}{CH}=CH_2$ (b) $\underset{\underset{Cl}{|}}{\overset{\overset{F}{|}}{C}}=CF_2$

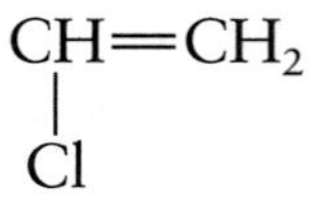

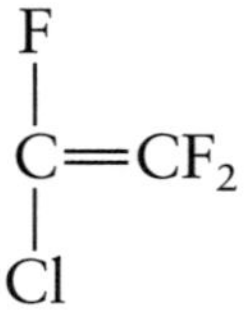

11.75 (a) $-OC-CO-NH-(CH_2)_4-NHCO-CO-NH-(CH_2)_4-NH-$

(b) $-OC-\underset{\underset{CH_3}{|}}{CH}-NH-OC-\underset{\underset{CH_3}{|}}{CH}-NH-$

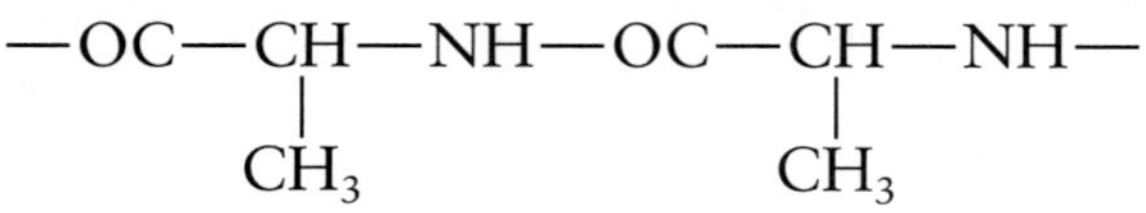

11.77 An isotactic polymer is a polymer in which the substituents are all on the same side of the chain.

A syndiotactic polymer is a polymer in which the substituent groups alternate, one side of the chain to the other.

An atactic polymer is a polymer in which the groups are randomly attached, one side or the other, along the chain.

11.79 block copolymer

11.81 Larger average molar mass corresponds to longer average chain length. Longer chain length allows for greater intertwining of the chains, making them more difficult to pull apart. This twining results in (a) higher softening points, (b) greater viscosity, and (c) greater mechanical strength.

11.83 Highly linear, unbranched chains allow for maximum interaction between chains. The greater the intermolecular contact between chains, the stronger the forces between them, and the greater the strength of the material.

Edible Polymers

11.85 (a) 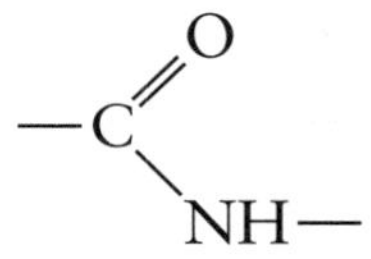 (b) amide (c) condensation

11.87 Side groups that contain hydroxyl, carbonyl, amino, and sulfide groups are all potentially capable of participating in hydrogen bonding that could contribute to the tertiary structure of the protein. Thus, serine, threonine, tyrosine, aspartic acid, glutamic acid, lysine, arginine, histidine, asparagine, and glutamine satisfy the criteria. Proline, and tryptophan generally do not contribute through hydrogen bonding because they are typically found in hydrophobic regions of proteins.

11.89

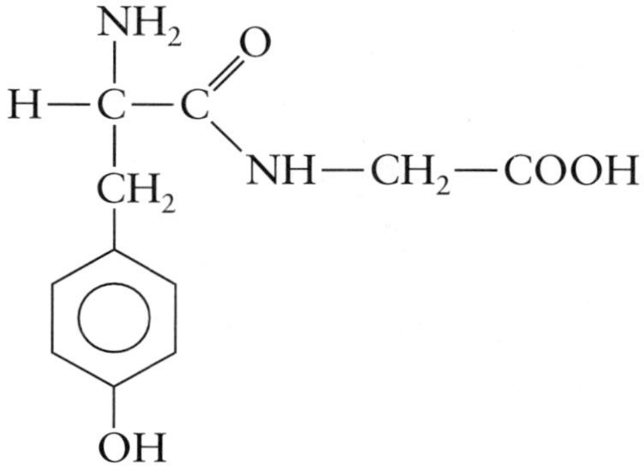

11.91

The functional groups are the alcohol, (—OH) and aldehyde

$$\left(\begin{array}{c} \diagdown \\ C = O \\ | \\ H \end{array} \right) \text{ groups.}$$

11.93 (a)

$$\begin{array}{ccccccccc} C & A & T & G & A & G & T & T & A \\ | & | & | & | & | & | & | & | & | \\ G & T & A & C & T & C & A & A & T \end{array}$$

(b)

$$\begin{array}{ccccccccc} T & G & A & A & T & T & G & C & A \\ | & | & | & | & | & | & | & | & | \\ A & C & T & T & A & A & C & G & T \end{array}$$

SUPPLEMENTARY EXERCISES

11.95 There are a large number and a wide variety of organic compounds because of the ability of carbon to form four bonds with as many as four different atoms or groups of atoms, the ability of carbon to bond directly to other carbon atoms to form long chains of carbon-carbon bonds (the basis for polymerization), and the ability of carbon-containing compounds to form a variety of isomers, compounds with the same molecular formula, but different structural formulas.

11.97 Aromatic carbon-carbon bonds are intermediate in length (139 pm) between a C—C single bond (154 pm) and a C=C double bond (134 pm). An aromatic ring is characterized by a delocalized π system, in contrast to the localized bonds present in aliphatic hydrocarbons.

11.99 number of moles of H $= \left(\dfrac{3.32 \text{ g H}_2\text{O}}{18.02 \text{ g H}_2\text{O/mol H}_2\text{O}} \right) \times \left(\dfrac{2 \text{ mol H}}{1 \text{ mol H}_2\text{O}} \right)$

$$= 0.369 \text{ mol H}$$

number of moles of C $= \left(\dfrac{6.48 \text{ g CO}_2}{44.01 \text{ g CO}_2\text{/mol CO}_2} \right) \times \left(\dfrac{1 \text{ mol C}}{1 \text{ mol CO}_2} \right) = 0.147 \text{ mol C}$

$$\dfrac{0.369 \text{ mol H}}{0.147 \text{ mol C}} = 2.51 \left(\dfrac{\text{mol H}}{\text{mol C}} \right) = \dfrac{5 \text{ mol H}}{2 \text{ mol C}}$$

Therefore, the empirical formula is C_2H_5. The molecular formula might be C_4H_{10}, which matches the general formula for alkanes, C_nH_{2n+2}. The compound cannot be an alkene or alkyne, because they all have mol H/mol C ratios less than 2.5.

11.101 (a)

$$\begin{array}{c} \text{H} \quad \text{CH}_3 \\ \text{C} \\ \text{H}-\text{C}-\text{C}-\text{H} \\ \text{H} \qquad \text{H} \end{array}$$

(b)

2,4,6-trimethylbenzene ring with H_3C, CH_3, CH_3, CH_3 substituents

(c) $CH_3CH_2CH_2-\overset{\displaystyle CH_3}{\underset{\displaystyle \text{(phenyl)}}{\overset{|}{\underset{|}{C}}}}-CH_3$

(d) cyclohexene ring structure

(e) $CH_3-\overset{\displaystyle }{\underset{\displaystyle CH_3}{\overset{|}{C}}}=CHCH_3$

(f) toluene ring with CH_3 and Br substituents

11.103

$$\underset{\text{(2-butyne)}}{H-\overset{H}{\underset{H}{C}}-C\equiv C-\overset{H}{\underset{H}{C}}-H} + 2HBr \longrightarrow H-\overset{H}{\underset{H}{C}}-\overset{Br}{\underset{H}{C}}-\overset{Br}{\underset{H}{C}}-\overset{H}{\underset{H}{C}}-H$$

11.105 (a)

$$H-\overset{H}{\underset{H}{C}}-\overset{H}{\underset{H}{C}}-O-\overset{H}{\underset{H}{C}}-\overset{H}{\underset{H}{C}}-H \qquad H-\overset{H}{\underset{H}{C}}-\overset{H}{\underset{H}{C}}-\overset{H}{\underset{H}{C}}-\overset{H}{\underset{H}{C}}-O-H$$

Diethyl ether   1-Butanol

(b) The principal forces between both of these compounds and water resulting in their solubility are London forces. Both molecules are likely to have very similar London forces with water because both contain the same atoms in a similar structural arrangement. However, 1-butanol can also undergo hydrogen bonding with itself, so the molecules are held together strongly in the liquid state, thereby resulting in a relatively high (117°C) boiling point.

11.107

$$HO-\langle\bigcirc\rangle-CH_2OH \xrightarrow[\text{organic solvent}]{Na_2Cr_2O_7(aq),\ H^+} HO-\langle\bigcirc\rangle-CHO$$

11.109

$$H-\overset{H}{\underset{H}{C}}-\overset{H}{C}=\overset{H}{C}-\overset{H}{\underset{H}{C}}-\overset{H}{\underset{H}{C}}-H + HBr \longrightarrow H-\overset{H}{\underset{H}{C}}-\overset{H}{\underset{H}{C}}-\overset{H}{\underset{Br}{C}}-\overset{H}{\underset{H}{C}}-\overset{H}{\underset{H}{C}}-H$$

$$H-\underset{\underset{H}{|}}{\overset{\overset{H}{|}}{C}}-\underset{}{\overset{\overset{H}{|}}{C}}=\underset{\underset{H}{|}}{\overset{\overset{H}{|}}{C}}-\underset{\underset{H}{|}}{\overset{\overset{H}{|}}{C}}-\underset{\underset{H}{|}}{\overset{\overset{H}{|}}{C}}-H \;+\; HBr \longrightarrow\; H-\underset{\underset{H}{|}}{\overset{\overset{H}{|}}{C}}-\underset{\underset{Br}{|}}{\overset{\overset{H}{|}}{C}}-\underset{\underset{H}{|}}{\overset{\overset{H}{|}}{C}}-\underset{\underset{H}{|}}{\overset{\overset{H}{|}}{C}}-\underset{\underset{H}{|}}{\overset{\overset{H}{|}}{C}}-H$$

The first reaction produces 3-bromopentane. The second reaction produces 2-bromopentane.

11.111 Polyalkenes < polyesters < polyamides, due to the increasing strength of intermolecular forces between the chains. The three types of polymer have about the same London forces if their chains are about the same length. However, polyesters also have dipole forces contributing to the strength of intermolecular forces, and polyamides form very strong hydrogen bonds between their chains.

11.113 (a) Primary structure is the sequence of amino acids along a protein chain. Secondary structure is the conformation of the protein or the manner in which the chain is coiled or layered as a result of interactions between amide and carboxy groups. Tertiary structure is the shape into which sections of the proteins twist and intertwine as a result of interactions between side groups of the amino acids in the protein. If the protein consists of several polypeptide units, then the manner in which the units stick together is the quaternary structure.

(b) The primary structure is held together by covalent bonds. Intermolecular forces provide the major stabilizing force of the secondary structure. The tertiary structure is maintained by a combination of London forces, hydrogen bonding, and sometimes ion-ion interactions. The same forces are responsible for the quaternary structure.

CHALLENGING EXERCISES

11.115 $CH_3(CH_2)_2CH(OH)CH_3 \xrightarrow[120°C]{H_2SO_4} H_2O(g) + CH_3(CH_2)_2CH=CH_2$

11.117

11.119 Condensation polymerization involves the loss of a small molecule, often water or HCl, when monomers are added together. 1,2-Benzenedicarboxylic acid reacts with ethylene glycol to yield

138

$$\left[\text{CH}_2\text{—CH}_2\text{—O—}\underset{\underset{\text{O}}{\|}}{\text{C}}\,\cdots\,\overset{\overset{\text{O}}{\|}}{\text{C}}\text{—O—CH}_2\text{—CH}_2\text{—O—}\overset{\overset{\text{O}}{\|}}{\text{C}}\,\cdots\,\underset{\underset{\text{O}}{\|}}{\text{C}}\text{—O} \right]$$

whereas Dacron is

$$\left[\text{CH}_2\text{—CH}_2\text{—O—}\overset{\overset{\text{O}}{\|}}{\text{C}}\!\!-\!\!\bigcirc\!\!-\!\!\overset{\overset{\text{O}}{\|}}{\text{C}}\text{—O—CH}_2\text{—CH}_2\text{—O—}\overset{\overset{\text{O}}{\|}}{\text{C}}\!\!-\!\!\bigcirc\!\!-\!\!\overset{\overset{\text{O}}{\|}}{\text{C}}\text{—O} \right]$$

The properties of these two polymers would be similar except that Dacron, as a result of its more linear molecular structure, can be more readily spun into yarn.

CHAPTER 12
THE PROPERTIES OF SOLUTIONS

EXERCISES

Solubility

12.1 Both water and methanol are capable of hydrogen bonding, and they readily hydrogen bond to each other. Thus they intermingle at the molecular level. Toluene, on the other hand, cannot hydrogen bond to methanol. The much weaker London forces between methanol and toluene result in only limited solubility.

12.3 (a) water, because of strong ion-dipole interactions (b) benzene, because of stronger London forces (c) water, because of the hydrophilic head group ($-CO_2^-$) of CH_3COOH in water

12.5 (a) hydrophilic, because of hydrogen bonding (b) hydrophobic, because it is nonpolar (c) hydrophobic, because it is nonpolar (d) hydrophilic, because of the polar $-COOH$ group

12.7 (a) Grease is composed principally of nonpolar hydrocarbons, which are expected to dissolve in gasoline (also a nonpolar hydrocarbon mixture) but not in the very polar water.
(b) Soaps are long-chain molecules with both polar and nonpolar ends. The polar end of the soap dissolves in water, and the nonpolar end dissolves in the nonpolar

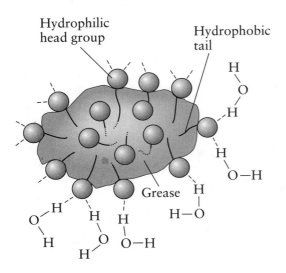

grease. As such, the soap serves as a "bridge" to "connect" the grease to the water so that it can be washed away. See Fig. 12.6 and the similar figure here.

Gas Solubility

12.9 In each case, solubility $= S = P \times k_H$.

(a) $S = (50 \text{ kPa O}_2) \times \left(\dfrac{1 \text{ atm}}{101 \text{ kPa}}\right) \times \left(\dfrac{1.3 \times 10^{-3} \text{ mol}}{(\text{L} \cdot \text{atm})}\right) = 6.4 \times 10^{-4} \text{ mol} \cdot \text{L}^{-1}$

(b) $S = (500 \text{ Torr CO}_2) \times \left(\dfrac{1 \text{ atm}}{760 \text{ Torr}}\right) \times \left(\dfrac{2.3 \times 10^{-2} \text{ mol}}{(\text{L} \cdot \text{atm})}\right)$

$\quad = 1.5 \times 10^{-2} \text{ mol} \cdot \text{L}^{-1}$

(c) $S = (0.10 \text{ atm CO}_2) \times \left(\dfrac{2.3 \times 10^{-2} \text{ mol}}{(\text{L} \cdot \text{atm})}\right) = 2.3 \times 10^{-3} \text{ mol} \cdot \text{L}^{-1}$

12.11 amount (moles) of CO_2 released $= 0.355 \text{ L} \times 2.3 \times 10^{-2} \text{ mol} \cdot \text{L}^{-1} \cdot \text{atm}^{-1}$

$\qquad\qquad\qquad\qquad\qquad\qquad\qquad\quad \times 3.00 \text{ atm} = 2.4\overline{4} \times 10^{-2} \text{ mol}$

$V = \dfrac{nRT}{P} = \dfrac{2.4\overline{4} \times 10^{-2} \text{ mol} \times 0.082\,06 \text{ L} \cdot \text{atm} \cdot \text{K}^{-1} \cdot \text{mol}^{-1} \times 293 \text{ K}}{1.00 \text{ atm}} = 0.59 \text{ L}$

12.13 We represent the equilibrium as; $CO_2(aq) \rightleftharpoons CO_2(g)$.

(a) If the partial pressure of CO_2 in the air above the solution is doubled; the equilibrium (above) will shift to the left, and the concentration of CO_2 in solution will double.

(b) If the total pressure of the gas is increased by the addition of nitrogen, no change in the equilibrium (above) will occur; the partial pressure of CO_2 is unchanged, and the concentration is unchanged.

12.15 (a) mass of 1 L of solution $= 1 \text{ L} \times \left(\dfrac{1 \text{ mL}}{10^{-3} \text{ L}}\right) \times \left(\dfrac{1.00 \text{ g}}{\text{mL}}\right)$

$\qquad\qquad\qquad\qquad\qquad = 1.00 \times 10^3 \text{g} = 1.00 \text{ kg}$

concentration (ppm) $= \left(\dfrac{4 \text{ mg}}{1 \text{ L}}\right) \times \left(\dfrac{1 \text{ L}}{1.00 \text{ kg}}\right) = 4 \text{ mg} \cdot \text{kg}^{-1} = 4 \text{ ppm}$

(b) concentration (mol $\cdot$ L^{-1}) $= \left(\dfrac{4 \text{ mg}}{1 \text{ kg}}\right) \times \left(\dfrac{1.00 \text{ kg}}{1 \text{ L}}\right)$

$\qquad\qquad\qquad\qquad \times \left(\dfrac{10^{-3} \text{ g}}{1 \text{ mg}}\right) \times \dfrac{1 \text{ mol O}_2}{32.00 \text{ g O}_2} = 1.2\overline{5} \times 10^{-4} \text{ mol} \cdot \text{L}^{-1}$

$P_{O_2} = \dfrac{S}{k_H} = \dfrac{1.2\overline{5} \times 10^{-4} \text{ mol} \cdot \text{L}^{-1}}{1.3 \times 10^{-3} \text{ mol} \cdot \text{L}^{-1} \cdot \text{atm}^{-1}} = 0.1 \text{ atm}$

(c) $P_{air} = P_{O_2} \times \left(\dfrac{1 \text{ atm air}}{0.21 \text{ atm O}_2} \right) = 0.1 \text{ atm} \times \left(\dfrac{1 \text{ atm air}}{0.21 \text{ atm O}_2} \right) = 0.5 \text{ atm air}$

Enthalpy of Solution

12.17 Ion hydration enthalpies for ions of the same charge within a group of elements become progressively less negative (or more positive) as we proceed down a group. This trend parallels increasing ion size. Because hydration energy is an ion-dipole interaction, it should be highest for small, high charge density ions.

12.19 (a) Negative; exothermic means enthalpy is released, which by convention is negative

(b) $Li_2SO_4(s) \rightleftharpoons 2Li^+(aq) + SO_4^{2-}(aq) + heat$

(c) Exothermic values of solution enthalpy generally result from systems with low lattice enthalpy and high enthalpy of hydration.

12.21 Table 12.3 applies to very dilute solutions. We assume here that 10.0 g of compound in 100.0 g of water is sufficiently dilute.

(a) $NaCl \longrightarrow Na^+(aq) + Cl^-(aq) \qquad \Delta H_{sol} = +3.9 \text{ kJ} \cdot \text{mol}^{-1}$

$\Delta H = (10.0 \text{ g NaCl}) \times \left(\dfrac{3.9 \text{ kJ}}{1 \text{ mol NaCl}} \right) \times \left(\dfrac{1 \text{ mol NaCl}}{58.5 \text{ g NaCl}} \right) \times \left(\dfrac{10^3 \text{ J}}{1 \text{ kJ}} \right)$

$= 6.7 \times 10^2 \text{ J} = +6.7 \times 10^2 \text{ J for NaCl} = -6.7 \times 10^2 \text{ J for water}$

(b) $NaBr \longrightarrow Na^+(aq) + Br^-(aq) \qquad \Delta H_{sol} = -0.6 \text{ kJ} \cdot \text{mol}^{-1}$

$\Delta H = (10.0 \text{ g NaBr}) \times \left(\dfrac{-0.6 \text{ kJ}}{1 \text{ mol NaBr}} \right) \times \left(\dfrac{1 \text{ mol NaBr}}{103 \text{ g NaBr}} \right) \times \left(\dfrac{10^3 \text{ J}}{1 \text{ kJ}} \right)$

$= -60 \text{ J (1 sf) for NaBr} = +60 \text{ J (1 sf) for water}$

(c) $AlCl_3 \longrightarrow Al^{3+}(aq) + 3Cl^-(aq) \qquad \Delta H_{sol} = -329 \text{ kJ} \cdot \text{mol}^{-1}$

$\Delta H = (10.0 \text{ g AlCl}_3) \times \left(\dfrac{-329 \text{ kJ}}{1 \text{ mol AlCl}_3} \right) \times \left(\dfrac{1 \text{ mol AlCl}_3}{133.5 \text{ g AlCl}_3} \right) \times \left(\dfrac{10^3 \text{ J}}{1 \text{ kJ}} \right)$

$= -2.46 \times 10^4 \text{ J} = -2.46 \times 10^4 \text{ J for AlCl}_3 = +2.46 \times 10^4 \text{ J for water}$

(d) $NH_4NO_3 \longrightarrow NH_4^+(aq) + NO_3^-(aq) \qquad \Delta H_{sol} = 25.7 \text{ kJ} \cdot \text{mol}^{-1}$

$\Delta H = (10.0 \text{ g NH}_4\text{NO}_3) \times \left(\dfrac{25.7 \text{ kJ}}{1 \text{ mol NH}_4\text{NO}_3} \right) \times \left(\dfrac{1 \text{ mol NH}_4\text{NO}_3}{80.1 \text{ g NH}_4\text{NO}_3} \right) \times \left(\dfrac{10^3 \text{ J}}{1 \text{ kJ}} \right)$

$= 3.21 \times 10^3 \text{ J} = +3.21 \times 10^3 \text{ J for NH}_4\text{NO}_3 = -3.21 \times 10^3 \text{ J for water}$

12.23 The enthalpy of solution of $SrCl_2$ is the sum of the lattice enthalpy and the enthalpy of hydration.

$$SrCl_2(s) \longrightarrow Sr^+(g) + 2Cl^-(g) \qquad \Delta H_L = +2153 \text{ kJ}$$
$$Sr^+(g) + 2Cl^-(g) \longrightarrow Sr^+(aq) + 2Cl^-(aq) \qquad \Delta H_{hyd} = -2204 \text{ kJ}$$
$$SrCl_2(s) \longrightarrow Sr^+(aq) + 2Cl^-(aq) \qquad \Delta H_{sol} = -51 \text{ kJ}$$

12.25

Metal (M) chloride	ΔH_{sol} (kJ·mol^{-1})	Solubility	Radius of M^+
LiCl	-37.0	most soluble	smallest
NaCl	$+3.9$	soluble	
AgCl	$+65.5$	insoluble	largest

The enthalpies of solution of the alkali metal chlorides become more positive as the cation becomes larger and less strongly hydrated by water. All the alkali metal chlorides are soluble in water, but AgCl is not. AgCl has a very positive enthalpy of solution. When dissolving is highly endothermic, the small increase in disorder due to solution formation may not be enough to compensate for the decrease in disorder of the surroundings and a solution does not form. Thus, we might expect solubility to decrease with large positive increases in enthalpy of solution. This is the case for AgCl.

12.27 (a) The disorder in the system increases. This is true of any solution process, be it exothermic or endothermic. In dissolving exothermically, the energy (enthalpy) of the system decreases.

(b) The disorder in the surroundings increases as energy is dispersed into it from the system. Thus, both the energy and disorder increase when a solute dissolves exothermically.

Measures of Concentration

12.29
$$\text{molarity} = \frac{\text{number of moles of solute}}{\text{volume of solution in liters}}$$

(a) $\text{molarity} = \left(\dfrac{50.0 \text{ g KNO}_3}{1.50 \text{ L soln}}\right) \times \left(\dfrac{1 \text{ mol KNO}_3}{101.1 \text{ g KNO}_3}\right) = 0.330 \text{ mol·L}^{-1}$

(b) $\text{molarity} = \left(\dfrac{10.0 \text{ g glucose}}{250 \text{ mL soln}}\right) \times \left(\dfrac{1 \text{ mL}}{10^{-3} \text{ L}}\right) \times \left(\dfrac{1 \text{ mol glucose}}{180 \text{ g glucose}}\right)$
$$= 0.222 \text{ mol·L}^{-1}$$

12.31 (a) $\text{mass (g)} = (1.0 \text{ L}) \times \left(\dfrac{0.10 \text{ mol NaCl}}{1 \text{ L}}\right) \times \left(\dfrac{58.4 \text{ g NaCl}}{1 \text{ mol NaCl}}\right) = 5.8 \text{ g NaCl}$

(b) $\text{mass (g)} = (250 \text{ mL}) \times \left(\dfrac{10^{-3} \text{ L}}{1 \text{ mL}}\right) \times \left(\dfrac{0.10 \text{ mol CaCl}_2}{1 \text{ L}}\right) \times \left(\dfrac{111 \text{ g CaCl}_2}{1 \text{ mol CaCl}_2}\right)$
$$= 2.8 \text{ g CaCl}_2$$

(c) mass (g) = $(500 \text{ mL}) \times \left(\dfrac{10^{-3} \text{ L}}{1 \text{ mL}}\right) \times \left(\dfrac{0.63 \text{ mol } C_6H_{12}O_6}{1 \text{ L}}\right)$

$\qquad\qquad\qquad \times \left(\dfrac{180 \text{ g } C_6H_{12}O_6}{1 \text{ mol } C_6H_{12}O_6}\right) = 57 \text{ g } C_6H_{12}O_6$

12.33 general formula: mass % of A $= \dfrac{\text{mass of A in solution}}{\text{total mass of solution}} \times 100\%$

(a) mass % NaCl $= \dfrac{4.0 \text{ g NaCl}}{100 \text{ g solution}} \times 100\% = 4.0\% \text{ NaCl}$

(b) mass % NaCl $= \dfrac{4.0 \text{ g NaCl}}{4.0 \text{ g NaCl} + 100 \text{ g } H_2O} \times 100\% = 3.8\% \text{ NaCl}$

(c) mass % $C_{12}H_{22}O_{11} = \dfrac{1.66 \text{ g } C_{12}H_{22}O_{11}}{1.66 \text{ g } C_{12}H_{22}O_{11} + 200 \text{ g } H_2O} \times 100\%$

$\qquad\qquad\qquad\qquad = 0.823\% \text{ } C_{12}H_{22}O_{11}$

12.35 general formula: $x_{\text{solute}} = \dfrac{n_{\text{solute}}}{n_{\text{solvent}} + n_{\text{solute}}}$

(a) $n_{H_2O} = (25.0 \text{ g } H_2O) \times \left(\dfrac{1 \text{ mol } H_2O}{18.0 \text{ g } H_2O}\right) = 1.39 \text{ mol } H_2O$ (solute)

$n_{C_2H_5OH} = (50.0 \text{ g } C_2H_5OH) \times \left(\dfrac{1 \text{ mol } C_2H_5OH}{46.0 \text{ g } C_2H_5OH}\right)$

$\qquad\qquad = 1.09 \text{ mol } C_2H_5OH$ (solvent)

Then, $x_{H_2O} = \dfrac{1.39 \text{ mol } H_2O}{1.39 \text{ mol } H_2O + 1.09 \text{ mol } C_2H_5OH} = 0.560$

Therefore, $x_{C_2H_5OH} = 0.440$

(b) $n_{H_2O} = (25.0 \text{ g } H_2O) \times \left(\dfrac{1 \text{ mol } H_2O}{18.0 \text{ g } H_2O}\right) = 1.39 \text{ mol } H_2O$

$n_{CH_3OH} = (50.0 \text{ g } CH_3OH) \times \left(\dfrac{1 \text{ mol } CH_3OH}{32 \text{ g } CH_3OH}\right) = 1.56 \text{ mol } CH_3OH$

Then, $x_{H_2O} = \dfrac{1.39 \text{ mol } H_2O}{1.39 \text{ mol } H_2O + 1.56 \text{ mol } CH_3OH} = 0.470$

Therefore, $x_{CH_3OH} = 0.530$

(c) 0.10 m $C_6H_{12}O_6(aq) = 0.10 \text{ mol } C_6H_{12}O_6$ per 1 kg solvent (H_2O)

$n_{H_2O} = (1 \text{ kg } H_2O) \times \left(\dfrac{10^3 \text{ g}}{1 \text{ kg}}\right) \times \left(\dfrac{1 \text{ mol } H_2O}{18.0 \text{ g } H_2O}\right) = 55.6 \text{ mol } H_2O$

Then, $x_{C_6H_{12}O_6} = \dfrac{0.10 \text{ mol } C_6H_{12}O_6}{0.10 \text{ mol } C_6H_{12}O_6 + 55.6 \text{ mol } H_2O} = 1.8 \times 10^{-3}$

Therefore, $x_{H_2O} = 1.000 - 1.8 \times 10^{-3} = 0.998 \approx 1.0$ (2 sf)

12.37   general formula: molality $= \dfrac{\text{number of moles of solute}}{\text{mass of solvent (kg)}} = \dfrac{n_{solute}}{mass_{solvent}}$

This formula can be used to solve for n_{solute}.

(a) $n_{NaCl} = (10.0 \text{ g NaCl}) \times \left(\dfrac{1 \text{ mol NaCl}}{58.5 \text{ g NaCl}} \right) = 1.71 \times 10^{-1} \text{ mol NaCl}$

molality $= \dfrac{1.71 \times 10^{-1} \text{ mol NaCl}}{(250 \text{ g}) \times \left(\dfrac{1 \text{ kg}}{10^3 \text{ g}} \right) \text{ H}_2\text{O}} = 6.84 \times 10^{-1} \text{ } m$

(b)   molality $= \dfrac{0.48 \text{ mol KOH}}{(50.0 \text{ g H}_2\text{O}) \times \left(\dfrac{1 \text{ kg}}{10^3 \text{ g}} \right)} = 9.6 \text{ } m$

(c) $n_{urea} = (1.94 \text{ g CO(NH}_2)_2) \times \left(\dfrac{1 \text{ mol CO(NH}_2)_2}{60.0 \text{ g} \cdot \text{mol}^{-1} \text{ CO(NH}_2)_2} \right)$

$= 3.23 \times 10^{-2} \text{ mol CO(NH}_2)_2$

molality $= \dfrac{3.23 \times 10^{-2} \text{ mol CO(NH}_2)_2}{(200 \text{ g H}_2\text{O}) \times \left(\dfrac{1 \text{ kg}}{10^3 \text{ g}} \right)} = 0.162 \text{ } m$

12.39   general formula: molality $= \dfrac{\text{number of moles of solute}}{\text{mass of solvent (kg)}} = \dfrac{n_{solute}}{mass_{solvent} \text{ (kg)}}$

n_{solute} can be solved from this formula.

(a) $0.200 \text{ } m \text{ solute} = \dfrac{n_{ZnCl_2}}{(150 \text{ g}) \times \left(\dfrac{1 \text{ kg}}{10^3 \text{ g}} \right)}$

$n_{ZnCl_2} = 0.030$ and $(0.030 \text{ mol ZnCl}_2) \times \left(\dfrac{137 \text{ g ZnCl}_2}{1 \text{ mol ZnCl}_2} \right) = 4.11 \text{ g ZnCl}_2$

(b) $3.0 \text{ mass } \% = \dfrac{\text{mass KClO}_3}{\text{mass KClO}_3 + 20.0 \text{ g H}_2\text{O}}$

$\times 100 \%$ mass $KClO_3 = 0.62$ g (2 sf)

(c) $3.0 \text{ } m \text{ solute} = \dfrac{n_{KClO_3}}{(20.0 \text{ g H}_2\text{O}) \times \left(\dfrac{1 \text{ kg}}{10^3 \text{ g}} \right)}$

$n_{KClO_3} = 0.060$ and $(0.060 \text{ mol KClO}_3) \times \left(\dfrac{122.6 \text{ g KClO}_3}{1 \text{ mol KClO}_3} \right) = 7.36 \text{ g KClO}_3$

12.41   (a) $x_{solute} = \dfrac{n_{solute}}{n_{solvent} + n_{solute}}$

$n_{C_2H_5OH} = (25.0 \text{ g C}_2\text{H}_5\text{OH}) \times \left(\dfrac{1 \text{ mol C}_2\text{H}_5\text{OH}}{46.0 \text{ g C}_2\text{H}_5\text{OH}} \right) = 0.543 \text{ mol C}_2\text{H}_5\text{OH}$

$$n_{H_2O} = (150 \text{ g } H_2O) \times \left(\frac{1 \text{ mol } H_2O}{18.0 \text{ g } H_2O}\right) = 8.33 \text{ mol } H_2O$$

$$x_{C_2H_5OH} = \frac{0.543 \text{ mol } C_2H_5OH}{0.543 \text{ mol } C_2H_5OH + 8.33 \text{ mol } H_2O} = 0.0612$$

$$x_{H_2O} = 1.000 - 0.0612 = 0.939$$

(b) molality $= \dfrac{n_{solute}}{\text{mass solvent (kg)}}$

molality of ethanol $= \left(\dfrac{0.543 \text{ mol } C_2H_5OH}{150 \text{ g } H_2O}\right) \times \left(\dfrac{10^3 \text{ g } H_2O}{1 \text{ kg } H_2O}\right)$

$$= 3.62 \; m \; C_2H_5OH$$

12.43 general formula: $x_A = \dfrac{n_A}{n_A + n_B + n_C + \; \dots}$

(a) $0.10 \; m \; NaCl(aq) \equiv 0.10 \text{ mol } Na^+ + 0.10 \text{ mol } Cl^-$
$$+ \; 10^3 \text{ g } H_2O \text{ (or 55.6 mol } H_2O)$$

$$x_{Na^+} = x_{Cl^-} = \frac{0.10 \text{ mol}}{0.10 \text{ mol } Na^+ + 0.10 \text{ mol } Cl^- + 55.6 \text{ mol } H_2O} = 1.8 \times 10^{-3}$$

$$x_{H_2O} = \frac{55.6 \text{ mol}}{0.10 \text{ mol } Na^+ + 0.10 \text{ mol } Cl^- + 55.6 \text{ mol } H_2O} = 0.996 \text{ or } \sim 1.0 \text{ (2 sf)}$$

(b) $0.20 \text{ m } Na_2CO_3 \equiv 0.40 \text{ mol } Na^+ + 0.20 \text{ mol } CO_3^{2-}$
$$+ \; 10^3 \text{ g } H_2O \text{ (or 55.6 mol)}$$

$$x_{Na^+} = \frac{0.40 \text{ mol } Na^+}{0.40 \text{ mol } Na^+ + 0.20 \text{ mol } CO_3^{2-} + 55.6 \text{ mol } H_2O} = 7.1 \times 10^{-3}$$

$$x_{CO_3^{2-}} = \frac{7.1 \times 10^{-3}}{2} = 3.6 \times 10^{-3}$$

$$x_{H_2O} = \frac{55.6 \text{ mol } H_2O}{0.40 \text{ mol } Na^+ + 0.20 \text{ mol } CO_3^{2-} + 55.6 \text{ mol } H_2O} = 0.99$$

(c) Assume 100 g of solution. Then 10.0 mass % $KNO_3(aq)$
$$= 10.0 \text{ g } KNO_3 + 90.0 \text{ g } H_2O$$

$$n_{KNO_3} = n_{K^+} = n_{NO_3^-} = (10.0 \text{ g } KNO_3) \times \left(\frac{1 \text{ mol } KNO_3}{101 \text{ g } KNO_3}\right) = 0.099 \text{ mol}$$

$$n_{H_2O} = (90.0 \text{ g } H_2O) \times \left(\frac{1 \text{ mol } H_2O}{18.0 \text{ g } H_2O}\right) = 5.00 \text{ mol } H_2O$$

$$x_{K^+} = x_{NO_3^-} = \frac{0.099 \text{ mol}}{0.099 \text{ mol } K^+ + 0.099 \text{ mol } NO_3^- + 5.00 \text{ mol } H_2O} = 1.9 \times 10^{-2}$$

$$x_{H_2O} = \frac{5.00 \text{ mol } H_2O}{0.099 \text{ mol } K^+ + 0.099 \text{ mol } NO_3^- + 5.00 \text{ mol } H_2O} = 0.96 \text{ (2 sf)}$$

12.45 (a) Assume 1 L of solution. The mass of the solute, $(NH_4)_2SO_4$, is then

$$\text{mass of solute} = (0.35 \text{ mol } (NH_4)_2SO_4) \times \left(\frac{132 \text{ g } (NH_4)_2SO_4}{1 \text{ mol } (NH_4)_2SO_4}\right) \times \left(\frac{1 \text{ kg}}{10^3 \text{ g}}\right)$$

$$= 0.046\overline{2} \text{ kg } (NH_4)_2SO_4$$

$$\text{mass of solution} = (1 \text{ L}) \times \left(\frac{1 \text{ mL}}{10^{-3} \text{ L}}\right) \times \left(\frac{1.027 \text{ g}}{1.0 \text{ mL}}\right) \times \left(\frac{1 \text{ kg}}{10^3 \text{ g}}\right)$$

$$= 1.027 \text{ kg solution}$$

$$\text{mass of solvent} = 1.027 \text{ kg soln} - 0.046\overline{2} \text{ kg solute} = 0.981 \text{ kg solvent}$$

$$\text{molality} = \frac{n_{solute}}{\text{mass of solvent (kg)}} = \frac{0.35 \text{ mol } (NH_4)_2SO_4}{0.981 \text{ kg solvent}} = 0.36 \text{ mol} \cdot \text{kg}^{-1}$$

(b) The number of moles of solvent (water) is

$$0.981 \text{ kg} \times \left(\frac{10^3 \text{ g}}{1 \text{ kg}}\right) \times \left(\frac{1 \text{ mol } H_2O}{18.02 \text{ g } H_2O}\right) = 54.4 \text{ mol } H_2O$$

$$x_{(NH_4)_2SO_4} = \frac{0.35 \text{ mol}}{0.35 \text{ mol} + 54.4 \text{ mol}} = 0.0064$$

Vapor-Pressure Lowering

12.47 Let $P^* = P_{pure}$, sucrose = solute, H_2O = solvent

(a) $x_{solute} = 0.10,$ $\quad x_{solvent} = 0.90$

$P = (x_{solvent})(P^*)$

$P^*_{H_2O} = 760 \text{ Torr at } 100°C$

$P = (0.90) \times (760 \text{ Torr}) = 684 \text{ Torr}$

(b) $\text{molality} = \dfrac{n_{sucrose}}{\text{mass } H_2O \text{ (kg)}} = 0.10 \, m = \dfrac{0.10 \text{ mol sucrose}}{1 \text{ kg } H_2O}$

$$n_{H_2O} = (1 \text{ kg } H_2O) \times \left(\frac{10^3 \text{ g}}{1 \text{ kg}}\right) \times \left(\frac{1 \text{ mol } H_2O}{18 \text{ g } H_2O}\right) = 55.6 \text{ mol } H_2O$$

$$x_{solute} = \frac{0.10 \text{ mol sucrose}}{0.10 \text{ mol sucrose} + 55.6 \text{ mol } H_2O} = 1.8 \times 10^{-3}$$

Therefore, $x_{solvent} = 1 - 1.8 \times 10^{-3} = 0.998$

$P = (x_{solvent})(P^*)$

$P^*_{H_2O} = 760 \text{ Torr at } 100°C$

$P = (0.998) \times (760 \text{ Torr}) = 759 \text{ Torr}$

12.49 Each calculation requires the determination of the mole fraction of the solvent, $x_{solvent}$, to be used in Raoult's law:

$$P = x_{\text{solvent}} \times P_{\text{pure}} \quad (\text{let } P_{\text{pure}} = P^* \text{ below}) \quad \text{and} \quad x_{\text{solvent}} = \frac{n_{\text{solvent}}}{n_{\text{solute}} + n_{\text{solvent}}}$$

(a) 1.0% ethylene glycol, $C_2H_4(OH)_2$, in water is 1.0 g ethylene glycol and 99 g H_2O, in 100 g of solution

$x_{\text{solvent}} =$

$$\frac{(99 \text{ g } H_2O) \times \left(\dfrac{1 \text{ mol } H_2O}{18.0 \text{ g } H_2O}\right)}{(1.0 \text{ g } C_2H_4(OH)_2) \times \left(\dfrac{1 \text{ mol } C_2H_4(OH)_2}{62.0 \text{ g } C_2H_4(OH)_2}\right) + (99 \text{ g } H_2O) \times \left(\dfrac{1 \text{ mol } H_2O}{18.0 \text{ g } H_2O}\right)}$$

$$= 0.99\overline{6}$$

$P = (x_{\text{solvent}}) \times (P^*)$

$P^*_{H_2O} = 4.48$ Torr at 0°C

$P = (0.99\overline{6}) \times (4.48 \text{ Torr}) = 4.4\overline{6}$ Torr ≈ 4.5 Torr

(b) 0.10 m NaOH = 0.10 mol NaOH in 1 kg H_2O; 2 mol particles per 1 mol NaOH ($i = 2$); 1000 g H_2O = 55.6 mol H_2O

$$x_{\text{solvent}} = \frac{55.6 \text{ mol } H_2O}{(0.10 \text{ mol NaOH}) \times (2) + 55.6 \text{ mol } H_2O} = 0.99\overline{6}$$

$P = (x_{\text{solvent}}) \times (P^*)$

$P^*_{H_2O} = 355$ Torr at 80°C

$P = (0.99\overline{6}) \times (355 \text{ Torr}) = 3.5 \times 10^2$ Torr

(c) x_{solvent}

$$= \frac{(100 \text{ g } H_2O) \times \left(\dfrac{1 \text{ mol } H_2O}{18.0 \text{ g } H_2O}\right)}{(6.6 \text{ g CO(NH}_2)_2) \times \left(\dfrac{1 \text{ mol CO(NH}_2)_2}{60.0 \text{ g CO(NH}_2)_2}\right) + 100 \text{ g } H_2O \times \left(\dfrac{1 \text{ mol } H_2O}{18.0 \text{ g } H_2O}\right)}$$

$$= 0.98$$

$P = (x_{\text{solvent}}) \times (P^*)$

$P^*_{H_2O} = 9.21$ Torr at 10°C

$P = (0.98) \times (9.21 \text{ Torr}) = 9.03$ Torr

Therefore, $\Delta P = 9.21$ Torr $- 9.03$ Torr $= 0.18$ Torr

12.51 Let $P^* = P_{\text{pure solvent}}$, $x =$ unknown molar mass of X (do not confuse with mole fraction)

(a) $P = (x_{\text{solvent}}) \times (P^*)$

$P = 94.8$ Torr $\quad P^* = 100.0$ Torr

$$x_{\text{solvent}} = \frac{P}{P^*} = \frac{94.8}{100.0} = 0.948 \quad \text{Therefore, } x_X = 1 - 0.948 = 0.052$$

(b) $x_{solvent} = \dfrac{\text{no. of mol solvent}}{\text{no. of mol benzene + no. of mol X}}$

$$= \dfrac{(100\ g) \times \left(\dfrac{1\ \text{mol benzene}}{78.0\ \text{g benzene}}\right)}{(100\ g) \times \left(\dfrac{1\ \text{mol benzene}}{78.0\ \text{g benzene}}\right) + (8.05\ g) \times \left(\dfrac{1\ \text{mol X}}{x\ \text{grams}}\right)}$$

$$0.948 = \dfrac{1.28\ \text{mol}}{1.28\ \text{mol} + \left(\dfrac{8.05}{x}\right)\ \text{mol}}$$

Solve for x (take reciprocals of both sides).
After taking reciprocals,

$$1.05\overline{5} = 1 + \dfrac{8.05\ g}{1.28\ x\ g}$$

$$0.055 = \dfrac{8.05\ g}{1.28\ x\ g}$$

$$x = 11\overline{4}\ g$$

molar mass of X $= \dfrac{x\ g}{\text{mol}} = 11\overline{4}\ g \cdot mol^{-1} = 1.1 \times 10^2\ g \cdot mol^{-1}$

Boiling-Point Elevation

12.53 ΔT = boiling-point elevation, m = molality
(a) $\Delta T = k_b m = 0.51\ K \cdot kg \cdot mol^{-1} \times 0.10\ mol \cdot kg^{-1} = 0.051\ K = 0.051°C$
new bp $= 100°C + 0.051°C = 100.051°C$
(b) $\Delta T = ik_b m$, $i = 2$
$\Delta T = 2 \times 0.51\ K \cdot kg \cdot mol^{-1} \times 0.22\ mol \cdot kg^{-1} = 0.22\ K = 0.22°C$
new bp $= 100°C + 0.22°C = 100.22°C$
(c) Solubility $= \dfrac{230\ mg}{100\ g} = \dfrac{2.30\ g}{1\ kg}$

molality $= \left(\dfrac{2.30\ g}{1\ kg}\right) \times \left(\dfrac{1\ \text{mol LiF}}{25.9\text{g LiF}}\right) = 0.0888\ mol \cdot kg^{-1}$
$\Delta T = ik_b m$, $i = 2$
$\Delta T = 2 \times 0.51\ K \cdot kg \cdot mol^{-1} \times 0.0888\ mol \cdot kg^{-1} = 0.091\ K = 0.091°C$
new bp $= 100°C + 0.091°C = 100.091°C$

12.55 $P^* = P_{\text{pure solvent}}$, m = molality, ΔT = boiling point elevation
(a) $\dfrac{P}{P^*} = x_{solvent} = x_{H_2O} = \dfrac{751\ \text{Torr}}{760\ \text{Torr}} = 0.988$ Therefore, $x_{solute} = 0.012$.

Hence, the solution contains 0.012 mol solute per 0.988 mol water. Then,

$$\text{mass } H_2O = 0.988 \text{ mol } H_2O \times \left(\frac{18.0 \text{ g } H_2O}{1 \text{ mol } H_2O}\right) = 17.8 \text{ g } H_2O$$

$$= 17.8 \times 10^{-3} \text{ kg } H_2O$$

$$m = \frac{0.012 \text{ mol solute}}{17.8 \times 10^{-3} \text{ kg } H_2O} = 0.67\overline{4} \text{ mol} \cdot \text{kg}^{-1}$$

$$\Delta T = k_b m = 0.51 \text{ K} \cdot \text{kg} \cdot \text{mol}^{-1} \times 0.67\overline{4} \text{ mol} \cdot \text{kg}^{-1} = 0.34 \text{ K} = 0.34°C$$

$$\text{bp} = 100°C + 0.34°C = 100.34°C$$

(b) $\dfrac{P}{P*} = x_{\text{solvent}} = x_{\text{benzene}} = \dfrac{740 \text{ Torr}}{760 \text{ Torr}} = 0.974$ Therefore, $x_{\text{solute}} = 0.026$.

Hence, solution contains 0.026 mol solute per 0.974 mol benzene. Then,

$$\text{mass benzene} = (0.974 \text{ mol solvent}) \times \left(\frac{78.0 \text{ g } C_6H_6}{1 \text{ mol } C_6H_6}\right)$$

$$= 76 \text{ g } C_6H_6 = 7.6 \times 10^{-2} \text{ kg } C_6H_6$$

$$m = \frac{0.026 \text{ mol solute}}{7.6 \times 10^{-2} \text{ kg benzene}} = 0.34\overline{2} \text{ mol} \cdot \text{kg}^{-1}$$

$$\Delta T = k_b m = 2.53 \text{ K} \cdot \text{kg} \cdot \text{mol}^{-1} \times 0.34\overline{2} \text{ mol} \cdot \text{kg}^{-1} = 0.86 \text{ K} = 0.86°C$$

$$\text{bp} = 80.1°C + 0.86°C = 81.0°C$$

12.57 ΔT_b = boiling-point elevation = $k_b m$, k_b (CCl$_4$) = 4.95 K · kg · mol^{-1}

$$m = \frac{\Delta T_b}{k_b} = \frac{(76.85 - 76.54) \text{ K}}{4.95 \text{ K} \cdot \text{kg} \cdot \text{mol}^{-1}} = 0.062\overline{4} \text{ mol} \cdot \text{kg}^{-1}$$

Let X = solute and n_X = number of moles of X in 100 g CCl$_4$ (0.100 kg CCl$_4$).

$$n_X = 0.100 \text{ kg } CCl_4 \times \left(\frac{0.0624 \text{ mol}}{1 \text{ kg } CCl_4}\right) = 6.2\overline{4} \times 10^{-3} \text{ mol X}$$

$$\text{molar mass of X} = \frac{1.05 \text{ g X}}{6.2\overline{4} \times 10^{-3} \text{ mol X}} = 16\overline{8} \text{ g} \cdot \text{mol}^{-1} \text{ or } 1.7 \times 10^{+2} \text{ g} \cdot \text{mol}^{-1}$$

12.59 (a) ΔT = freezing-point depression

$\Delta T = k_f m = 1.86 \text{ K} \cdot \text{kg} \cdot \text{mol}^{-1} \times 0.10 \text{ mol} \cdot \text{kg}^{-1} = 0.18\overline{6} \text{ K} = 0.19°C$

new fp = $0°C - 0.19°C = -0.19°C$

(b) $\Delta T = ik_f m$, $i = 2$

$\Delta T = 2 \times 1.86 \text{ K} \cdot \text{kg} \cdot \text{mol}^{-1} \times 0.22 \text{ mol} \cdot \text{kg}^{-1} = 0.82 \text{ K} = 0.82°C$

new fp = $0°C - 0.82°C = -0.82°C$

(c) 120 mg LiF per 100 g H$_2$O 1.20 g LiF per 1 kg H$_2$O

$$m = (1.20 \text{ g LiF}) \times \left(\frac{1 \text{ mol LiF}}{26.0 \text{ g LiF}}\right) = 0.0462 \text{ mol LiF in 1 kg } H_2O$$

$$= 0.0462 \text{ mol} \cdot \text{kg}^{-1}$$

$\Delta T = ik_f m = 2 \times 1.86 \ \text{K} \cdot \text{kg} \cdot \text{mol}^{-1} \times 0.0462 \ \text{mol} \cdot \text{kg}^{-1} = 0.172 \ \text{K} = 0.172°\text{C}$

new fp $= 0°\text{C} - 0.172°\text{C} = -0.172°\text{C}$

12.61 Let X = molecular substance

$$\left(\frac{1.14 \ \text{g X}}{100.0 \ \text{g camphor}}\right) \times \left(\frac{10^3 \ \text{g camphor}}{1 \ \text{kg camphor}}\right) = \frac{11.4 \ \text{g X}}{1 \ \text{kg camphor}}$$

$\Delta T = k_f m = 179.8°\text{C} - 177.3°\text{C} = 2.5°\text{C} = 2.5 \ \text{K}$

$$2.5 \ \text{K} = 39.7 \ \text{K} \cdot \text{kg} \cdot \text{mol}^{-1} \times \frac{11.4 \ \text{g X}}{\left(\dfrac{\text{molar mass X}}{1 \ \text{kg camphor}}\right)}$$

After rearranging, $0.0625 \ \text{mol X} = \dfrac{11.4 \ \text{g X}}{\text{molar mass X}}$

molar mass X $= \dfrac{11.4 \ \text{g X}}{0.0625 \ \text{mol X}} = 182 \ \text{g} \cdot \text{mol}^{-1}$

12.63 (a) $\Delta T_f = k_f m \quad \Delta T_b = k_b m$

$$\frac{\Delta T_b}{k_b} = m = \frac{\Delta T_f}{k_f} \quad \text{and} \quad \frac{\Delta T_b}{k_b} = \frac{\Delta T_f}{k_f}$$

$$\Delta T_f = \frac{k_f \Delta T_b}{k_b} = \frac{(1.90) \times (5.12°\text{C})}{2.53} = 3.8°\text{C} \quad \text{[units of } k_f \text{ and } k_b \text{ cancel]}$$

Therefore, fp $= 5.5°\text{C} - 3.8°\text{C} = 1.7°\text{C}$

(b) $\Delta T_f = k_f m$. Assume that the solute does not dissociate. Then,

$$m = \frac{\Delta T_f}{k_f} = \frac{3.04 \ \text{K}}{1.86 \ \text{K} \cdot \text{kg} \cdot \text{mol}^{-1}} = 1.63 \ \text{mol} \cdot \text{kg}^{-1}$$

(c) $\Delta T_b = k_f m$

$$m = \frac{\Delta T_f}{k_f} = \frac{1.94 \ \text{K}}{1.86 \ \text{K} \cdot \text{kg} \cdot \text{mol}^{-1}} = 1.04 \ \text{mol} \cdot \text{kg}^{-1} = \frac{1.04 \ \text{mol}}{1 \ \text{kg H}_2\text{O}}$$

so, in 200 g H_2O, the number of moles of solute is

$$(200 \ \text{g H}_2\text{O}) \times \left(\frac{1.04 \ \text{mol}}{1 \ \text{kg H}_2\text{O}}\right) \times \left(\frac{1 \ \text{kg}}{10^3 \ \text{g}}\right) = 0.208 \ \text{mol of the electrolyte.}$$

12.65 Assume 100 g of solution.

1.00% NaCl $\equiv$ 1.00 g NaCl per 100 g solution; therefore,

mass H_2O = mass solution $-$ mass NaCl

$\qquad = 100 \ \text{g} - 1.00 \ \text{g} = 99.0 \ \text{g H}_2\text{O}$

molality $= m = \left(\dfrac{1.00 \ \text{g NaCl}}{99.0 \ \text{g H}_2\text{O}}\right) \times \left(\dfrac{1 \ \text{mol NaCl}}{58.5 \ \text{g NaCl}}\right) \times \left(\dfrac{10^3 \ \text{g}}{1 \ \text{kg}}\right) = 0.173 \ \text{mol} \cdot \text{kg}^{-1}$

(a) $\Delta T = ik_f m, \quad \Delta T = 0.593°\text{C} = 0.593 \ \text{K}$

$$i = \frac{\Delta T}{k_f m} = \frac{0.593 \text{ K}}{1.86 \text{ K} \cdot \text{kg} \cdot \text{mol}^{-1} \times 0.173 \text{ mol} \cdot \text{kg}^{-1}} = 1.84$$

(b) Actual ionic molality $= i \times m = 1.84 \times 0.173 \text{ mol} \cdot \text{kg}^{-1} = 0.318 \text{ mol} \cdot \text{kg}^{-1}$

(c) $i = 1.84$ corresponds to 84% dissociation. This can be seen by considering that 84% dissociation of one mole of NaCl leads to 0.84 mol of Na^+ ions and 0.84 mol of Cl^- ions, and 0.16 mol of undissociated NaCl ($0.84 + 0.84 + 0.16 = 1.84$).

12.67 $i = 1.075$ for 7.5% dissociation. This is seen by considering that 7.5% dissociation leads to 0.075 for fraction of positive ion, 0.075 for fraction of negative ion, and 0.925 for fraction of undissociated electrolyte ($0.075 + 0.075 + 0.925 = 1.075$)

$\Delta T = i k_f m = 1.075 \times 1.86 \text{ K} \cdot \text{kg} \cdot \text{mol}^{-1} \times 0.10 \text{ mol} \cdot \text{kg}^{-1} = 0.20 \text{ K} = 0.20°C$

Therefore, fp $= 0.00°C - 0.20°C = -0.20°C$

Osmosis and Osmometry

12.69 In each case $\Pi = i \times RT \times$ molarity. At 20°C, $T = 293$ K, $RT = 0.082\,06 \text{ L} \cdot \text{atm} \cdot \text{K}^{-1} \cdot \text{mol}^{-1} \times 293 \text{ K} = 24.05 \text{ L} \cdot \text{atm} \cdot \text{mol}^{-1}$

    (a) $\Pi = 1 \times 24.05 \text{ L} \cdot \text{atm} \cdot \text{mol}^{-1} \times 0.010 \text{ mol} \cdot \text{L}^{-1} = 0.24$ atm

    (b) $\Pi = 2 \times 24.05 \text{ L} \cdot \text{atm} \cdot \text{mol}^{-1} \times 1.0 \text{ mol} \cdot \text{L}^{-1} = 48$ atm

    (c) $\Pi = 3 \times 24.05 \text{ L} \cdot \text{atm} \cdot \text{mol}^{-1} \times 0.010 \text{ mol} \cdot \text{L}^{-1} = 0.72$ atm

12.71 $\Pi = i \times RT \times M, \quad M =$ molarity

$$M = \frac{\Pi}{iRT} = \frac{(3.74 \text{ Torr}) \times \left(\frac{1 \text{ atm}}{760 \text{ Torr}}\right)}{(1) \times \left(\frac{0.0821 \text{ L} \cdot \text{atm}}{\text{K} \cdot \text{mol}}\right) \times (273 + 27) \text{ K}} = 2.0 \times 10^{-4} \text{ mol} \cdot \text{L}^{-1}$$

and $\left(\frac{0.40 \text{ g polypeptide}}{1.0 \text{ L}}\right) \times \left(\frac{1 \text{ L}}{2.0 \times 10^{-4} \text{ mol}}\right) = 2.0 \times 10^3 \text{ g} \cdot \text{mol}^{-1}$

12.73 $\Pi = i \times RT \times M, \quad M =$ molarity

$$M = \frac{\Pi}{iRT} = \frac{(5.4 \text{ Torr}) \times \left(\frac{1 \text{ atm}}{760 \text{ Torr}}\right)}{(1) \times (0.0821 \text{ L} \cdot \text{atm K}^{-1} \cdot \text{mol}^{-1}) \times (273 + 20) \text{ K}} = 3.0 \times 10^{-4} \text{ mol} \cdot \text{L}^{-1}$$

Then, $(3.0 \times 10^{-4} \text{ mol} \cdot \text{L}^{-1}) \times \left(\frac{10^{-3} \text{ L}}{1 \text{ mL}}\right) \times (100 \text{ mL}) = 3.0 = 10^{-5} \text{ mol polymer}$

and molar mass $= \frac{0.10 \text{ g}}{3.0 \times 10^{-5} \text{ mol}} = 3.3 \times 10^3 \text{ g} \cdot \text{mol}^{-1}$

12.75 (a) $\Pi = iRTM = 1 \times 0.082\,06\ \text{L} \cdot \text{atm} \cdot \text{K}^{-1} \cdot \text{mol}^{-1} \times 293\ \text{K} \times 0.050\ \text{mol} \cdot \text{L}^{-1}$
$$= 1.2\ \text{atm}$$

(b) $\Pi = 2 \times 0.082\,06\ \text{L} \cdot \text{atm} \cdot \text{K}^{-1} \cdot \text{mol}^{-1} \times 293\ \text{K} \times 0.0010\ \text{mol} \cdot \text{L}^{-1}$
$$= 0.048\ \text{atm}$$

(c) $\text{molarity of solution} = \left(\dfrac{2.3 \times 10^{-5}\ \text{g}}{100\ \text{g H}_2\text{O}}\right) \times \left(\dfrac{1\ \text{mol AgCN}}{134\ \text{g AgCN}}\right) \times \left(\dfrac{0.998\ \text{g}}{1\ \text{mL}}\right)$

$$\times \left(\dfrac{1\ \text{mL}}{10^{-3}\ \text{L}}\right) = 1.7 \times 10^{-6}\ \text{mol} \cdot \text{L}^{-1}$$

$\Pi = i \times RT \times M = (2) \times (0.0821\ \text{L} \cdot \text{atm} \cdot \text{K}^{-1} \cdot \text{mol}^{-1}) \times (273 + 20)\ \text{K}$
$$\times\ (1.7 \times 10^{-6}\ \text{mol} \cdot \text{L}^{-1}) = 8.2 \times 10^{-5}\ \text{atm}$$

SUPPLEMENTARY EXERCISES

12.77 $CuSO_4\ (s) \rightleftharpoons CuSO_4\ (aq)$

The equilibrium between solid and aqueous $CuSO_4$ is a dynamic process. Cu^{2+} and SO_4^{2-} ions continually leave the solid and are replaced with ions returning to the solid from solution. Because the surface area of the smaller crystals is larger, per gram, than that of the bigger crystals (see below), the ions leaving the solid surface preferentially come from the former (smaller) crystals. However, those returning to the solid surface have a greater chance of landing on a large crystal (per crystal) than a small one. So the large crystals grow at the expense of the small crystals without a change in the concentration of the solution.

The ratio of surface area to mass of a crystal, for a cubic crystal, can be determined as follows:

$$\frac{\text{surface area}}{\text{mass}} = \frac{\text{surface area}}{\text{density} \times \text{volume}} = \frac{6a^2}{d \times a^3} \propto \frac{1}{a}$$

a is the length of a side of the cube; $6/d$ is a constant. Thus, smaller crystals (smaller a) have a greater surface area to mass ratio.

12.79 (a) $0.33\ m\ CO(NH_2)_2 \equiv 0.33\ \text{mol}\ CO(NH_2)_2 + 1\ \text{kg (or }10^3\ \text{g)}\ H_2O$

$(0.33\ \text{mol}\ CO(NH_2)_2) \times \left(\dfrac{60\ \text{g}\ CO(NH_2)_2}{1\ \text{mol}\ CO(NH_2)_2}\right) = 20\ \text{g}\ CO(NH_2)_2$

$\text{mass \%} = \dfrac{20\ \text{g}\ CO(NH_2)_2}{20\ \text{g}\ CO(NH_2)_2 + 10^3\ \text{g}\ H_2O} \times 100\% = 1.96\%\ \text{or } 2.0\%\ \text{(2 sf)}$

(b) $x_{C_2H_5OH} = 0.28 = \dfrac{n_{C_2H_5OH}}{n_{C_2H_5OH} + n_{H_2O}}$

If we assume 1 mol H_2O, then $0.28 = \dfrac{n_{C_2H_5OH}}{n_{C_2H_5OH} + 1 \text{ mol}}$

Solving for $n_{C_2H_5OH}$ yields $n_{C_2H_5OH} = 0.39$ mol

mass $C_2H_5OH = (0.39 \text{ mol } C_2H_5OH) \times \left(\dfrac{46 \text{ g } C_2H_5OH}{1 \text{ mol } C_2H_5OH}\right)$

$= 17.9 \text{ g } C_2H_5OH \text{ or } 18 \text{ g (2 sf)}$

mass % $= \dfrac{18 \text{ g } C_2H_5OH}{18 \text{ g } C_2H_5OH + 18 \text{ g } H_2O} \times 100\% = 50\%$

(c) $1.04 \ m \ K_2SO_4(aq) \equiv 1.04 \text{ mol } K_2SO_4 + 1 \text{ kg (or } 10^3 \text{ g) } H_2O$

$(1.04 \text{ mol } K_2SO_4) \times \left(\dfrac{174 \text{ g } K_2SO_4}{1 \text{ mol } K_2SO_4}\right) = 181 \text{ g } K_2SO_4$

mass % $= \dfrac{181 \text{ g } K_2SO_4}{181 \text{ g } K_2SO_4 + 10^3 \text{ g } H_2O} \times 100\% = 15.3\%$

(d) $x_{HCl} = 0.11 = \dfrac{n_{HCl}}{n_{HCl} + n_{H_2O}}$

If we assume 1 mol H_2O, then $0.11 = \dfrac{n_{HCl}}{n_{HCl} + 1 \text{ mol}}$

Solving for n_{HCl} yields $n_{HCl} = 0.12\overline{4}$ mol

mass HCl $= 0.12\overline{4} \text{ mol HCl} \times \dfrac{36.5 \text{ g HCl}}{1 \text{ mol HCl}} = 4.5 \text{ g HCl}$

mass % $= \dfrac{4.5 \text{ g HCl}}{4.5 \text{ g HCl} + 18 \text{ g } H_2O} \times 100\% = 20\%$

12.81 Assume 100 g of solution.

(a) $10.0\% \ H_2SO_4 \equiv 10.0 \text{ g } H_2SO_4 \text{ per 100 g solution}$ and $\left(\dfrac{10.0 \text{ g } H_2SO_4}{100 \text{ g soln}}\right)$

$\times \left(\dfrac{1.07 \text{ g soln}}{1 \text{ mL}}\right) = \dfrac{10.7 \text{ g } H_2SO_4}{100 \text{ mL soln}}$

Therefore, $(6.32 \text{ g } H_2SO_4) \times \left(\dfrac{100 \text{ mL soln}}{10.7 \text{ g } H_2SO_4}\right) = 59.1 \text{ mL soln.}$

(b) $100 \text{ g soln} - 10.0 \text{ g } H_2SO_4 = 90.0 \text{ g } H_2O = 0.0900 \text{ kg } H_2O$

$n_{H_2SO_4} = \dfrac{10.0 \text{ g } H_2SO_4}{98.0 \text{ g } H_2SO_4/\text{mol } H_2SO_4} = 0.102 \text{ mol } H_2SO_4$

molality $= \dfrac{n_{H_2SO_4}}{\text{mass of soln (kg)}} = \dfrac{0.102 \text{ mol}}{0.0900 \text{ kg}} = 1.13 \text{ mol} \cdot \text{kg}^{-1}$

(c) From part (a), $\left(\dfrac{10.7 \text{ g } H_2SO_4}{100 \text{ mL soln}}\right) \times (300 \text{ mL soln}) = 32.1 \text{ g } H_2SO_4$

12.83 $2.0 \ m \ HNO_3 \equiv \dfrac{2 \text{ mol } HNO_3}{1 \text{ kg } H_2O}$ (assume density = 1.0)

$$\left(\frac{2.0 \text{ mol HNO}_3}{1 \text{ kg H}_2\text{O}}\right) \times \left(\frac{1 \text{ kg}}{10^3 \text{ g}}\right) \times \left(\frac{1 \text{ g}}{1 \text{ mL}}\right) \times (250 \text{ mL}) = 0.50 \text{ mol HNO}_3 \text{ required}$$

Then, $70\% \text{ HNO}_3 = \left(\frac{70 \text{ g HNO}_3}{100 \text{ g soln}}\right) \times \left(\frac{1 \text{ mol HNO}_3}{63 \text{ g HNO}_3}\right) = 0.011 \text{ mol HNO}_3 \text{ per g soln}$

and $(0.50 \text{ mol HNO}_3) \times \left(\frac{1 \text{ g soln}}{0.011 \text{ mol HNO}_3}\right) = 45 \text{ g of } 70\% \text{ HNO}_3 \text{ soln.}$

12.85 $0.50 \ m \text{ NaCl} = \dfrac{0.50 \text{ mol NaCl}}{1 \text{ kg H}_2\text{O}} = \dfrac{0.50 \text{ mol NaCl}}{(1 \text{ kg H}_2\text{O}) \times \left(\dfrac{1 \text{ mol H}_2\text{O}}{18.0 \text{ g H}_2\text{O}}\right)}$

$$= \frac{0.50 \text{ mol Na}^+ + 0.50 \text{ mol Cl}^-}{55.6 \text{ mol H}_2\text{O}}$$

$x_{\text{H}_2\text{O}} = \dfrac{55.6 \text{ mol H}_2\text{O}}{55.6 \text{ mol H}_2\text{O} + 1.00 \text{ mol ions}} = 0.982$

Then at 30°C, $P = x\,P_{\text{pine H}_2\text{O}} = 0.982 \times 31.82 \text{ Torr} = 31.3 \text{ Torr}$

at 100°C, $P = 0.982 \times 760 \text{ Torr} = 746 \text{ Torr}$

at 0°C, $P = 0.982 \times 4.58 \text{ Torr} = 4.50 \text{ Torr}$

12.87 Let p = dichlorobenzene = cmpd.

(a) $\Delta T = 5.48°\text{C} - 1.20°\text{C} = 4.28°\text{C} = 4.28\text{K}$ and $\Delta T = k_f m$

$m = \dfrac{\Delta T}{k_f} = \dfrac{4.28 \text{ K}}{5.12 \text{ K} \cdot \text{kg} \cdot \text{mol}^{-1}} = 0.836 \text{ (mol cmpd)} \cdot \text{kg}^{-1}$

$0.836 \text{ (mol cmpd)} \cdot \text{kg}^{-1} \times \left(\dfrac{1 \text{ kg}}{10^3 \text{ g}}\right) = 8.36 \times 10^{-4} \text{ (mol cmpd)}/(1 \text{ g benzene})$

Then molar mass cmpd $= \left(\dfrac{10.0 \text{ g cmpd}}{80.0 \text{ g benzene}}\right) \times \left(\dfrac{1 \text{ g benzene}}{8.36 \times 10^{-4} \text{ mol cmpd}}\right)$

$= 149 \text{ g} \cdot \text{mol}^{-1}$

(b) $\dfrac{\text{molar mass cmpd}}{\text{molar mass C}_3\text{H}_2\text{Cl}} = \dfrac{149 \text{ g} \cdot \text{mol}^{-1}}{73.5 \text{ g} \cdot \text{mol}^{-1}} \approx 2$

Therefore, the formula is $C_6H_4Cl_2$.

(c) For $C_6H_4Cl_2$, molar mass $= 146.99 \text{ g} \cdot \text{mol}^{-1}$.

12.89 (a) Assume 100 g sample.

$59.0\% \text{ C, therefore, } (59.0 \text{ g C}) \times \left(\dfrac{1 \text{ mol C}}{12.0 \text{ g C}}\right) = 4.92 \text{ mol C}$

$26.2\% \text{ O, therefore, } (26.2 \text{ g O}) \times \left(\dfrac{1 \text{ mol O}}{16.0 \text{ g O}}\right) = 1.64 \text{ mol O}$

$7.10\% \text{ H, therefore, } (7.10 \text{ g H}) \times \left(\dfrac{1 \text{ mol H}}{1.01 \text{ g H}}\right) = 7.03 \text{ mol H}$

7.65% N, therefore, $(7.65 \text{ g N}) \times \left(\dfrac{1 \text{ mol N}}{14.0 \text{ g N}} \right) = 0.546 \text{ N}$

Dividing by 0.546 gives C:O:H:N = 9:3:12.9:1. Therefore, the empirical formula is $C_9H_{13}O_3N$. The molar mass of the empirical formula is 183 g · mol^{-1}.

(b) $m = \dfrac{\Delta T}{k_f} = \dfrac{0.50 \text{ K}}{5.12 \text{ K} \cdot \text{kg} \cdot \text{mol}^{-1}} = 0.098 \text{ mol} \cdot \text{kg}^{-1}$

Therefore, $\left(\dfrac{0.098 \text{ mol adrenaline}}{1 \text{ kg solvent}} \right) \times \left(\dfrac{1 \text{ kg solvent}}{10^3 \text{ g solvent}} \right) =$

$\dfrac{9.8 \times 10^{-5} \text{ mol adrenaline}}{1 \text{ g solvent}}$ and $\left(\dfrac{0.64 \text{ g adrenaline}}{36.0 \text{ g solvent}} \right) \times$

$\left(\dfrac{1 \text{ g solvent}}{9.8 \times 10^{-5} \text{ mol adrenaline}} \right) = 18\overline{1} \text{ g} \cdot \text{mol}^{-1} = 1.8 \times 10^2 \text{ g} \cdot \text{mol}^{-1}.$

(c) $\dfrac{\text{molar mass}}{\text{empirical molar mass}} = \dfrac{18\overline{1} \text{ g} \cdot \text{mol}^{-1}}{183 \text{ g} \cdot \text{mol}^{-1}} \sim 1.$ Therefore, $C_9H_{13}O_3N.$

12.91 $\Pi = i \times RT \times M$

molarity $= M = \dfrac{\Pi}{iRT} = \dfrac{(1.2 \text{ Torr}) \times \left(\dfrac{1 \text{ atm}}{760 \text{ Torr}} \right)}{(1) \times \left(\dfrac{0.0821 \text{ L} \cdot \text{atm}}{\text{K} \cdot \text{mol}} \right) \times (273 + 20) \text{ K}} = 6.6 \times 10^{-5} \text{ mol} \cdot \text{L}^{-1}$

and $\left(\dfrac{0.166 \text{ g catalase}}{10 \text{ mL H}_2\text{O}} \right) \times \left(\dfrac{1 \text{ mL}}{10^{-3} \text{ L}} \right) \times \left(\dfrac{1 \text{ L}}{6.6 \times 10^{-5} \text{ mol}} \right) = 2.5 \times 10^5 \text{ g} \cdot \text{mol}^{-1}$ (2 sf)

12.93 The hypotonic (too dilute) solution will cause a net flow of solvent into the cells in an effort to equalize the osmotic pressure between the inside and outside of the cell. The cell will burst and die.

The hypertonic (too concentrated) solution will cause a net flow of solvent out of the cells in an effort to equalize the osmotic pressure between the inside and outside of the cell. The cell will shrink and die.

12.95 $\Pi = i \times RT \times M, \quad M = \text{molarity} = \dfrac{n_{\text{solute}}}{V_{\text{soln}} (\text{L})}, \quad n_{\text{solute}} = \dfrac{\text{mass}_{\text{solute}}}{\text{molar mass}}$

Putting these relations all together yields $\Pi = iRT \times \left(\dfrac{\text{mass}_{\text{solute}}}{\text{molar mass} \times V_{\text{soln}}} \right).$

Solving for molar mass: molar mass $= \dfrac{iRT \times \text{mass}_{\text{solute}}}{\Pi \times V_{\text{soln}}}.$

Thus, the determination of the molar mass of a solute requires only a measurement of mass, volume, temperature, and osmotic pressure. Osmotic pressures are generally quite large; hence, this quantity, like all the others mentioned, can be determined quite accurately, yielding accurate molar masses. Boiling-point elevations and freezing-point depressions are usually quite small and hence cannot often be measured with great accuracy, so molar masses determined from them are often not accurate.

CHALLENGING EXERCISES

12.97 When a drop of aqueous solution containing $Ca(HCO_3)_2$ seeps through the ceiling of a cave, it encounters a situation in which the partial pressure of CO_2 is less than required for the equilibrium in the reaction
$$Ca(HCO_3)_2(aq) \rightleftharpoons CaCO_3(s) + CO_2(aq) + H_2O(l)$$
to be maintained. The concentration of CO_2 (aq) in the aqueous solution decreases below the equilibrium value in accordance with Henry's law, $S = k_H \times P_{CO_2}$. The CO_2 then escapes as a gas, driving the equilibrium above to the right with $CaCO_3$ (s) precipitating and extending downward from the ceiling in the form of a stalactite. Stalagmite formation is similar, except here the drop falls to the floor of the cave and the precipitate grows upward.

12.99 $\Delta T = ik_f m$ and 5.00% soln $\equiv \dfrac{5.00 \text{ g } CH_3COOH}{95.0 \text{ g } H_2O}$

$$\left(\frac{5.00 \text{ g } CH_3COOH}{95.0 \text{ g } H_2O}\right) \times \left(\frac{10^3 \text{ g}}{1 \text{ kg}}\right) \times \left(\frac{1 \text{ mol}}{60.0 \text{ g } CH_3COOH}\right)$$

$$= 0.877 \text{ mol} \cdot \text{kg}^{-1} \, CH_3COOH$$

$$i = \frac{\Delta T}{k_f m} = \frac{1.576 \text{ K}}{1.86 \text{ K} \cdot \text{kg} \cdot \text{mol}^{-1} \times 0.877 \text{ mol} \cdot \text{kg}^{-1}} = 0.966$$

A van't Hoff factor just slightly less than 1 indicates association, rather than dissociation, in solution. Association among polar CH_3COOH molecules reduces the effective number of particles in solution.

12.101 (a) $\Pi = i \times RT \times M$

$$M = \frac{\Pi}{iRT} = \frac{(5.22 \text{ cm}) \times \left(\dfrac{1 \text{ atm}}{76 \text{ cm}}\right) \times \left(\dfrac{0.998 \text{ g} \cdot \text{mL}^{-1} \text{ soln}}{13.6 \text{ g} \cdot \text{mL}^{-1} \text{ Hg}}\right)}{(1) \times \left(\dfrac{0.0821 \text{ L} \cdot \text{atm}}{\text{K} \cdot \text{mol}}\right) \times (273 + 20) \text{ K}}$$

$$= 2.10 \times 10^{-4} \text{ mol} \cdot \text{L}^{-1}$$

Then, $M = \left(\dfrac{0.010 \text{ mol protein}}{10 \text{ mL } H_2O}\right) \times \left(\dfrac{1 \text{ mL}}{10^{-3} \text{ L}}\right) \times \left(\dfrac{1 \text{ L}}{2.10 \times 10^{-4} \text{ mol}}\right)$

$$= 4.77 \times 10^3 \text{ g} \cdot \text{mol}^{-1}$$

(b) molality $= m = \left(\dfrac{2.10 \times 10^{-4} \text{ mol}}{1 \text{ L}}\right) \times \left(\dfrac{10^{-3} \text{ L}}{1 \text{ mL}}\right) \times \left(\dfrac{1 \text{ mL}}{0.998 \text{ g}}\right) \times \left(\dfrac{10^3 \text{ g}}{1 \text{ kg}}\right)$

$\qquad = 2.10 \times 10^{-4} \text{ mol} \cdot \text{kg}^{-1}$

$\Delta T = ik_f m = 1 \times 1.86 \text{ K} \cdot \text{kg} \cdot \text{mol}^{-1} \times 2.10 \times 10^{-4} \text{ mol} \cdot \text{kg}^{-1}$

$\qquad = 3.90 \times 10^{-4} \text{ K}$

fp $= 0.00°\text{C} - 3.90 \times 10^{-4}°\text{C} = -3.90 \times 10^{-4}°\text{C}$

(c) The small ΔT of part (b) cannot be measured accurately; hence, the molar mass determined from it cannot be accurate. Therefore, the osmotic pressure, which can be measured accurately (3 sf), is the superior method for the determination of the molar mass.

12.103 (a) $P = x_{\text{solvent}} P_{\text{pure solvent}}$, $P_{\text{pure solvent}} = 760$ Torr at 80.1°C

$x_{\text{solvent}} = \dfrac{P}{P_{\text{pure solvent}}} = \dfrac{740 \text{ Torr}}{760 \text{ Torr}} = 0.974$

$x_{\text{solute}} = 1 - 0.974 - 0.026$

We need to calculate the molarity of the solute in solution to use in the formula $\Pi = i \times RT \times M$ (assume $i = 1$). Consider a solution of 0.026 mol solute and 0.974 mol benzine; assume that the volume of the solution is the same as the volume of 0.974 mol of pure benzene.

volume $= 0.974 \text{ mol C}_6\text{H}_6 \times \left(\dfrac{78.12 \text{ g C}_6\text{H}_6}{1 \text{ mol C}_6\text{H}_6}\right) \times \left(\dfrac{1.00 \text{ mL C}_6\text{H}_6}{0.88 \text{ g}}\right)$

$\qquad = 86.5 \text{ mL} = 0.0865 \text{ L}$

molarity $= \dfrac{0.026 \text{ mol}}{0.0865 \text{ L}} = 0.30 \text{ mol} \cdot \text{L}^{-1}$

$\Pi = 1 \times 0.082\,06 \text{ L} \cdot \text{atm} \cdot \text{K}^{-1} \cdot \text{mol}^{-1} \times 293 \text{ K} \times 0.30 \text{ mol} \cdot \text{L}^{-1} = 7.2 \text{ atm}$

(b) $\Delta T = ik_f m$, solve for m = molality, assume $i = 1$

$m = \dfrac{\Delta T}{ik_f} = \dfrac{0.1 \text{ K}}{1 \times 5.12 \text{ K} \cdot \text{kg} \cdot \text{mol}^{-1}} = 0.01\overline{95} \text{ mol} \cdot \text{kg}^{-1}$

We need to convert molality to molarity. Given that $d_{\text{soln}} = d_{\text{C}_6\text{H}_6}$ $= 0.88 \text{ g} \cdot \text{cm}^{-3} = 0.88 \text{ g} \cdot \text{mL}^{-1}$, we have

$\left(\dfrac{0.01\overline{95} \text{ mol solute}}{1 \text{ kg C}_6\text{H}_6}\right) \times \left(\dfrac{1 \text{ kg}}{10^3 \text{ g}}\right) \times \left(\dfrac{0.88 \text{ g}}{1 \text{ mL}}\right) \times \left(\dfrac{1 \text{ mL}}{10^{-3} \text{ L}}\right)$

$\qquad\qquad\qquad\qquad\qquad\qquad\qquad\qquad\qquad = 1.\overline{7} \times 10^{-2} \text{ mol} \cdot \text{L}^{-1}$

$\Pi = i \times RT \times M$

$\qquad = 1 \times 0.082\,06 \text{ L} \cdot \text{atm} \cdot \text{K}^{-1} \cdot \text{mol}^{-1} \times 283 \text{ K} \times 1.\overline{7} \times 10^{-2} \text{ mol} \cdot \text{L}^{-1}$

$\qquad = 0.4 \text{ atm}$

(c) $\Pi = 0.4 \text{ atm} \times \left(\dfrac{760 \text{ mm}}{1 \text{ atm}}\right) \times \left(\dfrac{13.6 \text{ g} \cdot \text{cm}^{-3}}{0.88 \text{ g} \cdot \text{cm}^{-3}}\right) = 5 \times 10^3 \text{ mm C}_6\text{H}_6$

$\qquad\qquad\qquad\qquad\qquad\qquad\qquad\qquad\qquad = 5 \text{ m C}_6\text{H}_6$

CHAPTER 13
CHEMICAL EQUILIBRIUM

EXERCISES

Equilibrium and Equilibrium Constants

13.1 (a) At the molecular level, chemical equilibrium is a dynamic process and interconversion of reactants and products continues to occur. However, at the macroscopic level, no change in concentrations of reactants and products is observable at equilibrium, because the rates of product and reactant formation are equal.

(b) At a fixed temperature, the equilibrium constant is truly a constant, independent of concentrations. However, if the concentration of a reactant is increased, the concentrations of other chemical species involved in the reaction will change, and more product will form; that is, the concentrations adjust because the equilibrium constant remains the same.

13.3 The concentrations of reactants and products stop changing when equilibrium has been attained. Equilibrium occurs when the forward and reverse rates of reaction are equal, a condition that will always be reached eventually, given enough time. At equilibrium, the concentrations of reactants and products have reached the values dictated by the equilibrium constant. We can think of the difference of concentrations of reactants and products from their equilibrium values as a kind of driving force for the reaction to proceed. When that difference is 0, as it is at equilibrium, this driving force is also 0, and the concentrations no longer continue to change. The nature of this driving force is discussed in more detail in Chapter 16.

13.5 The equilibrium composition in each system will be that which results in the same value of K. Thus, (d) and its inverse, (e), are identical in the two containers, but (a), (b), and (c) will be different, because the second container contains five times as much material.

(f) The time required to reach equilibrium might be different in the two containers. There is no fixed simple relation between the time required to reach equilibrium and the concentration of reactant.

A more detailed analysis of (a) through (e) follows. The equilibrium constant for this reaction in this exercise is

$$K_c = \frac{[O_2(g)]^3}{[O_3(g)]^2}$$

In terms of the change in concentration, x, that has occurred at equilibrium, we can write

$$K_c = \frac{(\frac{3}{2}x)^3}{(0.10 - x)^2} \quad \text{in the first container}$$

$$K_c = \frac{(\frac{3}{2}x)^3}{(0.50 - x)^2} \quad \text{in the second container}$$

The change, x, is different in the two cases.

(a) Because the volume is the same, the amount (moles) of O_2, $n_{O_2} = [O_2] \times$ volume, is larger in the second experiment.

(b) Because K_c is a constant and the denominator is larger in the second case, the numerator must also be larger. So the concentration of O^2 ($= \frac{3}{2}x$) is larger in the second case.

(c) Although $[O_2]^3/[O_3]^2$ is the same, $[O_2]/[O_3]$ will be different. This can be seen by solving the two K_c expressions above for x and then calculating the ratio. The ratio depends on K_c, which is needed to obtain its numerical value.

(d) Because K_c is a constant, $[O_2]^3/[O_3]^2$ is the same.

(e) Because $[O_2]^3/[O_3]^2$ is the same, its reciprocal must be the same.

13.7 (a) $K_c = \dfrac{[COCl][Cl]}{[CO][Cl_2]}$ (b) $K_c = \dfrac{[HBr]^2}{[H_2][Br_2]}$ (c) $K_c = \dfrac{[SO_2]^2[H_2O]^2}{[O_2]^3[H_2S]^2}$

13.9 $N_2(g) + 3H_2(g) \rightleftharpoons 2NH_3(g)$ $\quad K_p = \dfrac{P^2_{NH_3}}{P_{N_2}P^3_{H_2}} = 41$

(a) $K_{p(a)} = \dfrac{P_{N_2}P^3_{H_2}}{P^2_{NH_3}}$ Therefore, $K_{p(a)} = 1/K_p = 1/41 = 0.024$

(b) $K_{p(b)} = \dfrac{P_{NH_3}}{P^{1/2}_{N_2}P^{3/2}_{H_2}}$ Therefore, $K_{p(b)} = \sqrt{K_p} = 6.4$

(c) $K_{p(c)} = \dfrac{P^4_{NH_3}}{P^2_{N_2}P^6_{H_2}}$ Therefore, $K_{p(c)} = K_p^2 = 41^2 = 1.7 \times 10^3$

Equilibrium Constants from Equilibrium Amounts

13.11 $K_c = \dfrac{[HI]^2}{[H_2][I_2]}$

first case: $K_c = \dfrac{(1.37 \times 10^{-2})^2}{(6.47 \times 10^{-3})(5.94 \times 10^{-4})} = 48.8$

second case: $K_c = \dfrac{(1.69 \times 10^{-2})^2}{(3.84 \times 10^{-3})(1.52 \times 10^{-3})} = 48.9$

third case: $K_c = \dfrac{(1.00 \times 10^{-2})^2}{(1.43 \times 10^{-3})(1.43 \times 10^{-3})} = 48.9$

13.13 (a) $2NOCl(g) \rightleftharpoons 2NO(g) + Cl_2(g)$ $\Delta n = 1$

$K_c = \dfrac{K_p}{(RT)^{\Delta n}} = \dfrac{K_p}{[0.082\ 06\ (T/K)]^{\Delta n}} = \dfrac{1.8 \times 10^{-2}}{(0.082\ 06 \times 500)} = 4.4 \times 10^{-4}$

(b) $CaCO_3(s) \rightleftharpoons CaO(s) + CO_2(g)$ $\Delta n = 1$

$K_c = \dfrac{167}{(0.082\ 06 \times 1073)} = 1.90$

Heterogeneous Equilibria

13.15 All the equilibria are heterogeneous, because in each case more than one phase is involved in the equilibrium.

(a) $K_p = P_{H_2S}P_{NH_3}$ (b) $K_p = P_{NH_3}^2 P_{CO_2}$ (c) $K_p = P_{O_2}$

13.17 (a) $K_c = \dfrac{1}{[Cl_2]}$ (b) $K_c = [N_2O][H_2O]^2$ (c) $K_c = [CO_2]$

The Extent and Direction of Reactions

13.19 $H_2(g) + I_2(g) \rightleftharpoons 2HI(g)$ $K_c = 160$ at 500°C

$K_c = \dfrac{[HI]^2}{[H_2][I_2]} = 160$ and $[H_2] = \dfrac{[HI]^2}{K_c[I_2]} = \dfrac{(2.21 \times 10^{-3})^2}{(160)(1.46 \times 10^{-3})} = 2.09 \times 10^{-5}$ mol·L^{-1}

13.21 $PCl_5(g) \rightleftharpoons PCl_3(g) + Cl_2(g)$

$K_p = \dfrac{P_{PCl_3}P_{Cl_2}}{P_{PCl_5}} = 25$ Therefore, $P_{PCl_3} = \dfrac{K_p P_{PCl_5}}{P_{Cl_2}} = \dfrac{(25)(0.15)}{0.20} = 19$ atm

13.23 (a) $K_c = 160$ at 500°C; the reaction is $H_2(g) + I_2(g) \rightleftharpoons 2HI(g)$

$$Q_c = \frac{[HI]^2}{[H_2][I_2]} = \frac{(2.4 \times 10^{-3})^2}{(4.8 \times 10^{-3}) \times (2.4 \times 10^{-3})} = 0.50$$

(b) no, $Q_c \neq K_c$

(c) $Q_c < K_c$; tendency to form products

13.25 For the reaction $2SO_2(g) + O_2(g) \rightleftharpoons 2SO_3(g)$

(a) $Q_c = \dfrac{[SO_3]^2}{[SO_2]^2[O_2]} = \dfrac{(1.00 \times 10^{-4}/0.500)^2}{(1.20 \times 10^{-3}/0.500)^2 \times (5.0 \times 10^{-4}/0.500)} = 6.94$

(b) $Q_c < K_c$; therefore more $SO_3(g)$ will form.

Equilibrium Constants from Initial Amounts

13.27 $2HI(g) \rightleftharpoons H_2(g) + I_2(g)$ $K_c = \dfrac{[H_2][I_2]}{[HI]^2}$

$[HI] = \left(\dfrac{1.90 \text{ g HI}}{2.00 \text{ L}}\right) \times \left(\dfrac{1 \text{ mol HI}}{127.9 \text{ g HI}}\right) = 7.43 \times 10^{-3} \text{ mol} \cdot L^{-1}$

$[I_2] = [H_2] = (\frac{1}{2}) \times$ (mol HI reacted)

$= \frac{1}{2} \times \left(\dfrac{0.0172 \text{ mol}}{2.00 \text{ L}} - 7.43 \times 10^{-3} \text{ mol} \cdot L^{-1}\right) = 5.85 \times 10^{-4} \text{ mol} \cdot L^{-1}$

Then, $K_c = \dfrac{5.85 \times 10^{-4} \times 5.85 \times 10^{-4}}{(7.43 \times 10^{-3})^2} = 6.20 \times 10^{-3}$

13.29 $NH_2CO_2NH_4(s) \rightleftharpoons 2NH_3(g) + CO_2(g)$ $K_c = [NH_3]^2[CO_2]$

$[CO_2] = \left(\dfrac{17.4 \text{ mg CO}_2}{250 \text{ mL}}\right) \times \left(\dfrac{10^{-3} \text{ g}}{1 \text{ mg}}\right) \times \left(\dfrac{1 \text{ mol CO}_2}{44.0 \text{ g CO}_2}\right) \times \left(\dfrac{1 \text{ mL}}{10^{-3} \text{ L}}\right)$

$= 1.58 \times 10^{-3} (\text{mol CO}_2) \cdot L^{-1}$

$[NH_3] = 1.58 \times 10^{-3}(\text{mol CO}_2) \cdot L^{-1} \times \left(\dfrac{2 \text{ mol NH}_3}{1 \text{ mol CO}_2}\right) = 3.16 \times 10^{-3} (\text{mol NH}_3) \cdot L^{-1}$

Substituting in the expression for K_c, $K_c = (3.16 \times 10^{-3})^2 \times (1.58 \times 10^{-3}) = 1.58 \times 10^{-8}$.

13.31 $CH_3COOH(l) + C_2H_5OH(l) \rightleftharpoons CH_3COOC_2H_5(l) + H_2O(l)$

In each case, $K_c = \dfrac{[CH_3COOC_2H_5][H_2O]}{[CH_3COOH][C_2H_5OH]}$.

On the assumption that the only water present is there as a result of the reaction, then in each case the equilibrium concentration of water is the same as that of $CH_3COOC_2H_5(l)$; that is, $[H_2O] = [CH_3COOC_2H_5]$

first case: $K_c = \dfrac{(0.171)^2}{(1.00 - 0.171) \times (0.180 - 0.171)} = 3.9$

second case: $K_c = \dfrac{(0.667)^2}{(1.00 - 0.667) \times (1.00 - 0.667)} = 4.0$

third case: $\dfrac{(0.966)^2}{(1.00 - 0.966) \times (8.00 - 0.966)} = 3.9$

Equilibrium Table Calculations

13.33 (a) initial concentration $Cl_2 = \dfrac{2.0 \times 10^{-3} \text{ mol}}{2.0 \text{ L}} = 1.0 \times 10^{-3} \text{ mol} \cdot L^{-1}$

Concentration $(\text{mol} \cdot L^{-1})$	$Cl_2(g)$	$\rightleftharpoons$	$2Cl(g)$	$K_c = 1.2 \times 10^{-7}$ at 1000 K
initial	1.0×10^{-3}		0	
change	$-x$		$+2x$	
equil.	$1.0 \times 10^{-3} - x$		$2x$	

so $K_c = \dfrac{[Cl]^2}{[Cl_2]} = \dfrac{(2x)^2}{(1.0 \times 10^{-3} - x)} = 1.2 \times 10^{-7}$

Assume in $(1.0 \times 10^{-3} - x)$, that x is negligible as a result of the small K_c, and then $4x^2 = (1.0 \times 10^{-3}) \times (1.2 \times 10^{-7})$.

Then $x = 5.5 \times 10^{-6} \text{ mol} \cdot L^{-1}$ = amount/L decomposed.

equilibrium concentrations: $2x = [Cl] = 1.1 \times 10^{-5} \text{ mol} \cdot L^{-1}$

$[Cl_2] \approx 1.0 \times 10^{-3} \text{ mol} \cdot L^{-1}$

% decomposition $= \dfrac{\text{amount/L decomposed}}{\text{initial amount/L}} \times 100\% = \dfrac{5.5 \times 10^{-6} \text{ mol} \cdot L^{-1}}{1.0 \times 10^{-3} \text{ mol} \cdot L^{-1}}$

$\times 100\% = 0.55\%$

(b) Initial concentration of $F_2 = \dfrac{2.0 \times 10^{-3} \text{ mol}}{2.0 \text{ L}} = 1.0 \times 10^{-3} \text{ mol} \cdot L^{-1}$

Concentration $(\text{mol} \cdot L^{-1})$	$F_2(g)$	$\rightleftharpoons$	$2F(g)$	$K_c = 1.2 \times 10^{-4}$ at 1000 K
initial	1.0×10^{-3}		0	
change	$-x$		$+2x$	
equil.	$1.0 \times 10^{-3} - x$		$2x$	

so $K_c = \dfrac{[F]^2}{[F_2]} = \dfrac{(2x)^2}{(1.0 \times 10^{-3} - x)} = 1.2 \times 10^{-4}$

In this case, x is *not* negligible.

$4x^2 = (1.0 \times 10^{-3}) \times (1.2 \times 10^{-4}) - 1.2 \times 10^{-4}x$

$4x^2 + 1.2 \times 10^{-4}x - 1.2 \times 10^{-7} = 0$

Solve the quadratic: $x = 1.59 \times 10^{-4} \text{ mol} \cdot L^{-1}$ = amount/L decomposed.

equilibrium concentrations: $2x = [F] = 3.18 \times 10^{-4} \text{ mol} \cdot L^{-1}$

$[F_2] \approx 1.0 \times 10^{-3} - x = 8.41 \times 10^{-4} \text{ mol} \cdot L^{-1}$

$$\% \text{ decomposition} = \frac{1.59 \times 10^{-4} \text{ mol} \cdot \text{L}^{-1}}{8.41 \times 10^{-4} \text{ mol} \cdot \text{L}^{-1}} \times 100\% = 19\%$$

(c) Cl_2 is more stable at 1000 K than F_2 is.

13.35

Concentration

(mol·L⁻¹)	2HBr(g) $\rightleftharpoons$	H₂(g) +	Br₂(g)	$K_c = 7.7 \times 10^{-11}$ at 500 K
initial	1.2×10^{-3}	0	0	
change	$-2x$	$+x$	$+x$	
equil.	$1.2 \times 10^{-3} - 2x$	x	x	

$$K_c = \frac{[H_2][Br_2]}{[HBr]^2} = \frac{(x)(x)}{(1.2 \times 10^{-3} - 2x)^2} = 7.7 \times 10^{-11}$$

In the term $(1.2 \times 10^{-3} - 2x)$, $2x$ is negligible.

$x^2 = 1.11 \times 10^{-16}$

$x = 1.1 \times 10^{-8} = [H_2] = [Br_2]$

$2x = 2.2 \times 10^{-8} \text{ mol} \cdot \text{L}^{-1} = \text{amount/L decomposed}$

$[HBr] = 1.2 \times 10^{-3} \text{ mol} \cdot \text{L}^{-1} - 2 \times (1.1 \times 10^{-8}) \approx 1.2 \times 10^{-3} \text{ mol} \cdot \text{L}^{-1}$

$$\% \text{ decomposition} = \frac{\text{amount/L decomposed}}{\text{initial concentration of reactant}} \times 100\% = \frac{2.2 \times 10^{-8} \text{ mol} \cdot \text{L}^{-1}}{1.2 \times 10^{-3} \text{ mol} \cdot \text{L}^{-1}}$$
$$\times 100\% = 1.8 \times 10^{-3}\%$$

The percentage decomposition is close to negligible.

13.37 (a) $[PCl_5] = \dfrac{n_{PCl_5}}{\text{Vol(L)}} = \dfrac{1.0 \text{ g } PCl_5/208 \text{ g} \cdot \text{mol}^{-1}}{0.250 \text{ L}} = 1.9 \times 10^{-2} \text{ mol} \cdot \text{L}^{-1}$

= initial concentration

Concentration (mol·L⁻¹)	PCl₅(g) $\rightleftharpoons$	PCl₃(g) +	Cl₂(g)
initial	1.9×10^{-2}	0	0
change	$-x$	$+x$	$+x$
equil.	$1.9 \times 10^{-2} - x$	x	x

$$K_c = \frac{K_p}{(RT)^{\Delta n}} = \frac{0.36}{(0.0821) \times (400)^I} = 1.1 \times 10^{-2} \quad \text{and,} \quad K_c = \frac{x^2}{1.9 \times 10^{-2} - x}$$

$x^2 + 1.1 \times 10^{-2}x - 2.1 \times 10^{-4} = 0$

equilibrium concentration: $x = [PCl_3] = [Cl_2] = 1.0 \times 10^{-2} \text{ mol} \cdot \text{L}^{-1}$

$[PCl_5] = 1.9 \times 10^{-2} - 1.0 \times 10^{-2}$

$= 9.0 \times 10^{-3} \text{ mol} \cdot \text{L}^{-1}$

(b) $x = \text{amount/L decomposed} = 1.0 \times 10^{-2} \text{ mol} \cdot \text{L}^{-1}$

$$\% \text{ decomposition} = \frac{1.0 \times 10^{-2} \text{ mol} \cdot \text{L}^{-1}}{1.9 \times 10^{-2} \text{ mol} \cdot \text{L}^{-1}} \times 100\% = 53\%$$

13.39   initial $[NH_3] = \dfrac{0.400 \text{ mol}}{2.0 \text{ L}} = 0.200 \text{ mol} \cdot L^{-1}$

Concentration $(mol \cdot L^{-1})$ $NH_4HS(s)$	$\rightleftharpoons$	$NH_3(g)$	$+$	$H_2S(g)$
initial	—	0.200		0
change	—	$+x$		$+x$
equil.	—	$0.200 + x$		x

$K_c = [NH_3][H_2S] = 1.6 \times 10^{-4}$

$(0.200 + x) \times (x) = 1.6 \times 10^{-4}$

$x^2 + 0.200x - 1.6 \times 10^{-4} = 0$

equilibrium concentrations: $x = 8.0 \times 10^{-4} \text{ mol} \cdot L^{-1} = [H_2S]$

$\qquad\qquad 0.200 + 8.0 \times 10^{-4} = 0.200 \text{ mol} \cdot L^{-1} = [NH_3]$

13.41   initial concentrations: $[PCl_5] = \dfrac{0.200 \text{ mol}}{4.00 \text{ L}} = 0.0500 \text{ mol} \cdot L^{-1}$

$[PCl_3] = \dfrac{0.600 \text{ mol}}{4.00 \text{ L}} = 0.150 \text{ mol} \cdot L^{-1}$

$[Cl_2] = 0$

Concentration $(mol \cdot L^{-1})$	$PCl_5(g)$	$\rightleftharpoons$	$PCl_3(g)$	$+$	$Cl_2(g)$
initial	0.050		0.150		0
change	$-x$		$+x$		$+x$
equil.	$0.050 - x$		$0.150 + x$		x

$K_c = \dfrac{[PCl_3][Cl_2]}{[PCl_5]} = 33.3 = \dfrac{(0.150 + x) \times (x)}{(0.050 - x)}$

$1.665 - 33.3x = x^2 + 0.15x$, and $x^2 + 33.45x - 1.665 = 0$

equilibrium concentrations: $x = 4.97 \times 10^{-2} \text{ mol} \cdot L^{-1} = [Cl_2]$

$\qquad\qquad 0.15 + 4.97 \times 10^{-2} = 2.00 \times 10^{-1} \text{ mol} \cdot L^{-1} = [PCl_3]$

$\qquad\qquad 0.050 - 4.97 \times 10^{-2} = 2.98 \times 10^{-4} \text{ mol} \cdot L^{-1} = [PCl_5]$

13.43

Concentration $(mol \cdot L^{-1})$	$N_2(g)$	$+$	$O_2(g)$	$\rightleftharpoons$	$2NO(g)$
initial	0.114		0.114		0
change	$-x$		$-x$		$+2x$
equil.	$0.114 - x$		$0.114 - x$		$2x$

$K_c = \dfrac{[NO]^2}{[N_2][O_2]} = 1.00 \times 10^{-5} = \dfrac{(2x)^2}{(0.114 - x) \times (0.114 - x)} = 1.00 \times 10^{-5}$

$4x^2 = (1.00 \times 10^{-5}) \times (x^2 - 0.228x + 0.013)$

$\quad = 1.00 \times 10^{-5}x^2 - 2.28 \times 10^{-6}x + 1.3 \times 10^{-7}$

$4x^2 + 2.28 \times 10^{-6}x - 1.3 \times 10^{-7} = 0$

Solving the quadratic equation, $x = 1.80 \times 10^{-4} \text{ mol} \cdot \text{L}^{-1}$

equilibrium concentrations: $2x = 3.60 \times 10^{-4} \text{ mol} \cdot \text{L}^{-1} = [\text{NO}]$

$0.114 - x \approx 0.114 \text{ mol} \cdot \text{L}^{-1} = [\text{N}_2] = [\text{O}_2]$

13.45 $\text{H}_2(g) + \text{I}_2(g) \rightleftharpoons 2\text{HI}(g)$

0.400 mol $\text{H}_2 \times 0.60 = 0.240$ mol H_2 reacted

Therefore, 0.240 mol I_2 reacted and 0.480 mol HI formed

0.400 mol H_2 initial $- 0.240$ mol H_2 reacted $= 0.160$ mol H_2 at equilibrium

1.60 mol I_2 initial $- 0.240$ mol I_2 reacted $= 1.36$ mol I_2 at equilibrium

$$K_c = \frac{[\text{HI}]^2}{[\text{H}_2][\text{I}_2]} = \frac{\left(\dfrac{0.480 \text{ mol}}{3.00 \text{ L}}\right)^2}{\left(\dfrac{0.160 \text{ mol}}{3.00 \text{ L}}\right) \times \left(\dfrac{1.36 \text{ mol}}{3.00 \text{ L}}\right)} = 1.06$$

13.47   initial concentrations:

$$[\text{CO}] = \left(\frac{0.28 \text{ g CO}}{2.0 \text{ L}}\right) \times \left(\frac{1 \text{ mol CO}}{28.01 \text{ g CO}}\right) = 5.0 \times 10^{-3} \text{ mol} \cdot \text{L}^{-1}$$

$$[\text{O}_2] = \left(\frac{0.032 \text{ g O}_2}{2.0 \text{ L}}\right) \times \left(\frac{1 \text{ mol O}_2}{32.0 \text{ g O}_2}\right) = 5.0 \times 10^{-4} \text{ mol} \cdot \text{L}^{-1}$$

$[\text{CO}_2] = 0 \text{ mol} \cdot \text{L}^{-1}$

Concentration $(\text{mol} \cdot \text{L}^{-1})$	$2\text{CO}(g)$	$+$	$\text{O}_2(g)$	$\rightleftharpoons$	$2\text{CO}_2(g)$
initial	5.0×10^{-3}		5.0×10^{-4}		0
change	$-2x$		$-x$		$+2x$
equil.	$5.0 \times 10^{-3} - 2x$		$5.0 \times 10^{-4} - x$		$2x$

$$K_c = \frac{(2x)^2}{(5.0 \times 10^{-3} - 2x)^2 \times (5.0 \times 10^{-4} - x)} = 0.66$$

This expression results in a cubic equation. Assume that x is small relative to the other values in the denominator. Then, an approximate quadratic expression is

$$0.66 = \frac{4x^2}{(5.0 \times 10^{-3})^2 \times (5.0 \times 10^{-4})}$$

$4x^2 = (0.66) \times (1.25 \times 10^{-8}) = 8.25 \times 10^{-9}$

$x^2 = 2.06 \times 10^{-9}$

$x = 4.5 \times 10^{-5} \text{ mol} \cdot \text{L}^{-1}$

equilibrium concentrations: $2x = 9.0 \times 10^{-5} \text{ mol} \cdot \text{L}^{-1} \approx [\text{CO}_2]$

$[\text{CO}] \approx 4.9 \times 10^{-3} \text{ mol} \cdot \text{L}^{-1}$,

$[\text{O}_2] = 4.5 \times 10^{-4} \text{ mol} \cdot \text{L}^{-1}$

It is instructive to compare these values to those obtained from the solution to the full cubic equation. This solution can be easily obtained from any of a number of mathematical software packages as well as by many hand-held calculators. The full cubic is (after multiplication and expansion of the terms in K_c above):

$$2.64x^3 + 3.985x^2 + 2.31 \times 10^{-5}x - 8.25 \times 10^{-9} = 0$$

The solution is $x = 4.2\overline{7} \times 10^{-5} \ mol \cdot L^{-1}$. Then,

$2x = 8.5\overline{4} \times 10^{-5} \ mol \cdot L^{-1} = [CO_2]$

$5.0 \times 10^{-3} - 2x = 4.9\overline{1} \times 10^{-3} \ mol \cdot L^{-1} = [CO]$

$5.0 \times 10^{-4} - x = 4.5\overline{7} \times 10^{-4} \ mol \cdot L^{-1}$

$\qquad\qquad\qquad = 4.6 \times 10^{-4} \ mol \cdot L^{-1} = [O_2]$

Comparing these results with the approximate one above, we see no measurable difference in $[CO]$, very little in $[O_2]$, but about 5% difference in $[CO_2]$. So for $[CO_2]$, the approximation may not be adequate, depending on the accuracy required.

13.49

Concentration $(mol \cdot L^{-1})$	$CH_3COOH(l)$	$+ \ C_2H_5OH(l)$	$\rightleftharpoons CH_3COOC_2H_5(l)$	$+ \ H_2O(l)$
initial	0.32	6.3	0	0
change	$-x$	$-x$	$+x$	$+x$
equil.	$0.32 - x$	$6.3 - x$	x	x

$$K_c = 4.0 = \frac{[CH_3COOC_2H_5][H_2O]}{[CH_3COOH][C_2H_5OH]} = \frac{(x)(x)}{(0.32 - x)(6.3 - x)}$$

$x^2 = 4.0(x^2 - 6.62x + 2.02) = 4x^2 - 26.5x + 8.08$

$3x^2 - 26.5x + 8.08 = 0$

solving the quadratic yields $x = 0.316$ or $\approx 0.32 \ mol \cdot L^{-1}$

equilibrium concentrations:

$$[CH_3COOC_2H_5] = [H_2O] \approx 0.32 \ mol \cdot L^{-1}$$
$$[CH_3COOH] = 0.32 \ mol \cdot L^{-1} - 0.32 \ mol \cdot L^{-1} \approx 0 \ mol \cdot L^{-1}$$
$$[C_2H_5OH] = 6.3 \ mol \cdot L^{-1} - 0.32 \ mol \cdot L^{-1} \approx 6 \ mol \cdot L^{-1}$$

Effect of Added Reagents

13.51 (a) According to Le Chatelier's principle, an increase in the partial pressure of CO_2, a product, will favor a shift in the equilibrium to the left, thus decreasing the partial pressure of H_2.

(b) According to Le Chatelier's principle, a decrease in the partial pressure of CO, a reactant, will favor a shift in the equilibrium to the left, thus decreasing the partial pressure of CO_2.

(c) According to Le Chaterlier's principle, an increase in the concentration of one of the reactants, CO, will favor the formation of products; thus the H_2 concentration will increase.

(d) Nothing; the equilibrium constant is a constant independent of concentrations.

13.53

Change	Quantity	Effect
add NO	amount of H_2O	decrease
add NO	amount of O_2	increase
remove H_2O	amount of NO	increase
remove O_2	amount of NH_3	increase
add NH_3	K_c	no change
remove NO	amount of NH_3	decrease
add NH_3	amount of O_2	decrease

Response to Pressure

13.55 General statement: If the number of moles of gaseous products and reactants are equal, no pressure effect will be observed. When the numbers of moles of gaseous products and reactants are not equal, an *increase* in pressure will favor the direction having the smaller number of moles of gas.

(a) reactants favored; smaller number of moles of gas
(b) reactants favored; smaller number of moles of gas
(c) reactants favored; smaller number of moles of gas
(d) no effect; same number of moles on each side
(e) reactants favored; smaller number of moles of gas

13.57 (a) The partial pressure of NH_3 increases when the partial pressure of NO increases. According to Le Chatelier's principle, an increase in partial pressure of a product shifts the equilibrium to the left, thereby favoring the production of reactant, NH_3.

(b) When the partial pressure of NH_3 decreases, the partial pressure of O_2 increases. According to Le Chatelier's principle, a decrease in the partial pressure of one of the reactants shifts the equilibrium to the left, thereby favoring the production of O_2.

13.59 As the pressure is increased, the more dense form of SiO_2 (quartz) is favored because it occupies the smallest volume per gram of material.

Response to Temperature

13.61 General Principle: According to Le Chatelier's principle, the reaction will shift in the direction of the substances having the higher internal energy when the temperature is increased. Thus for an exothermic reaction, an increase in temperature favors the reactants; whereas, for an endothermic reaction, the products are favored.

(a) products favored (endothermic reaction)

(b) products favored (see Table 13.2); K increases with temperature

(c) reactants favored (exothermic reaction)

(d) reactants favored (exothermic reaction)

13.63 At 700 K, K_p is smaller than at 600 K. A smaller K_p means less product is formed, so the amount of ammonia will be less at 700 K than at 600 K.

SUPPLEMENTARY EXERCISES

13.65 (a) $Q_c = \dfrac{[SO_2]}{[O_2]}$ $\qquad$ $Q_p = \dfrac{P_{SO_2}}{P_{O_2}}$

(b) $Q_c = \dfrac{[SO_2][H_2O]}{[SO_3][H_2]}$ $\qquad$ $Q_p = \dfrac{P_{SO_2}P_{H_2O}}{P_{SO_3}P_{H_2}}$

(c) $Q_c = \dfrac{[WCl_6][H_2]^3}{[HCl]^6}$ $\qquad$ $Q_p = \dfrac{P_{WCl_6}P_{H_2}^3}{P_{HCl}^6}$

13.67 $2SO_2(g) + O_2(g) \rightleftharpoons 2SO_3(g)$ $\qquad$ $K_p = 3.0 \times 10^4, \quad \Delta n = -1$

Therefore, for $2SO_3(g) \rightleftharpoons 2SO_2(g) + O_2(g)$ $\qquad$ $K_p = \dfrac{1}{3.0 \times 10^4}$,

so, $SO_3(g) \rightleftharpoons SO_2(g) + \frac{1}{2}O_2(g)$ $\qquad$ $K_p = \sqrt{\dfrac{1}{3.0 \times 10^4}} = 5.8 \times 10^{-3}, \quad \Delta n = \frac{1}{2}$.

(a) $K_c = \dfrac{K_p}{(RT)^{\Delta n}} = \dfrac{3.0 \times 10^4}{(0.0821 \times 700)^{-1}} = 1.7 \times 10^6$

(b) $K_c = \dfrac{K_p}{(RT)^{\Delta n}} = \dfrac{5.8 \times 10^{-3}}{\sqrt{0.0821 \times 700}} = 7.7 \times 10^{-4}$

13.69 $Q_c = \dfrac{[NH_3]^2}{[N_2][H_2]^3} = \dfrac{(0.500)^2}{(3.00) \times (2.00)^3} = 0.0104$ and $Q_c < K_c$ (because $0.0104 < 0.060$).

Therefore, the reaction is not at equilibrium, and there is a tendency to form the product (NH_3) at the expense of the reactants (N_2 and H_2).

13.71 $Cl_2(g) + Br_2(g) \rightleftharpoons 2BrCl(g)$ and $K_c = 0.031 = \dfrac{[BrCl]^2}{[Cl_2][Br_2]}$

Let $x = [Br_2]$.

$$0.031 = \frac{(0.097)^2}{(0.22) \times (x)}$$

$$[Br_2] = x = \frac{(0.097)^2}{(0.22) \times (0.031)} = 1.4 \ mol \cdot L^{-1} \ (2 \ sf)$$

13.73 initial concentrations:

$$[CO] = \frac{2.00 \ mol}{10.0 \ L} = 0.200 \ mol \cdot L^{-1}$$

$$[H_2] = \frac{3.00 \ mol}{10.0 \ L} = 0.300 \ mol \cdot L^{-1}$$

equilibrium concentration: $\quad [CH_4] = \dfrac{0.478 \ mol}{10.0 \ L} = 0.0478 \ mol \cdot L^{-1}$

Concentration $(mol \cdot L^{-1})$	$CO(g)$	$+$	$3H_2(g)$	$\rightleftharpoons$	$CH_4(g)$	$+$	$H_2O(g)$
initial	0.200		0.300		0		0
change	-0.0478		-3×0.0478		$+0.0478$		$+0.0478$
equil.	$0.152\overline{2}$		$0.156\overline{6}$		0.0478		0.0478

$$K_c = \frac{[CH_4][H_2O]}{[CO][H_2]^3} = \frac{(0.0478)^2}{0.152\overline{2} \times (0.156\overline{6})^3} = 3.97$$

13.75

Concentration $(mol \cdot L^{-1})$	$SO_2(g)$	$+$	$NO_2(g)$	$\rightleftharpoons$	$NO(g)$	$+$	$SO_3(g)$
initial	$\dfrac{0.100 \ mol}{5.00 \ L}$		$\dfrac{0.200 \ mol}{5.00 \ L}$		$\dfrac{0.100 \ mol}{5.00 \ L}$		$\dfrac{0.150 \ mol}{5.00 \ L}$
change	$-x$		$-x$		$+x$		$+x$
equil.	$\dfrac{0.100 \ mol}{5.00 \ L} - x$		$\dfrac{0.200 \ mol}{5.00 \ L} - x$		$\dfrac{0.100 \ mol}{5.00 \ L} + x$		$\dfrac{0.150 \ mol}{5.00 \ L} + x$

$$K_c = 85.0 = \frac{[NO][SO_3]}{[SO_2][NO_2]} = \frac{\left(\dfrac{0.100 \ mol}{5.00 \ L} + x\right) \times \left(\dfrac{0.150 \ mol}{5.00 \ L} + x\right)}{\left(\dfrac{0.100 \ mol}{5.00 \ L} - x\right) \times \left(\dfrac{0.200 \ mol}{5.00 \ L} - x\right)}$$

$$85.0 = \frac{(0.020 + x) \times (0.0300 + x)}{(0.0200 - x) \times (0.0400 - x)} = \frac{x^2 + 0.0500x + 6.00 \times 10^{-4}}{x^2 - 0.0600x + 8.00 \times 10^{-4}}$$

$$x^2 + 0.0500x + 6.00 \times 10^{-4} = 85.0x^2 - 5.10x + 6.80 \times 10^{-2}$$

$$84.0x^2 - 5.15x + 6.74 \times 10^{-2} = 0$$

Solving the quadratic yields $x = 0.0189$.

equilibrium concentrations:
$[NO] = 0.0200 + 0.0189 = 0.0389 \text{ mol} \cdot L^{-1}$
$[SO_3] = 0.0300 + 0.0189 = 0.0489 \text{ mol} \cdot L^{-1}$
$[SO_2] = 0.0200 - 0.0189 = 0.0011 \text{ mol} \cdot L^{-1}$
$[NO_2] = 0.0400 - 0.0189 = 0.0211 \text{ mol} \cdot L^{-1}$

13.77 $2N_2O(g) + 3O_2(g) \rightleftharpoons 4NO_2(g)$

(a) at equilibrium:

$[NO_2] = 0.0200 \text{ mol} \cdot L^{-1}$

$[N_2O] = 0.0200 \text{ mol} \cdot L^{-1} - (0.0200 \text{ mol} \cdot L^{-1}) \times \left(\dfrac{2 \text{ mol } N_2O}{4 \text{ mol } NO_2}\right)$

$\qquad = 0.0100 \text{ mol} \cdot L^{-1}$

$[O_2] = 0.0560 \text{ mol} \cdot L^{-1} - (0.0200 \text{ mol} \cdot L^{-1}) \times \left(\dfrac{3 \text{ mol } O_2}{4 \text{ mol } N_2O}\right)$

$\qquad = 0.0410 \text{ mol} \cdot L^{-1}$

(b) $K_c = \dfrac{[NO_2]^4}{[N_2O]^2[O_2]^3} = \dfrac{(0.0200)^4}{(0.0100)^2(0.0410)^3} = 23.2$

13.79 $PCl_3(g) + Cl_2(g) \rightleftharpoons PCl_5(g)$

$Q_c = \dfrac{[PCl_5]}{[PCl_3][Cl_2]} = \dfrac{\left(\dfrac{1.5 \text{ mol}}{0.500 \text{ L}}\right)}{\left(\dfrac{3.0 \text{ mol}}{0.500 \text{ L}}\right) \times \left(\dfrac{0.50 \text{ mol}}{0.500 \text{ L}}\right)} = 0.50$

(a) If $K_c = 0.56$, then $Q_c < K_c$ and the reaction is not at equilibrium.

(b) The reaction will proceed to the right, to produce more product.

(c)

Concentration $(\text{mol} \cdot L^{-1})$	$PCl_3(g)$ +	$Cl_2(g)$ $\rightleftharpoons$	$PCl_5(g)$
initial	6.0	1.0	3.0
change	$-x$	$-x$	$+x$
equil.	$6.0 - x$	$1.0 - x$	$3.0 + x$

$K_c = 0.56 = \dfrac{(3.0 + x)}{(6.0 - x) \times (1.0 - x)}$

$3.0 + x = (0.56) \times (x^2 - 7.0x + 6) = 0.56x^2 - 3.92x + 3.36$

$0.56x^2 - 4.92x + 0.36 = 0$

Solving the quadratic, we get $x = 0.074$.

equilibrium concentrations:

$[PCl_5] = 3.0 \text{ mol} \cdot L^{-1} + 0.074 \text{ mol} \cdot L^{-1} \approx 3.1 \text{ mol} \cdot L^{-1}$
$[PCl_3] = 6.0 \text{ mol} \cdot L^{-1} - 0.074 \text{ mol} \cdot L^{-1} \approx 5.9 \text{ mol} \cdot L^{-1}$
$[Cl_2] = 1.0 \text{ mol} \cdot L^{-1} - 0.074 \text{ mol} \cdot L^{-1} \approx 0.9 \text{ mol} \cdot L^{-1}$

13.81 Pressure (atm) $2HCl(g) \rightleftharpoons H_2(g) + Cl_2(g)$

initial	0.22	0	0
change	$-2x$	$+x$	$+x$
equil.	$0.22 - 2x$	x	x

$$K_p = 3.2 \times 10^{-34} = \frac{P_{H_2}P_{Cl_2}}{P_{HCl}^2} = \frac{(x) \times (x)}{(0.22 - x)^2}$$

Because K_p is very small, $(0.22 - x) \approx 0.22$.

$$3.2 \times 10^{-34} = \frac{x^2}{(0.22)^2}$$

$$x^2 = 1.5 \times 10^{-35}$$

equilibrium partial pressures: $x = 3.9 \times 10^{-18}$ atm $= P_{H_2} = P_{Cl_2}$

$$P_{HCl} \approx 0.22 \text{ atm}$$

13.83 (a) $n_{NOCl} = 30.1 \text{ g NOCl} \times \dfrac{1 \text{ mol NOCl}}{65.5 \text{ g NOCl}} = 0.459\overline{5} \text{ mol NOCl}$

$$\text{initial } P_{NOCl} = \frac{nRT}{V} = \frac{0.459\overline{5} \text{ mol} \times 0.082\,06 \text{ L} \cdot \text{atm} \cdot \text{K}^{-1} \cdot \text{mol}^{-1} \times 500 \text{ K}}{0.200 \text{ L}}$$

$$= 94.2\overline{7} \text{ atm}$$

Pressure (atm) $2NOCl(g) \rightleftharpoons 2NO(g) + Cl_2(g)$

initial	$94.2\overline{7}$	0	0
change	$-2x$	$+2x$	$+x$
equil.	$94.2\overline{7} - 2x$	$2x$	x

$$K_p = 1.13 \times 10^{-3} = \frac{P_{NO}^2 P_{Cl_2}}{P_{NOCl}^2} = \frac{(2x)^2 \times x}{(94.2\overline{7} - 2x)^2}$$

Because K_p is small, we can approximate this expression by neglecting $2x$ in the denominator.

$$K_p = 1.13 \times 10^{-3} = \frac{4x^3}{(94.2\overline{7})^2}$$

$$x = \sqrt[3]{\frac{1.13 \times 10^{-3} \times (94.2\overline{7})^2}{4}} = 1.36 \text{ atm} = P_{Cl_2}$$

$2x = 2 \times 1.36 \text{ atm} = 2.72 \text{ atm} = P_{NO}$

$94.2\overline{7} \text{ atm} - 2x = 94.2\overline{7} \text{ atm} - 2.72 \text{ atm} = 91.6 \text{ atm} = P_{NOCl}$

(b) % decomposition $= \dfrac{(94.3 - 91.6) \text{ atm}}{94.3 \text{ atm}} \times 100\% = 2.9\%$

13.85 (a) shift toward reactants

(b) no effect (number of moles of gaseous reactants and products equal)

(c) shift toward products

(d) shift toward products (reaction is endothermic; $+\Delta H$)

(e) no effect (solid, not in equilibrium expression)

(f) shift toward products

(g) shift toward reactants

13.87 $CO(g) + 2H_2(g) \rightleftharpoons CH_3OH(g) \qquad K_c = 1.1 \times 10^{-2}$

(a) $Q_c = \dfrac{[CH_3OH]}{[CO][H_2]^2} = \dfrac{\left(\dfrac{0.180}{3.00}\right)}{\left(\dfrac{0.150}{3.00}\right) \times \left(\dfrac{0.0900}{3.00}\right)^2} = \dfrac{(0.0600)}{(0.0500) \times (0.0300)^2}$

$= 1.3 \times 10^3$

As the reaction approaches equilibrium, the molar concentration of CH_3OH will decrease, because $Q_c > K_c$ (reactants are favored).

(b)

Concentration $(mol \cdot L^{-1})$	$CO(g)$	$+$	$2H_2(g)$	$\rightleftharpoons$	$CH_3OH(g)$
initial	0.0500		0.0300		0.0600
change	$+x$		$+2x$		$-x$
equil.	$0.0500 + x$		$0.0300 + 2x$		$0.0600 - x$

$K_c = 1.1 \times 10^{-2} = \dfrac{(0.0600 - x)}{(0.0500 + x) \times (0.0300 + 2x)^2}$

Expanding the equation yields $x^3 - 0.0200x^2 - 22.728\ 55x + 1.3636\ 251 = 0$. Solution of this cubic equation yields $x = 0.0600$. Therefore,

$[CO] = 0.0500 + 0.0600 = 0.1100 \ mol \cdot L^{-1}$

$[H_2] = 0.0300 + 2 \times 0.0600 = 0.150 \ mol \cdot L^{-1}$

$[CH_3OH] = 0.0600 + 0.0600 \approx 0 \ mol \cdot L^{-1}$

13.89

Concentration	$N_2O_4(g)$	$\rightleftharpoons$	$2NO_2(g)$
initial	$\left(\dfrac{2.50\ g}{2.00\ L}\right)\left(\dfrac{1\ mol}{92.0\ g}\right)$		0
change	$-x$		$+2x$
equil.	$1.36 \times 10^{-2} mol \cdot L^{-1} - x$		$2x$

$K_c = \dfrac{[NO_2]^2}{[N_2O_4]} = \dfrac{(2x)^2}{(1.36 \times 10^{-2} - x)} = 4.66 \times 10^{-3}$

$4x^2 = 6.33 \times 10^{-5} - 4.66 \times 10^{-3}x$

$4x^2 + 4.66 \times 10^{-3}x - 6.33 \times 10^{-5} = 0$

Solving the quadratic yields $x = 3.44 \times 10^{-3}$.

$2x = 6.88 \times 10^{-3} \text{ mol} \cdot \text{L}^{-1} = [NO_2]$

$1.36 \times 10^{-2} - 3.44 \times 10^{-3} = 1.02 \times 10^{-2} \text{ mol} \cdot \text{L}^{-1} = [N_2O_4]$

CHALLENGING EXERCISES

13.91 $A + B \rightleftharpoons C + D$ at 100°C.   Let x = ester.

Reactant	A	B	C	D
initial	A	B	0	0
change	$-x$	$-x$	$+x$	$+x$
equil.	$A - x$	$B - x$	x	x

$$K_c = \frac{[C][D]}{[A][B]} = \frac{(x)(x)}{(A - x)(B - x)}$$

$$K_c = \frac{x^2}{(A - x)(B - x)}$$

$$x^2 = K_c(A - x)(B - x)$$
$$= K_c[(AB) - (Ax) - (Bx) + x^2]$$
$$= K_c(AB) - (A + B)K_cx + K_cx^2$$

$$x^2 - K_cx^2 = K_c(AB) - (A + B)K_cx$$

$$(1 - K_c)x^2 + (A + B)K_cx - K_c(AB) = 0 \quad \text{(a quadratic equation)}$$

If A = 1.0 mol, B = 0.5 mol, K_c = 3.5, and assuming V = constant, the number of moles of ester, x, can be directly solved for: x = 0.42 mol.

13.93   (a) $K_c = \dfrac{[NO_2]^2}{[N_2O_4]} = \dfrac{(2.13)^2}{0.405} = 11.2$

(b)

Concentration	$N_2O_4(g)$ $\rightleftharpoons$	$2NO_2$
initial (mol · L^{-1})	0.405	3.13
change (mol · L^{-1})	$+x$	$-2x$
equil. (mol · L^{-1})	$0.405 + x$	$3.13 - 2x$

As can be seen from the equilibrium table, $[N_2O_4]$ will increase, as will $[NO_2]$ ($2x$ should be <1.00), but K_c remains constant.

(c) $K_c = 11.2 = \dfrac{(3.13 - 2x)^2}{0.405 + x}$

This expression rearranges to the quadratic $4x^2 - 23.72x + 5.2609 = 0$, which yields $x = 0.231 \text{ mol} \cdot \text{L}^{-1}$. This answer is consistent with $2x < 1.00 \text{ mol} \cdot \text{L}^{-1}$. The final equilibrium concentrations are

$[N_2O_4] = 0.405 + x = (0.405 + 0.231) \text{ mol} \cdot \text{L}^{-1} = 0.636 \text{ mol} \cdot \text{L}^{-1}$

$[NO_2] = 3.13 - 2x = (3.13 - 2 \times 0.231) \text{ mol} \cdot \text{L}^{-1} = 2.67 \text{ mol} \cdot \text{L}^{-1}$

13.95 $NH_4HS(s) \longrightarrow NH_3(g) + H_2S(g)$

$K_P = P_{NH_3} P_{H_2S}$

$P_{NH_3} = P_{H_2S} = \dfrac{1}{2} P$

$K_P = \dfrac{1}{4} P^2$

$\ln\left(\dfrac{K_P'}{K_P}\right) = \ln\left(\dfrac{P'}{P}\right) = \dfrac{\Delta H°}{R} \times \left(\dfrac{1}{T} - \dfrac{1}{T'}\right)$

Solve $\ln\left(\dfrac{501}{919}\right)^2 = \dfrac{\Delta H°}{R} \times \left(\dfrac{1}{308.8} - \dfrac{1}{298.3}\right)$ for $\Delta H°$, then look for T such that

$\ln k = \ln 760$

$\ln\left(\dfrac{501}{919}\right) = -0.607 = \dfrac{\Delta H°}{2R} \times \left(\dfrac{-10.5}{(308.8) \times (298.3)}\right) K^{-1}$

$\Delta H° = \dfrac{(-0.607) \times (8.31) \times (308.8) \times (298.3)}{-10.5} = 8.86 \times 10^4 \, J \cdot mol^{-1}$

Then $\ln\left(\dfrac{760}{501}\right)^2 = 0.417 = \dfrac{88600}{8.31} \times \left(\dfrac{T_b - 298.3}{(298.3)T_b}\right)$

$\left(\dfrac{(0.417) \times (8.31) \times (298.3)}{44300}\right) T_b = T_b - 298.3$

$0.0233 T_b = T_b - 298.3$

$T_b(1 - 0.0233) = 298.3$

$T_b = \dfrac{298.3}{0.9767} = 305.4 \, K$

CHAPTER 14
PROTONS IN TRANSITION: ACIDS AND BASES

EXERCISES

Unless stated otherwise, assume that all solutions are aqueous and that the temperature is 25°C.

Brønsted Acids and Bases

14.1 (a) amphiprotic (b) base (c) base (d) acid

14.3 (a) $CH_3NH_3^+$ (b) $NH_2NH_3^+$ (c) H_2CO_3 (d) CO_3^{2-} (e) $C_6H_5O^-$
(f) $CH_3CO_2^-$

14.5 (a)
$$\underset{acid_1}{H_2SO_4} + \underset{base_2}{H_2O} \longrightarrow \underset{acid_2}{H_3O^+} + \underset{base_1}{HSO_4^-}$$
conjugate (outer), conjugate (inner)

(b)
$$\underset{acid_1}{C_6H_5NH_3^+} + \underset{base_2}{H_2O} \rightleftharpoons \underset{acid_2}{H_3O^+} + \underset{base_1}{C_6H_5NH_2}$$
conjugate (outer), conjugate (inner)

(c)
$$\underset{acid_1}{H_2PO_4^-} + \underset{base_2}{H_2O} \rightleftharpoons \underset{acid_2}{H_3O^+} + \underset{base_1}{HPO_4^{2-}}$$
conjugate (outer), conjugate (inner)

(d)
$$\underset{acid_1}{HCOOH} + \underset{base_2}{H_2O} \rightleftharpoons \underset{acid_2}{H_3O^+} + \underset{base_1}{HCO_2^-}$$
conjugate (outer), conjugate (inner)

(e)
$$\overset{\text{conjugate}}{\overbrace{\underset{\substack{\text{acid}_1}}{NH_2NH_3^+} + \underset{\substack{\text{base}_2}}{H_2O} \rightleftharpoons \underset{\substack{\text{acid}_2}}{H_3O^+} + \underset{\substack{\text{base}_1}}{NH_2NH_2}}}$$

conjugate

14.7 (a) HCO_3^-, as an acid:

$$\overset{\text{conjugate}}{\overbrace{\underset{\substack{\text{acid}_1}}{HCO_3^-} + \underset{\substack{\text{base}_2}}{H_2O} \rightleftharpoons \underset{\substack{\text{acid}_2}}{H_3O^+} + \underset{\substack{\text{base}_1}}{CO_3^{2-}}}}$$

conjugate

HCO_3^-, as a base:

$$\overset{\text{conjugate}}{\overbrace{\underset{\substack{\text{acid}_1}}{H_2O} + \underset{\substack{\text{base}_2}}{HCO_3^-} \rightleftharpoons \underset{\substack{\text{acid}_2}}{H_2CO_3} + \underset{\substack{\text{base}_1}}{OH^-}}}$$

conjugate

(b) HPO_4^{2-}, as an acid:

$$\overset{\text{conjugate}}{\overbrace{\underset{\substack{\text{acid}_1}}{HPO_4^{2-}} + \underset{\substack{\text{base}_2}}{H_2O} \rightleftharpoons \underset{\substack{\text{acid}_2}}{H_3O^+} + \underset{\substack{\text{base}_1}}{PO_4^{3-}}}}$$

conjugate

HPO_4^{2-}, as a base:

$$\overset{\text{conjugate}}{\overbrace{\underset{\substack{\text{acid}_1}}{H_2O} + \underset{\substack{\text{base}_2}}{HPO_4^{2-}} \rightleftharpoons \underset{\substack{\text{acid}_2}}{H_2PO_4^-} + \underset{\substack{\text{base}_1}}{OH^-}}}$$

conjugate

14.9 (a) Brønsted acid: HNO_3

Brønsted base: HPO_4^{2-}

(b) conjugate base to HNO_3: NO_3^-

conjugate acid to HPO_4^{2-}: $H_2PO_4^-$

Autoprotolysis of Water

14.11 In each case, use $K_w = [H_3O^+][OH^-] = 1.0 \times 10^{-14}$, then

$$[OH^-] = \frac{K_w}{[H_3O^+]} = \frac{1.0 \times 10^{-14}}{[H_3O^+]}$$

(a) $[OH^-] = \dfrac{1.0 \times 10^{-14}}{3.1 \times 10^{-2}} = 3.2 \times 10^{-13} \text{ mol} \cdot L^{-1}$

(b) $[OH^-] = \dfrac{1.0 \times 10^{-14}}{1.0 \times 10^{-4}} = 1.0 \times 10^{-10}$ mol $\cdot$ L^{-1}

(c) $[OH^-] = \dfrac{1.0 \times 10^{-14}}{0.20} = 5.0 \times 10^{-14}$ mol $\cdot$ L^{-1}

14.13 (a) $K_w = 2.5 \times 10^{-14} = [H_3O^+][OH^-] = x^2$, where $x = [H_3O^+] = [OH^-]$
$x = \sqrt{2.5 \times 10^{-14}} = 1.5\overline{8} \times 10^{-7} = 1.6 \times 10^{-7}$ mol $\cdot$ L^{-1}
pH $= -\log[H_3O^+] = 6.80$
(b) $[OH^-] = [H_3O^+] = 1.5\overline{8} \times 10^{-7} = 1.6 \times 10^{-7}$ mol $\cdot$ L^{-1}
pOH $= -\log[OH^-] = 6.80$

pH and pOH of Strong Acids and Bases

14.15 Because HCl is a strong acid, $[HCl]_0 = [H_3O^+] = [Cl^-]$, where $[HCl]_0 =$ nominal concentration of HCl

$[HCl]_0 = \dfrac{0.48 \text{ mol}}{0.500 \text{ L}} = 0.96$ mol $\cdot$ L$^{-1} = [H_3O^+] = [Cl^-]$

$[OH^-] = \dfrac{K_w}{[H_3O^+]} = \dfrac{1.0 \times 10^{-14}}{0.96} = 1.0 \times 10^{-14}$ mol $\cdot$ L^{-1}

14.17 Because Ba(OH)$_2$ is a strong base, Ba(OH)$_2$ (aq) $\longrightarrow$ Ba^{2+}(aq) + 2OH$^-$(aq), 100%.
Then, $[Ba(OH)_2]_0 = [Ba^{2+}]$, $[OH^-] = 2 \times [Ba(OH)_2]$, where $[Ba(OH)_2]_0 =$ nominal concentration of Ba(OH)$_2$.

amount (moles) of Ba(OH)$_2 = \dfrac{0.50 \text{ g}}{171.36 \text{ g} \cdot \text{mol}^{-1}} = 2.9 \times 10^{-3}$ mol

$[Ba(OH)_2]_0 = \dfrac{2.9 \times 10^{-3} \text{ mol}}{0.100 \text{ L}} = 2.9 \times 10^{-2}$ mol $\cdot$ L$^{-1} = [Ba^{2+}]$

$[OH^-] = 2 \times [Ba(OH)_2]_0 = 2 \times 2.9 \times 10^{-2}$ mol $\cdot$ L$^{-1} = 5.8 \times 10^{-2}$ mol $\cdot$ L^{-1}

$[H_3O^+] = \dfrac{K_w}{[OH-]} = \dfrac{1.0 \times 10^{-14}}{5.8 \times 10^{-2}} = 1.7 \times 10^{-13}$ mol $\cdot$ L^{-1}

14.19 Because pH $= -\log[H_3O^+]$, $\log[H_3O^+] = -$pH. Taking the antilogs of both sides gives $[H_3O^+] = 10^{-pH}$ mol $\cdot$ L^{-1}
(a) $[H_3O^+] = 10^{-3.3} = 5.0 \times 10^{-4}$ mol $\cdot$ L^{-1}
(b) $[H_3O^+] = 10^{-6.7}$ mol $\cdot$ L$^{-1} = 2 \times 10^{-7}$ mol $\cdot$ L^{-1}
(c) $[H_3O^+] = 10^{-4.4}$ mol $\cdot$ L$^{-1} = 4 \times 10^{-5}$ mol $\cdot$ L^{-1}
(d) $[H_3O^+] = 10^{-5.3}$ mol $\cdot$ L$^{-1} = 5 \times 10^{-6}$ mol $\cdot$ L^{-1}
(e) (b) $<$ (d) $<$ (c) $<$ (a)

14.21 $pH = -\log[H_3O^+]$, $pOH = 14.00 - pH$

(a) $pH = -\log(2.0 \times 10^{-5}) = 4.70$, $pOH = 14.00 - pH = 14.0 - 4.70 = 9.30$

(b) $pH = -\log(1.0) = 0.00$, $pOH = 14.00 - 0.00 = 14.00$

(c) $pH = -\log(5.0 \times 10^{-14}) = 13.3$, $pOH = 14.00 - 13.3 = 0.7$

(d) $pH = -\log(5.02 \times 10^{-5}) = 4.30$, $pOH = 14.00 - 4.30 = 9.70$

14.23 $[\text{acid}]_0$ = nominal concentration of acid

$[\text{base}]_0$ = nominal concentration of base

(a) $[HNO_3]_0 = [H_3O^+] = 0.010 \text{ mol} \cdot L^{-1}$; HNO_3 is a strong acid.

$pH = -\log(0.010) = 2.00$, $pOH = 14.00 - 2.00 = 12.00$

(b) $[HCl]_0 = [H_3O^+] = 0.22 \text{ mol} \cdot L^{-1}$; HCl is a strong acid.

$pH = -\log(0.22) = 0.66$, $pOH = 14.00 - 0.66 = 13.34$

(c) $[OH^-] = 2 \times [Ba(OH)_2] = 2 \times 1.0 \times 10^{-3} \text{ M} = 2.0 \times 10^{-3} \text{ mol} \cdot L^{-1}$

$pOH = -\log(2.0 \times 10^{-3}) = 2.70$, $pH = 14.00 - 2.70 = 11.30$

(d) $[KOH]_0 = [OH^-]$; KOH is a strong base.

$$[OH^-] = \left(\frac{10.0 \text{ mL}}{250 \text{ mL}}\right) \times (0.022 \text{ mol} \cdot L^{-1}) = 8.8 \times 10^{-4} \text{ mol} \cdot L^{-1}$$

$pOH = -\log(8.8 \times 10^{-4}) = 3.06$, $pH = 14.00 - 3.06 = 10.94$

(e) $[NaOH]_0 = [OH^-]$; NaOH is a strong base.

$$\text{number of moles of NaOH} = \frac{0.0140 \text{ g}}{40.0 \text{ g} \cdot mol^{-1}} = 3.50 \times 10^{-4} \text{ mol}$$

$$[NaOH]_0 = \frac{3.50 \times 10^{-4} \text{ mol}}{0.250 \text{ L}} = 1.40 \times 10^{-3} \text{ mol} \cdot L^{-1} = [OH^-]$$

$pOH = -\log(1.40 \times 10^{-3}) = 2.854$, $pH = 14.00 - 2.854 = 11.15$

(f) $[HBr]_0 = [H_3O^+]$; HBr is a strong acid.

$$[H_3O^+] = \left(\frac{50 \text{ mL}}{250 \text{ mL}}\right) \times (0.000\ 43 \text{ mol} \cdot L^{-1}) = 8.6 \times 10^{-5} \text{ mol} \cdot L^{-1}$$

$pH = -\log(8.6 \times 10^{-5}) = 4.07$, $pOH = 14.00 - 4.07 = 9.93$

Acidity and Basicity Constants

14.25

	Name	Formula	K_a	pK_a
(a)	formic acid	HCOOH	1.8×10^{-4}	3.75
(b)	acetic acid	CH_3COOH	1.8×10^{-5}	4.74
(c)	trichloroacetic acid	CCl_3COOH	3.0×10^{-1}	0.52
(d)	benzoic acid	C_6H_5COOH	6.5×10^{-5}	4.19

The larger K_a, the stronger the acid; therefore acetic acid < benzoic acid < formic acid < trichloroacetic acid.

14.27 $pK_{a1} = -\log K_{a1}$; therefore, after taking antilogs, $K_{a1} = 10^{-pK_{a1}}$

Acid	pK_{a1}	K_{a1}
(a) H_3PO_4	2.12	7.6×10^{-3}
(b) H_3PO_3	2.00	0.010
(c) H_2SeO_3	2.46	3.5×10^{-3}
(d) H_2SeO_4	1.92	0.012

The larger K_{a1}, the stronger the acid; therefore $H_2SeO_3 < H_3PO_4 < H_3PO_3 < H_2SeO_4$

14.29 The weakest acid has the strongest conjugate base and vice versa.

(a) $HSeO_3^-$, hydrogen selenite ion, strongest

$HSeO_4^-$, hydrogen selenate ion, weakest

(b) $HSeO_3^-$, $K_b = \dfrac{K_w}{K_a} = \dfrac{1.0 \times 10^{-14}}{3.5 \times 10^{-3}} = 2.9 \times 10^{-12}$

$HSeO_4^-$, $K_b = \dfrac{1.0 \times 10^{-14}}{0.012} = 8.3 \times 10^{-13}$

(c) $HSeO_3^-$, strongest base corresponds to highest pH.

Structures and Strengths of Acids

14.31 For oxoacids, the greater the number of highly electronegative O-atoms attached to the central atom, the stronger the acid. This effect is related to the increased oxidation number of the central atom as the number of O atoms increases. Therefore, HIO_3 is the stronger acid, with the lower pK_a.

14.33 (a) HCl is the stronger acid, because its bond strength is much weaker than the bond in HF, and bond strength is the dominant factor in determining the strength of binary acids.

(b) $HClO_2$ is stronger; there is one more O atom attached to the Cl atom in $HClO_2$ than in HClO. The additional O in $HClO_2$ helps to pull the electron of the H atom out of the H—O bond. The oxidation state of Cl is higher in $HClO_2$ than in HClO.

(c) $HClO_2$ is stronger; Cl has a greater electronegativity than Br, making the H—O bond $HClO_2$ more polar than in $HBrO_2$.

(d) $HClO_4$ is stronger; Cl has a greater electronegativity than P (see Example 14.4 in the text).

(e) HNO_3 is stronger. The explanation is the same as that for part (b). HNO_3 has one more O atom.

(f) H_2CO_3 is stronger; C has greater electronegativity than Ge. See part (c).

14.35 (a) The —CCl_3 group that is bonded to the carboxyl group, —COOH, in trichloroacetic acid, is more electron withdrawing than the —CH_3 group in acetic acid. Thus, trichloroacetic acid is the stronger acid.

(b) The —CH_3 group in acetic acid has electron-donating properties, which means that it is less electron withdrawing than the —H attached to the carboxyl group in formic acid, HCOOH. Thus, formic acid is a slightly stronger acid than acetic acid. However, it is not nearly as strong as trichloroacetic acid. The order is

$$CCl_3COOH \gg HCOOH > CH_3COOH$$

14.37 The larger the K_a, the stronger the corresponding acid. 2,4,6-Trichlorophenol is the stronger acid because the chlorines have a greater electron-withdrawing power than the hydrogens they replaced in the unsubstituted phenol.

14.39 The larger the pK_a of an acid, the stronger the corresponding conjugate base; hence, the order is aniline < ammonia < methylamine < ethylamine. Although one should not draw conclusions from such a small data set, we might suggest the possibility that

(1) arylamines < ammonia < alkylamines

(2) methyl < ethyl < etc.

(Arylamines are amines in which the nitrogen of the amine is attached to a benzene ring.)

Weak Acid and Weak Base Calculations

Refer to Tables 14.2 and 14.5 for the appropriate K_a and K_b values for the following exercises.

14.41 (a)

Concentration (mol · L^{-1})	C_6H_5COOH	+ H_2O $\rightleftharpoons$	H_3O^+	+ $C_6H_5CO_2^-$
initial	0.20	—	0	0
change	$-x$	—	$+x$	$+x$
equilibrium	$0.20 - x$	—	x	x

$$K_a = \frac{[H_3O^+][C_6H_5CO_2^-]}{[C_6H_5COOH]} = \frac{x \cdot x}{0.20 - x} \approx \frac{x^2}{0.20} = 6.5 \times 10^{-5}$$

$$x = [H_3O^+] = \sqrt{0.20 \times 6.5 \times 10^{-5}} = 3.6 \times 10^{-3} \text{ mol} \cdot L^{-1}$$

$$[OH^-] = \frac{K_w}{[H_3O^+]} = \frac{1.0 \times 10^{-14}}{3.6 \times 10^{-3}} = 2.8 \times 10^{-12} \text{ mol} \cdot L^{-1}$$

(b) Concentration (mol·L^{-1}) $H_2O + NH_2NH_2 \rightleftharpoons NH_2NH_3^+ + OH^-$

initial	—	0.20	0	0
change	—	$-x$	$+x$	$+x$
equilibrium	—	$0.20 - x$	x	x

$$K_b = \frac{[NH_2NH_3^+][OH^-]}{[NH_2NH_2]} = \frac{x \cdot x}{0.20 - x} \approx \frac{x^2}{0.20} = 1.7 \times 10^{-6}$$

$$x = [OH^-] = \sqrt{0.20 \times 1.7 \times 10^{-6}} = 5.8 \times 10^{-4} \text{ mol·L}^{-1}$$

$$[H_3O^+] = \frac{K_w}{[OH^-]} = \frac{1.0 \times 10^{-14}}{5.8 \times 10^{-4}} = 1.7 \times 10^{-11} \text{ mol·L}^{-1}$$

(c) Concentration (mol·L^{-1}) $H_2O + (CH_3)_3N \rightleftharpoons (CH_3)_3NH^+ + OH^-$

initial	—	0.20	0	0
change	—	$-x$	$+x$	$+x$
equilibrium	—	$0.20 - x$	x	x

$$K_b = \frac{[(CH_3)_3NH^+][OH^-]}{[(CH_3)_3N]} = \frac{x \cdot x}{0.20 - x} \approx \frac{x^2}{0.20} = 6.5 \times 10^{-5}$$

$$x = [OH^-] = \sqrt{0.20 \times 6.5 \times 10^{-5}} = 3.6 \times 10^{-3} \text{ mol·L}^{-1}$$

$$[H_3O^+] = \frac{1.0 \times 10^{-14}}{3.6 \times 10^{-3}} = 2.8 \times 10^{-12} \text{ mol·L}^{-1}$$

14.43 (a) Concentration (mol·L^{-1}) $HCOOH + H_2O \rightleftharpoons H_3O^+ + HCO_2^-$

initial	0.20	—	0	0
change	$-x$	—	$+x$	$+x$
equilibrium	$0.20 - x$	—	x	x

$$K_a = \frac{[H_3O^+][HCO_2^-]}{[HCOOH]} = \frac{x \cdot x}{0.20 - x} \approx \frac{x^2}{0.20} = 1.8 \times 10^{-4}$$

$$x = [H_3O^+] = \sqrt{0.20 \times 1.8 \times 10^{-4}} = 6.0 \times 10^{-3} \text{ mol·L}^{-1}$$

$$pH = -\log(6.0 \times 10^{-3}) = 2.22$$

(b) Concentration (mol·L^{-1}) $H_2O + NH_2NH_2 \rightleftharpoons NH_2NH_3^+ + OH^-$

initial	—	0.12	0	0
change	—	$-x$	$+x$	$+x$
equilibrium	—	$0.12 - x$	x	x

$$K_b = \frac{[NH_2NH_3^+][OH^-]}{[NH_2NH_2]} = \frac{x \cdot x}{0.12 - x} \approx \frac{x^2}{0.12} = 1.7 \times 10^{-6}$$

$$x = [OH^-] = \sqrt{0.12 \times 1.7 \times 10^{-6}} = 4.5 \times 10^{-4} \text{ mol·L}^{-1}$$

$$pOH = -\log(4.5 \times 10^{-4}) = 3.35, \quad pH = 14.00 - 3.35 = 10.65$$

(c) Concentration ($mol \cdot L^{-1}$) $\quad C_6H_5COOH + H_2O \rightleftharpoons H_3O^+ + C_6H_5CO_2^-$

initial	0.15	—	0	0
change	$-x$	—	$+x$	$+x$
equilibrium	$0.15 - x$	—	x	x

$$K_a = \frac{[H_3O^+][C_6H_5CO_2^-]}{[C_6H_5COOH]} = \frac{x^2}{0.15 - x} \approx \frac{x^2}{0.15} = 6.5 \times 10^{-5}$$

$$x = [H_3O^+] = \sqrt{0.15 \times 6.5 \times 10^{-5}} = 3.1 \times 10^{-3} \; mol \cdot L^{-1}$$

$$pH = -\log(3.1 \times 10^{-3}) = 2.51$$

(d) Concentration ($mol \cdot L^{-1}$) $\quad H_2O + C_{10}H_{14}N_2 \rightleftharpoons C_{10}H_{14}N_2H^+ + OH^-$

initial	—	0.0034	0	0
change	—	$-x$	$+x$	$+x$
equilibrium	—	$0.0058 - x$	x	x

$$K_b = \frac{[C_{10}H_{14}N_2H^+][OH^-]}{[C_{10}H_{14}N_2]} = \frac{x^2}{0.0034 - x} \approx \frac{x^2}{0.0034} = 1.0 \times 10^{-6}$$

$$x = \sqrt{0.0034 \times 1.0 \times 10^{-6}} = 5.8 \times 10^{-5} \; mol \cdot L^{-1} = [OH^-]$$

$$pOH = -\log(5.8 \times 10^{-5}) = 4.24, \quad pH = 14.00 - 4.23 = 9.77$$

14.45 (a) Concentration ($mol \cdot L^{-1}$) $\quad CH_3COOH + H_2O \rightleftharpoons H_3O^+ + CH_3CO_2^-$

initial	0.15	—	0	0
change	$-x$	—	$+x$	$+x$
equilibrium	$0.15 - x$	—	x	x

$$K_a = 1.8 \times 10^{-5} = \frac{[H_3O^+][CH_3CO_2^-]}{[CH_3COOH]} = \frac{x^2}{0.15 - x} \approx \frac{x^2}{0.15}$$

$$x = [H_3O^+] = 1.6 \times 10^{-3} \; mol \cdot L^{-1}$$

$$pH = -\log(1.6 \times 10^{-3}) = 2.80, \quad pOH = 14.00 - 2.80 = 11.20$$

(b) The equilibrium table for (b) is similar to that for (a).

$$K_a = 3.0 \times 10^{-1} = \frac{[H_3O^+][CCl_3CO_2^-]}{[CCl_3COOH]} = \frac{x^2}{0.15 - x}$$

$$\text{or } x^2 + 3.0 \times 10^{-1}x - 0.045 = 0$$

$$x = \frac{-3.0 \times 10^{-1} \pm \sqrt{(3.0 \times 10^{-1})^2 - (4)(-0.045)}}{2} = 0.11\overline{0}, \; -0.41\overline{0}$$

The negative root is not possible and can be eliminated.

$$x = [H_3O^+] = 0.11\overline{0} \; mol \cdot L^{-1}$$

$$pH = -\log(0.11\overline{0}) = 0.96, \quad pOH = 14.00 - 0.96 = 13.04$$

(c) Concentration $(mol \cdot L^{-1})$ $HCOOH + H_2O \rightleftharpoons H_3O^+ + HCO_2^-$

	initial			
initial	0.15	—	0	0
change	$-x$	—	$+x$	$+x$
equilibrium	$0.15 - x$	—	x	x

$$K_a = \frac{[H_3O^+][HCO_2^-]}{[HCOOH]} = \frac{x \cdot x}{0.15 - x} \approx \frac{x^2}{0.15} = 1.8 \times 10^{-4}$$

$$x = [H_3O^+] = \sqrt{0.15 \times 1.8 \times 10^{-4}} = 5.2 \times 10^{-3}\ mol \cdot L^{-1}$$

$$pH = -\log(5.2 \times 10^{-3}) = 2.28, \quad pOH = 14.00 - 2.28 = 11.72$$

14.47 (a) Concentration $(mol \cdot L^{-1})$ $H_2O + NH_3 \rightleftharpoons NH_4^+ + OH^-$

	initial			
initial	—	0.10	0	0
change	—	$-x$	$+x$	$+x$
equilibrium	—	$0.10 - x$	x	x

$$K_b = \frac{[NH_4^+][OH^-]}{[NH_3]} = \frac{x \cdot x}{0.10 - x} \approx \frac{x^2}{0.10} = 1.8 \times 10^{-5}$$

$$x = [OH^-] = \sqrt{0.10 \times 1.8 \times 10^{-5}} = 1.3 \times 10^{-3}\ mol \cdot L^{-1}$$

$$pOH = -\log(1.3 \times 10^{-3}) = 2.89, \quad pH = 14.00 - 2.89 = 11.11$$

$$\text{percentage protonation} = \frac{1.3 \times 10^{-3}}{0.10} \times 100\% = 1.3\%$$

(b) Concentration $(mol \cdot L^{-1})$ $NH_2OH + H_2O \rightleftharpoons {}^+NH_3OH + OH^-$

	initial			
initial	0.017	—	0	0
change	$-x$	—	$+x$	$+x$
equilibrium	$0.017 - x$	—	x	x

$$K_b = 1.1 \times 10^{-8} = \frac{x^2}{0.017 - x} \approx \frac{x^2}{0.017}$$

$$x = [OH^-] = 1.3\overline{7} \times 10^{-5}\ mol \cdot L^{-1}$$

$$pOH = -\log(1.3\overline{7} \times 10^{-5}) = 4.86, \quad pH = 14.00 - 4.86 = 9.14$$

$$\text{percentage protonation} = \frac{1.3\overline{7} \times 10^{-5}}{0.017} \times 100\% = 0.081\%$$

(c) See the solution to Exercise 14.41 (c), which involves the same aqueous solution of $(CH_3)_3N$.

$$[OH^-] = 3.6 \times 10^{-3}\ mol \cdot L^{-1}$$

$$pOH = -\log(3.6 \times 10^{-3}) = 2.44, \quad pH = 14.00 - 2.44 = 11.56$$

$$\text{percentage protonation} = \frac{3.6 \times 10^{-3}}{0.20} \times 100\% = 1.8\%$$

(d) $pK_b = 14.00 - pK_a = 14.00 - 8.21 = 5.79, \quad K_b = 1.6 \times 10^{-6}$

$$codeine + H_2O \rightleftharpoons codeineH^+ + OH^-$$

$$K_b = 1.6 \times 10^{-6} = \frac{x^2}{0.020 - x} \approx \frac{x^2}{0.020}$$

$$x = [\text{OH}^-] = 1.7\overline{8} \times 10^{-4} \text{ mol} \cdot \text{L}^{-1}$$

$$\text{pOH} = -\log(1.7\overline{8} \times 10^{-4}) = 3.74, \quad \text{pH} = 14.00 - 3.74 = 10.26$$

$$\text{percentage protonation} = \frac{1.7\overline{8} \times 10^{-4}}{0.020} \times 100\% = 0.89\%$$

14.49 (a) $\text{HClO}_2 + \text{H}_2\text{O} \rightleftharpoons \text{H}_3\text{O}^+ + \text{ClO}_2^-$

$$[\text{H}_3\text{O}^+] = [\text{ClO}_2^-] = 10^{-\text{pH}} = 10^{-1.2} = 0.06\overline{3} \text{ mol} \cdot \text{L}^{-1}$$

$$K_a = \frac{[\text{H}_3\text{O}^+][\text{ClO}_2^-]}{[\text{HClO}_2]} = \frac{(0.06\overline{3})^2}{0.10 - 0.063} = 0.1\overline{1} = 0.1 \text{ (1 sf)}$$

$$pK_a = -\log(0.1\overline{1}) = 1.0$$

(b) $\text{C}_3\text{H}_7\text{NH}_2 + \text{H}_2\text{O} \rightleftharpoons \text{C}_3\text{H}_7\text{NH}_3^+ + \text{OH}^-$

$$\text{pOH} = 14.00 - 11.86 = 2.14$$

$$[\text{C}_3\text{H}_7\text{NH}_3^+] = [\text{OH}^-] = 10^{-2.14} = 7.2\overline{4} \times 10^{-3} \text{ mol} \cdot \text{L}^{-1}$$

$$K_b = \frac{[\text{C}_3\text{H}_7\text{NH}_3^+][\text{OH}^-]}{[\text{C}_3\text{H}_7\text{NH}_2]} = \frac{(7.2\overline{4} \times 10^{-3})^2}{0.10 - 7.2\overline{4} \times 10^{-3}} = 5.7 \times 10^{-4}$$

$$pK_b = -\log(5.7 \times 10^{-4}) = 3.25$$

14.51 (a) $\text{pH} = 4.6, \quad [\text{H}_3\text{O}^+] = 10^{-\text{pH}} = 10^{-4.6} = 2.\overline{5} \times 10^{-5} \text{ mol} \cdot \text{L}^{-1}$

Let x = nominal concentration of HClO, then

Concentration	HClO	+ H$_2$O $\rightleftharpoons$	H$_3$O$^+$	+	ClO$^-$
nominal conc.	x	—	0		0
at equil.	$x - 2.\overline{5} \times 10^{-5}$	—	$2.\overline{5} \times 10^{-5}$		$2.\overline{5} \times 10^{-5}$

$$K_a = 3.0 \times 10^{-8} = \frac{(2.\overline{5} \times 10^{-5})^2}{x - 2.\overline{5} \times 10^{-5}}$$

Solve for x; $x = \dfrac{(2.5 \times 10^{-5})^2 + 2.\overline{5} \times 10^{-5} \times 3.0 \times 10^{-8}}{3.0 \times 10^{-8}}$

$$= 2 \times 10^{-2} \text{ mol} \cdot \text{L}^{-1} = 0.02 \text{ mol} \cdot \text{L}^{-1}$$

(b) $\text{pOH} = 14.00 - \text{pH} = 14.00 - 10.2 = 3.8$

$$[\text{OH}^-] = 10^{-\text{pOH}} = 10^{-3.8} = 1.\overline{6} \times 10^{-4}$$

Let x = nominal concentration of NH$_2$NH$_2$, then

Concentration	NH$_2$NH$_2$	+ H$_2$O $\rightleftharpoons$	NH$_2$NH$_3^+$	+	OH$^-$
nominal conc.	x	—	0		0
at equil.	$x - 1.\overline{6} \times 10^{-4}$	—	$1.\overline{6} \times 10^{-4}$		$1.\overline{6} \times 10^{-4}$

$$K_b = 1.7 \times 10^{-6} = \frac{(1.\overline{6} \times 10^{-4})^2}{x - 1.\overline{6} \times 10^{-4}}$$

Solve for x; $x = 1.\overline{52} \times 10^{-2}$ mol $\cdot$ L^{-1} = 0.02 mol $\cdot$ L^{-1}

14.53

Concentration (mol $\cdot$ L^{-1})	C_6H_5COOH +	H_2O $\rightleftharpoons$	H_3O^+ +	$C_6H_5CO_2^-$
initial	0.110	—	0	0
change	$-x$	—	$+x$	$+x$
equilibrium	$0.110 - x$	—	x	x

$x = 0.024 \times 0.110$ mol $\cdot$ L^{-1} = $[H_3O^+]$ = $[C_6H_5CO_2^-]$

$$K_a = \frac{[H_3O^+][C_6H_5COO^-]}{[C_6H_5COOH]} = \frac{(0.024 \times 0.110)^2}{(1 - 0.024) \times 0.110} = \frac{(2.6\overline{4} \times 10^{-3})^2}{0.107\overline{4}} = 6.5 \times 10^{-5}$$

pH $= -\log(2.6\overline{4} \times 10^{-3}) = 2.58$

14.55 H_2O + octylamine $\rightleftharpoons$ octylamineH$^+$ + OH$^-$

The change in the concentration of octylamine is $x = 0.067 \times 0.10 = 0.0067$ mol $\cdot$ L^{-1}.
Thus the equilibrium table is

Concentration (mol $\cdot$ L^{-1})	H_2O +	octylamine $\rightleftharpoons$	octylamineH$^+$ +	OH$^-$
initial	—	0.10	0	0
change	—	-0.0067	$+0.0067$	$+0.0067$
equilibrium	—	$0.10 - 0.0067$	0.0067	0.0067

The equilibrium concentrations are

[octylamine] $= 0.10 - 0.067 \times 0.10 = 0.09\overline{3}$ mol $\cdot$ L^{-1}

[OH$^-$] $=$ [octylamineH$^+$] $= 0.0067$ mol $\cdot$ L^{-1}

pOH $= -\log(0.0067) = 2.17$,   pH $= 14.00 - 2.17 = 11.83$

$$K_b = \frac{[\text{octylamineH}^+][OH^-]}{[\text{octylamine}]} = \frac{(6.7 \times 10^{-3})^2}{0.09\overline{3}} = 5 \times 10^{-4}$$

Polyprotic Acids

14.57 (a) $H_2SO_4 + H_2O \longrightarrow H_3O^+ + HSO_4^-$
$HSO_4^- + H_2O \rightleftharpoons H_3O^+ + SO_4^{2-}$
(b) $H_3AsO_4 + H_2O \rightleftharpoons H_3O^+ + H_2AsO_4^-$
$H_2AsO_4^- + H_2O \rightleftharpoons H_3O^+ + HAsO_4^{2-}$
$HAsO_4^{2-} + H_2O \rightleftharpoons H_3O^+ + AsO_4^{3-}$
(c) $C_6H_4(COOH)_2 + H_2O \rightleftharpoons H_3O^+ + C_6H_4(COOH)CO_2^-$
$C_6H_4(COOH)CO_2^- + H_2O \rightleftharpoons H_3O^+ + C_6H_4(CO_2)_2^{2-}$

14.59 The initial concentrations of HSO_4^- and H_3O^+ are both 0.15 mol $\cdot$ L^{-1} as a result of the complete ionization of H_2SO_4 in the first step. The second ionization is incomplete.

Concentration $(mol \cdot L^{-1})$	HSO_4^-	$+ H_2O \rightleftharpoons$	H_3O^+	$+ SO_4^{2-}$
initial	0.15	—	0.15	0
change	$-x$	—	$+x$	$+x$
equilibrium	$0.15 - x$	—	$0.15 + x$	x

$$K_{a2} = 1.2 \times 10^{-2} = \frac{[H_3O^+][SO_4^{2-}]}{[HSO_4^-]} = \frac{(0.15 + x)(x)}{0.15 - x}$$

$$x^2 + 0.162x - 1.8 \times 10^{-3} = 0$$

$$x = \frac{-0.162 + \sqrt{(0.162)^2 + (4)(1.8 \times 10^{-3})}}{2} = 0.0104 \text{ mol} \cdot L^{-1}$$

$$[H_3O^+] = 0.15 + x = (0.15 + 0.0104) \text{mol} \cdot L^{-1} = 0.16 \text{ mol} \cdot L^{-1}$$

$$pH = -\log(0.16) = 0.80$$

14.61 (a) Because $K_{a2} \ll K_{a1}$, the second ionization can be ignored.

Concentration $(mol \cdot L^{-1})$	H_2CO_3	$+ H_2O \rightleftharpoons$	H_3O^+	$+ HCO_3^-$
initial	0.0010	—	0	0
change	$-x$	—	$+x$	$+x$
equilibrium	$0.0010 - x$	—	x	x

$$K_{a1} = \frac{[H_3O^+][HCO_3^-]}{[H_2CO_3]} = \frac{x^2}{0.0010 - x} \approx \frac{x^2}{0.0010} = 4.3 \times 10^{-7}$$

$$x = [H_3O^+] = 2.1 \times 10^{-5} \text{ mol} \cdot L^{-1}$$

$$pH = -\log(2.1 \times 10^{-5}) = 4.68$$

(b) Because $K_{a2} \ll K_{a1}$, the second ionization can be ignored.

Concentration $(mol \cdot L^{-1})$	$(COOH)_2$	$+ H_2O \rightleftharpoons$	H_3O^+	$+ (COOH)CO_2^-$
initial	0.10	—	0	0
change	$-x$	—	$+x$	$+x$
equilibrium	$0.10 - x$	—	x	x

$$K_{a1} = 5.9 \times 10^{-2} = \frac{[H_3O^+][(COOH)CO_2^-]}{[(COOH)_2]} = \frac{x^2}{0.10 - x}$$

$$x^2 + 5.9 \times 10^{-2}x - 5.9 \times 10^{-3} = 0$$

$$x = \frac{-5.9 \times 10^{-2} + \sqrt{(5.9 \times 10^{-2})^2 + (4)(5.9 \times 10^{-3})}}{2} = 0.052\overline{8} \text{ mol} \cdot L^{-1}$$

$$pH = -\log(0.052\overline{8}) = 1.28$$

(c) Because $K_{a2} \ll K_{a1}$, the second ionization can be ignored.

Concentration $(mol \cdot L^{-1})$	H_2S	$+ H_2O \rightleftharpoons$	H_3O^+	$+ HS^-$
equilibrium	$0.20 - x$	—	x	x

$$K_{a1} = 1.3 \times 10^{-7} = \frac{[H_3O^+][HS^-]}{[H_2S]} = \frac{x^2}{0.20 - x} \approx \frac{x^2}{0.20}$$

$x = [\text{H}_3\text{O}^+] = 1.6 \times 10^{-4} \text{ mol} \cdot \text{L}^{-1}$

$\text{pH} = -\log(1.6 \times 10^{-4}) = 3.79$

SUPPLEMENTARY EXERCISES

14.63 $[\text{H}_3\text{O}^+] = [\text{OH}^-]$

14.65 (a)
$$\overset{\text{conjugate}}{\underbrace{}}$$
$$\underset{\text{acid}_1}{\text{C}_2\text{H}_5\text{COOH}} + \underset{\text{base}_2}{\text{H}_2\text{O}} \rightleftharpoons \underset{\text{acid}_2}{\text{H}_3\text{O}^+} + \underset{\text{base}_1}{\text{C}_2\text{H}_5\text{CO}_2^-}$$
conjugate

(b)
conjugate
$$\underset{\text{acid}_1}{\text{HClO}_3} + \underset{\text{base}_2}{\text{H}_2\text{O}} \rightleftharpoons \underset{\text{acid}_2}{\text{H}_3\text{O}^+} + \underset{\text{base}_1}{\text{ClO}_3^-}$$
conjugate

(c)
conjugate
$$\underset{\text{acid}_1}{\text{C}_8\text{H}_7\text{O}_2\text{COOH}} + \underset{\text{base}_2}{\text{H}_2\text{O}} \rightleftharpoons \underset{\text{acid}_2}{\text{H}_3\text{O}^+} + \underset{\text{base}_1}{\text{C}_8\text{H}_7\text{O}_2\text{CO}_2^-}$$
conjugate

(d)
conjugate
$$\underset{\text{acid}_1}{\text{H}_2\text{O}} + \underset{\text{base}_2}{\text{C}_8\text{H}_{10}\text{N}_4\text{O}_2} \rightleftharpoons \underset{\text{acid}_2}{\text{C}_8\text{H}_{10}\text{N}_4\text{O}_2\text{H}^+} + \underset{\text{base}_1}{\text{OH}^-}$$
conjugate

(e)
conjugate
$$\underset{\text{acid}_1}{\text{H}_2\text{O}} + \underset{\text{base}_2}{\text{C}_5\text{H}_5\text{N}} \rightleftharpoons \underset{\text{acid}_2}{\text{C}_5\text{H}_5\text{NH}^+} + \underset{\text{base}_1}{\text{OH}^-}$$
conjugate

14.67 (a) If a solution is a concentrated solution of an acid with $[\text{H}_3\text{O}^+] > 1$ M, the pH will be negative.

(b) If a solution is very basic, with $[\text{OH}^-] > 1$ M (which means $[\text{H}_3\text{O}^+] < 10^{-14}$ M), the pH will be greater than 14.

14.69 $\text{pH} = -\log[\text{H}_3\text{O}^+]$; therefore, $[\text{H}_3\text{O}^+] = 10^{-\text{pH}} \text{ mol} \cdot \text{L}^{-1}$

(a) $10^{-9.33} \text{ mol} \cdot \text{L}^{-1} = 4.7 \times 10^{-10} \text{ mol} \cdot \text{L}^{-1}$

(b) $10^{-7.95} \text{ mol} \cdot \text{L}^{-1} = 1.1 \times 10^{-8} \text{ mol} \cdot \text{L}^{-1}$

(c) $10^{-0.01}$ mol $\cdot$ L^{-1} $= 0.98$ mol $\cdot$ L^{-1}

(d) $10^{-4.33}$ mol $\cdot$ L^{-1} $= 4.7 \times 10^{-5}$ mol $\cdot$ L^{-1}

(e) $10^{-1.99}$ mol $\cdot$ L^{-1} $= 0.010$ mol $\cdot$ L^{-1}

(f) $10^{-11.95}$ mol $\cdot$ L^{-1} $= 1.1 \times 10^{-12}$ mol $\cdot$ L^{-1}

14.71 Both CH_3COOH and HNO_2 are monoprotic acids; therefore, for solutions with the same concentration of acid, the one with the larger K_a will have the greater percentage ionization.

$K_a(HNO_2) = 4.3 \times 10^{-4}$ (greater)

$K_a(CH_3COOH) = 1.8 \times 10^{-5}$

14.73 (a) $C_6H_5OH + H_2O \rightleftharpoons H_3O^+ + C_6H_5O^-$

$NH_4^+ + H_2O \rightleftharpoons H_3O^+ + NH_3$

(b) $pK_a(C_6H_5OH) = -\log(1.3 \times 10^{-10}) = 9.89$

$pK_a(NH_4^+) = -\log(5.6 \times 10^{-10}) = 9.25$

(c) NH_4^+ is the stronger acid; it has the smaller pK_a and the larger K_a.

14.75 (a) $HBrO_4$, because Br is slightly more electronegative than I.

(b) HI, because H—I is a weaker bond than H—F.

(c) HIO_3; because I has more oxygens attached to it in HIO_3 than in HIO_2.

(d) H_2SeO_4; because Se is more electronegative than As.

14.77 Let B = base; $B + H_2O \rightleftharpoons BH^+ + OH^-$

pOH $= 14.00 - 10.05 = 3.95$

The equilibrium concentrations are

$[OH^-] = [BH^+] = 10^{-pOH}$ mol $\cdot$ L^{-1} $= 10^{-3.95}$ mol $\cdot$ L^{-1} $= 1.1\overline{2} \times 10^{-4}$ mol $\cdot$ L^{-1}

initial concentration of B: $[B]_0 = \left(\dfrac{0.150 \text{ g}}{0.0500 \text{ L}}\right) \times \left(\dfrac{1 \text{ mol}}{31.06 \text{ g}}\right) = 0.0966$ mol $\cdot$ L^{-1}

equilibrium concentration of B: $[B] = (0.0966 - 1.1\overline{2} \times 10^{-4})$ mol $\cdot$ L^{-1}

$= 0.0965$ mol $\cdot$ L^{-1}

Concentration (mol $\cdot$ L^{-1})	H$_2$O	+	B	$\rightleftharpoons$	BH$^+$	+	OH$^-$
initial	—		0.0966		0		0
change	—		$-1.1\overline{2} \times 10^{-4}$		$+1.1\overline{2} \times 10^{-4}$		$+1.1\overline{2} \times 10^{-4}$
equilibrium	—		$0.0966 - 1.1\overline{2} \times 10^{-4}$		$1.1\overline{2} \times 10^{-4}$		$1.1\overline{2} \times 10^{-4}$

$K_b = \dfrac{[BH^+][OH^-]}{[B]} = \dfrac{(1.1\overline{2} \times 10^{-4})^2}{0.0965} = 1.3 \times 10^{-7}$

$pK_b = -\log(1.3 \times 10^{-7}) = 6.89, \quad pK_a(BH^+) = 14.00 - 6.89 = 7.11$

$\text{percentage protonation} = \dfrac{1.1\overline{2} \times 10^{-4}}{0.0965} \times 100\% = 0.12\%$

CHALLENGING EXERCISES

14.79 (a) $D_2O + D_2O \rightleftharpoons D_3O^+ + OD^-$

(b) $K_w = [D_3O^+][OD^-] = 1.35 + 10^{-15}, \quad pK_w = -\log K_w = 14.870$

(c) $[D_3O^+] = [OD^-] = \sqrt{1.35 \times 10^{-15}} = 3.67 \times 10^{-8} \text{ mol} \cdot L^{-1}$

(d) $pD = -\log(3.67 \times 10^{-8}) = 7.435 = pOD$

(e) $pD + pOD = pK_w(D_2O) = 14.870$

14.81 (a)

Concentration $(\text{mol} \cdot L^{-1})$	H_2O +	B	$\rightleftharpoons$ BH^+	+ OH^-
initial	—	0.025	0	0
change	—	$-x$	$+x$	$+x$
equilibrium	—	$0.025 - x$	x	x

$pOH = 14.0 - 11.6 = 2.4, \quad x = [OH^-] = [BH^+] = 10^{-2.4} \text{ mol} \cdot L^{-1} = 4.\overline{0} \times 10^{-3} \text{ mol} \cdot L^{-1}$

$K_b = \dfrac{[BH^+][OH^-]}{[BH]} = \dfrac{(4.\overline{0} \times 10^{-3})^2}{(0.025 - 4.\overline{0} \times 10^{-3})} = 7.\overline{6} \times 10^{-4}$

$pK_b = -\log(7.\overline{6} \times 10^{-4}) = 3.1, \quad pK_a = 14.0 - 3.1 = 10.9$

(b) Let T = thiazole

Concentration $(\text{mol} \cdot L^{-1})$	H_2O +	T	$\rightleftharpoons$ TH^+	+ OH^-
initial	—	0.0010	0	0
change	—	$-x$	$+x$	$+x$
equilibrium	—	$0.0010 - x$	x	x

$x = 5.2 \times 10^{-5} \times 0.0010 \text{ mol} \cdot L^{-1} = [TH^+] \neq [OH^-]$

This is a case where the autoprotolysis of water cannot be ignored. $[OH^-]$ is not the same as [thiazolate ion].

$K_b = \dfrac{[TH^+][OH^-]}{[T]}, \quad K_w = [H_3O^+][OH^-] = 1.0 \times 10^{-14}$

Electroneutrality requires $[TH^+] + [H_3O^+] - [OH^-] = 0$,

giving $[OH^-] = 5.2 \times 10^{-8} + \dfrac{(1.0 \times 10^{-14})}{[OH^-]}$.

Let $y = [OH^-]$, then $y^2 - 5.2 \times 10^{-8}y - 1.0 \times 10^{-14} = 0$.

$y = \dfrac{5.2 \times 10^{-8} + \sqrt{(5.2 \times 10^{-8})^2 + 4.0 \times 10^{-14}}}{2}$

$= 1.2\overline{9} \times 10^{-7} \text{ mol} \cdot L^{-1} = [OH^-]$

$$K_b = \frac{5.2 \times 10^{-8} \times 1.29 \times 10^{-7}}{0.0010} = 6.7 \times 10^{-12}$$

$$[H_3O^+] = \frac{1.0 \times 10^{-14}}{1.29 \times 10^{-7}} = 7.8 \times 10^{-8} \text{ mol} \cdot L^{-1}$$

$$pH = -\log(7.8 \times 10^{-8}) = 7.11$$

14.83 (a)

Concentration (mol · L^{-1})	B(OH)$_3$	+	2H$_2$O	$\rightleftharpoons$ H$_3$O$^+$	+ B(OH)$_4^-$
initial	1.0×10^{-4}	—		0	0
change	$-x$	—		$+x$	$+x$
equilibrium	$1.0 \times 10^{-4} - x$	—		x	x

$$K_a = 7.2 \times 10^{-10} = \frac{[H_3O^+][B(OH)_4^-]}{[B(OH)_3]} = \frac{x^2}{1.0 \times 10^{-4} - x} \approx \frac{x^2}{1.0 \times 10^{-4}}$$

$$x = [H_3O^+] = 2.7 \times 10^{-7} \text{ mol} \cdot L^{-1}$$

$$pH = -\log(2.7 \times 10^{-7}) = 6.57$$

Note: This value of $[H_3O^+]$ is not much different from the value for pure water, 1.0×10^{-7} mol · L^{-1}; hence, it is at the lower limit of safely ignoring the contribution to $[H_3O^+]$ from the autoprotolysis of water. The exercise should be solved by simultaneously considering both equilibria.

Concentration (mol · L^{-1})	B(OH)$_3$	+	2H$_2$O	$\rightleftharpoons$ H$_3$O$^+$	+ B(OH)$_4^-$
equilibrium	$1.0 \times 10^{-14} - x$	—		x	y

Concentration (mol · L^{-1})	2H$_2$O	$\rightleftharpoons$ H$_3$O$^+$	+ OH$^-$
equilibrium	—	x	z

Because there are now two contributions to $[H_3O^+]$, $[H_3O^+]$ is no longer equal to $[B(OH)_4]$, nor is it equal to $[OH^-]$, as in pure water. To avoid a cubic equation, x will again be ignored relative to 1.0×10^{-4} mol · L^{-1}. This approximation is justified by the approximate calculation above and because K_a is very small relative to 1.0×10^{-4}. Let $a =$ initial concentration of B(OH)$_3$, then

$$K_a = 7.2 \times 10^{-10} = \frac{xy}{a-x} \approx \frac{xy}{a} \text{ or } y = \frac{aK_a}{x}$$

$$K_w = 1.0 \times 10^{-14} = xz$$

Electroneutrality requires $x = y + z$ or $z = x - y$; hence, $K_w = xz = x(x - y)$. Substituting for y from above:

$$x \times \left(x - \frac{aK_a}{x}\right) = K_w$$

$$x^2 - aK_a = K_w$$

$$x^2 = K_w + aK_a$$

$$x = \sqrt{K_w + aK_a} = \sqrt{1.0 \times 10^{-14} + 1.0 \times 10^{-4} \times 7.2 \times 10^{-10}}$$

$$x = 2.8\overline{6} \times 10^{-7} \text{ mol} \cdot \text{L}^{-1} = [H_3O^+]$$
$$pH = -\log(2.8\overline{6} \times 10^{-7}) = 6.54$$

This value is slightly, but measurably, different from the value 6.57 obtained by ignoring the contribution to $[H_3O^+]$ from water.

(b) In this case, the second ionization can safely be ignored; $K_{a2} \ll K_{a1}$.

Concentration (mol·L^{-1})	H_3PO_4	+ H_2O	$\rightleftharpoons H_3O^+$	+ $H_2PO_4^-$
initial	0.015	—	0	0
change	$-x$	—	$+x$	$+x$
equilibrium	$0.015 - x$	—	x	x

$$K_{a1} = 7.6 \times 10^{-3} = \frac{x^2}{0.015 - x}$$
$$x^2 + 7.6 \times 10^{-3}x - 1.14 \times 10^{-4} = 0$$
$$x = [H_3O^+] = \frac{-7.6 \times 10^{-3} + \sqrt{(7.6 \times 10^{-3})^2 + 4.56 \times 10^{-4}}}{2}$$
$$= 7.5\overline{3} \times 10^{-3} \text{ mol} \cdot \text{L}^{-1}$$
$$pH = -\log(7.5\overline{3} \times 10^{-3}) = 2.12$$

(c) In this case, the second ionization can safely be ignored; $K_{a2} \ll K_{a1}$.

Concentration (mol·L^{-1})	H_2SO_3	+ H_2O	$\rightleftharpoons H_3O^+$	+ HSO_3^-
initial	0.1	—	0	0
change	$-x$	—	$+x$	$+x$
equilibrium	$0.1 - x$	—	x	x

$$K_{a1} = 1.5 \times 10^{-2} = \frac{x^2}{0.10 - x}$$
$$x^2 + 1.5 \times 10^{-2}x - 1.5 \times 10^{-3} = 0$$
$$x = [H_3O^+] = \frac{-1.5 \times 10^{-2} + \sqrt{(1.5 \times 10^{-2})^2 + 6.0 \times 10^{-3}}}{2} = 0.032 \text{ mol} \cdot \text{L}^{-1}$$
$$pH = -\log(0.032) = 1.49$$

14.85 In this case, the second ionization can safely be ignored for the calculation of $[H_3O^+]$, $[OH^-]$, $[H_2SO_3]$, and $[HSO_3^-]$ because $K_{a2} \ll K_{a1}$. However, it must be used in the calculation of $[SO_3^{2-}]$.

Concentration (mol·L^{-1})	H_2SO_3	+ H_2O	$\rightleftharpoons H_3O^+$	+ HSO_3^-
initial	0.1	—	0	0
change	$-x$	—	$+x$	$+x$
equilibrium	$0.1 - x$	—	x	x

$$K_{a1} = 1.5 \times 10^{-2} = \frac{x^2}{0.10 - x}$$

$$x^2 + 1.5 \times 10^{-2}x - 1.5 \times 10^{-3} = 0$$

$$x = [H_3O^+] = \frac{-1.5 \times 10^{-2} + \sqrt{(1.5 \times 10^{-2})^2 + 6.0 \times 10^{-3}}}{2} = 0.032 \ \text{mol} \cdot \text{L}^{-1}$$

$$[H_3O^+] = [HSO_3^-] = 0.032 \ \text{mol} \cdot \text{L}^{-1}$$

$$[OH^-] = \frac{1.0 \times 10^{-14}}{0.032} = 3.1 \times 10^{-13} \ \text{mol} \cdot \text{L}^{-1}$$

$$[H_2SO_3] = 0.10 - 0.032 = 0.068 \ \text{mol} \cdot \text{L}^{-1}$$

The second ionization is required to produce SO_3^{2-}.

Equilibrium concentrations are $[HSO_3^-] = 0.032 - x$, $[H_3O^+] = 0.032 + x$, and $[SO_3^{2-}] = x$

$$K_{a2} = 1.2 \times 10^{-7} = \frac{(0.032 + x)(x)}{0.032 - x} \approx x = [SO_3^{2-}]$$

$$[SO_3^{2-}] = 1.2 \times 10^{-7} \ \text{mol} \cdot \text{L}^{-1}$$

14.87 $\Delta H^\circ = +57 \ \text{kJ} \cdot \text{mol}^{-1}$ (where 1 mol refers to the reaction as written)

$$\ln K_w' - \ln K_w = \frac{\Delta H^\circ}{R}\left(\frac{T' - T}{TT'}\right)$$

$$2.303 \log K_w' - 2.303 \log K_w = \frac{\Delta H^\circ}{R}\left(\frac{T' - T}{TT'}\right)$$

$$\log K_w' - \log K_w = \frac{\Delta H^\circ}{2.303R}\left(\frac{T' - T}{TT'}\right)$$

$$-\log K_w' - (-\log K_w) = \frac{-\Delta H^\circ}{2.303R}\left(\frac{T' - T}{TT'}\right)$$

$$pK_w' - pK_w = \frac{\Delta H^\circ}{2.303R}\left(\frac{T' - T}{TT'}\right)$$

$$pK_w' - pK_w = \frac{-\Delta H^\circ}{2.303R}\left(\frac{T' - T}{TT'}\right)$$

$$pK_w' = pK_w - \frac{\Delta H^\circ}{2.303R}\left(\frac{T' - T}{TT'}\right)$$

$$pK_w' = 14.00 - \frac{57 \ \text{kJ} \cdot \text{mol}^{-1}}{2.303 \times 0.008 \ 31 \ \text{kJ} \cdot \text{K}^{-1} \cdot \text{mol}^{-1}}\left[\frac{(373 - 298) \ \text{K}}{298 \ \text{K} \times 373 \ \text{K}}\right]$$

$$pK_w' = 14.00 - 2.01 = 11.99$$

$$pH = pOH = \frac{11.99}{2} = 6.00$$

CHAPTER 15
SALTS IN WATER

The values for the acidity and basicity constants are listed in Tables 14.2 and 14.5. Unless stated otherwise, take the solutions to be aqueous and at 25°C.

EXERCISES

Ions as Acids and Bases

15.1 (a) pH < 7, acidic; $NH_4^+(aq) + H_2O(l) \rightleftharpoons H_3O^+(aq) + NH_3(aq)$

(b) pH > 7, basic; $H_2O(l) + CO_3^{2-}(aq) \rightleftharpoons HCO_3^-(aq) + OH^-(aq)$

(c) pH > 7, basic; $H_2O(l) + F^-(aq) \rightleftharpoons HF(aq) + OH^-(aq)$

(d) pH = 7, neutral; K^+ is not an acid, Br^- is not a base

(e) pH < 7, acidic; $Al(H_2O)_6^{3+}(aq) + H_2O(l) \rightleftharpoons H_3O^+(aq) + Al(H_2O)_5OH^{2+}(aq)$

(f) pH < 7, acidic; $Cu(H_2O)_6^{2+}(aq) + H_2O(l) \rightleftharpoons H_3O^+(aq) + Cu(H_2O)_5OH^+(aq)$

15.3 In each case, determine whether the ion is a weak acid or a weak base. Its acidity or basicity constant is then calculated from the K_b or K_a of its conjugate base or acid, using $K_a \times K_b = K_w$. K_b and K_a data are from Table 14.2.

(a) $K_a \times K_b = K_w$; conjugate base is NH_3.

$$K_a = \frac{K_w}{K_b} = \frac{1.00 \times 10^{-14}}{1.8 \times 10^{-5}} = 5.6 \times 10^{-10}$$

(b) $K_a \times K_b = K_w$; conjugate acid is HCO_3^-.

$$K_b = \frac{K_w}{K_{a2}} = \frac{1.00 \times 10^{-14}}{5.6 \times 10^{-11}} = 1.8 \times 10^{-4}$$

(c) $K_a \times K_b = K_w$; conjugate acid is HF.

$$K_b = \frac{K_w}{K_a} = \frac{1.00 \times 10^{-14}}{3.5 \times 10^{-4}} = 2.9 \times 10^{-11}$$

(d) $K_a \times K_b = K_w$; conjugate acid is $HClO$.

$$K_b = \frac{K_w}{K_a} = \frac{1.00 \times 10^{-14}}{3.0 \times 10^{-8}} = 3.3 \times 10^{-7}$$

(e) $K_a \times K_b = K_w$; conjugate acid is H_2CO_3.

$$K_b = \frac{K_w}{K_a} = \frac{1.00 \times 10^{-14}}{4.3 \times 10^{-7}} = 2.3 \times 10^{-8}$$

(f) $K_a \times K_b = K_w$; conjugate base is $(CH_3)_3N$.

$$K_a = \frac{K_w}{K_b} = \frac{1.00 \times 10^{-14}}{6.5 \times 10^{-5}} = 1.5 \times 10^{-10}$$

15.5 (a) $K_b = \dfrac{K_w}{K_a} = \dfrac{1.00 \times 10^{-14}}{1.8 \times 10^{-5}} = 5.6 \times 10^{-10}$

Concentration (mol · L^{-1})	$CH_3CO_2^-(aq)$	$+ H_2O(l)$	$\rightleftharpoons HCH_3CO_2(aq)$	$+ OH^-(aq)$
initial	0.20	—	0	0
change	$-x$	—	$+x$	$+x$
equilibrium	$0.20 - x$	—	x	x

$$K_b = \frac{[HCH_3CO_2][OH^-]}{[CH_3CO_2^-]} = 5.6 \times 10^{-10} = \frac{x^2}{0.20 - x} \approx \frac{x^2}{0.20}$$

$x = 1.1 \times 10^{-5} = [OH^-]$, $pOH = -\log(1.1 \times 10^{-5}) = 4.98$

$pH = 14.00 - pOH = 14.00 - 4.98 = 9.02$

(b) $K_a = \dfrac{K_w}{K_b} = \dfrac{1.00 \times 10^{-14}}{1.8 \times 10^{-5}} = 5.6 \times 10^{-10}$

Concentration (mol · L^{-1})	$NH_4^+(aq)$	$+ H_2O(l)$	$\rightleftharpoons H_3O^+(aq)$	$+ NH_3(aq)$
initial	0.10	—	0	0
change	$-x$	—	$+x$	$+x$
equilibrium	$0.10 - x$	—	x	x

$$K_a = \frac{[H_3O^+][NH_3]}{[NH_4Cl]} = 5.6 \times 10^{-10} = \frac{x^2}{0.10 - x} \approx \frac{x^2}{0.10}$$

$x^2 = 5.6 \times 10^{-11}$

$x = 7.4\overline{8} \times 10^{-6}$ mol · L^{-1} = $[H_3O^+]$

$pH = -\log(7.4\overline{8} \times 10^{-6}) = 5.13$

(c)

Concentration (mol · L^{-1})	$Al(H_2O)_6^{3+}(aq)$	$+ H_2O(l)$	$\rightleftharpoons H_3O^+(aq)$	$+ Al(H_2O)_5OH^{2+}(aq)$
initial	0.10	—	0	0
change	$-x$	—	$+x$	$+x$
equilibrium	$0.10 - x$	—	x	x

$$K_a = \frac{[H_3O^+][Al(H_2O)_5OH^{2+}]}{[Al(H_2O)_6^{3+}]} = 1.4 \times 10^{-5} = \frac{x^2}{0.10 - x} \approx \frac{x^2}{0.10}$$

$x^2 = 1.42 \times 10^{-6}$

$x = \sqrt{1.4 \times 10^{-6}} = 1.2 \times 10^{-3}$ mol · L^{-1} = $[H_3O^+]$

$pH = -\log(1.2 \times 10^{-3}) = 2.92$

(d) Concentration $(mol \cdot L^{-1})$ $H_2O(l) + CN^-(aq) \rightleftharpoons HCN(aq) + OH^-(aq)$

initial	—	0.15	0	0
change	—	$-x$	$+x$	$+x$
equilibrium	—	$0.15 - x$	x	x

$$K_b = \frac{K_w}{K_a} = \frac{1.00 \times 10^{-14}}{4.9 \times 10^{-10}} = 2.0 \times 10^{-5} = \frac{[HCN][OH^-]}{[CN^-]} = \frac{x^2}{0.15 - x} \approx \frac{x^2}{0.15}$$

$$x^2 = (0.15) \times (2.0 \times 10^{-5}) = 3.0 \times 10^{-6}$$

$$x = [OH^-] = 1.7 \times 10^{-3} \; mol \cdot L^{-1}$$

$$pOH = -\log(1.7 \times 10^{-3}) = 2.76, \quad pH = 11.24$$

15.7 (a) 250 mL of solution contains 10.0 g $KC_2H_3O_2$, molar mass = 98.146 $g \cdot mol^{-1}$

$$(10.0 \; g \; KC_2H_3O_2) \times \left(\frac{1 \; mol \; KC_2H_3O_2}{98.146 \; g \; KC_2H_3O_2} \right)$$

$$\times \left(\frac{1}{0.250 \; L} \right) = 0.408 \; M \; KC_2H_3O_2$$

Concentration $(mol \cdot L^{-1})$ $H_2O(l) + C_2H_3O_2^-(aq) \rightleftharpoons HC_2H_3O_2(aq) + OH^-(aq)$

initial	—	0.408	0	0
change	—	$-x$	$+x$	$+x$
equilibrium	—	$0.408 - x$	x	x

$$\frac{1.0 \times 10^{-14}}{1.8 \times 10^{-5}} = \frac{x^2}{0.408 - x} \approx \frac{x^2}{0.408}$$

$$[OH^-] = 1.5 \times 10^{-5} \; mol \cdot L^{-1}$$

$$[H_3O^+] = 6.7 \times 10^{-10} \; mol \cdot L^{-1}$$

$$pH = -\log(6.7 \times 10^{-10}) = 9.18$$

(b) 100 mL of solution contains 5.75 g NH_4Br, molar mass = 97.9 $g \cdot mol^{-1}$

$$(5.75 \; g \; NH_4Br) \times \left(\frac{1 \; mol \; NH_4Br}{97.9 \; g \; NH_4Br} \right) \times \left(\frac{1}{0.100 \; L} \right) = 0.587 \; M \; NH_4Br$$

Concentration $(mol \cdot L^{-1})$ $NH_4^+(aq) + H_2O(l) \rightleftharpoons NH_3(aq) + H_3O^+(aq)$

initial	0.587	—	0	0
change	$-x$	—	$+x$	$+x$
equilibrium	$0.587 - x$	—	x	x

$$\frac{1.0 \times 10^{-14}}{1.8 \times 10^{-5}} = \frac{x^2}{0.587 - x} \approx \frac{x^2}{0.587}$$

$$[H_3O^+] = 1.8 \times 10^{-5} \; mol \cdot L^{-1}$$

$$pH = -\log(1.8 \times 10^{-5}) = 4.74$$

15.9 (a) $\dfrac{0.200 \; mol \cdot L^{-1} \; NaCH_3CO_2 \times 0.200 \; L}{0.500 \; L} = 0.0800 \; mol \cdot L^{-1}$

Concentration
$(mol \cdot L^{-1})$ $\quad H_2O(l) + CH_3CO_2^-(aq) \rightleftharpoons CH_3COOH(aq) + OH^-(aq)$

initial	—	0.0800	0	0
change	—	$-x$	$+x$	$+x$
equilibrium	—	$0.0800 - x$	x	x

$$K_b = \frac{K_w}{K_a} = \frac{1.00 \times 10^{-14}}{1.8 \times 10^{-5}} = 5.6 \times 10^{-10} = \frac{[CH_3COOH][OH^-]}{[CH_3CO_2^-]}$$

$$5.6 \times 10^{-10} = \frac{x^2}{0.0800 - x} \approx \frac{x^2}{0.0800}$$

$$x^2 = 4.4 \times 10^{-11}$$

$$x = 6.7 \times 10^{-6} \ mol \cdot L^{-1} = [CH_3COOH]$$

(b) $\left(\dfrac{5.75 \text{ g } NH_4Br}{400 \text{ mL}}\right) \times \left(\dfrac{1 \text{ mL}}{10^{-3} \text{ L}}\right) \times \left(\dfrac{1 \text{ mol } NH_4Br}{97.9 \text{ g } NH_4Br}\right)$

$$= 0.147 \ (mol \ NH_4Br) \cdot L^{-1}$$

Concentration $(mol \cdot L^{-1})$ $\quad NH_4^+(aq) + H_2O(l) \rightleftharpoons H_3O^+(aq) + NH_3(aq)$

initial	0.147	—	0	0
change	$-x$	—	$+x$	$+x$
equilibrium	$0.147 - x$	—	x	x

$$K_a = \frac{K_w}{K_b} = \frac{1.00 \times 10^{-14}}{1.8 \times 10^{-5}} = 5.6 \times 10^{-10} = \frac{[NH_3][H_3O^+]}{[NH_4^+]}$$

$$5.6 \times 10^{-10} = \frac{x^2}{0.147 - x} \approx \frac{x^2}{0.147}$$

$$x^2 = 8.2 \times 10^{-11}$$

$$x = 9.1 \times 10^{-6} \ mol \cdot L^{-1} = [H_3O^+] \text{ and } pH = -\log(9.1 \times 10^{-6}) = 5.04$$

15.11 (a) When solid sodium acetate is added to an acetic acid solution, the concentration of H_3O^+ decreases because the equilibrium

$$HC_2H_3O_2(aq) + H_2O(l) \rightleftharpoons H_3O^+(aq) + C_2H_3O_2^-(aq)$$

shifts to the left to relieve the stress imposed by the increase of $[C_2H_3O_2^-]$ (Le Chatelier's principle).

(b) When HCl is added to a benzoic acid solution, the percentage of benzoic acid that is deprotonated decreases because the equilibrium

$$C_6H_5COOH(aq) + H_2O(l) \rightleftharpoons H_3O^+(aq) + C_6H_5CO_2^-(aq)$$

shifts to the left to relieve the stress imposed by the increased $[H_3O^+]$ (Le Chatelier's principle).

(c) When solid NH_4Cl is added to an ammonia solution, the concentration of OH^- decreases because the equilibrium

$$NH_3(aq) + H_2O(l) \rightleftharpoons NH_4^+(aq) + OH^-(aq)$$

shifts to the left to relieve the stress imposed by the increased $[NH_4^+]$ (Le Chatelier's principle). Because $[OH^-]$ decreases, $[H_3O^+]$ increases and pH decreases.

15.13 (a) $pH = pK_a + \log\left(\dfrac{[base]_0}{[acid]_0}\right) = pK_a + \log\left(\dfrac{[\text{lactate ion}]}{[\text{lactic acid}]}\right)$

$pH = pK_a = 3.08, \quad K_a = 8.4 \times 10^{-4}$

(b) Let $x = [\text{lactate ion}] = [L^-]$ and $y = [H_3O^+]$.

Concentration $(mol \cdot L^{-1})$	HL(aq)	+ H₂O(l) ⇌	H₃O⁺(aq)	+ L⁻(aq)
initial	$2x$	—	—	x
change	$-y$	—	$+y$	$+y$
equilibrium	$2x - y$	—	y	$y + x$

$K_a = \dfrac{[H_3O^+][L^-]}{[HL]} = \dfrac{(y)(y + x)}{(2x - y)} \approx \dfrac{(y)(x)}{(2x)} = 8.4 \times 10^{-4}$

$y = 2(8.4 \times 10^{-4}) \approx 1.68 \times 10^{-3} \text{ mol} \cdot L^{-1} \approx [H_3O^+]$

$pH \approx 2.77$

15.15 (a)

Concentration $(mol \cdot L^{-1})$	HBrO(aq)	+ H₂O(l) ⇌	H₃O⁺(aq)	+ BrO⁻(aq)
initial	0.20	—	0	0.10
change	$-x$	—	$+x$	$+x$
equilibrium	$0.20 - x$	—	x	$0.10 + x$

$K_a = \dfrac{[H_3O^+][BrO^-]}{[HBrO]} = \dfrac{(x)(0.10 + x)}{(0.20 - x)} = 2.0 \times 10^{-9} \approx \dfrac{[H_3O^+](0.10)}{(0.20)}$

$[H_3O^+] \approx 4.0 \times 10^{-9} \text{ mol} \cdot L^{-1}$

(b)

Concentration $(mol \cdot L^{-1})$	(CH₃)₂NH(aq)	+ H₂O(l) ⇌	(CH₃)₂NH₂⁺(aq)	+ OH⁻(aq)
initial	0.010	—	0.150	0
change	$-x$	—	$+x$	$+x$
equilibrium	$0.010 - x$	—	$0.150 + x$	x

$K_b = \dfrac{[(CH_3)_2NH_2^+][OH^-]}{[(CH_3)_2NH]} = \dfrac{(0.150 + x)(x)}{(0.010 - x)} = 5.4 \times 10^{-4} \approx \dfrac{(0.150)[OH^-]}{(0.010)}$

$[OH^-] \approx 3.6 \times 10^{-5} \text{ mol} \cdot L^{-1}$

Because $[H_3O^+] = \dfrac{K_w}{[OH^-]} = \dfrac{1.00 \times 10^{-14}}{3.6 \times 10^{-5}} = 2.8 \times 10^{-10} \text{ mol} \cdot L^{-1}$

(c)

Concentration $(mol \cdot L^{-1})$	HBrO(aq)	+ H₂O(l) ⇌	H₃O⁺(aq)	+ BrO⁻(aq)
initial	0.10	—	0	0.20
change	$-x$	—	$+x$	$+x$
equilibrium	$0.10 - x$	—	x	$0.20 + x$

$$K_a = \frac{[H_3O^+][BrO^-]}{[HBrO]} = \frac{(x)(0.20 + x)}{(0.10 - x)} = 2.0 \times 10^{-9} \approx \frac{[H_3O^+](0.20)}{0.10}$$

$$[H_3O^+] = 1.0 \times 10^{-9} \text{ mol} \cdot L^{-1}$$

(d) Concentration

(mol · L^{-1})	(CH$_3$)$_2$NH(aq)	+ H$_2$O(l)	$\rightleftharpoons$ (CH$_3$)$_2$NH$_2^+$(aq)	+ OH$^-$(aq)
initial	0.020	—	0.030	0
change	$-x$	—	$+x$	$+x$
equilibrium	$0.020 - x$	—	$0.030 + x$	x

$$K_b = \frac{[(CH_3)_2NH_2^+][OH^-]}{[(CH_3)_2NH]} = \frac{(0.030 + x)(x)}{(0.020 - x)} = 5.4 \times 10^{-4} \approx \frac{(0.030)[OH^-]}{(0.020)}$$

$$[OH^-] \approx 3.6 \times 10^{-4} \text{ mol} \cdot L^{-1}$$

$$[H_3O^+] = \frac{K_w}{[OH^-]} = \frac{1.00 \times 10^{-14}}{3.6 \times 10^{-4}} = 2.8 \times 10^{-11} \text{ mol} \cdot L^{-1}$$

15.17 In each case, the equilibrium involved is

$$HSO_4^-(aq) + H_2O(l) \rightleftharpoons H_3O^+(aq) + SO_4^{2-}(aq)$$

$HSO_4^-(aq)$ and $SO_4^{2-}(aq)$ are conjugate acid and base; therefore, the pH calculation is most easily performed with the Henderson-Hasselbalch equation:

$$pH = pK_a + \log\left(\frac{[\text{base}]}{[\text{acid}]}\right) = pK_a + \log\left(\frac{[SO_4^{2-}]}{[HSO_4^-]}\right)$$

(a) $pH = 1.92 + \log\left(\dfrac{0.80 \text{ mol} \cdot L^{-1}}{0.40 \text{ mol} \cdot L^{-1}}\right) = 2.22$, $pOH = 14.00 - 2.22 = 11.78$

(b) $pH = 1.92 + \log\left(\dfrac{0.20 \text{ mol} \cdot L^{-1}}{0.40 \text{ mol} \cdot L^{-1}}\right) = 1.62$, $pOH = 12.38$

(c) $pH = pK_a = 1.92$, $pOH = 12.08$

15.19 $\left(\dfrac{1.0 \text{ g NaF}}{0.025 \text{ L}}\right) \times \left(\dfrac{1 \text{ mol NaF}}{42 \text{ g NaF}}\right) = 0.95 \text{ (mol NaF)} \cdot L^{-1}$

Concentration (mol · L^{-1})	HF(aq)	+ H$_2$O(l)	$\rightleftharpoons$ H$_3$O$^+$(aq)	+ F$^-$(aq)
initial	0.40	—	0	0.95
change	$-x$	—	$+x$	$+x$
equilibrium	$0.40 - x$	—	x	$0.95 + x$

$$K_a = \frac{[H_3O^+][F^-]}{[HF]} = \frac{(x)(0.95 + x)}{(0.40 - x)} \approx \frac{(x)(0.95)}{(0.40)} = 3.5 \times 10^{-4}$$

$$x \approx 1.48 \times 10^{-4} \text{ mol} \cdot L^{-1} \approx [H_3O^+]$$

$$pH = -\log[H_3O^+] = -\log(1.48 \times 10^{-4}) = 3.83$$

change in pH = $3.83 - 1.93 = 1.90$

15.21 (a) $HCN(aq) + H_2O(l) \rightleftharpoons H_3O^+(aq) + CN^-(aq)$

total volume = 100 mL = 0.100 L

moles of HCN = 0.0200 L × 0.050 mol·L^{-1} = 1.0 × 10^{-3} mol HCN

moles of NaCN = 0.0800 L × 0.030 mol·L^{-1} = 2.4 × 10^{-3} mol NaCN

$$\text{initial } [HCN]_0 = \frac{1.0 \times 10^{-3} \text{ mol}}{0.100 \text{ L}} = 1.0 \times 10^{-2} \text{ mol·L}^{-1}$$

$$\text{initial } [CN^-]_0 = \frac{2.4 \times 10^{-3} \text{ mol}}{0.100 \text{ L}} = 2.4 \times 10^{-2} \text{ mol·L}^{-1}$$

Concentration (mol·L^{-1})	HCN(aq)	+ H$_2$O(l) $\rightleftharpoons$	H$_3$O$^+$(aq)	+ CN$^-$(aq)
initial	1.0 × 10^{-2}	—	0	2.4 × 10^{-2}
change	−x	—	+x	+x
equilibrium	1.0 × 10^{-2} − x	—	x	2.4 × 10^{-2} + x

$$K_a = \frac{[H_3O^+][CN^-]}{[HCN]} = \frac{(x)(2.4 \times 10^{-2} + x)}{(1.0 \times 10^{-2} - x)} \approx \frac{(x)(2.4 \times 10^{-2})}{(1.0 \times 10^{-2})} = 4.9 \times 10^{-10}$$

$x \approx 2.0 \times 10^{-10}$ mol·L^{-1} ≈ [H$_3$O$^+$]

pH = −log[H$_3$O$^+$] = −log(2.0 × 10^{-10}) = 9.69

(b) The solution here is the same as for part (a), except for the initial concentrations:

$$[HCN]_0 = \frac{0.0800 \text{ L} \times 0.030 \text{ mol·L}^{-1}}{0.100 \text{ L}} = 2.4 \times 10^{-2} \text{ mol·L}^{-1}$$

$$[CN^-]_0 = \frac{0.0200 \text{ L} \times 0.050 \text{ mol·L}^{-1}}{0.100 \text{ L}} = 1.0 \times 10^{-2} \text{ mol·L}^{-1}$$

$$K_a = 4.9 \times 10^{-10} = \frac{(x)(1.0 \times 10^{-2})}{(2.4 \times 10^{-2})}$$

$x = [H_3O^+] = 1.1\overline{8} \times 10^{-9}$ mol·L^{-1}

pH = −log(1.1$\overline{8}$ × 10^{-9}) = 8.93

(c) $[HCN]_0 = [NaCN]_0$ after mixing; therefore,

$$K_a = 4.9 \times 10^{-10} = \frac{(x)[NaCN]_0}{[HCN]_0} = x = [H_3O^+]$$

pH = pK_a = −log(4.9 × 10^{-10}) = 9.31

Strong Acid-Strong Base Titrations

15.23 In each case, the net ionic reaction is $H_3O^+(aq) + OH^-(aq) \longrightarrow 2H_2O(l)$; therefore, the neutralization requires 1 mol H$_3$O$^+$ = 1 mol OH$^-$

(a) number of moles of H$_3$O$^+$ (from the acid) = (0.025 L) × (0.30 mol·L^{-1})

$$= 7.5 \times 10^{-3} \text{ mol H}_3\text{O}^+$$

number of moles of OH$^-$ (from the base) = (0.025 L) × (0.20 mol·L^{-1})

$$= 5.0 \times 10^{-3} \text{ mol OH}^-$$

excess $H_3O^+ = (7.5 \times 10^{-3} - 5.0 \times 10^{-3})$ mol $H_3O^+ = 2.5 \times 10^{-3}$ mol H_3O^+

$[H_3O^+] = \dfrac{2.5 \times 10^{-3} \text{ mol } H_3O^+}{0.050 \text{ L}} = 0.050 \text{ mol} \cdot L^{-1}$

$pH = -\log(0.050) = 1.30$

(b) number of moles of H_3O^+ (from the acid) $= (0.025 \text{ L}) \times (0.15 \text{ mol} \cdot L^{-1})$
$$= 3.7\overline{5} \times 10^{-3} \text{ mol } H_3O^+$$

number of moles of OH^- (from the base) $= (0.050 \text{ L}) \times (0.15 \text{ mol} \cdot L^{-1})$
$$= 7.5 \times 10^{-3} \text{ mol } OH^-$$

excess $OH^- = (7.5 \times 10^{-3} - 3.7\overline{5} \times 10^{-3})$ mol $OH^- = 3.7\overline{5} \times 10^{-3}$ mol OH^-

$[OH^-] = \dfrac{3.7\overline{5} \times 10^{-3} \text{ mol } OH^-}{0.075 \text{ L}} = 0.050 \text{ mol} \cdot L^{-1}$

$pOH = -\log(0.050) = 1.30, \quad pH = 14.00 - 1.30 = 12.70$

$[H_3O^+] = 2.0 \times 10^{-3}$

(c) moles of H_3O^+ (from the acid) $= 0.0217 \text{ L} \times 0.27 \text{ mol} \cdot L^{-1}$
$$= 5.8\overline{6} \times 10^{-3} \text{ mol } H_3O^+$$

moles of OH^- (from the base) $= 0.0100 \text{ L} \times 0.30 \text{ mol} \cdot L^{-1}$
$$= 3.0\overline{0} \times 10^{-3} \text{ mol } OH^-$$

excess $H_3O^+ = (5.8\overline{6} \times 10^{-3} - 3.0\overline{0} \times 10^{-3})$ mol $= 2.9 \times 10^{-3}$ mol

$[H_3O^+] = \dfrac{2.9 \times 10^{-3} \text{ mol } H_3O^+}{0.0317 \text{ L}} = 0.090 \text{ mol} \cdot L^{-1}$

$pH = -\log(2.9 \times 10^{-3}) = 1.04$

15.25 $[NaOH]_0 = \left(\dfrac{14.0 \text{ g NaOH}}{0.250 \text{ L}}\right) \times \left(\dfrac{1 \text{ mol NaOH}}{40.0 \text{ g NaOH}}\right) = 1.40 \text{ mol} \cdot L^{-1} = [OH^-]_0$

moles of OH^- (from the base) $= (0.0250 \text{ L}) \times (1.40 \text{ (mol } OH^-) \cdot L^{-1})$
$$= 0.0350 \text{ mol } OH^-$$

moles of H_3O^+ (from the acid) $= (0.0500 \text{ L}) \times (0.20 \text{ mol } H_3O^+ \cdot L^{-1})$
$$= 0.010 \text{ mol } H_3O^+$$

excess $OH^- = (0.0350 - 0.010)$ mol $OH^- = 0.025$ mol OH^-

$[OH^-] = \dfrac{0.025 \text{ mol } OH^-}{(0.050 + 0.025) \text{ L}} = 0.33 \text{ mol} \cdot L^{-1}$

$pOH = -\log(0.33) = 0.48, \quad pH = 14.00 - 0.48 = 13.52$

15.27 1 mol $H_3O^+ = 1$ mol OH^- in neutralization, hence 1 mol HCl = 1 mol KOH.

moles of HCl required $= (0.0250 \text{ L KOH}) \times \left(\dfrac{0.0497 \text{ mol KOH}}{1 \text{ L KOH}}\right) \times \left(\dfrac{1 \text{ mol HCl}}{1 \text{ mol KOH}}\right)$
$$= 1.24 \times 10^{-3} \text{ mol HCl}$$

$$\text{volume of HCl required} = \frac{1.24 \times 10^{-3} \text{ mol HCl}}{0.0631 \text{ mol} \cdot \text{L}^{-1}} = 0.0197 \text{ L HCl} = 19.7 \text{ mL HCl}$$

15.29 initial pH $= -\log(0.10) = 1.00$

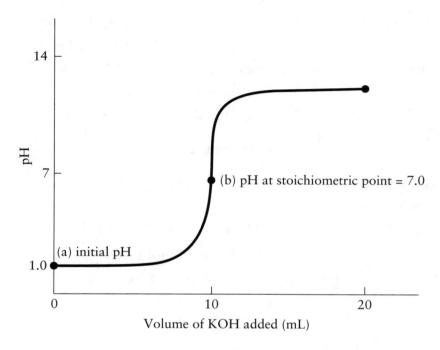

15.31 $\text{HCl(aq)} + \text{NaOH(aq)} \longrightarrow \text{H}_2\text{O(l)} + \text{Na}^+\text{(aq)} + \text{Cl}^-\text{(aq)}$

(a) volume of HCl $= (\tfrac{1}{2}) \times (25.0 \text{ mL}) \times \left(\dfrac{10^{-3} \text{ L}}{1 \text{ mL}}\right) \times \left(\dfrac{0.110 \text{ mol NaOH}}{1 \text{ L}}\right)$

$\qquad\qquad \times \left(\dfrac{1 \text{ mol HCl}}{1 \text{ mol NaOH}}\right) \times \left(\dfrac{1 \text{ L HCl}}{0.150 \text{ mol HCl}}\right) = 9.17 \times 10^{-3} \text{ L HCl}$

(b) $2 \times 9.17 \times 10^{-3} \text{ L} = 0.0183 \text{ L}$

(c) volume $= (0.0250 + 0.0183) \text{ L} = 0.0433 \text{ L}$

$[\text{Na}^+] = (0.0250 \text{ L}) \times \left(\dfrac{0.110 \text{ mol NaOH}}{1 \text{ L}}\right) \times \left(\dfrac{1 \text{ mol Na}^+}{1 \text{ mol NaOH}}\right) \times \left(\dfrac{1}{0.0433 \text{ L}}\right)$

$\qquad = 0.0635 \text{ mol} \cdot \text{L}^{-1}$

(d) number of moles of H_3O^+ (from acid) $= (0.0200 \text{ L}) \times \left(\dfrac{0.150 \text{ mol}}{1 \text{ L}}\right)$

$\qquad\qquad\qquad\qquad = 3.00 \times 10^{-3} \text{ mol H}_3\text{O}^+$

number of moles of OH^- (from base) $= (0.0250 \text{ L}) \times \left(\dfrac{0.110 \text{ mol Na}^+}{1 \text{ L}}\right)$

$\qquad\qquad\qquad\qquad = 2.75 \times 10^{-3} \text{ mol OH}^-$

excess $\text{H}_3\text{O}^+ = (3.00 - 2.75) \times 10^{-3} \text{ mol} = 2.5 \times 10^{-4} \text{ mol H}_3\text{O}^+$

$[\text{H}_3\text{O}^+] = \dfrac{2.5 \times 10^{-4} \text{ mol}}{0.0450 \text{ L}} = 5.5\overline{6} \times 10^{-3} \text{ mol} \cdot \text{L}^{-1}$

$\text{pH} = -\log(5.5\overline{6} \times 10^{-3}) = 2.26$

15.33 $HCl(aq) + NaOH(aq) \longrightarrow H_2O(l) + Na^+(aq) + Cl^-(aq)$

(a) moles of HCl = $(2.54 \text{ g NaOH}) \times \left(\dfrac{1 \text{ mol NaOH}}{40.0 \text{ g NaOH}}\right) \times \left(\dfrac{1 \text{ mol HCl}}{1 \text{ mol NaOH}}\right)$

$= 6.35 \times 10^{-2} \text{ mol HCl}$

volume of HCl = $\dfrac{6.35 \times 10^{-2} \text{ mol}}{0.150 \text{ mol} \cdot L^{-1}} = 0.423 \text{ L} = 423 \text{ mL}$

(b) moles of Cl^- = $0.423 \text{ L} \times \left(\dfrac{0.150 \text{ mol HCl}}{1 \text{ L}}\right) \times \left(\dfrac{1 \text{ mol } Cl^-}{1 \text{ mol HCl}}\right)$

$= 6.34 \times 10^{-2} \text{ mol } Cl^-$

$[Cl^-] = \dfrac{6.34 \times 10^{-2} \text{ mol } Cl^-}{(0.423 + 0.025) \text{ L}} = 0.142 \text{ mol} \cdot L^{-1}$

15.35 mass of pure NaOH = $(0.0158 \text{ L HCl}) \times \left(\dfrac{0.107 \text{ mol HCl}}{1 \text{ L HCl}}\right)$

$\times \left(\dfrac{1 \text{ mol NaOH}}{1 \text{ mol HCl}}\right) \times \left(\dfrac{40.0 \text{ g NaOH}}{1 \text{ mol NaOH}}\right) \times \left(\dfrac{200 \text{ mL}}{20 \text{ mL}}\right) = 0.676 \text{ g}$

percentage purity = $\dfrac{0.676 \text{ g}}{0.968 \text{ g}} \times 100\% = 69.8\%$

15.37 (a) pOH = $-\log(0.110) = 0.959$, pH = $14.00 - 0.959 = 13.04$

(b) initial moles of OH^- (from base) = $(0.0250 \text{ L}) \times \left(\dfrac{0.110 \text{ mol}}{1 \text{ L}}\right)$

$= 2.75 \times 10^{-3} \text{ mol } OH^-$

moles of H_3O^+ added = $(0.0050 \text{ L}) \times \left(\dfrac{0.150 \text{ mol}}{1 \text{ L}}\right) = 7.5 \times 10^{-4} \text{ mol } H_3O^+$

excess OH^- = $(2.75 - 0.75) \times 10^{-3} \text{ mol} = 2.00 \times 10^{-3} \text{ mol } OH^-$

$[OH^-] = \dfrac{2.00 \times 10^{-3} \text{ mol}}{0.030 \text{ L}} = 0.066\overline{7} \text{ mol} \cdot L^{-1}$

pOH = $-\log(0.066\overline{7}) = 1.18$, pH = $14.00 - 1.18 = 12.82$

(c) moles of H_3O^+ added = $2 \times 7.5 \times 10^{-4} \text{ mol} = 1.50 \times 10^{-3} \text{ mol } H_3O^+$

excess OH^- = $(2.75 - 1.50) \times 10^{-3} \text{ mol} = 1.25 \times 10^{-3} \text{ mol } OH^-$

$[OH^-] = \dfrac{1.25 \times 10^{-3} \text{ mol}}{0.035 \text{ L}} = 0.035\overline{7} \text{ mol} \cdot L^{-1}$

pOH = $-\log(0.035\overline{7}) = 1.45$, pH = $14.00 - 1.45 = 12.55$

(d) pH = 7.00

volume of HCl at stoichiometric point = $(2.75 \times 10^{-3} \text{ mol NaOH})$

$\times \left(\dfrac{1 \text{ mol HCl}}{1 \text{ mol NaOH}}\right) \times \left(\dfrac{1 \text{ L HCl}}{0.150 \text{ mol HCl}}\right) = 0.0183 \text{ L}$

(e) $[H_3O^+] = (0.0050 \text{ L}) \times \left(\dfrac{0.150 \text{ mol}}{1 \text{ L}}\right) \times \left(\dfrac{1}{(0.0250 + 0.0183 + 0.0050) \text{ L}}\right)$

$\qquad = 0.015\bar{5} \text{ mol} \cdot \text{L}^{-1}$

$\text{pH} = -\log(0.015\bar{5}) = 1.81$

(f) $[H_3O^+] = \left(\dfrac{0.010 \text{ L}}{0.0533 \text{ L}}\right) \times \left(\dfrac{0.150 \text{ mol}}{1 \text{ L}}\right) = 0.028\bar{1} \text{ mol} \cdot \text{L}^{-1}$

$\text{pH} = -\log(0.028\bar{1}) = 1.55$

Weak Acid-Strong Base and Weak Base-Strong Acid Titrations

15.39 (a)

Concentration $(\text{mol} \cdot \text{L}^{-1})$	$CH_3COOH(aq)$	$+ H_2O(l)$	$\rightleftharpoons H_3O^+(aq)$	$+ CH_3CO_2^-(aq)$
initial	0.10	—	0	0
change	$-x$	—	$+x$	$+x$
equilibrium	$0.10 - x$	—	x	x

$K_a = \dfrac{[H_3O^+][CH_3CO_2^-]}{[CH_3COOH]} = 1.8 \times 10^{-5} = \dfrac{x^2}{0.10 - x} \approx \dfrac{x^2}{0.10}$

$x^2 = 1.8 \times 10^{-6}$

$x = 1.3 \times 10^{-3} \text{ mol} \cdot \text{L}^{-1} = [H_3O^+]$

initial $\text{pH} = -\log(1.3 \times 10^{-3}) = 2.87$

(b) moles of $CH_3COOH = (0.0250 \text{ L}) \times (0.10 \text{ M})$

$\qquad = 2.50 \times 10^{-3} \text{ mol } CH_3COOH$

moles of $NaOH = (0.0100 \text{ L}) \times (0.10 \text{ M}) = 1.0 \times 10^{-3} \text{ mol } OH^-$

So, $\dfrac{1.50 \times 10^{-3} \text{ mol } CH_3COOH}{0.0350 \text{ L}} = 4.29 \times 10^{-2} \text{ mol} \cdot \text{L}^{-1}$

and $\dfrac{1.0 \times 10^{-3} \text{ mol } CH_3CO_2^-}{0.0350 \text{ L}} = 2.86 \times 10^{-2} \text{ mol} \cdot \text{L}^{-1}$

Then, consider equilibrium, $K_a = \dfrac{[H_3O^+][CH_3CO_2^-]}{[CH_3COOH]}$

Concentration $(\text{mol} \cdot \text{L}^{-1})$	$CH_3COOH(aq)$	$+ H_2O(l)$	$\rightleftharpoons H_3O^+(aq)$	$+ CH_3CO_2^-(aq)$
initial	4.29×10^{-2}	—	0	2.86×10^{-2}
change	$-x$	—	$+x$	$+x$
equilibrium	$4.29 \times 10^{-2} - x$	—	x	$2.86 \times 10^{-2} + x$

$1.8 \times 10^{-5} = \dfrac{(x)(x + 2.86 \times 10^{-2})}{(4.29 \times 10^{-2} - x)}$; assume $+x$ and $-x$ negligible.

$[H_3O^+] = x = 2.7 \times 10^{-5} \text{ mol} \cdot \text{L}^{-1}$ and $\text{pH} = -\log(2.7 \times 10^{-5}) = 4.56$

(c) Because acid and base concentrations are equal, their volumes are equal at the stoichiometric point. Therefore, 25.0 mL NaOH are required to reach the stoichiometric point and 12.5 mL NaOH are required to reach half the stoichiometric point.

(d) At the half stoichiometric point, $pH = pK_a$ and $pH = 4.75$

(e) 25.0 mL; see part (c)

(f) The final pH is that of 0.050 M $NaCH_3CO_2$.

Concentration (mol·L^{-1})	$H_2O(l)$ +	$CH_3CO_2^-(aq)$	$\rightleftharpoons$ $CH_3COOH(aq)$ +	$OH^-(aq)$
initial	—	0.050	0	0
change	—	$-x$	$+x$	$+x$
equilibrium	—	$0.050 - x$	x	x

$$K_b = \frac{K_w}{K_a} = \frac{1.00 \times 10^{-14}}{1.8 \times 10^{-5}} = 5.6 \times 10^{-10} = \frac{x^2}{0.050 - x} \approx \frac{x^2}{0.050}$$

$x^2 = 2.8 \times 10^{-11}$

$x = 5.5 \times 10^{-6}$ mol·L^{-1} = $[OH^-]$

$pOH = 5.28$, $pH = 14.00 - 5.28 = 8.72$

(g) thymol blue; $pK_{in} = 8.9$
or phenolphthalein; $pK_{in} = 9.4$ } close to stoichiometric point pH of 8.72

15.41 (a) $K_b = \dfrac{[NH_4^+][OH^-]}{[NH_3]} = 1.8 \times 10^{-5}$

Concentration (mol·L^{-1})	$H_2O(l)$ +	$NH_3(aq)$	$\rightleftharpoons$ $NH_4^+(aq)$ +	$OH^-(aq)$
initial	—	0.15	0	0
change	—	$-x$	$+x$	$+x$
equilibrium	—	$0.15 - x$	x	x

$$1.8 \times 10^{-5} = \frac{x^2}{0.15 - x} \approx \frac{x^2}{0.15}$$

$[OH^-] = x = 1.6 \times 10^{-3}$ mol·L^{-1}

$pOH = 2.78$, initial $pH = 14.00 - 2.78 = 11.22$

(b) moles of $NH_3 = (0.0150 \text{ L}) \times (0.15 \text{ mol·L}^{-1}) = 2.25 \times 10^{-3}$ mol NH_3

moles of $HCl = (0.0150 \text{ L}) \times (0.10 \text{ mol·L}^{-1}) = 1.5 \times 10^{-3}$ mol HCl

$$\frac{(2.25 \times 10^{-3} - 1.5 \times 10^{-3}) \text{ mol NH}_3}{0.0300 \text{ L}} = 2.5 \times 10^{-2} \text{ (mol NH}_3) \cdot \text{L}^{-1}$$

$$\frac{1.5 \times 10^{-3} \text{ mol HCl}}{0.0300 \text{ L}} = 5.0 \times 10^{-2} \text{ mol HCl} \cdot \text{L}^{-1} \approx 5.0 \times 10^{-2} \text{ (mol NH}_4^+) \cdot \text{L}^{-1}$$

Then, consider the equilibrium.

Concentration (mol·L^{-1})	$H_2O(l)$ +	$NH_3(aq)$	$\rightleftharpoons$	$NH_4^+(aq)$ +	$OH^-(aq)$
initial	—	2.5×10^{-2}		5.0×10^{-2}	0
change	—	$-x$		$+x$	$+x$
equilibrium	—	$2.5 \times 10^{-2} - x$		$5.0 \times 10^{-2} + x$	x

$$K_b = \frac{[NH_4^+][OH^-]}{[NH_3]} = 1.8 \times 10^{-5}$$

$$= \frac{(x)(5.0 \times 10^{-2} + x)}{(2.5 \times 10^{-2} - x)}; \text{ assume } +x \text{ and } -x \text{ are negligible.}$$

$[OH^-] = x = 9.0 \times 10^{-6} \text{ mol} \cdot L^{-1}$ and pOH $= 5.05$

Therefore, pH $= 14.00 - 5.05 = 8.95$

(c) At the stoichiometric point, moles NH_3 = moles HCl.

$$\text{volume HCl added} = \frac{(0.15 \text{ mol } NH_3 \cdot L^{-1})(0.0150 \text{ L})}{0.10 \text{ mol HCl} \cdot L^{-1}} = 0.0225 \text{ L HCl}$$

Therefore, halfway to the stoichiometric point, volume HCl added $=$ 22.5/2 $= 11.25$ mL

(d) At half stoichiometric point, pOH $= pK_b$ and pOH $= 4.75$.

Therefore, pH $= 14.00 - 4.75 = 9.25$.

(e) 22.5 mL; see part (c)

(f) $NH_4^+(aq) + H_2O(l) \rightleftharpoons H_3O^+(aq) + NH_3(aq)$

The initial moles of NH_3 have now been converted to moles NH_4^+ in a (15 + 22.5 = 37.5) mL volume

$$[NH_4^+] = \frac{2.25 \times 10^{-3} \text{ mol}}{0.0375 \text{ L}} = 0.060 \text{ mol} \cdot L^{-1}$$

$$K_a = \frac{K_w}{K_b} = \frac{1.00 \times 10^{-14}}{1.8 \times 10^{-5}} = 5.6 \times 10^{-10}$$

Concentration (mol·L^{-1})	$NH_4^+(aq)$	$+ H_2O(l)$	$\rightleftharpoons$	$H_3O^+(aq)$	$+ NH_3(aq)$
initial	0.060	—		0	0
change	$-x$	—		$+x$	$+x$
equilibrium	$0.060 - x$	—		x	x

$$K_a = 5.6 \times 10^{-10} = \frac{x^2}{0.060 - x} \approx \frac{x^2}{0.060}$$

$x = [H_3O^+] = 5.8 \times 10^{-6} \text{ mol} \cdot L^{-1}$

pH $= -\log(5.8 \times 10^{-6}) = 5.24$

(g) methyl red or bromocresol green

15.43 (a) Let HL = lactic acid; then, HL(aq) + $H_2O(l) \rightleftharpoons H_3O^+(aq) + L^-(aq)$

$$K_a = \frac{[H_3O^+][L^-]}{[HL]} = 8.4 \times 10^{-4}$$

Concentration (mol·L^{-1})	HL(aq)	$+ H_2O(l)$	$\rightleftharpoons$	$H_3O^+(aq)$	$+ L^-(aq)$
initial	0.110	—		0	0
change	$-x$	—		$+x$	$+x$
equilibrium	$0.110 - x$	—		x	x

$$8.4 \times 10^{-4} = \frac{x^2}{0.110 - x} \approx \frac{x^2}{0.110}$$

$[H_3O^+] = x = 9.6 \times 10^{-3} \text{ mol} \cdot L^{-1}$

initial pH $= -\log(9.6 \times 10^{-3}) = 2.02$

(b) moles of HL $= (0.0250 \text{ L}) \times (0.110 \text{ M}) = 2.75 \times 10^{-3}$ mol HL

moles of NaOH $= (0.0050 \text{ L}) \times (0.150 \text{ M}) = 7.5 \times 10^{-4}$ mol NaOH

$$[HL] = \frac{2.00 \times 10^{-3} \text{ mol HL}}{0.0300 \text{ L}} = 6.67 \times 10^{-2} \text{ mol HL} \cdot L^{-1}$$

$$[L^-] = \frac{7.5 \times 10^{-4} \text{ mol } L^-}{0.0300 \text{ L}} = 2.5 \times 10^{-2} \text{ mol } L^- \cdot L^{-1}$$

Then, consider the equilibrium.

Concentration

(mol $\cdot$ L^{-1})	HL(aq)	+	H$_2$O(l) $\rightleftharpoons$ H$_3$O$^+$(aq)	+	L$^-$(aq)
initial	6.67×10^{-2}	—	0		2.5×10^{-2}
change	$-x$	—	$+x$		$+x$
equilibrium	$6.67 \times 10^{-2} - x$	—	x		$2.5 \times 10^{-2} + x$

$K_a = \dfrac{[H_3O^+][L^-]}{[HL]} = 8.4 \times 10^{-4} = \dfrac{(x)(x + 2.5 \times 10^{-2})}{(6.67 \times 10^{-2} - x)}$; $+x$ and $-x$ negligible

$[H_3O^+] = x = 2.24 \times 10^{-3} \text{ mol} \cdot L^{-1}$

pH $= -\log(2.24 \times 10^{-3}) = 2.65$

(c) moles of HL $= (0.0250 \text{ L}) \times (0.110 \text{ mol} \cdot L^{-1}) = 2.75 \times 10^{-3}$ mol HL

moles of NaOH $= (0.0100 \text{ L}) \times (0.150 \text{ mol} \cdot L^{-1}) = 1.50 \times 10^{-3}$ mol NaOH

$$[HL] = \frac{1.25 \times 10^{-3} \text{ mol HL}}{0.0350 \text{ L}} = 3.57 \times 10^{-2} \text{ mol HL} \cdot L^{-1}$$

$$[L^-] = \frac{1.50 \times 10^{-3} \text{ mol } L^-}{0.0350 \text{ L}} = 4.28 \times 10^{-2} \text{ mol } L^- \cdot L^{-1}$$

Then, consider the equilibrium.

Concentration

(mol $\cdot$ L^{-1})	HL(aq)	+	H$_2$O(l) $\rightleftharpoons$ H$_3$O$^+$(aq)	+	L$^-$(aq)
initial	3.57×10^{-2}	—	0		4.28×10^{-2}
change	$-x$	—	$+x$		$+x$
equilibrium	$3.57 \times 10^{-2} - x$	—	x		$4.28 \times 10^{-2} + x$

$K_a = \dfrac{[H_3O^+][L^-]}{[HL]} = 8.4 \times 10^{-4} = \dfrac{(x)(x + 4.28 \times 10^{-2})}{(3.57 \times 10^{-2} - x)}$; $+x$ and $-x$ negligible

$[H_3O^+] = x = 7.01 \times 10^{-4} \text{ mol} \cdot L^{-1}$

pH $= -\log(7.01 \times 10^{-4}) = 3.15$

(d) At the stoichiometric point, moles acid = moles base = moles L$^-$

volume base $= \dfrac{(0.110 \text{ mol acid} \cdot L^{-1}) \times (0.0250 \text{ L acid})}{0.150 \text{ mol base} \cdot L^{-1}} = 0.0184 \text{ L base}$

$$K_b = \frac{K_w}{K_a} = \frac{1.00 \times 10^{-14}}{8.4 \times 10^{-4}} = 1.19 \times 10^{-11}$$

$$[L^-] = \frac{2.75 \times 10^{-3} \text{ mol} \cdot L^-}{(0.025 + 0.0184) \text{ L}} = 6.34 \times 10^{-2} \text{ mol } L^- \cdot L^{-1}$$

Concentration (mol · L^{-1})	H$_2$O(l)	+	L$^-$(aq)	$\rightleftharpoons$	HL(aq)	+	OH$^-$(aq)
initial	—		6.34×10^{-2}		0		0
change	—		$-x$		$+x$		$+x$
equilibrium	—		$6.34 \times 10^{-2} - x$		x		x

$$1.19 \times 10^{-11} = \frac{[HL][OH^-]}{[L^-]} = \frac{x^2}{6.34 \times 10^{-2} - x} \approx \frac{x^2}{6.34 \times 10^{-2}}$$

$$[OH^-] = x = 8.68 \times 10^{-7} \text{ mol} \cdot L^{-1}$$

$$pOH = -\log(8.68 \times 10^{-7}) = 6.06, \quad pH = 14.00 - 6.06 = 7.94$$

(e) At 5.0 mL base beyond the stoichiometric point, consider only strong base.

$$\text{molar concentration of OH}^- = \frac{(0.0050 \text{ L}) \times (0.150 \text{ mol} \cdot L^{-1})}{0.0250 \text{ L} + 0.0234 \text{ L}}$$

$$= 1.55 \times 10^{-2} \text{ mol} \cdot L^{-1}$$

$$pOH = -\log(1.55 \times 10^{-2}) = 1.81, \quad pH = 14.00 - 1.81 = 12.19$$

(f) At 10.0 mL base beyond stoichiometric point, consider only strong base.

$$\text{molar concentration of OH}^- = \frac{(0.0100 \text{ L}) \times (0.150 \text{ mol} \cdot L^{-1})}{0.0250 \text{ L} + 0.0284 \text{ L}}$$

$$= 2.81 \times 10^{-2} \text{ mol} \cdot L^{-1}$$

$$pOH = -\log(2.81 \times 10^{-2}) = 1.55, \quad pH = 14.00 - 1.55 = 12.45$$

(g) phenol red, pK_{in} = 7.9 (close to pH = 7.94)

Indicators

For the pH ranges over which common indicators change color, see Table 15.3.

15.45 (a) methyl orange, pK_{in} = 3.4; 3.2–4.4

(b) litmus, pK_{in} = 6.5; 5.0–8.0

(c) methyl red, pK_{in} = 5.0; 4.8–6.0

(d) phenolphthalein, pK_{in} = 9.4; 8.2–10.0

Values are from Table 15.3.

15.47 At the stoichiometric point, the volume of solution will have doubled; therefore, the concentration of CH$_3$CO$_2^-$ will be 0.10 M. The equilibrium is

Concentration (mol · L^{-1})	CH$_3$CO$_2^-$(aq)	+ H$_2$O(l)	$\rightleftharpoons$	HCH$_3$CO$_2$(aq)	+	OH$^-$(aq)
initial	0.10	—		0		0
change	$-x$	—		$+x$		$+x$
equilibrium	$0.10 - x$	—		x		x

$$K_b = \frac{K_w}{K_a} = \frac{1.00 \times 10^{-14}}{1.8 \times 10^{-5}} = 5.6 \times 10^{-10}$$

$$K_b = \frac{[HCH_3CO_2][OH^-]}{[CH_3CO_2^-]} = \frac{x^2}{0.10 - x} \approx \frac{x^2}{0.10} = 5.6 \times 10^{-10}$$

$$x = 7.5 \times 10^{-6} \text{ mol} \cdot \text{L}^{-1} = [OH^-]$$

$$pOH = -\log(7.5 \times 10^{-6}) = 5.13, \quad pH = 14.00 - 5.13 = 8.87$$

From Table 15.3, we see that this pH value lies within the range for phenolphthalein, so that indicator would be suitable; the others would not.

Buffers

15.49 (a) not a buffer; strong acid/salt of strong acid and strong base

(b) weak acid/conjugate base; hence, a buffer:

$$HClO(aq) + H_2O(l) \rightleftharpoons H_3O^+(aq) + ClO^-(aq)$$

(c) weak base/conjugate acid; hence, a buffer:

$$(CH_3)_3N(aq) + H_2O(l) \rightleftharpoons (CH_3)_3NH^+(aq) + OH^-(aq)$$

(d) After partial neutralization, we have a weak acid (CH_3COOH) and its salt ($NaCH_3CO_2$) in solution. Thus, weak acid/conjugate base, hence, a buffer:

$$CH_3COOH(aq) + H_2O(l) \rightleftharpoons H_3O^+(aq) + CH_3CO_2^-(aq)$$

(e) not a buffer; complete neutralization results in a salt and water

15.51 In a solution containing $HClO(aq)$ and $ClO^-(aq)$, the following equilibrium occurs:

$$HClO(aq) + H_2O(l) \rightleftharpoons H_3O^+(aq) + ClO^-(aq)$$

The ratio $[ClO^-]/[HClO]$ is related to pH, as given by the Henderson-Hasselbalch equation:

$$pH = pK_a + \log\left(\frac{[ClO^-]}{[HClO]}\right), \text{ or}$$

$$\log\left(\frac{[ClO^-]}{[HClO]}\right) = pH - pK_a = 6.50 - 7.53 = -1.03$$

$$\frac{[ClO^-]}{[HClO]} = 9.3 \times 10^{-2}$$

15.53 The rule of thumb we use is that the effective range of a buffer is roughly within plus or minus one pH unit of the pK_a of the acid. Therefore,

(a) $pK_a = 3.08$; pH range, 2–4

(b) $pK_a = 4.19$; pH range, 3–5

(c) $pK_{a3} = 12.68$; pH range, 11.5–13.5

(d) $pK_{a2} = 7.21$; pH range, 6–8

(e) $pK_b = 7.97$, $pK_a = 6.03$; pH range, 5–7

15.55 Choose a buffer system in which the conjugate acid has a pK_a close to the desired pH. Therefore,

(a) $HClO_2$ and $NaClO_2$, $pK_a = 2.00$

(b) NaH_2PO_4 and Na_2HPO_4, $pK_{a2} = 7.21$

(c) $CH_2ClCOOH$ and $NaCH_2ClCO_2$, $pK_a = 2.85$

(d) Na_2HPO_4 and Na_3PO_4, $pK_a = 12.68$

15.57 (a) $HCO_3^-(aq) + H_2O(l) \rightleftharpoons CO_3^{2-}(aq) + H_3O^+(aq)$

$$K_{a2} = \frac{[H_3O^+][CO_3^{2-}]}{[HCO_3^-]}, \quad pK_{a2} = 10.25$$

$$pH = pK_{a2} + \log\left(\frac{[CO_3^{2-}]}{[HCO_3^-]}\right)$$

$$\log\left(\frac{[CO_3^{2-}]}{[HCO_3^-]}\right) = pH - pK_{a2} = 11.0 - 10.25 = 0.75$$

$$\frac{[CO_3^{2-}]}{[HCO_3^-]} = 5.6$$

(b) $[CO_3^{2-}] = 5.6 \times [HCO_3^-] = 5.6 \times 0.100 \text{ mol} \cdot L^{-1} = 0.56 \text{ mol} \cdot L^{-1}$

moles of CO_3^{2-} = moles of $K_2CO_3 = 0.56 \text{ mol} \cdot L^{-1} \times 1 \text{ L} = 0.56 \text{ mol}$

mass of $K_2CO_3 = 0.56 \text{ mol} \times \left(\frac{138 \text{ g } K_2CO_3}{1 \text{ mol } K_2CO_3}\right) = 77 \text{ g } K_2CO_3$

(c) $[HCO_3^-] = \dfrac{[CO_3^{2-}]}{5.6} = \dfrac{0.100 \text{ mol} \cdot L^{-1}}{5.6} = 1.7\overline{9} \times 10^{-2} \text{ mol} \cdot L^{-1}$

moles of HCO_3^- = moles of $KHCO_3 = 1.7\overline{9} \times 10^{-2} \text{ mol} \cdot L^{-1} \times 1 \text{ L}$

$$= 1.7\overline{9} \times 10^{-2} \text{ mol}$$

mass $KHCO_3 = 1.7\overline{9} \times 10^{-2} \text{ mol} \times 100 \text{ g} \cdot \text{mol}^{-1} = 1.8 \text{ g } KHCO_3$

(d) $[CO_3^{2-}] = 5.6 \times [HCO_3^-]$

moles HCO_3^- = moles $KHCO_3 = 0.100 \text{ mol} \cdot L^{-1} \times 0.100 \text{ L} = 1.00 \times 10^{-2} \text{ mol}$

Because the final total volume is the same for both $KHCO_3$ and K_2CO_3, the number of moles of K_2CO_3 required is $5.6 \times 1.00 \times 10^{-2} \text{ mol} = 5.6 \times 10^{-2} \text{ mol}$. Thus,

$$\text{volume of } K_2CO_3 \text{ solution} = \frac{5.6 \times 10^{-2} \text{ mol}}{0.200 \text{ mol} \cdot L^{-1}} = 0.28 \text{ L} = 2.8 \times 10^2 \text{ mL}$$

15.59 $CH_3COOH(aq) + H_2O(l) \rightleftharpoons H_3O^+(aq) + CH_3CO_2^-(aq)$

$$K_a = \frac{[H_3O^+][CH_3CO_2^-]}{[CH_3COOH]}$$

$$pH = pK_a + \log\left(\frac{[CH_3CO_2^-]}{[CH_3COOH]}\right)$$

(a) $pH = pK_a + \log\left(\dfrac{0.10}{0.10}\right) = pK_a = 4.75$

(b) 3.0 mmol NaOH = 3.0×10^{-3} mol NaOH (strong base) produces 3.0×10^{-3} mol $CH_3CO_2^-$ from CH_3COOH (assume no volume change)

0.10 mol·$L^{-1} \times 0.100$ L = 1.0×10^{-2} mol CH_3COOH initially

0.10 mol·$L^{-1} \times 0.100$ L = 1.0×10^{-2} mol $CH_3CO_2^-$ initially

after adding NaOH:

$$[CH_3COOH] = \frac{(1.0 \times 10^{-2} - 3.0 \times 10^{-3})\ \text{mol}}{0.100\ \text{L}} = \frac{7.0 \times 10^{-3}\ \text{mol}}{0.100\ \text{L}}$$
$$= 7.0 \times 10^{-2}\ \text{mol·L}^{-1}$$

$$[CH_3CO_2^-] = \frac{(1.0 \times 10^{-2} + 3.0 \times 10^{-3})\ \text{mol}}{0.100\ \text{L}} = \frac{1.3 \times 10^{-2}\ \text{mol}}{0.100\ \text{L}}$$
$$= 1.3 \times 10^{-1}\ \text{mol·L}^{-1}$$

$$pH = 4.75 + \log\left(\frac{1.3 \times 10^{-1}}{7.0 \times 10^{-2}}\right)$$

$pH = 4.75 + 0.27 = 5.02$ ($\Delta pH = 0.27$)

(c) 6.0 mmol HNO_3 = 6.0×10^{-3} mol HNO_3 (strong acid) produces 6.0×10^{-3} mol CH_3COOH from $CH_3CO_2^-$ (assume no volume change)

after adding HNO_3:

$$[CH_3COOH] = \frac{(1.0 \times 10^{-2} + 6.0 \times 10^{-3})\ \text{mol}}{0.100\ \text{L}} = \frac{1.6 \times 10^{-2}\ \text{mol}}{0.100\ \text{L}}$$
$$= 1.6 \times 10^{-1}\ \text{mol·L}^{-1}$$

$$[CH_3CO_2^-] = \frac{(1.0 \times 10^{-2} - 6.0 \times 10^{-3})\ \text{mol}}{0.100\ \text{L}} = \frac{4.0 \times 10^{-3}\ \text{mol}}{0.100\ \text{L}}$$
$$= 4.0 \times 10^{-2}\ \text{mol·L}^{-1}$$

$$pH = 4.75 + \log\left(\frac{4.0 \times 10^{-2}}{1.6 \times 10^{-1}}\right)$$

$pH = 4.75 - 0.60 = 4.15$ ($\Delta pH = -0.60$)

15.61 (a) $pH = pK_a + \log\left(\dfrac{[CH_3CO_2^-]}{[CH_3COOH]}\right)$ (see Exercise 15.59)

$pH = pK_a + \log\left(\dfrac{0.10}{0.10}\right) = 4.75$ (initial pH) final pH: $(0.0100 \text{ L})(0.950 \text{ mol} \cdot \text{L}) = 9.5 \times 10^{-3}$ mol NaOH (strong base)

produces 9.5×10^{-3} mol $CH_3CO_2^-$ from CH_3COOH

$0.10 \text{ mol} \cdot \text{L}^{-1} \times 0.100 \text{ L} = 1.0 \times 10^{-2}$ mol CH_3COOH initially

$0.10 \text{ mol} \cdot \text{L}^{-1} \times 0.100 \text{ L} = 1.0 \times 10^{-2}$ mol $CH_3CO_2^-$ initially

after adding NaOH:

$$[CH_3COOH] = \frac{(1.0 \times 10^{-2} - 9.5 \times 10^{-3}) \text{ mol}}{0.110 \text{ L}} = 4.55 \times 10^{-3} \text{ mol} \cdot \text{L}^{-1}$$

$$[CH_3CO_2^-] = \frac{(1.0 \times 10^{-2} + 9.5 \times 10^{-3}) \text{ mol}}{0.110 \text{ L}} = 1.78 \times 10^{-1} \text{ mol} \cdot \text{L}^{-1}$$

$$\text{pH} = 4.75 + \log\left(\frac{1.78 \times 10^{-1} \text{ mol} \cdot \text{L}^{-1}}{4.55 \times 10^{-3} \text{ mol} \cdot \text{L}^{-1}}\right) = 4.75 + 1.59 = 6.34$$

(b) $(0.0200 \text{ L}) \times (0.10 \text{ mol} \cdot \text{L}^{-1}) = 2.00 \times 10^{-3}$ mol HNO_3 (strong acid)

produces 2.00×10^{-3} mol CH_3COOH from $CH_3CO_2^-$

after adding HNO_3 [see part (a) of this exercise]:

$$[CH_3COOH] = \frac{(1.0 \times 10^{-2} + 2.00 \times 10^{-3}) \text{ mol}}{0.120 \text{ L}} = 1.00 \times 10^{-1} \text{ mol} \cdot \text{L}^{-1}$$

$$[CH_3CO_2^-] = \frac{(1.0 \times 10^{-2} - 2.00 \times 10^{-3}) \text{ mol}}{0.120 \text{ L}} = 6.67 \times 10^{-2} \text{ mol} \cdot \text{L}^{-1}$$

$$\text{pH} = 4.75 + \log\left(\frac{6.67 \times 10^{-2} \text{ mol} \cdot \text{L}^{-1}}{1.00 \times 10^{-1} \text{ mol} \cdot \text{L}^{-1}}\right) = 4.75 - 0.17 = 4.58$$

$$\Delta\text{pH} = -0.17$$

Solubility Products

The values for the solubility products of various sparingly soluble salts are listed in Table 15.5.

15.63 (a) $K_{sp} = [Ag^+][Br^-]$

(b) $K_{sp} = [Ag^+]^2[S^{2-}]$

(c) $K_{sp} = [Ca^{2+}][OH^-]^2$

(d) $K_{sp} = [Ag^+]^2[CrO_4^{2-}]$

15.65 (a) The solubility equilibrium is $[AgBr(s) \rightleftharpoons Ag^+(aq) + Br^-(aq)$.

$[Ag^+] = [Br^-] = 8.8 \times 10^{-7} \text{ mol} \cdot \text{L}^{-1} = S = $ solubility

$K_{sp} = [Ag^+][Br^-] = (8.8 \times 10^{-7})(8.8 \times 10^{-7}) = 7.7 \times 10^{-13}$

(b) The solubility equilibrium is $PbCrO_4(s) \rightleftharpoons Pb^{2+}(aq) + CrO_4^{2-}(aq)$

$[Pb^{2+}] = 1.3 \times 10^{-7} \text{ mol} \cdot \text{L}^{-1} = S, \quad [CrO_4^{2-}] = 1.3 \times 10^{-7} \text{ mol} \cdot \text{L}^{-1} = S$

$K_{sp} = [Pb^{2+}][CrO_4^{2-}] = (1.3 \times 10^{-7})(1.3 \times 10^{-7}) = 1.7 \times 10^{-14}$

(c) The solubility equilibrium is $Ba(OH)_2(s) \rightleftharpoons Ba^{2+}(aq) + 2OH^-(aq)$

$[Ba^{2+}] = 0.11 \text{ mol} \cdot L^{-1} = S$, $[OH^-] = 0.22 \text{ mol} \cdot L^{-1} = 2S$

$K_{sp} = [Ba^{2+}][OH^-]^2 = (0.11)(0.22)^2 = 5.3 \times 10^{-3}$

(d) The solubility equilibrium is $MgF_2(s) \rightleftharpoons Mg^{2+}(aq) + 2F^-(aq)$

$[Mg^{2+}] = 1.2 \times 10^{-3} \text{ mol} \cdot L^{-1} = S$, $[F^-] = 2.4 \times 10^{-3} \text{ mol} \cdot L^{-1} = 2S$

$K_{sp} = [Mg^{2+}][F^-]^2 = (1.2 \times 10^{-3})(2.4 \times 10^{-3})^2 = 6.9 \times 10^{-9}$

15.67 (a) Equilibrium equation: $Ag_2S(s) \rightleftharpoons 2Ag^+(aq) + S^{2-}(aq)$

$K_{sp} = [Ag^+]^2[S^{2-}] = (2S)^2 (S) = 4S^3 = 6.3 \times 10^{-51}$

$S = 1.2 \times 10^{-17} \text{ mol} \cdot L^{-1}$

(b) Equilibrium equation: $CuS(s) \rightleftharpoons Cu^{2+}(aq) + S^{2-}(aq)$

$K_{sp} = [Cu^{2+}][S^{2-}] = S \times S = S^2 = 1.3 \times 10^{-36}$

$S = 1.1 \times 10^{-18} \text{mol} \cdot L^{-1}$

(c) Equilibrium equation: $CaCO_3(s) \rightleftharpoons Ca^{2+}(aq) + CO_3^{2-}(aq)$

$K_{sp} = [Ca^{2+}][CO_3^{2-}] = S \times S = S^2 = 8.7 \times 10^{-9}$

$S = 9.3 \times 10^{-5} \text{ mol} \cdot L^{-1}$

15.69 $Tl_2CrO_4(s) \rightleftharpoons 2Tl^+(aq) + CrO_4^{2-}(aq)$

$[CrO_4^{2-}] = S = 6.3 \times 10^{-5} \text{ mol} \cdot L^{-1}$

$[Tl^+] = 2S = 2(6.3 \times 10^{-5}) \text{ mol} \cdot L^{-1}$

$K_{sp} = [Tl^+]^2[CrO_4^{2-}] = (2S)^2 \times (S)$

$K_{sp} = [2(6.3 \times 10^{-5})]^2 \times (6.3 \times 10^{-5}) = 1.0 \times 10^{-12}$

Common-Ion Effect

15.71 (a)

Concentration (mol $\cdot$ L^{-1})	AgCl(s) $\rightleftharpoons$	Ag$^+$(aq) +	Cl$^-$(aq)
initial	—	0	0.20
change	—	+S	+S
equilibrium	—	S	S + 0.20

$K_{sp} = [Ag^+][Cl^-] = (S) \times (S + 0.20) = 1.6 \times 10^{-10}$

Assume S in S + 0.20 is negligible, so $0.20 S = 1.6 \times 10^{-10}$

$S = 8.0 \times 10^{-10} \text{ mol} \cdot L^{-1} = [Ag^+] = $ molar solubility of AgCl in 0.20 M NaCl

(b)

Concentration (mol $\cdot$ L^{-1})	Hg$_2$Cl$_2$(s) $\rightleftharpoons$	Hg$_2^{2+}$(aq) +	2Cl$^-$(aq)
initial	—	0	0.10
change	—	+S	+2S
equilibrium	—	S	0.10 + 2S

$K_{sp} = [Hg_2^{2+}][Cl^-]^2 = (S) \times (2S + 0.10)^2 = 1.3 \times 10^{-18}$

Assume $2S$ in $2S + 0.10$ is negligible, so $0.010S = 1.3 \times 10^{-18}$

$S = 1.3 \times 10^{-16}$ mol $\cdot$ L^{-1} = [Hg$_2^{2+}$] = molar solubility of Hg$_2$Cl$_2$ in 0.10 M NaCl

(c) Concentration (mol $\cdot$ L^{-1}) PbCl$_2$(s) $\rightleftharpoons$ Pb^{2+}(aq) + 2Cl$^-$(aq)

initial	—	0	$2 \times 0.10 = 0.20$
change	—	$+S$	$+S$
equilibrium	—	S	$S + 0.20$

$K_{sp} = [\text{Pb}^{2+}][\text{Cl}^-]^2 = S \times (S + 0.20)^2 = 1.6 \times 10^{-5}$

S may not be negligible relative to 0.20, so the full cubic form may be required. We do it both ways:

For $S^3 + 0.40\,S^2 + 4 \times 10^{-2}S - 1.6 \times 10^{-5} = 0$, the solution by standard methods is $S = 4.0 \times 10^{-4}$ mol $\cdot$ L^{-1}.

If S had been neglected, the answer would have been the same, 4.0×10^{-4}, to within two significant figures.

(d) Concentration (mol $\cdot$ L^{-1}) Fe(OH)$_2$(s) $\rightleftharpoons$ Fe^{2+}(aq) + 2OH$^-$(aq)

initial	—	1.0×10^{-4}	0
change	—	$+S$	$+2S$
equilibrium	—	$1.0 \times 10^{-4} + S$	$2S$

$K_{sp} = [\text{Fe}^{2+}][\text{OH}^-]^2 = (S + 1.0 \times 10^{-4}) \times (2S)^2 = 1.6 \times 10^{-14}$

Assume S in $S + 1.0 \times 10^{-4}$ is negligible, so $4S^2 \times 1.0 \times 10^{-4} = 1.6 \times 10^{-14}$

$S^2 = 4 \times 10^{-11}$

$S = 6.3 \times 10^{-6}$ mol $\cdot$ L^{-1} = molar solubility of Fe(OH)$_2$ in 1.0×10^{-4} M FeCl$_2$

15.73 (a) Ag$^+$(aq) + Cl$^-$(aq) $\rightleftharpoons$ AgCl(s)

Concentration (mol $\cdot$ L^{-1})	Ag$^+$	Cl$^-$
initial	0	1.0×10^{-5}
change	$+x$	0
equilibrium	x	1.0×10^{-5}

$K_{sp} = [\text{Ag}^+][\text{Cl}^-] = 1.6 \times 10^{-10} = (x)(1.0 \times 10^{-5})$

$x = [\text{Ag}^+] = 1.6 \times 10^{-5}$ mol $\cdot$ L^{-1}

(b) mass AgNO$_3$ = $\left(\dfrac{1.6 \times 10^{-5} \text{ mol AgNO}_3}{1 \text{ L}} \right) \times \left(\dfrac{10^{-3} \text{ L}}{1 \text{ mL}} \right) \times (100 \text{ mL})$

$\times \left(\dfrac{170 \text{ g AgNO}_3}{1 \text{ mol AgNO}_3} \right) \times \left(\dfrac{1 \text{ } \mu\text{g}}{10^{-6} \text{ g}} \right) = 2.7 \times 10^2 \text{ } \mu\text{g AgNO}_3$

15.75 Ni^{2+}(aq) + 2OH$^-$(aq) $\rightleftharpoons$ Ni(OH)$_2$(s)

Concentration ($mol \cdot L^{-1}$)	Ni^{2+}	OH^-
initial	0.010	0
change	0	$+x$
equilibrium	0.010	x

$K_{sp} = [Ni^{2+}][OH^-]^2 = 6.5 \times 10^{-18} = (0.010)(x)^2$

$[OH^-] = x = \sqrt{\dfrac{6.5 \times 10^{-18}}{0.010}} = 2.5 \times 10^{-8} \; mol \cdot L^{-1}$

$pOH = -\log(2.5 \times 10^{-8}) = 7.59, \quad pH = 14.00 - 7.59 = 6.41$

15.77 $\quad [Mg^{2+}] = \left(\dfrac{1.3 \; \mu g \; Mg^{2+}}{1 \; L}\right) \times \left(\dfrac{10^{-6} \; g \; Mg^{2+}}{1 \; \mu g \; Mg^{2+}}\right) \times \left(\dfrac{1 \; mol \; Mg^{2+}}{24.3 \; g \; Mg^{2+}}\right)$

$\qquad\qquad = 5.3 \times 10^{-8} \; mol \; Mg^{2+} \cdot L^{-1}$

$Mg(OH)_2(s) \rightleftharpoons Mg^{2+}(aq) + 2OH^-(aq)$

$K_{sp} = [Mg^{2+}][OH^-]^2 = 1.1 \times 10^{-11} = (5.3 \times 10^{-8}) \times [OH^-]^2$

$[OH^-] = \sqrt{\dfrac{1.1 \times 10^{-11}}{5.3 \times 10^{-8}}} = 1.4 \times 10^{-2} \; mol \cdot L^{-1}$

$pOH = -\log(1.4 \times 10^{-2}) = 1.84$, and $pH \geq 12.16$

Predicting Precipitation Reactions

15.79 (a) $Ag^+(aq) + Cl^-(aq) \rightleftharpoons AgCl(s), \quad [Ag^+][Cl^-] = K_{sp}$

$Q_{sp} = \left[\dfrac{(0.073 \; L)(0.0040 \; mol \cdot L^{-1})}{0.100 \; L}\right] \times \left[\dfrac{(0.027 \; L)(0.0010 \; mol \cdot L^{-1})}{0.100 \; L}\right]$

$\qquad = (2.9 \times 10^{-3}) \times (2.7 \times 10^{-4}) = 7.8 \times 10^{-7}$

will precipitate, because $Q_{sp} (7.8 \times 10^{-7}) > K_{sp} (1.6 \times 10^{-10})$

(b) $Ca^{2+}(aq) + SO_4^{2-}(aq) \rightleftharpoons CaSO_4(s), \quad [Ca^{2+}][SO_4^{2-}] = K_{sp}$

$Q_{sp} = \left[\dfrac{(0.0100 \; L) \times (0.0030 \; mol \cdot L^{-1})}{0.111 \; L}\right] \times \left[\dfrac{(0.0010 \; L) \times (1.0 \; mol \cdot L^{-1})}{0.111 \; L}\right]$

$\qquad = (2.7 \times 10^{-4}) \times (9.0 \times 10^{-3}) = 2.4 \times 10^{-6}$

will not precipitate, because $Q_{sp} (2.4 \times 10^{-6}) < K_{sp}(2.4 \times 10^{-5})$

15.81 $\left(\dfrac{1 \; mL}{20 \; drops}\right) \times 1 \; drop = 0.05 \; mL = 0.05 \times 10^{-3} \; L = 5 \times 10^{-5} \; L$

and $(5 \times 10^{-5} \; L)(0.010 \; mol \cdot L^{-1}) = 5 \times 10^{-7} \; mol \; NaCl = 5 \times 10^{-7} \; mol \; Cl^-$

(a) $Ag^+(aq) + Cl^-(aq) \rightleftharpoons AgCl(s), \quad [Ag^+][Cl^-] = K_{sp}$

$$Q_{sp} = \left[\frac{(0.010\ \text{L}) \times (0.0040\ \text{mol} \cdot \text{L}^{-1})}{0.010\ \text{L}} \right] \times \left[\frac{5 \times 10^{-7}\ \text{mol}}{0.010\ \text{L}} \right]$$

$$= (4.0 \times 10^{-3}) \times (5 \times 10^{-5}) = 2 \times 10^{-7}$$

will precipitate, because Q_{sp} (2×10^{-7}) $> K_{sp}$ (1.6×10^{-10})

(b) $Pb^{2+}(aq) + 2Cl^-(aq) \rightleftharpoons PbCl_2(s)$, $[Pb^{2+}][Cl^-]^2 = K_{sp}$

$$Q_{sp} = \left[\frac{(0.0100\ \text{L}) \times (0.0040\ \text{mol} \cdot \text{L}^{-1})}{0.010\ \text{L}} \right] \times \left[\frac{5 \times 10^{-7}\ \text{mol}}{0.010\ \text{L}} \right]^2$$

$$= (4.0 \times 10^{-3}) \times (2.\overline{5} \times 10^{-9}) = 1 \times 10^{-11}$$

will not precipitate, because Q_{sp} (1×10^{-11}) $< K_{sp}$ (1.6×10^{-5})

15.83 (a) $K_{sp}[\text{Ni(OH)}_2] < K_{sp}[\text{Mg(OH)}_2] < K_{sp}[\text{Ca(OH)}_2]$

This is the order for the solubility products of these hydroxides. Thus, order of precipitation is (first to last): Ni(OH)_2, Mg(OH)_2, Ca(OH)_2

(b) $K_{sp}[\text{Ni(OH)}_2] = 6.5 \times 10^{-18} = [\text{Ni}^{2+}][\text{OH}^-]^2$

$$[\text{OH}^-]^2 = \frac{6.5 \times 10^{-18}}{0.0010} = 6.5 \times 10^{-15}$$

$[\text{OH}^-] = 8.1 \times 10^{-8}$

$\text{pOH} = -\log[\text{OH}^-] = 7.09 \approx 7$, $\text{pH} \approx 7$

$K_{sp}[\text{Mg(OH)}_2] = 1.1 \times 10^{-11} = [\text{Mg}^{2+}][\text{OH}^-]^2$

$$[\text{OH}^-] = \sqrt{\frac{1.1 \times 10^{-11}}{0.0010}} = 1.0\overline{5} \times 10^{-4}$$

$\text{pOH} = -\log(1.0\overline{5} \times 10^{-4}) = 3.98 \approx 4$, $\text{pH} = 14 - 4 \approx 10$

$K_{sp}[\text{Ca(OH)}^2] = 5.5 \times 10^{-6} = [\text{Ca}^{2+}][\text{OH}^-]^2$

$$[\text{OH}^-] = \sqrt{\frac{5.5 \times 10^{-6}}{0.0010}} = 7.4 \times 10^{-2}$$

$\text{pOH} = -\log(7.4 \times 10^{-2}) = 1.13 \approx 1$, $\text{pH} = 14 - 1 \approx 13$

Dissolving Precipitates

15.85 $\text{AgBr}(s) \rightleftharpoons \text{Ag}^+(aq) + \text{Br}^-(aq)$ $\qquad\qquad K_{sp} = 7.7 \times 10^{-13}$

$\underline{\text{Ag}^+(aq) + 2\text{CN}^-(aq) \rightleftharpoons \text{Ag(CN)}_2^-(aq)} \qquad\qquad K_f = 5.6 \times 10^8$

$\text{AgBr}(s) + 2\text{CN}^-(aq) \rightleftharpoons \text{Ag(CN)}_2^-(aq) + \text{Br}^-(aq) \qquad K = 4.3 \times 10^{-4}$

hence, $K = \dfrac{[\text{Ag(CN)}_2^-][\text{Br}^-]}{[\text{CN}^-]^2} = 4.3 \times 10^{-4}$

Concentration (mol $\cdot$ L^{-1})	AgBr(s) +	2CN$^-$(aq) $\rightleftharpoons$	Ag(CN)$_2^-$(aq) +	Br$^-$(aq)
initial	—	0.10	0	0
change	—	$-2S$	$+S$	$+S$
equilibrium	—	$0.10 - 2S$	S	S

$$\frac{[Ag(CN)_2^-][Br^-]}{[CN^-]^2} = \frac{S^2}{(0.10 - 2S)^2} = 4.3 \times 10^{-4}$$

$$\frac{S}{0.10 - 2S} = \sqrt{4.3 \times 10^{-4}} = 2.1 \times 10^{-2}$$

$$S = 2.1 \times 10^{-3} - 4.2 \times 10^{-2}S$$

$$1.04S = 2.1 \times 10^{-3}$$

$$S = 2.1 \times 10^{-3} \text{ mol} \cdot \text{L}^{-1} = \text{molar solubility of AgBr}$$

15.87 (a) pH = 7.0; $[OH^-] = 1.0 \times 10^{-7}$ mol·L^{-1}

$$Al3^+(aq) + 3OH^-(aq) \rightleftharpoons Al(OH)_3(s)$$

$$[Al3^+][OH^-]^3 = K_{sp} = 1.0 \times 10^{-33}$$

$$S \times (10^{-7})^3 = 1.0 \times 10^{-33}$$

$$S = \frac{1.0 \times 10^{-33}}{1 \times 10^{-21}} = 1.0 \times 10^{-12} \text{ mol} \cdot \text{L}^{-1} = [Al^{3+}]$$

= molar solubility of Al(OH)$_3$ at pH = 7.0

(b) pH = 4.5; pOH = 9.5; $[OH^-] = 3.2 \times 10^{-10}$ mol·L^{-1}

$$[Al^{3+}][OH^-] = K_{sp} = 1.0 \times 10^{-33}$$

$$S \times (3.2 \times 10^{-10})^3 = 1.0 \times 10^{-33}$$

$$S = \frac{1.0 \times 10^{-33}}{3.3 \times 10^{-29}} = 3.0 \times 10^{-5} \text{ mol} \cdot \text{L}^{-1} = [Al^{3+}]$$

= molar solubility of Al(OH)$_3$ at pH = 4.5

(c) pH = 7.0; $[OH^-] = 1.0 \times 10^{-7}$ mol·L^{-1}

$$Zn^{2+}(aq) + 2OH^-(aq) \rightleftharpoons Zn(OH)_2(s)$$

$$[Zn^{2+}][OH^-]^2 = K_{sp} = 2.0 \times 10^{-17}$$

$$S \times (1.0 \times 10^{-7})^2 = 2.0 \times 10^{-17}$$

$$S = \frac{2.0 \times 10^{-17}}{1.0 \times 10^{-14}} = 2.0 \times 10^{-3} \text{ mol} \cdot \text{L}^{-1} = [Zn^{2+}]$$

= molar solubility of Zn(OH)$_2$ at pH = 7.0

(d) pH = 6.0; pOH = 8.0; $[OH^-] = 1.0 \times 10^{-8}$ mol·L^{-1}

$$[Zn^{2+}][OH^-]^2 = 2.0 \times 10^{-17} = K_{sp}$$

$$S \times (1.0 \times 10^{-8})^2 = 2.0 \times 10^{-17}$$

$$S = \frac{2.0 \times 10^{-17}}{1.0 \times 10^{-16}} = 2.0 \times 10^{-1} = 0.20 \text{ mol} \cdot \text{L}^{-1} = [Zn^{2+}]$$

= molar solubility of Zn(OH)$_2$ at pH = 6.0

15.89 (a) Multiply the second equilibrium equation by 2 and add to the first equilibrium. Then

$$CaF_2(s) + 2H_2O(l) \rightleftharpoons Ca^{2+}(aq) + 2HF(aq) + 2OH^-(aq)$$

$K = K_{sp}K_b^2 = 4.0 \times 10^{-11} \times (2.9 \times 10^{-11})^2 = 3.3\overline{6} \times 10^{-32} = 3.4 \times 10^{-32}$

(b) $K = [Ca^{2+}][HF]^2[OH^-]^2$

$3.3\overline{6} \times 10^{-32} = (S)(2S)^2(1.0 \times 10^{-7})^2$

$3.3\overline{6} \times 10^{-18} = 4S^3$

$S = [Ca^{2+}] = 9.4 \times 10^{-7} \text{ mol} \cdot L^{-1} = $ molar solubility of CaF_2 at pH = 7.0

(c) $K = [Ca^{2+}][HF]^2[OH^-]^2$

$3.3\overline{6} \times 10^{-32} = (S)(2S)^2(1.0 \times 10^{-9})^2$

$3.3\overline{6} \times 10^{-14} = 4S^3$

$S = [Ca^{2+}] = 2.0 \times 10^{-5} \text{ mol} \cdot L^{-1} = $ molar solubility of CaF_2 at pH = 5.0

SUPPLEMENTARY EXERCISES

15.91 (a) KI is neutral, because neither K^+ or I^- is acidic or basic

(b) CsF is basic, because F^- is basic

(c) CrI_3 is acidic, because $Cr(H_2O)_6^{3+}$ is an acid

(d) $C_6H_5NH_3Cl$ is acidic, because $C_6H_5NH_3^+$ is the conjugate acid of $C_6H_5NH_2$

(e) Na_2CO_3 is basic, because CO_3^{2-} is a base

(f) $Cu(NO_3)_2$ is acidic, because $Cu(H_2O)_6^{2+}$ is an acid

15.93 Let NaB = sodium barbiturate, HB = barbituric acid

$[B^-] = [NaB] = \left(\dfrac{10.0 \text{ mg}}{250 \text{ mL}}\right) \times \left(\dfrac{1 \text{ mL}}{10^{-3} \text{ L}}\right) \times \left(\dfrac{10^{-3} \text{ g}}{1 \text{ mg}}\right) \times \left(\dfrac{1 \text{ mol}}{150 \text{ g}}\right)$

$= 2.67 \times 10^{-4} \text{ mol} \cdot L^{-1}$

pH = 7.71, pOH = 6.29, $[OH^-] = 5.0 \times 10^{-7} \text{ mol} \cdot L^{-1}$

Concentration

$(\text{mol} \cdot L^{-1})$	$B^-(aq)$	+	$H_2O(l) \rightleftharpoons$	$OH^-(aq)$	+	$HB(aq)$
initial	2.67×10^{-4}		—	0		0
change	-5.0×10^{-7}		—	$+5.0 \times 10^{-7}$		$+5.0 \times 10^{-7}$
equilibrium	$2.67 \times 10^{-4} - 5.0 \times 10^{-7}$		—	5.0×10^{-7}		5.0×10^{-7}

Assume $[OH^-] = [HB]$.

(a) % protonation $= \dfrac{[HB]}{[B^-]_0} \times 100\% = \dfrac{5.0 \times 10^{-7}}{2.67 \times 10^{-4}} \times 100\% = 0.19\%$

(b) $K_b = \dfrac{K_w}{K_a} = \dfrac{[OH^-][HB]}{[B^-]}$

$K_a = \dfrac{K_w[B^-]}{[OH^-][HB]} = \dfrac{(1.0 \times 10^{-14}) \times (2.67 \times 10^{-4} - 5.0 \times 10^{-7})}{(5.0 \times 10^{-7})^2} = 1.1 \times 10^{-5}$

15.95 The presence of K^+ and Cl^- ions does not affect the pH. Total volume of solution = 200 mL + 150 mL = 350 mL.

moles of Na_3PO_4 = 0.20 L $\times$ 0.27 mol $\cdot$ L^{-1} = 5.4 $\times$ 10^{-2} mol

molar concentration of Na_3PO_4 = $\dfrac{5.4 \times 10^{-2} \text{ mol}}{0.350 \text{ L}}$ = 0.154 mol $\cdot$ L^{-1}

Concentration (mol $\cdot$ L^{-1}) $H_2O(l)$ +	PO_4^{3-}(aq)	$\rightleftharpoons$ HPO_4^{2-}(aq) +	OH^-(aq)
initial —	0.154	0	0
change —	$-x$	$+x$	$+x$
equilibrium —	$0.154 - x$	x	x

$K_b = \dfrac{K_w}{K_a} = \dfrac{[HPO_4^{2-}][OH^-]}{[PO_4^{3-}]} = \dfrac{x^2}{0.154 - x}$

$\dfrac{1.0 \times 10^{-14}}{4.2 \times 10^{-13}} = \dfrac{x^2}{0.154 - x} = 2.4 \times 10^{-2}$ (x cannot be neglected)

$x^2 + 2.4 \times 10^{-2}x - 3.7 \times 10^{-3} = 0$

Solving this quadratic yields $[OH^-] = x = 5.0 \times 10^{-2}$ mol $\cdot$ L^{-1}; pOH
$= -\log(5.0 \times 10^{-2}) = 1.30$; pH = 14.00 - 1.30 = 12.70.

15.97 The strong acid, HCl, will protonate the HCO_2^- ion.

moles of HCl = 0.0040 L $\times$ 0.070 mol $\cdot$ L^{-1} = 2.8 $\times$ 10^{-4} mol HCl (H^+)

moles of HCO_2^- = 0.060 L $\times$ 0.10 mol $\cdot$ L^{-1} = 6.0 $\times$ 10^{-3} mol HCO_2^-

After protonation, there are $(6.0 - 0.28) \times 10^{-3}$ mol HCO_2^- =
5.7 $\times$ 10^{-3} mol HCO_2^- and 2.8 $\times$ 10^{-4} mol HCOOH.

$[HCO_2^-] = \dfrac{5.7 \times 10^{-3} \text{ mol}}{0.0640 \text{ L}}$ = 8.9 $\times$ 10^{-2} mol $\cdot$ L^{-1}

$[HCOOH] = \dfrac{2.8 \times 10^{-4} \text{ mol}}{0.0640 \text{ L}}$ = 4.4 $\times$ 10^{-3} mol $\cdot$ L^{-1}

Concentration (mol $\cdot$ L^{-1})	HCOOH(aq) +	$H_2O(l)$ $\rightleftharpoons$	H_3O^+(aq) +	HCO_2^-(aq)
initial	4.4×10^{-3}	—	0	8.9×10^{-2}
change	$-x$	—	$+x$	$+x$
equilibrium	$4.4 \times 10^{-3} - x$	—	x	$8.9 \times 10^{-2} + x$

$K_a = 1.8 \times 10^{-4} = \dfrac{[H_3O^+][HCO_2^-]}{[HCOOH]} = \dfrac{(x)(8.9 \times 10^{-2} + x)}{(4.4 \times 10^{-2} - x)}$

Assume that $+x$ and $-x$ are negligible; so $1.8 \times 10^{-4} = \dfrac{(8.9 \times 10^{-2}) \times (x)}{4.4 \times 10^{-3}} = 20.2x$

$[H_3O^+] = x = 8.8 \times 10^{-6}$ mol $\cdot$ L^{-1}

$[HCOOH] = 4.4 \times 10^{-3} - 8.8 \times 10^{-6} \approx 4.4 \times 10^{-3}$ mol $\cdot$ L^{-1}

pH = $-\log(8.8 \times 10^{-6})$ = 5.06

15.99 The end point of an acid-base titration is the pH at which the indicator color change is observed. The stoichiometric point is the pH at which an exactly equivalent amount of titrant (in moles) has been added to the solution being titrated.

15.101 $HNO_3 + NaOH \longrightarrow NaNO_3 + H_2O$

moles of HNO_3 = $(0.0210 \text{ L}) \times \left(\dfrac{3.0 \text{ mol } HNO_3}{1 \text{ L}}\right)$ = 0.063 mol HNO_3

moles of NaOH = $(0.0252 \text{ L}) \times \left(\dfrac{2.5 \text{ mol NaOH}}{1 \text{ L}}\right)$ = 0.063 mol NaOH

To within experimental error, there is complete neutralization; therefore, pH = 7.00.

15.103 (a) pH = $-\log(0.020)$ = 1.70

(b) initial moles of H_3O^+ = $0.020 \text{ L} \times 0.020 \text{ mol} \cdot \text{L}^{-1}$ = 4.0×10^{-4} mol

moles of OH^- added = $0.005\ 00 \text{ L} \times 0.035 \text{ mol} \cdot \text{L}^{-1}$ = $1.7\overline{5} \times 10^{-4}$ mol

excess H_3O^+ = $(4.0 \times 10^{-4} - 1.7\overline{5} \times 10^{-4})$ mol = $2.2\overline{5} \times 10^{-4}$ mol

$[H_3O^+]$ = $\dfrac{2.2\overline{5} \times 10^{-4} \text{ mol}}{(0.020 + 0.0050) \text{ L}}$ = 9.0×10^{-3} mol $\cdot \text{L}^{-1}$

pH = $-\log(9.0 \times 10^{-3})$ = 2.05

(c) moles of OH^- added = $2 \times 1.7\overline{5} \times 10^{-4}$ mol = $3.5\overline{0} \times 10^{-4}$ mol

excess H_3O^+ = $(4.0 \times 10^{-4} - 3.5\overline{0} \times 10^{-4})$ mol = $5.\overline{0} \times 10^{-5}$ mol

$[H_3O^+]$ = $\dfrac{5.\overline{0} \times 10^{-5} \text{ mol}}{0.030 \text{ L}}$ = $1.\overline{7} \times 10^{-3}$ mol $\cdot \text{L}^{-1}$

pH = $-\log(1.\overline{7} \times 10^{-3})$ = 2.8

(d) moles of OH^- added = $3 \times 1.7\overline{5} \times 10^{-4}$ = 5.25×10^{-4} mol

excess OH^- = $(5.25 \times 10^{-4} - 4.0 \times 10^{-4})$ mol = 1.25×10^{-4} mol

$[OH^-]$ = $\dfrac{1.25 \times 10^{-4} \text{ mol}}{0.035 \text{L}}$ = $3.5\overline{7} \times 10^{-3}$ mol $\cdot \text{L}^{-1}$

pOH = $-\log(3.5\overline{7} \times 10^{-3})$ = 2.45, pH = $14.00 - 2.45$ = 11.55

(e) moles of OH^- added = $4 \times 1.75 \times 10^{-4}$ mol = 7.00×10^{-4} mol

excess OH^- = $(7.00 \times 10^{-4} - 4.0 \times 10^{-4})$ mol = 3.0×10^{-4} mol

$[OH^-]$ = $\dfrac{3.0 \times 10^{-4} \text{ mol}}{0.040 \text{ L}}$ = 7.5×10^{-3} mol $\cdot \text{L}^{-1}$

pOH = $-\log(7.5 \times 10^{-3})$ = 2.12, pH = $14.00 - 2.12$ = 11.88

(f) volume of KOH = $(4.0 \times 10^{-4} \text{ mol HCl}) \times \left(\dfrac{1 \text{ mol KOH}}{1 \text{ mol HCl}}\right)$

$\times \left(\dfrac{1 \text{ L KOH}}{0.035 \text{ mol KOH}}\right)$ = $0.011\overline{4}$ L KOH = 11 mL KOH

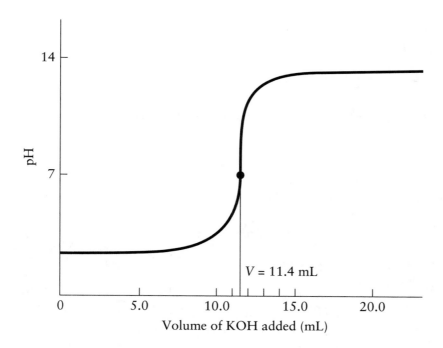

$V = 11.4$ mL

Volume of KOH added (mL)

15.105 $HBrO(aq) + OH^-(aq) \rightleftharpoons H_2O(l) + BrO^-(aq)$

(a) at the stoichiometric point, moles of OH^- = moles of HBrO

$$\text{volume NaOH} = \frac{(0.010\ 00\ \text{L}) \times (0.0633\ \text{mol} \cdot \text{L}^{-1})}{0.0400\ \text{mol} \cdot \text{L}^{-1}}$$

1.58×10^{-2} L NaOH

(b) at the stoichiometric point,

$$\frac{\text{mol BrO}^-}{\text{volume}} = \frac{(0.010\ 00\ \text{L}) \times (0.0633\ \text{mol} \cdot \text{L}^{-1})}{0.0258\ \text{L}} = 2.4 \times 10^{-2}\ \text{mol} \cdot \text{L}^{-1}$$

Concentration

$(\text{mol} \cdot \text{L}^{-1})$	$BrO^-(aq)$	+	$H_2O(l)$	$\rightleftharpoons$	$HBrO(aq)$	+	$OH^-(aq)$
initial	2.4×10^{-2}		—		0		0
change	$-x$		—		$+x$		$+x$
equilibrium	$2.4 \times 10^{-2} - x$		—		x		x

$$K_b = \frac{K_w}{K_a} = \frac{1.0 \times 10^{-14}}{2.0 \times 10^{-9}} = 5.0 \times 10^{-6} = \frac{x^2}{2.4 \times 10^{-2} - x} \approx \frac{x^2}{2.4 \times 10^{-2}}$$

$[OH^-] = x = \sqrt{(5.0 \times 10^{-6}) \times (2.4 \times 10^{-2})} = 3.5 \times 10^{-4}\ \text{mol} \cdot \text{L}^{-1}$

$pOH = -\log(3.5 \times 10^{-4}) = 3.46$, $pH = 14.00 - 3.46 = 10.54$

(c) alizarin yellow R, $pK_{in} = 11.2$

15.107 Let novocaine = N; $N(aq) + H_2O(l) \rightleftharpoons HN^+(aq) + OH^-(aq)$

$$K_b = \frac{[HN^+][OH^-]}{[N]}$$

$pK_a = pK_w - pK_b = 14.00 - 5.05 = 8.95$

$$pH = pK_a + \log\left(\frac{[N]}{[HN^+]}\right)$$

$$\log\left(\frac{[N]}{[HN^+]}\right) = pH - pK_a = 7.4 - 8.95 = -1.55$$

Therefore, the ratio of the concentrations of novocaine and its conjugate acid is
$[N]/[HN^+] = 10^{-1.55} = 2.8 \times 10^{-2}$.

15.109 $CH_3COOH(aq) + H_2O(l) \rightleftharpoons H_3O^+(aq) + CH_3CO_2^-(aq)$

$$K_a = \frac{[H_3O^+][CH_3CO_2^-]}{[CH_3COOH]} \text{ and } pH = pK_a + \log\frac{[CH_3CO_2^-]}{[CH_3COOH]} = pK_a + \log\left(\frac{0.50}{0.150}\right)$$

$$= 4.75 + 0.52 = 5.27 \quad \text{(initial pH)}$$

(a) $(0.0100 \text{ L}) \times (1.2 \text{ mol} \cdot \text{L}^{-1}) = 1.2 \times 10^{-2}$ mol HCl added (a strong acid)
produces 1.2×10^{-2} mol CH_3COOH from $CH_3CO_2^-$ after adding HCl

$$[CH_3COOH] = \frac{(0.100 \text{ L}) \times (0.150 \text{ mol} \cdot \text{L}^{-1})}{0.110 \text{ L}} + \frac{1.2 \times 10^{-2} \text{ mol}}{0.110 \text{ L}}$$

$$= 0.245 \text{ mol} \cdot \text{L}^{-1}$$

$$[CH_3CO_2^-] = \frac{(0.100 \text{ L}) \times (0.50 \text{ mol} \cdot \text{L}^{-1})}{0.110 \text{ L}} - \frac{1.2 \times 10^{-2} \text{ mol}}{0.110 \text{ L}} = 0.345 \text{ mol} \cdot \text{L}^{-1}$$

$$pH = 4.75 + \log\left(\frac{0.345}{0.245}\right) = 4.75 + 0.15 = 4.90 \quad \text{(after adding HCl)}$$

(b) $(0.0500 \text{ L})(0.095 \text{ mol} \cdot \text{L}^{-1}) = 4.7 \times 10^{-3}$ mol NaOH added (a strong base)
produces 4.7×10^{-3} mol $CH_3CO_2^-$ from CH_3COOH after adding NaOH

$$[CH_3COOH] = \frac{(0.100 \text{ L}) \times (0.150 \text{ mol} \cdot \text{L}^{-1})}{0.1500 \text{ L}} - \frac{4.7 \times 10^{-3} \text{ mol}}{0.150 \text{ L}}$$

$$= 6.9 \times 10^{-2} \text{ mol} \cdot \text{L}^{-1}$$

$$[CH_3CO_2^-] = \frac{(0.100 \text{ L}) \times (0.50 \text{ mol} \cdot \text{L}^{-1})}{0.150 \text{ L}} + \frac{4.7 \times 10^{-3} \text{ mol}}{0.150 \text{ L}}$$

$$= 3.6 \times 10^{-1} \text{ mol} \cdot \text{L}^{-1}$$

$$pH = 4.75 + \log\left(\frac{3.6 \times 10^{-1}}{6.9 \times 10^{-2}}\right) = 4.75 + 0.72 = 5.47 \quad \text{(after adding base)}$$

15.111 Equilibrium equation: $HCO_3^-(aq) + H_2O(l) \rightleftharpoons H_3O^+(aq) + CO_3^{2-}(aq)$

$$K_a = \frac{[H_3O^+][CO_3^{2-}]}{[HCO_3^-]}$$

$$pH = pK_a + \log\left(\frac{[CO_3^{2-}]}{[HCO_3^-]}\right)$$

$$10 = -\log(5.6 \times 10^{-11}) + \log\left(\frac{[CO_3^{2-}]}{[HCO_3^-]}\right)$$

$$\log\left(\frac{[CO_3^{2-}]}{[HCO_3^-]}\right) = 10 - 10.25 = -0.25$$

$$\frac{[CO_3^{2-}]}{[HCO_3^-]} = 0.56$$

Then prepare a solution containing Na_2CO_3 and $NaHCO_3$ in a molar ratio of $0.56:1$.

15.113 (a) $Ag_2S(s) \rightleftharpoons 2Ag^+(aq) + S^{2-}(aq)$

$K_{sp} = [Ag^+]^2[S^{2-}] = (2S)^2 \times (S) = 4S^3$

$6.3 \times 10^{-51} = 4S^3$

$S = \sqrt[3]{\frac{6.3 \times 10^{-51}}{4}} = 1.2 \times 10^{-17}$ mol $\cdot$ L^{-1} = $[S^{2-}]$ = molar solubility of Ag_2S

(b) $6.3 \times 10^{-51} = (2S + 2.0 \times 10^{-4})^2 \times (S) \approx (2.0 \times 10^{-4})^2 S$

$S = \frac{6.3 \times 10^{-51}}{(2.0 \times 10^{-4})^2} = 1.6 \times 10^{-43}$ mol $\cdot$ L^{-1} = $[S^{2-}]$

= molar solubility of Ag_2S in 2.0×10^{-4} M $AgNO_3$

(c) mass of $Ag_2S = 1.6 \times 10^{-43}$ mol $\cdot$ L^{-1} $\times$ 10.0 L $\times \left(\frac{248 \text{ g } Ag_2S}{1 \text{ mol } Ag_2S}\right)$

$= 3.96 \times 10^{-40}$ g

This is less than the mass of one formula unit of Ag_2S.

15.115 $CaF_2(s) \rightleftharpoons Ca^{2+}(aq) + 2F^-(aq)$

$[Ca^{2+}][F^-]^2 = Q_{sp}$

$(2 \times 10^{-4}) \times (5 \times 10^{-5})^2 = 5 \times 10^{-13} = Q_{sp}$

Because Q_{sp} (5×10^{-13}) is less than K_{sp} (4.0×10^{-11}), no precipitate will form.

15.117 $Mg(OH)_2(s) \rightleftharpoons Mg^{2+}(aq) + 2OH^-(aq)$

Concentration (mol $\cdot$ L^{-1})	Mg^{2+}	OH^-
initial	0	0
change	$+S$	$+2S$
equilibrium	S	$2S$

$K_{sp} = [Mg^{2+}][OH^-]^2 = 1.1 \times 10^{-11} = (S)(2S)^2 = 4S^3$

$S = \sqrt[3]{\frac{1.1 \times 10^{-11}}{4}} = 1.4 \times 10^{-4}$ mol $\cdot$ L^{-1}

Then $[OH^-] = 2S = 2.8 \times 10^{-4}$ mol $\cdot$ L^{-1}; pOH $= -\log(2.8 \times 10^{-4}) = 3.55$; and pH

$= 14.00 - 3.55 = 10.45$.

15.119 moles of $Ag^+ = (0.100\ L) \times (1.0 \times 10^{-4}\ mol \cdot L^{-1}) = 1.0 \times 10^{-5}\ mol\ Ag^+$
in 0.200 L

moles of $CO_3^{2-} = (0.100\ L) \times (1.0 \times 10^{-4}\ mol \cdot L^{-1}) = 1.0 \times 10^{-5}\ mol\ CO_3^{2-}$ in 0.200 L

$Ag_2CO_3(s) \rightleftharpoons 2Ag^+(aq) + CO_3^{2-}(aq)$

$[Ag^+]^2[CO_3^{2-}] = Q_{sp}$

$\left(\dfrac{1.0 \times 10^{-5}}{0.200}\right)^2 \left(\dfrac{1.0 \times 10^{-5}}{0.200}\right) = 1.25 \times 10^{-13} = Q_{sp}$

Because Q_{sp} (1.25×10^{-13}) is less than K_{sp} (6.2×10^{-12}), no precipitate will form.

CHALLENGING EXERCISES

15.121 (a) Tartaric acid is a diprotic acid as shown in the following equilibria.
Let H_2T = tartaric acid.

$H_2T(aq) + OH^-(aq) \rightleftharpoons HT^-(aq) + H_2O(l)$
$HT^-(aq) + OH^-(aq) \rightleftharpoons T^{2-}(aq) + H_2O(l)$

Therefore, titration of tartaric acid is a two-step process, and there are two stoichiometric points, around each of which there is a sharp rise in the pH curve.

(b) $[H_2T] = \dfrac{(0.0170\ L) \times (0.100\ mol \cdot L^{-1})}{0.0250\ L} = 0.0680\ mol \cdot L^{-1}$

(c) After 17.0 mL of KOH was added, the first stoichiometric point was reached, hence all H_2T was converted to HT^-.

$[HT^-] = \dfrac{(0.0170\ L) \times (0.100\ mol \cdot L^{-1})}{(0.0250\ L + 0.0170\ L)} = 4.0 \times 10^{-2}\ mol \cdot L^{-1}$

Concentration (mol·L^{-1})	HT$^-$(aq)	+	H$_2$O(l) $\rightleftharpoons$	T^{2-}(aq) +	H$_3$O$^+$(aq)
initial	4.0×10^{-2}		—	0	0
change	$-x$		—	$+x$	$+x$
equilibrium	$4.0 \times 10^{-2} - x$		—	x	x

$K_{a2} = 1.5 \times 10^{-5} = \dfrac{x^2}{4.0 \times 10^{-2} - x} \approx \dfrac{x^2}{4.0 \times 10^{-2}}$

$[H_3O^+] = x = \sqrt{(1.5 \times 10^{-5}) \times (4.0 \times 10^{-2})} = 7.8 \times 10^{-4}\ mol \cdot L^{-1}$

$pH = -\log(7.8 \times 10^{-4}) = 3.11$

(d) after 34.0 mL, all $H_2T \rightarrow T^{2-}$

$[T^{2-}] = \dfrac{(0.0170\ L) \times (0.100\ mol \cdot L^{-1})}{(0.0250\ L + 0.0340\ L)} = 2.88 \times 10^{-2}\ mol \cdot L^{-1}$

Concentration (mol·L^{-1})	T^{-2}(aq)	+	H$_2$O(l) $\rightleftharpoons$	HT$^-$(aq) +	OH$^-$(aq)
initial	2.88×10^{-2}		—	0	0
change	$-x$		—	$+x$	$+x$
equilibrium	$2.88 \times 10^{-2} - x$		—	x	x

$$K_b = 6.7 \times 10^{-10} = \frac{x^2}{2.88 \times 10^{-2} \times x} \approx \frac{x^2}{2.88 \times 10^{-2}}$$

$$[OH^-] = x = \sqrt{(6.7 \times 10^{-10}) \times (2.88 \times 10^{-2})} = 4.4 \times 10^{-6} \text{ mol} \cdot L^{-1}$$

$$pOH = -\log(4.4 \times 10^{-6}) = 5.36, \quad pH = 14.00 - 5.36 = 8.64$$

(e) $[T^{2-}] = 2.88 \times 10^{-2} - 4.4 \times 10^{-6} \approx 2.88 \times 10^{-2} \text{ mol} \cdot L^{-1}$

(f) $pH = pK_a = 3.22$ (half stoichiometric point)

15.123 (1) first stoichiometric point: $OH^-(aq) + H_2SO_4(aq) \longrightarrow H_2O(l) + HSO_4^-(aq)$.
Then, since the volume of the solution has doubled, $[HSO_4^-] = 0.10$ M,

Concentration (mol·L^{-1})	$HSO_4^-(aq)$ +	$H_2O(l)$ ⇌	$SO_4^{2-}(aq)$ +	$H_3O^+(aq)$
initial	0.10	—	0	0
change	$-x$	—	$+x$	$+x$
equilibrium	$0.10 - x$	—	x	x

$$K_{a2} = 0.012 = \frac{x^2}{0.10 - x}$$

$$0.0012 - 0.012x = x^2$$

$$x^2 + 0.012x - 0.0012 = 0$$

$$x = \frac{-0.012 + \sqrt{(0.012)^2 + (4) \times (0.0012)}}{2}$$

$$x = [H_3O^+] = 0.029 \text{ mol} \cdot L^{-1}$$

$$pH = -\log(0.029) = 1.54$$

(2) second stoichiometric point: $HSO_4^-(aq) + OH^-(aq) \longrightarrow SO_4^{2-}(aq) + H_2O(l)$. Then, since the volume of the solution has increased by an equal amount again,

Concentration (mol·L^{-1})	$SO_4^{2-}(aq)$ +	$H_2O(l)$ ⇌	$HSO_4^-(aq)$ +	$OH^-(aq)$
initial	0.067	—	0	1×10^{-7}
change	$-x$	—	$+x$	$+x$
equilibrium	$0.067 - x$	—	x	$1 \times 10^{-7} + x$

$$K_b = 8.3 \times 10^{-3} = \frac{(x)(1 \times 10^{-7} + x)}{0.067 - x}$$

$$5.6 \times 10^{-14} - 8.3 \times 10^{-13} x = 1 \times 10^{-7} x + x^2$$

$$x^2 + 1 \times 10^{-7}x - 5.6 \times 10^{-14} = 0$$

$$x = \frac{-1 \times 10^{-7} + \sqrt{(1 \times 10^{-7})^2 + (4) \times (5.6 \times 10^{-14})}}{2}$$

$$x = [HSO_4^-] = 1.9 \times 10^{-7} \text{ mol} \cdot L^{-1}$$

$$[OH^-] = 1.0 \times 10^{-7} + 1.9 \times 10^{-7} = 2.9 \times 10^{-7} \text{ mol} \cdot L^{-1}$$

$$pOH = -\log(2.9 \times 10^{-7}) = 6.54, \quad pH = 14.00 - 6.54 = 7.46$$

15.125 $CH_3COOH(aq) + N_2H_4(aq) \rightleftharpoons N_2H_5^+(aq) + CH_3CO_2^-(aq)$

(a) $K_c = \dfrac{[N_2H_5^+][CH_3CO_2^-]}{[N_2H_4][CH_3COOH]} = \dfrac{[N_2H_5^+][OH^-]}{[N_2H_4]}$

$$\times \frac{[H_3O^+][CH_3CO_2^-]}{[CH_3COOH]} \times \frac{1}{[H_3O^+][OH^-]}$$

$K_c = K_a(\text{acetic acid}) \times K_b(\text{hydrazine}) \times \dfrac{1}{K_w} = \dfrac{K_aK_b}{K_w} = \dfrac{(1.8 \times 10^{-5})(1.7 \times 10^{-6})}{1.0 \times 10^{-14}}$

$= 3.1 \times 10^3$

(b) $-\log K_c = -\log[N_2H_5^+] - \log\left(\dfrac{[CH_3CO_2^-]}{[N_2H_4][CH_3COOH]}\right)$

15.127 (a) $ZnS(s) + 2H_2O(l) \rightleftharpoons Zn^{2+}(aq) + H_2S(aq) + 2OH^-(aq)$

$K = K_{sp}K_{a1}K_{a2} = (1.6 \times 10^{-24}) \times (9.3 \times 10^{-22}) = 1.5 \times 10^{-45}$

(b) $pH = 7.0$; $[H_3O^+] = 1.0 \times 10^{-7}\ \text{mol} \cdot L^{-1} = [OH^-]$

$K = [Zn^{2+}][H_2S][OH^-]^2 = 1.5 \times 10^{-45}$

$K = S(0.1) \times (1.0 \times 10^{-7})^2 = 1.5 \times 10^{-45}$

$S = \dfrac{1.5 \times 10^{-45}}{1.0 \times 10^{-15}} = 1.5 \times 10^{-30}\ \text{mol} \cdot L^{-1} = [Zn^{2+}]$

$= $ molar solubility of ZnS at $pH = 7.0$ in a saturated H_2S solution

(c) $pH = 10.0$; $pOH = 4$; $[OH^-] = 1.0 \times 10^{-4}\ \text{mol} \cdot L^{-1}$

$K = [Zn^{2+}][H_2S][OH^-]^2 = 1.5 \times 10^{-45}$

$K = S(0.1) \times (1.0 \times 10^{-4})^2 = 1.5 \times 10^{-45}$

$S = \dfrac{1.5 \times 10^{-45}}{1.0 \times 10^{-9}} = 1.5 \times 10^{-36}\ \text{mol} \cdot L^{-1} = [Zn^{2+}]$

$= $ molar solubility of ZnS at $pH = 10.0$ in a saturated H_2S solution

CHAPTER 16
ENERGY IN TRANSITION: THERMODYNAMICS

EXERCISES

The First Law of Thermodynamics

16.1   (a) isolated   (b) closed   (c) isolated

16.3 q is positive (heat added to system), w is positive (work done on system)
$\Delta U = q + w = 550 \text{ kJ} + 700 \text{ kJ} = 1250 \text{ kJ}$

16.5   For the gas in the cylinder,

$q = 20 \text{ min} \times 100 \text{ J} \cdot \text{s}^{-1} \times \left(\dfrac{60 \text{ s}}{1 \text{ min}} \right)$

$= 1.2 \times 10^5 \text{ J}$ (heat added to the system is positive)

$w = -P \times \Delta V = -1.0 \text{ atm} \times (2.5 - 2.0) \text{ L} \times \dfrac{101 \text{ J}}{1 \text{ L} \cdot \text{atm}} = -50.5 \text{ J}$

$\Delta U = q + w = 1.2 \times 10^5 \text{ J} - 50.5 \text{ J} \approx 1.2 \times 10^5 \text{ J}$

16.7   Work is done by the reacting system; therefore, w is negative for the system.
$q = \Delta U - w = -892.4 \text{ kJ} - (-492 \text{ kJ}) = -400 \text{ kJ}$

16.9   Work done by the system is negative; thus, $w = -28 \text{ kJ}$.
$\Delta H = \Delta U + P\Delta V = \Delta U - w \quad [w = -P\Delta V]$
$\Delta H = -65 \text{ kJ} - (-28 \text{ kJ}) = -37 \text{ kJ}$

Entropy

16.11   (a) HBr(g)   [Br contains more elementary particles than F does]
(b) NH_3(g)   [NH_3 is a more complex structure]
(c) I_2(l)   [liquids have more disorder than solids do]
(d) Ar(g) at 1.00 atm   [there is more randomness in a gas at low pressure]

16.13 $C(s) < H_2O(s) < H_2O(l) < H_2O(g)$

Ice has a more complex crystalline structure than carbon (either as diamond or graphite) and so has a higher entropy. $H_2O(l)$ has more disorder than $H_2O(s)$; in turn, $H_2O(g)$ has more disorder than $H_2O(l)$.

16.15   (a) The entropy decreases. The number of molecules of gas decreases as a result of the reaction. Hence, the disorder of the system decreases.

(b) The gaseous state is more disordered than the solid state; hence, the entropy of the system increases.

(c) As water cools, the amplitude of the random motion of the molecules decreases; hence, the entropy decreases.

16.17   (a) $\Delta S° = \dfrac{\Delta H°_{freeze}}{T_f} = \dfrac{-\Delta H°_{fus}}{T_f} = \dfrac{-6.01\ \text{kJ}\cdot\text{mol}^{-1}}{273.2\ \text{K}} = \dfrac{-6.01 \times 10^3\ \text{J}\cdot\text{mol}^{-1}}{273.2\ \text{K}}$

$= -22.0\ \text{J}\cdot\text{K}^{-1}\cdot\text{mol}^{-1}$

(b) $\Delta S°_{sys} = n\left(\dfrac{\Delta H°_{vap}}{T_b}\right)$

$n = (50.0\ \text{g}) \times \left(\dfrac{1\ \text{mol}}{46.07\ \text{g}}\right) = 1.08\overline{5}\ \text{mol}$

$\Delta H°_{vap} = 43.5\ \text{kJ}\cdot\text{mol}^{-1}$

$\Delta S°_{sys} = (1.08\overline{5}\ \text{mol}) \times \left(\dfrac{4.35 \times 10^4\ \text{J}\cdot\text{mol}^{-1}}{351.5\ \text{K}}\right) = 134\ \text{J}\cdot\text{K}^{-1}$

16.19   (a) $\Delta S°_r = 2S°_m(H_2O, g) - \{2S°_m(H_2, g) + S°_m(O_2, g)\}$

$= \{2 \times 188.83 - (2 \times 130.68 + 205.14)\}\ \text{J}\cdot\text{K}^{-1}\cdot\text{mol}^{-1}$

$= -88.84\ \text{J}\cdot\text{K}^{-1}\cdot\text{mol}^{-1}$

The entropy change is negative because the number of moles of gas has decreased by one.

(b) $\Delta S°_r = 2S°_m(CO_2, g) - \{2S°_m(CO, g) + S°_m(O_2, g)\}$

$= \{2 \times 213.7 - (2 \times 197.67 + 205.1)\}\ \text{J}\cdot\text{K}^{-1}\cdot\text{mol}^{-1}$

$= (427.4 - 395.34 - 205.1)\ \text{J}\cdot\text{K}^{-1}\cdot\text{mol}^{-1} = -173.0\ \text{J}\cdot\text{K}^{-1}\cdot\text{mol}^{-1}$

The entropy change is negative because the number of moles of gas has decreased by one.

(c) $\Delta S°_r = S°_m(CaO, s) + S°_m(CO_2, g) - S°_m(CaCO_3, s)$

$= (39.8 + 213.7 - 92.9)\ \text{J}\cdot\text{K}^{-1}\cdot\text{mol}^{-1} = 160.6\ \text{J}\cdot\text{K}^{-1}\cdot\text{mol}^{-1}$

The entropy change is positive because the number of moles of gas has increased by one.

(d) $\Delta S_r^\circ = 3S_m^\circ(KClO_4, s) + S_m^\circ(KCl, s) - 4S_m^\circ(KClO_3, s)$

$= (3 \times 151.0 + 82.6 - 4 \times 143.1) \, J \cdot K^{-1} \cdot mol^{-1}$

$= -36.8 \, J \cdot K^{-1} \cdot mol^{-1}$

It is not immediately apparent, but the four moles of solid products are more ordered than the four moles of solid reactants.

Entropy Change in the Surroundings

16.21 (a) ΔH is negative, because heat leaves the coffee as it cools. Therefore, $\Delta S_{surr} = -\Delta H/T$ is positive. Although ΔS of the system is negative, ΔS_{surr} is positive and of a greater magnitude, because the surroundings are at a lower temperature than the system (coffee). Therefore, $\Delta S_{tot} = \Delta S + \Delta S_{surr}$ is positive and the process is spontaneous.

(b) No energy in the form of heat is transferred to or from the surroundings, so $\Delta S_{surr} = 0$. But ΔS of the system is positive as a result of the greater disorder generated by the mixing of the two substances. Thus, $\Delta S_{tot} = \Delta S_{surr} + \Delta S = 0 + \Delta S$ is positive and the process is spontaneous.

(c) When gasoline burns, both ΔS of the system and ΔS_{surr} are positive; hence, ΔS_{tot} is positive. ΔS of the system is positive, because the number of moles of gas increases as $CO_2(g)$ and $H_2O(g)$ are formed by the combustion process. ΔS_{surr} is positive, because the reaction is exothermic and much heat is transferred to the surroundings:

$$\Delta S_{surr} = \frac{-\Delta H}{T} = +(\Delta H = -)$$

Because $\Delta S_{tot} = \Delta S + \Delta S_{surr}$ is positive, the process is spontaneous.

(d) The interdiffusion of two gases results in an increase is disorder: the gases are all mixed up. Hence, ΔS of the system is positive. $\Delta S_{surr} = 0$, because there is no energy transferred as heat; thus, $\Delta S_{tot} = \Delta S + \Delta S_{surr} = \Delta S$ is positive and the process is spontaneous.

16.23 (a) $\Delta S_{surr} = \dfrac{-\Delta H}{T} = \dfrac{-(-1.20 \times 10^5 \, J)}{298 \, K} = 403 \, J \cdot K^{-1}$

(b) $\Delta S_{surr} = \dfrac{-(-1.20 \times 10^5 \, J)}{373 \, K} = 322 \, J \cdot K^{-1}$

(c) $\Delta S_{surr} = \dfrac{-\Delta H}{T} = \dfrac{-100 \, J}{323 \, K} = -0.310 \, J \cdot K^{-1}$

16.25 (a) $100 \text{ W} = 100 \text{ J} \cdot \text{s}^{-1}$, $\quad \Delta S_{surr} = \dfrac{-\Delta H}{T}$

$$\text{rate of entropy generation} = \frac{\text{rate of heat generation}}{T} = \frac{-(-100 \text{ J} \cdot \text{s}^{-1})}{293 \text{ K}}$$

$$= 0.341 \text{ J} \cdot \text{K}^{-1} \cdot \text{s}^{-1}$$

(b) $\Delta S_{surr} = 0.341 \text{ J} \cdot \text{K}^{-1} \cdot \text{s}^{-1} \times \left(\dfrac{3600 \text{ s}}{1 \text{ h}}\right) \times \left(\dfrac{24 \text{ h}}{1 \text{ d}}\right) = 2.95 \times 10^4 \text{ J} \cdot \text{K}^{-1} \cdot \text{s}^{-1}$

(c) Less, because, in the equation $\Delta S_{surr} = -\Delta H/T$, if T is higher, then ΔS_{surr} is smaller.

16.27 (a) $\Delta S_{surr} = \dfrac{-\Delta H}{T} = \dfrac{-5 \text{ J}}{298 \text{ K}} = -0.01\overline{7} \text{ J} \cdot \text{K}^{-1} = -0.02 \text{ J} \cdot \text{K}^{-1}$

(b) $\Delta S_{surr} = \dfrac{-5 \text{ J}}{373 \text{ K}} = -0.01\overline{3} \text{ J} \cdot \text{K}^{-1} = -0.01 \text{ J} \cdot \text{K}^{-1}$

(c) As seen in parts (a) and (b), the magnitude of the entropy change in the surroundings is greater when the block is at 25°C. The same amount of heat has a greater effect on entropy changes at lower temperature. At high temperatures, matter is already more chaotic.

16.29 $\Delta S^{\circ}_{surr} = \dfrac{-\Delta H^{\circ}}{T} = \dfrac{-1.96 \times 10^3 \text{ J}}{298 \text{ K}} = -6.58 \text{ J} \cdot \text{K}^{-1}$

$\Delta S^{\circ} = -109.58 \text{ J} \cdot \text{K}^{-1}$

$\Delta S^{\circ}_{tot} = \Delta S^{\circ} + \Delta S^{\circ}_{surr} = (-109.58 - 6.58) \text{ J} \cdot \text{K}^{-1} = -116.16 \text{ J} \cdot \text{K}^{-1}$

According to the second law, this process is not spontaneous; ΔS°_{tot} is negative; that is, there has been a decrease in disorder.

16.31 Under constant temperature and pressure conditions, a negative value of ΔG_r corresponds to spontaneity.

$$\Delta G_r = \Delta H_r - T\Delta S_r$$

Frequently, the magnitude of ΔH_r is much greater than the magnitude of $T\Delta S_r$, so no matter what the sign of ΔS_r, ΔG_r will be negative if ΔH_r is negative, and the reaction will be spontaneous.

Free Energy

16.33 (a) $\Delta G = \Delta H - T\Delta S = (-) - (+)(+) = -$

(b) $\Delta G = (+) - (+)(+) = ?$ Sign cannot be predicted. It depends on the magnitudes of ΔH, T, and ΔS.

(c) A temperature change can affect the sign in (b) by altering the magnitude of the $-T\Delta S$ term in ΔG.

16.35 In each case, $\Delta S_{tot}^{\circ} = 0$, because these are equilibrium processes. Therefore, because

$$\Delta S_{tot}^{\circ} = \Delta S_{surr}^{\circ} + \Delta S_{sys}^{\circ} = 0$$
$$\Delta S_{sys}^{\circ} = -\Delta S_{surr}^{\circ}$$

(a) $\Delta S_{surr}^{\circ} = \dfrac{-1.0 \text{ mol} \times \Delta H_{vap}^{\circ}}{T_b} = \dfrac{-1.0 \text{ mol} \times 8.2 \times 10^3 \text{ J} \cdot \text{mol}^{-1}}{111.7 \text{ K}}$

$= -73 \text{ J} \cdot \text{K}^{-1}$

$\Delta S_{tot}^{\circ} = 0$, hence $\Delta S_{sys}^{\circ} = +73 \text{ J} \cdot \text{K}^{-1}$

(b) $\Delta S_{surr}^{\circ} = \dfrac{-1.0 \text{ mol} \times \Delta H_{fus}^{\circ}}{T_f} = \dfrac{-1.0 \text{ mol} \times 4.60 \times 10^3 \text{ J} \cdot \text{mol}^{-1}}{158.7 \text{ K}}$

$= -29 \text{ J} \cdot \text{K}^{-1}$

$\Delta S_{tot}^{\circ} = 0$, hence $\Delta S_{sys}^{\circ} = +29 \text{ J} \cdot \text{K}^{-1}$

(c) $\Delta S_{surr}^{\circ} = +29 \text{ J} \cdot \text{K}^{-1}$

$\Delta S_{sys}^{\circ} = -29 \text{ J} \cdot \text{K}^{-1}$

Freezing is the reverse of melting.

16.37 In each case, $\Delta S_{tot}^{\circ} = 0$, because these are equilibrium processes. Therefore, because

$$\Delta S_{tot}^{\circ} = \Delta S_{surr}^{\circ} + \Delta S_{sys}^{\circ} = 0$$
$$\Delta S_{sys}^{\circ} = -\Delta S_{surr}^{\circ}$$

(a) $\Delta S_{surr}^{\circ} = \dfrac{-1.0 \text{ mol} \times \Delta H_{vap}^{\circ}}{T_b} = \dfrac{-1.0 \text{ mol} \times 40.7 \times 10^3 \text{ J} \cdot \text{mol}^{-1}}{373.2 \text{ K}}$

$= -1.1 \times 10^2 \text{ J} \cdot \text{K}^{-1}$

$\Delta S_{tot}^{\circ} = 0$, hence, $\Delta S_{sys}^{\circ} = +1.1 \times 10^2 \text{ J} \cdot \text{K}^{-1}$

(b) $\Delta S_{surr}^{\circ} = \dfrac{-1.0 \text{ mol} \times \Delta H_{vap}^{\circ}}{T_b} = \dfrac{-1.0 \text{ mol} \times 23.4 \times 10^3 \text{ J} \cdot \text{mol}^{-1}}{239.7 \text{ K}}$

$= -98 \text{ J} \cdot \text{K}^{-1}$

$\Delta S_{tot}^{\circ} = 0$; hence, $\Delta S_{sys}^{\circ} = +98 \text{ J} \cdot \text{K}^{-1}$

(c) $\Delta S_{surr}^{\circ} = \dfrac{-1.0 \text{ mol} \times \Delta H_{vap}^{\circ}}{T_b} = \dfrac{-1.0 \text{ mol} \times 35.3 \times 10^3 \text{ J} \cdot \text{mol}^{-1}}{337.2 \text{ K}}$

$= -1.0 \times 10^2 \text{ J} \cdot \text{K}^{-1}$

$\Delta S_{tot}^{\circ} = 0$; hence, $\Delta S_{sys}^{\circ} = +1.0 \times 10^2 \text{ J} \cdot \text{K}^{-1}$

16.39 $\Delta S^\circ_{vap} = \dfrac{\Delta H^\circ_{vap}}{T_b}$

$T_b = \dfrac{\Delta H^\circ_{vap}}{\Delta S^\circ_{vap}} = \dfrac{2.04 \times 10^4 \ \text{J} \cdot \text{mol}^{-1}}{85.4 \ \text{J} \cdot \text{K}^{-1} \cdot \text{mol}^{-1}} = 239 \ \text{K or} -34°\text{C}$

16.41 $\Delta H^\circ_{vap} = T_b \times \Delta S^\circ_{vap}$
(a) $\Delta H^\circ_{vap} = 353 \ \text{K} \times 85 \ \text{J} \cdot \text{K}^{-1} \cdot \text{mol}^{-1} = 3.0 \times 10^4 \ \text{J} \cdot \text{mol}^{-1} = 30 \ \text{kJ} \cdot \text{mol}^{-1}$

(b) $\Delta S^\circ_{surr} = \dfrac{-n\Delta H^\circ_{vap}}{T_b} = \dfrac{-(10 \ \text{g}) \times \left(\dfrac{1 \ \text{mol}}{78.12 \ \text{g}}\right) \times (3.0 \times 10^4 \ \text{J} \cdot \text{mol}^{-1})}{353 \ \text{K}}$

$= -11 \ \text{J} \cdot \text{K}^{-1}$

Standard Reaction Free Energies

16.43 ΔS°_r data from Exercise 16.19. Assume $T = 298$ K.
(a) $\Delta H^\circ_r = 2\Delta H^\circ_f(\text{H}_2\text{O, g}) = 2 \times (-241.82 \ \text{kJ} \cdot \text{mol}^{-1}) = -483.64 \ \text{kJ} \cdot \text{mol}^{-1}$

$\Delta G^\circ_r = \Delta H^\circ_r - T\Delta S^\circ_r = -483.64 \ \text{kJ} \cdot \text{mol}^{-1} - 298 \ \text{K}$
$\times (-0.088 \ 84 \ \text{kJ} \cdot \text{K}^{-1} \cdot \text{mol}^{-1}) = -457.17 \ \text{kJ} \cdot \text{mol}^{-1}$

The negative sign indicates that the reaction is spontaneous (has $K > 1$) under standard conditions. The large magnitude of ΔG°_r implies that a temperature change is not likely to affect the spontaneity, but it is possible at very high temperatures.

(b) $\Delta H^\circ_r = 2 \times (-393.51 \ \text{kJ} \cdot \text{mol}^{-1}) - 2 \times (-110.53 \ \text{kJ} \cdot \text{mol}^{-1})$
$= -566.0 \ \text{kJ} \cdot \text{mol}^{-1}$

$\Delta G^\circ_r = \Delta H^\circ_r - T\Delta S^\circ_r = -566.0 \ \text{kJ} \cdot \text{mol}^{-1} - 298 \ \text{K} \times (-0.1730 \ \text{kJ} \cdot \text{K}^{-1} \cdot \text{mol}^{-1})$
$= -514.4 \ \text{kJ} \cdot \text{mol}^{-1}$

The negative sign indicates the reaction is spontaneous (has $K > 1$) under the standard conditions. The large magnitude of ΔG°_r implies that a temperature change is not likely to affect the spontaneity, but it is possible at very high temperatures.

(c) $\Delta H^\circ_r = -635.09 \ \text{kJ} \cdot \text{mol}^{-1} - 393.51 \ \text{kJ} \cdot \text{mol}^{-1} - (-1206.9 \ \text{kJ} \cdot \text{mol}^{-1})$
$= +178.3 \ \text{kJ} \cdot \text{mol}^{-1}$

$\Delta G^\circ_r = \Delta H^\circ_r - T\Delta S^\circ_r = +178.3 \ \text{kJ} \cdot \text{mol}^{-1} - 298 \ \text{K} \times 0.1606 \ \text{kJ} \cdot \text{K}^{-1} \cdot \text{mol}^{-1}$
$= +130.4 \ \text{kJ} \cdot \text{mol}^{-1}$

The positive sign of ΔG° implies that the reaction is not spontaneous (has $K < 1$) under standard conditions, but the magnitude indicates that, at a higher temperature, there could be a change in sign.

(d) $\Delta H_r^\circ = 3 \times (-432.75 \text{ kJ} \cdot \text{mol}^{-1}) + 1 \times (-436.75 \text{ kJ} \cdot \text{mol}^{-1})$
$$- 4 \times (-397.73 \text{ kJ} \cdot \text{mol}^{-1}) = -144.1 \text{ kJ} \cdot \text{mol}^{-1}$$
$\Delta G_r^\circ = \Delta H_r^\circ - T\Delta S_r^\circ = -144.1 \text{ kJ} \cdot \text{mol}^{-1} - (298 \text{ K})(-0.0368 \text{ kJ} \cdot \text{K}^{-1} \cdot \text{mol}^{-1})$
$$= -133.1 \text{ kJ} \cdot \text{mol}^{-1}$$

The negative sign implies that the reaction is spontaneous under standard conditions.

16.45 (a) $\frac{1}{2}N_2(g) + \frac{3}{2}H_2(g) \longrightarrow NH_3(g)$
$\Delta S_f^\circ = 1 \times 192.45 \text{ J} \cdot \text{K}^{-1} \cdot \text{mol}^{-1} - (\frac{1}{2} \times 191.61 \text{ J} \cdot \text{K}^{-1} \cdot \text{mol}^{-1} + \frac{3}{2}$
$\times 130.68 \text{ J} \cdot \text{K}^{-1} \cdot \text{mol}^{-1}) = -99.38 \text{ J} \cdot \text{K}^{-1} \cdot \text{mol}^{-1} = -0.099\,38 \text{ kJ} \cdot \text{K}^{-1} \cdot \text{mol}^{-1}$
$\Delta G_f^\circ = \Delta H_f^\circ - T\Delta S_f^\circ = -46.11 \text{ kJ} \cdot \text{mol}^{-1} - (298 \text{ K})(-0.099\,38 \text{ kJ} \cdot \text{K}^{-1} \cdot \text{mol}^{-1})$
$$= -16.5 \text{ kJ} \cdot \text{mol}^{-1}$$
(b) $H_2(g) + \frac{1}{2}O_2(g) \longrightarrow H_2O(g)$
$\Delta S_f^\circ = 1 \times 188.83 \text{ J} \cdot \text{K}^{-1} \cdot \text{mol}^{-1} - (1 \times 130.68 \text{ J} \cdot \text{K}^{-1} \cdot \text{mol}^{-1}$
$$+ \frac{1}{2} \times 205.14 \text{ J} \cdot \text{K}^{-1} \cdot \text{mol}^{-1}) = -44.42 \text{ J} \cdot \text{K}^{-1} \cdot \text{mol}^{-1}$$
$\Delta G_f^\circ = \Delta H_f^\circ - T\Delta S_f^\circ = -241.82 \text{ kJ} \cdot \text{mol}^{-1}$
$$- 298 \text{ K} \times (-0.044\,42 \text{ kJ} \cdot \text{K}^{-1} \cdot \text{mol}^{-1}) = -228.58 \text{ kJ} \cdot \text{mol}^{-1}$$
(c) $C(s) + \frac{1}{2}O_2(g) \longrightarrow CO(g)$
$\Delta S_f^\circ = 1 \times 197.67 \text{ J} \cdot \text{K}^{-1} \cdot \text{mol}^{-1} - (1 \times 5.740 \text{ J} \cdot \text{K}^{-1} \cdot \text{mol}^{-1} + \frac{1}{2}$
$\times 205.14 \text{ J} \cdot \text{K}^{-1} \cdot \text{mol}^{-1}) = 89.36 \text{ J} \cdot \text{K}^{-1} \cdot \text{mol}^{-1} = 0.089\,36 \text{ kJ} \cdot \text{K}^{-1} \cdot \text{mol}^{-1}$
$\Delta G_f^\circ = \Delta H_f^\circ - T\Delta S_f^\circ = -110.53 \text{ kJ} \cdot \text{mol}^{-1} - (298 \text{ K})(0.089\,36 \text{ kJ} \cdot \text{K}^{-1} \cdot \text{mol}^{-1})$
$$= -137.2 \text{ kJ} \cdot \text{mol}^{-1}$$
(d) $\frac{1}{2}N_2(g) + O_2(g) \longrightarrow NO_2(g)$
$\Delta S_f^\circ = 1 \times 240.06 \text{ J} \cdot \text{K}^{-1} \cdot \text{mol}^{-1} - (\frac{1}{2} \times 191.61 \text{ J} \cdot \text{K}^{-1} \cdot \text{mol}^{-1} + 1$
$\times 205.14 \text{ J} \cdot \text{K}^{-1} \cdot \text{mol}^{-1}) = -60.88 \text{ J} \cdot \text{K}^{-1} \cdot \text{mol}^{-1} = -0.060\,88 \text{ kJ} \cdot \text{K}^{-1} \cdot \text{mol}^{-1}$
$\Delta G_f^\circ = \Delta H_f^\circ - T\Delta S_f^\circ = 33.18 \text{ kJ} \cdot \text{mol}^{-1}$
$$- (298 \text{ K})(-0.060\,88 \text{ kJ} \cdot \text{K}^{-1} \cdot \text{mol}^{-1}) = 51.3 \text{ kJ} \cdot \text{mol}^{-1}$$

16.47 (a) $\Delta G_r^\circ = 2 \times \Delta G_f^\circ(SO_3, g) - 2 \times \Delta G_f^\circ(SO_2, g)$
$\Delta G_r^\circ = 2 \times (-371.06 \text{ kJ} \cdot \text{mol}^{-1}) - 2 \times (-300.19 \text{ kJ} \cdot \text{mol}^{-1})$
$\Delta G_r^\circ = -141.74 \text{ kJ} \cdot \text{mol}^{-1}$ spontaneous
(b) $\Delta G_r^\circ = \Delta G_f^\circ(CaO, s) + \Delta G_f^\circ(CO_2, g) - \Delta G_f^\circ(CaCO_3, s)$
$\Delta G_r^\circ = -604.03 \text{ kJ} \cdot \text{mol}^{-1} - 394.36 \text{ kJ} \cdot \text{mol}^{-1} - 1128.8 \text{ kJ} \cdot \text{mol}^{-1}$
$$= +130.4 \text{ kJ} \cdot \text{mol}^{-1} \text{ not spontaneous}$$
(c) $\Delta G_r^\circ = 1 \times \Delta G_f^\circ(SbCl_3, g) - 1 \times \Delta G_f^\circ(SbCl_5, g)$
$\Delta G_r^\circ = 1 \times (-301.2 \text{ kJ} \cdot \text{mol}^{-1}) - 1 \times (-334.29 \text{ kJ} \cdot \text{mol}^{-1})$

$\Delta G_r^\circ = 33.1$ kJ · mol^{-1} not spontaneous

(d) $\Delta G_r^\circ = 16 \times \Delta G_f^\circ(CO_2, g) + 18 \times \Delta G_f^\circ(H_2O, l) - 2 \times \Delta G_f^\circ(C_8H_{18}, l)$

$\Delta G_r^\circ = 16 \times (-394.36$ kJ · mol$^{-1}) + 18$
$$\times (-237.13 \text{ kJ} \cdot \text{mol}^{-1}) - 2 \times (6.4 \text{ kJ} \cdot \text{mol}^{-1})$$

$\Delta G_r^\circ = -10,590.9$ kJ · mol^{-1} spontaneous

Thermodynamic Stability

16.49 In each case, the decomposition reaction is the reverse of the formation reaction; therefore, in each case, $\Delta G_r^\circ = -\Delta G_f^\circ(cmpd)$. A negative value for ΔG_r° (decomposition) implies instability.

(a) $\Delta G_r^\circ = -\Delta G_f^\circ(PCl_5, g) = +305.0$ kJ · mol^{-1}; therefore, stable

(b) $\Delta G_r^\circ = -\Delta G_f^\circ(HCN, g) = -124.7$ kJ · mol^{-1}; therefore, unstable and will decompose

(c) $\Delta G_r^\circ = -\Delta G_f^\circ(NO, g) = -86.55$ kJ · mol^{-1}; therefore, unstable and will decompose

(d) $\Delta G_r^\circ = -\Delta G_f^\circ(SO_2, g) = +300.19$ kJ · mol^{-1}; therefore, stable

16.51 In each case, it is the $-T\Delta S_r^\circ$ term for the decomposition which determines the effect of temperature. $\Delta S_r^\circ(\text{decomposition}) = -\Delta S_r^\circ(\text{formation})$ and $-T\Delta S_r^\circ(\text{decomposition}) = T\Delta S_r^\circ(\text{formation})$. So if $\Delta S_r^\circ(\text{formation})$ is negative, the compound becomes more unstable when the temperature is raised.

(a) $P(s) + \frac{5}{2}Cl_2(g) \rightleftharpoons PCl_5(g)$

$\Delta S_r^\circ(\text{formation}) = 1 \times 364.6$ J · K^{-1} · mol^{-1} $- (1 \times 41.09$ J · K^{-1} · mol^{-1}
$$+ \frac{5}{2} \times 223.07 \text{ J} \cdot \text{K}^{-1} \cdot \text{mol}^{-1})$$

$\Delta S_r^\circ(\text{formation}) = -234.16$ J · K^{-1} · mol^{-1}; therefore, more unstable

(b) $\frac{1}{2}H_2(g) + C(s) + \frac{1}{2}N_2(g) \rightleftharpoons HCN(g)$

$\Delta S_r^\circ(\text{formation}) = 1 \times 201.78$ J · K^{-1} · mol^{-1} $- (\frac{1}{2} \times 130.68$ J · K^{-1} · mol^{-1}
$$+ 1 \times 5.74 \text{ J} \cdot \text{K}^{-1} \cdot \text{mol}^{-1} + \frac{1}{2} \times 191.61 \text{ J} \cdot \text{K}^{-1} \cdot \text{mol}^{-1})$$

$\Delta S_r^\circ(\text{formation}) = 34.90$ J · K^{-1} · mol^{-1}; therefore, more stable

(c) $\frac{1}{2}N_2(g) + \frac{1}{2}O_2(g) \rightleftharpoons NO(g)$

$\Delta S_r^\circ(\text{formation}) = 1 \times 210.76$ J · K^{-1} · mol^{-1} $- (\frac{1}{2} \times 191.61$ J · K^{-1} · mol^{-1}
$$+ \frac{1}{2} \times 205.14 \text{ J} \cdot \text{K}^{-1} \cdot \text{mol}^{-1})$$

$\Delta S_r^\circ(\text{formation}) = 12.39$ J · K^{-1} · mol^{-1}; therefore, more stable

(d) $S(s) + O_2(g) \rightleftharpoons SO_2(g)$

$$\Delta S_r^\circ(\text{formation}) = 1 \times 248.22 \text{ J} \cdot \text{K}^{-1} \cdot \text{mol}^{-1} - (1 \times 31.80 \text{ J} \cdot \text{K}^{-1} \cdot \text{mol}^{-1}$$
$$+ 1 \times 205.14 \text{ J} \cdot \text{K}^{-1} \cdot \text{mol}^{-1})$$

$\Delta S_r^\circ(\text{formation}) = 11.28 \text{ J} \cdot \text{K}^{-1} \cdot \text{mol}^{-1}$; therefore, more stable

16.53 $4KClO_3(s) \longrightarrow 3KClO_4(s) + KCl(s), \quad \Delta G_r^\circ(25°C) = -133.1 \text{ kJ} \cdot \text{mol}^{-1}$

From this value of ΔG_r°, calculated in Exercise 16.43d, we see that the reaction is already spontaneous at 25°C. The effect of a change in temperature is determined by the sign of ΔS_r°, as can be seen from $\Delta G_r^\circ = \Delta H_r^\circ - T\Delta S_r^\circ$.

$$\Delta S_r^\circ = 3 \times 151.0 \text{ J} \cdot \text{K}^{-1} \cdot \text{mol}^{-1} + 1 \times 82.59 \text{ J} \cdot \text{K}^{-1} \cdot \text{mol}^{-1} - 4 \times 143.41 \text{ J} \cdot \text{K}^{-1} \cdot \text{mol}^{-1}$$
$$= -38.05 \text{ J} \cdot \text{K} \cdot \text{mol}^{-1}$$

Because ΔS_r° is negative, increased temperature will make the decomposition less spontaneous.

Free Energy and Equilibrium

16.55 Free energy approaches a minimum for the total reacting system as equilibrium is approached. That is, G_{total} decreases until equilibrium is reached.

16.57 In each case, $\ln K_p = \dfrac{-\Delta G_r^\circ}{RT}$. ΔG_r° data from Exercise 16.43. $RT = 2.479 \text{ kJ} \cdot \text{mol}^{-1}$ at 25°C.

(a) $\ln K_p = \dfrac{-(-457.17 \text{ kJ} \cdot \text{mol}^{-1})}{2.479 \text{ kJ} \cdot \text{mol}^{-1}} = 184.4\overline{2}, \quad K_p = 1 \times 10^{80}$

(b) $\ln K_p = \dfrac{-(-514.4 \text{ kJ} \cdot \text{mol}^{-1})}{2.479 \text{ kJ} \cdot \text{mol}^{-1}} = 207.5\overline{0}, \quad K_p = 1 \times 10^{90}$

(c) $\ln K_p = \dfrac{-(+130.4 \text{ kJ} \cdot \text{mol}^{-1})}{2.479 \text{ kJ} \cdot \text{mol}^{-1}} = -52.60, \quad K_p = 1.4 \times 10^{-23}$

16.59 (a) $\Delta G_r^\circ = -RT \ln K_p = -8.314 \text{ J} \cdot \text{K}^{-1} \cdot \text{mol}^{-1} \times 400 \text{ K} \times \ln 41$
$$= -1.23 \times 10^4 \text{ J} \cdot \text{mol}^{-1} = -12.3 \text{ kJ} \cdot \text{mol}^{-1}$$

(b) $\Delta G_r^\circ = -RT \ln K_p = -8.314 \text{ J} \cdot \text{K}^{-1} \cdot \text{mol}^{-1} \times 700 \text{ K} \times \ln(3.0 \times 10^4)$
$$= -6.00 \times 10^4 \text{ J} \cdot \text{mol}^{-1} = -60.0 \text{ kJ} \cdot \text{mol}^{-1}$$

16.61 $\Delta G_r^\circ = 2 \times 86.55 \text{ kJ} \cdot \text{mol}^{-1} - 1 \times 97.9 \text{ kJ} \cdot \text{mol}^{-1} = +173.1 \text{ kJ} \cdot \text{mol}^{-1}$

$$\ln K_p = \frac{-\Delta G_r^\circ}{RT} = \frac{-(+173.1 \text{ kJ} \cdot \text{mol}^{-1})}{2.479 \text{ kJ} \cdot \text{mol}^{-1}} = -69.83$$

$K_p = 4.7 \times 10^{-31}$

$Q_p > K_p$; hence, there is a tendency to form reactants.

16.63 $\quad Q_c = \dfrac{[I]^2}{[I_2]} = \dfrac{(0.0084)^2}{0.026} = 2.7 \times 10^{-3}$

$Q_c < K_c$; therefore, the reaction is spontaneous in the direction of I(g).

$\Delta G_r = \Delta G_r^\circ + RT \ln Q_c \quad (\Delta G_r^\circ = -RT \ln K_c)$

$\quad = -RT \ln K_c + RT \ln Q_c$, hence,

$\Delta G_r = -RT \ln\left(\dfrac{K_c}{Q_c}\right) = -8.314 \ \text{J} \cdot \text{K}^{-1} \cdot \text{mol}^{-1} \times 1200 \ \text{K} \times \ln\left(\dfrac{6.8 \times 10^{-2}}{2.7 \times 10^{-3}}\right)$

$\quad = -32 \ \text{kJ} \cdot \text{mol}^{-1} \quad$ (confirming the spontaneity)

16.65 $\quad Q_p = \dfrac{P_{NH_3}^2}{P_{N_2} \cdot P_{H_2}^3} = \dfrac{(63)^2}{1.0 \times (4.2)^3} = 53.\overline{6}$

(a) $\Delta G_r = \Delta G_r^\circ + RT \ln Q_p \quad (\Delta G_r^\circ = -RT \ln K_p)$

$\quad = -RT \ln K_p + RT \ln Q_p$; hence,

$\Delta G_r = -RT \ln\left(\dfrac{K_p}{Q_p}\right) = -8.314 \ \text{J} \cdot \text{K}^{-1} \cdot \text{mol}^{-1} \times 400 \ \text{K} \times \ln\left(\dfrac{41}{53.\overline{6}}\right)$

$\quad = +0.89 \ \text{kJ} \cdot \text{mol}^{-1}$

(b) Because $Q_p > K_p$ and $\Delta G_r > 0$, reactants will be formed.

16.67 In each case, $\ln K_{sp} = \dfrac{-\Delta G_r^\circ}{RT} = \dfrac{-\Delta G_r^\circ}{2.479 \ \text{kJ} \cdot \text{mol}^{-1}}$, at 25°C

(a) $AgI(s) \rightleftharpoons Ag^+(aq) + I^-(aq)$

$\Delta G_r^\circ = 1 \times (77.11 \ \text{kJ} \cdot \text{mol}^{-1}) + 1 \times (-51.57 \ \text{kJ} \cdot \text{mol}^{-1})$

$\qquad\qquad\qquad\qquad -1 \times (-66.19 \ \text{kJ} \cdot \text{mol}^{-1}) = 91.73 \ \text{kJ} \cdot \text{mol}^{-1}$

$\ln K_{sp} = \dfrac{-\Delta G_r^\circ}{RT} = \dfrac{-91.73 \ \text{kJ} \cdot \text{mol}^{-1}}{2.479 \ \text{kJ} \cdot \text{mol}^{-1}} = -37.01$

$K_{sp} = 8.4 \times 10^{-17}$

(b) $CaCO_3(s) \rightleftharpoons Ca^{2+}(aq) + CO_3^{2-}(aq)$

$\Delta G_r^\circ = 1 \times (-553.58 \ \text{kJ} \cdot \text{mol}^{-1}) + 1 \times (-527.9 \ \text{kJ} \cdot \text{mol}^{-1})$

$\qquad\qquad\qquad\qquad -1 \times (-1127.8 \ \text{kJ} \cdot \text{mol}^{-1}) = 46.32 \ \text{kJ} \cdot \text{mol}^{-1}$

$\ln K_{sp} = \dfrac{-\Delta G_r^\circ}{RT} = \dfrac{-46.32 \ \text{kJ} \cdot \text{mol}^{-1}}{2.479 \ \text{kJ} \cdot \text{mol}^{-1}} = -18.68$

$K_{sp} = 7.7 \times 10^{-9}$

(c) $FeS(s) \rightleftharpoons Fe^{2+}(aq) + S^{2-}(aq)$

$\Delta G_r^\circ = 1 \times (-78.90 \ \text{kJ} \cdot \text{mol}^{-1}) + 1 \times (85.8 \ \text{kJ} \cdot \text{mol}^{-1})$

$\qquad\qquad\qquad\qquad -1 \times (-104.4 \ \text{kJ} \cdot \text{mol}^{-1}) = 107.3 \ \text{kJ} \cdot \text{mol}^{-1}$

$$\ln K_{sp} = \frac{-\Delta G_r^\circ}{RT} = \frac{-107.3 \text{ kJ} \cdot \text{mol}^{-1}}{2.479 \text{ kJ} \cdot \text{mol}^{-1}} = -43.28$$

$$K_{sp} = 1.6 \times 10^{-19}$$

(d) $Ca(OH)_2(s) \rightleftharpoons Ca^{2+}(aq) + 2OH^-(aq)$

$$\Delta G_r^\circ = 1 \times (-553.58 \text{ kJ} \cdot \text{mol}^{-1}) + 2 \times (-157.24 \text{ kJ} \cdot \text{mol}^{-1})$$
$$- 1 \times (-898.49 \text{ kJ} \cdot \text{mol}^{-1}) = 30.43 \text{ kJ} \cdot \text{mol}^{-1}$$

$$\ln K_{sp} = \frac{-\Delta G_r^\circ}{RT} = \frac{-(30.43 \text{ kJ} \cdot \text{mol}^{-1})}{2.479 \text{ kJ} \cdot \text{mol}^{-1}} = -12.28$$

$$K_{sp} = 4.7 \times 10^{-6}$$

16.69 $K_w = 1.00 \times 10^{-14}$ at 25°C

$$\Delta G_r^\circ = -RT \ln K_w = -2.479 \text{ kJ} \cdot \text{mol} \times \ln(1.00 \times 10^{-14})$$
$$= +79.91 \text{ kJ} \cdot \text{mol}^{-1}$$

16.71 (a) $\Delta G_r^\circ = \Delta H_r^\circ - T\Delta S_r^\circ$

$$= +57.2 \text{ kJ} - 298 \text{ K} \times (+0.175\,83 \text{ kJ} \cdot \text{K}^{-1} \cdot \text{mol}^{-1})$$
$$= 4.8 \text{ kJ} \cdot \text{mol}^{-1}$$

(b) $\Delta G_r^\circ = +57.2 \text{ kJ} - 348 \text{ K} \times (+0.175\,83 \text{ kJ} \cdot \text{K}^{-1} \cdot \text{mol}^{-1}) = -4.0 \text{ kJ} \cdot \text{mol}^{-1}$

(c) $0 = \Delta H_r^\circ - T\Delta S_r^\circ$

$$T = \frac{\Delta H_r^\circ}{\Delta S_r^\circ} = \frac{57.2 \text{ kJ} \cdot \text{mol}^{-1}}{0.175\,83 \text{ kJ} \cdot \text{K}^{-1} \cdot \text{mol}^{-1}} = 325 \text{ K} = 52°C$$

$$0 = -RT \ln K_p$$

$$\ln K_p = 0, \quad K_p = 1$$

16.73 (a) $2Cu^+(aq) \rightleftharpoons Cu^{2+}(aq) + Cu(s)$

$$\Delta G_r^\circ = \Delta G_f^\circ(Cu^{2+}, aq) - 2 \times \Delta G_f^\circ(Cu^+, aq) = 65.49 \text{ kJ} \cdot \text{mol}^{-1}$$
$$- 2 \times 49.98 \text{ kJ} \cdot \text{mol}^{-1} = -34.47 \text{ kJ} \cdot \text{mol}^{-1}$$

Clearly, there is a thermodynamic tendency for this to occur at 25°C.

(b) The tendency is greater at lower temperatures, because ΔH_r° and ΔS_r° are both negative.

16.75 (a) $\Delta G_r^\circ = 3 \times (-200 \text{ kJ} \cdot \text{mol}^{-1}) - 1 \times (-562 \text{ kJ} \cdot \text{mol}^{-1}) = -38 \text{ kJ} \cdot \text{mol}^{-1}$

Therefore, the reduction can occur, because $\Delta G_r^\circ < 0$.

(b) $\Delta G_r^\circ = 3 \times (-396 \text{ kJ} \cdot \text{mol}^{-1}) - 2 \times (-562 \text{ kJ} \cdot \text{mol}^{-1}) = -64 \text{ kJ} \cdot \text{mol}^{-1}$

Therefore, the reduction can occur, because $\Delta G_r^\circ < 0$.

SUPPLEMENTARY EXERCISES

16.77 (a) The internal energy of an open system could be increased by (1) adding matter to the system (all matter has internal energy); (2) doing work on the system; and (3) *adding* heat to the system. w and q are positive in (2) and (3), hence $\Delta U = q + w$ is positive for these processes, and the internal energy increases.
(b) Matter cannot be added to a closed system, so only (2) (doing work *on* the system) and (3) (adding heat) could be used to increase the internal energy.
(c) The internal energy of an isolated system cannot be changed.

16.79 (a) ΔU for a reaction is the change in internal energy of the reacting system, that is,

$$\Delta U = \text{total energy of products} - \text{total energy of reactants}$$

If the reaction is carried out under constant volume conditions, $\Delta U = q_V$. ΔH is defined in a similar manner. The ΔH for a reaction is the change in enthalpy of the reacting system, that is,

$$\Delta H = \text{total enthalpy of products} - \text{total enthalpy of reactants}$$

If the reaction is carried out under constant pressure conditions, $\Delta H = q_P$.
(b) $\Delta U = q_P + w$, so if $w = 0$, which it is at constant pressure and volume, then $\Delta U = q_P = \Delta H$, and ΔU and ΔH are the same.

16.81 Compressing a gas decreases the disorder in the gas. The smaller volume available to the gas molecules upon compression means that their positions can be more precisely known; the disorder in their positions has decreased and hence the entropy of the gas has decreased. The temperature is not a factor here as long as it is high enough for the vapor to remain a gas; upon liquefaction, however, there is a greater decrease in entropy.

16.83 (a) Decrease; there is one less mole of gas in the products.
(b) Most likely an increase, because there is a greater dispersal of solute ions in the products. However, in an aqueous solution, one also has to consider the effect of the solution process on the entropy of the water, which will probably decrease as a result of the association of water molecules with the charged ions. The water molecules are then less free, with less disorder, and experience a decrease in entropy. But this effect, which will be concentration dependent, is very likely overridden by the dispersal of the solute ions.

(c) Decrease; the number of moles of gas has decreased.

(d) Decrease; the number of moles of gas has decreased.

16.85 (a) $\Delta G_r^\circ = 2 \times (-200 \text{ kJ} \cdot \text{mol}^{-1}) - 1 \times (-762 \text{ kJ} \cdot \text{mol}^{-1}) = +362 \text{ kJ} \cdot \text{mol}^{-1}$
The positive sign means this reduction is not possible.

(b) $\Delta G_r^\circ = 1 \times (-396 \text{ kJ} \cdot \text{mol}^{-1}) - 1 \times (-762 \text{ kJ} \cdot \text{mol}^{-1}) = +366 \text{ kJ} \cdot \text{mol}^{-1}$
The positive sign means this reduction is not possible.

16.87 (a) $\Delta S_r^\circ = \dfrac{\Delta H_r^\circ - \Delta G_r^\circ}{T} = \dfrac{[-87.9 - (-37.2)] \text{ kJ} \cdot \text{mol}^{-1}}{298 \text{ K}}$

$\qquad = -0.170 \text{ kJ} \cdot \text{K}^{-1} \cdot \text{mol}^{-1} = -170 \text{ J} \cdot \text{K}^{-1} \cdot \text{mol}^{-1}$

(b) This result is reasonable, because the number of moles of gas decreases in the reaction.

16.89 (a) $\Delta H_r^\circ = 1 \times \Delta H_f^\circ(C_2H_6, g) - 1 \times \Delta H_f^\circ(C_2H_2, g)$

$\Delta H_r^\circ = 1 \times (-84.68 \text{ kJ} \cdot \text{mol}^{-1}) - 1 \times 226.73 \text{ kJ} \cdot \text{mol}^{-1} = -311.41 \text{ kJ} \cdot \text{mol}^{-1}$

$\Delta S_r^\circ = 1 \times S_m^\circ(C_2H_6, g) - 1 \times S_m^\circ(C_2H_2, g) - 2 \times S_m^\circ(H_2, g)$

$\Delta S_r^\circ = 1 \times 0.229\,60 \text{ kJ} \cdot \text{K}^{-1} \cdot \text{mol}^{-1} - 1 \times 0.200\,94 \text{ kJ} \cdot \text{K}^{-1} \cdot \text{mol}^{-1}$

$\qquad\qquad - 2 \times 0.130\,68 \text{ kJ} \cdot \text{K}^{-1} \cdot \text{mol}^{-1} = -0.2327 \text{ kJ} \cdot \text{K}^{-1} \cdot \text{mol}^{-1}$

(b) $\Delta G_r^\circ = -311.41 \text{ kJ} \cdot \text{mol}^{-1} - (298 \text{ K})(-0.2327 \text{ kJ} \cdot \text{K}^{-1} \cdot \text{mol}^{-1})$

$\qquad = -242.1 \text{ kJ} \cdot \text{mol}^{-1}$

(c) A negative ΔH_r° indicates that heat is released by this reaction. The negative ΔS_r° is due to the fact that the product consists of two fewer moles of gas than the reactants.

(d) $T = \dfrac{\Delta H_r^\circ}{\Delta S_r^\circ} = \dfrac{-311.41 \text{ kJ} \cdot \text{mol}^{-1}}{-0.2327 \text{ kJ} \cdot \text{K}^{-1} \cdot \text{mol}^{-1}} = 1338 \text{ K}$

This is the crossover temperature between a spontaneous process, $K > 1$, (assuming $\Delta G_r^\circ \approx \Delta G_r$) and a nonspontaneous process, $K < 1$. Above this temperature, the reaction is not spontaneous.

16.91 (a) $\Delta G^\circ = \Delta H^\circ - T\Delta S^\circ = -14.07 \text{ kJ} - (189 \text{ K})(-0.0480 \text{ J} \cdot \text{K}^{-1}) = -5.00 \text{ J}$

(b) $T = \dfrac{\Delta H^\circ}{\Delta S^\circ} = \dfrac{-14.07 \text{ kJ}}{-0.0480 \text{ kJ} \cdot \text{K}^{-1}} = 293 \text{ K}$

The two solid phases are in equilibrium with each other (under standard conditions) at this temperature.

(c) We assume that the given values of ΔH° and ΔS° can also be used at $0°C$: $\Delta G^\circ(0°C) = -14.07 \text{ kJ} - (273 \text{ K})(-0.0480 \text{ kJ} \cdot \text{K}^{-1}) = -0.97 \text{ kJ}$. Hence, solid (2) is favored at $0°C$.

16.93 (a) $PCl_3(l) \longrightarrow PCl_3(g)$

$\Delta H^\circ_{vap} = \Delta H^\circ_f(Cl_3, g) - \Delta H^\circ_f(PCl_3, l) = -287.0 \text{ kJ} \cdot \text{mol}^{-1} - (-319.7 \text{ kJ} \cdot \text{mol}^{-1})$

$\Delta H^\circ_{vap} = 32.7 \text{ kJ} \cdot \text{mol}^{-1} = 3.27 \times 10^4 \text{ J} \cdot \text{mol}^{-1}$

$\Delta S^\circ_{vap} = S^\circ_m(PCl_3, g) - S^\circ_m(PCl_3, l) = (311.78 - 217.18) \text{ J} \cdot \text{K}^{-1} \cdot \text{mol}^{-1}$

$\Delta S^\circ_{vap} = 94.60 \text{ J} \cdot \text{K}^{-1} \cdot \text{mol}^{-1}$

$T_b = \dfrac{\Delta H^\circ_{vap}}{\Delta S^\circ_{vap}} = \dfrac{3.27 \times 10^4 \text{ J} \cdot \text{mol}^{-1}}{94.60 \text{ J} \cdot \text{K}^{-1} \cdot \text{mol}^{-1}} = 346 \text{ K}$

(b) $\Delta H^\circ_{tr} = \Delta H^\circ_f(S, mono) - \Delta H^\circ_f(S, rhombic) = (0.33 - 0) \text{ kJ} \cdot \text{mol}^{-1}$
$= 3.3 \times 10^2 \text{ J} \cdot \text{mol}^{-1}$

$\Delta S^\circ_{tr} = S^\circ_m(S, mono) - S^\circ_m(S, rhombic) = (32.6 - 31.80) \text{ J} \cdot \text{K}^{-1} \cdot \text{mol}^{-1}$
$= 0.8 \text{ J} \cdot \text{K}^{-1} \cdot \text{mol}^{-1}$

$T_{tr} = \dfrac{\Delta H^\circ_{tr}}{\Delta S^\circ_{tr}} = \dfrac{3.3 \times 10^2 \text{ J} \cdot \text{mol}^{-1}}{0.8 \text{ J} \cdot \text{K}^{-1} \cdot \text{mol}^{-1}} = 4 \times 10^2 \text{ K}$

(c) $I_2(s) \longrightarrow I_2(g)$

$\Delta H^\circ_{sub} = \Delta H^\circ_f(I_2, g) - \Delta H^\circ_f(I_2, s) = (62.44 - 0) \text{ kJ} \cdot \text{mol}^{-1} = 62.44 \text{ kJ} \cdot \text{mol}^{-1}$

$\Delta S^\circ_{sub} = S^\circ_m(I_2, g) - S^\circ_m(I_2, s) = (260.69 - 116.14) \text{ J} \cdot \text{K}^{-1} \cdot \text{mol}^{-1}$
$= 144.55 \text{ J} \cdot \text{K}^{-1} \cdot \text{mol}^{-1}$

$T_{sub} = \dfrac{\Delta H^\circ_{sub}}{\Delta S^\circ_{sub}} = \dfrac{62.44 \times 10^3 \text{ J} \cdot \text{mol}^{-1}}{144.55 \text{ J} \cdot \text{K}^{-1} \cdot \text{mol}^{-1}} = 432 \text{ K}$

(d) $D_2O(l) \longrightarrow D_2O(g)$

$\Delta H^\circ_{vap} = \Delta H^\circ_f(D_2O, g) - \Delta H^\circ_f(D_2O, l) = [-249.20 - (-294.60)] \text{ kJ} \cdot \text{mol}^{-1}$
$= 45.40 \text{ kJ} \cdot \text{mol}^{-1}$

$\Delta S^\circ_{vap} = S^\circ_m(D_2O, g) - S^\circ_m(D_2O, l) = (198.34 - 75.94) \text{ J} \cdot \text{K}^{-1} \cdot \text{mol}^{-1}$
$= 122.40 \text{ J} \cdot \text{K}^{-1} \cdot \text{mol}^{-1}$

$T_b = \dfrac{\Delta H^\circ_{tr}}{\Delta S^\circ_{tr}} = \dfrac{4.540 \times 10^4 \text{ J} \cdot \text{mol}^{-1}}{122.40 \text{ J} \cdot \text{K}^{-1} \cdot \text{mol}^{-1}} = 370.9 \text{ K}$

16.95 (a) $\Delta G^\circ_r = -2 \times \Delta G^\circ_f(O_3, g) = -2 \times 163.2 \text{ kJ} \cdot \text{mol}^{-1} = -326.4 \text{ kJ} \cdot \text{mol}^{-1}$

$\Delta S^\circ_r = 3 \times S^\circ_m(O_2, g) - 2 \times S^\circ_m(O_3, g) = 3 \times 205.14 \text{ J} \cdot \text{K}^{-1} \cdot \text{mol}^{-1}$
$- 2 \times 238.93 \text{ J} \cdot \text{K}^{-1} \cdot \text{mol}^{-1} = +137.56 \text{ J} \cdot \text{K}^{-1} \cdot \text{mol}^{-1}$

(b) $\ln K_p = \dfrac{-\Delta G^\circ_r}{RT} = \dfrac{-(-326.4 \text{ kJ} \cdot \text{mol}^{-1})}{2.479 \text{ kJ} \cdot \text{mol}^{-1}} = 131.6\overline{7}$

$K_p = 1.\overline{5} \times 10^{57}$

(c) The conversion of ozone to oxygen is spontaneous; if no matter or energy were added, the ozone would be used up. The rate at which this occurs, however, is another matter; thermodynamics does not give kinetic information.

16.97 Data is from Table 16.2

(a) $H_2O(l) \rightleftharpoons H_2O(g)$

$\Delta S° = n_{H_2O} \times [S°_m(H_2O, g) - S°_m(H_2O, l)]$

$\quad = (1\text{ g})\left(\dfrac{1\text{ mol}}{18.02\text{ g}}\right)(196.9\text{ J}\cdot\text{K}^{-1}\cdot\text{mol}^{-1} - 86.8\text{ J}\cdot\text{K}^{-1}\cdot\text{mol}^{-1}) = +6.11\text{ J}\cdot\text{K}^{-1}$

(b) $H_2O(s) \rightleftharpoons H_2O(l)$

$\Delta S° = n_{H_2O} \times [S°_m(H_2O, l) - S°_m(H_2O, s)]$

$\Delta S° = 0.0555\text{ mol} \times [65.2\text{ J}\cdot\text{K}^{-1}\cdot\text{mol}^{-1} - 43.2\text{ J}\cdot\text{K}^{-1}\cdot\text{mol}^{-1}] = +1.22\text{ J}\cdot\text{K}^{-1}$

(c) The disorder of the gaseous state relative to the liquid state is much larger than that of the liquid state relative to the solid state. Both the solid and liquid states are compact states of matter.

CHALLENGING EXERCISES

16.99 $\Delta U = 0 = \Delta U_1 + \Delta U_2$

$\qquad\quad = q_1 + w_1 + q_2 + w_2$

$\qquad\quad = 50\text{ J} + 0 - 5\text{ J} + w_2$

$\qquad\quad = 45\text{ J} + w_2$

Therefore, $w_2 = -45\text{ J} = -P\Delta V$

$$P\Delta V = 45\text{ J} \times \frac{1\text{ L}\cdot\text{atm}}{101\text{ J}} = 0.44\overline{6}\text{ L}\cdot\text{atm}$$

$$\Delta V = \frac{0.44\overline{6}\text{ L}\cdot\text{atm}}{1\text{ atm}} = 0.45\text{ L}$$

This would have to be an expansion, because ΔV is positive.

16.101 (a) $\Delta G_{soln} = \Delta H_{soln} - T\Delta S_{soln}$

For the dissolving process to be spontaneous, ΔG_{soln} must be negative. Thus, a positive ΔH_{soln} does not favor the solution process.

(b) Because the solution is spontaneous, ΔG_{soln} must be negative and ΔS_{soln} must be positive.

(c) At constant temperature, heat is dispersed in the system, as is matter. Both dispersals contribute to $\Delta S_{sys} = \Delta S_{soln}$, but the dispersal of matter (locational disorder) is the dominant factor.

(d) Because the surroundings participate in the solution process only as a source of heat, the entropy change of the surroundings is primarily a result of the dispersal of thermal energy.

(e) The driving force for the dissolution is the dispersal of matter, thus resulting in a positive ΔS.

16.103 (a) $\Delta G^\circ_{vap} = 0$; pure liquid water and pure water vapor are in equilibrium at 100°C and 1 atm pressure.

(b) See Exercise 16.98. For vaporization, the equilibrium constant $K_p = P$. We may use Raoult's law to calculate the vapor pressure of water in the glucose solution. We first calculate the mole fraction of water and then use it in

$$P_{H_2O} = x_{H_2O}P^\circ_{H_2O} = x_{H_2O} \times 1.00 \text{ atm}$$

Assume 100 g of solution, then 90 g H_2O and 10 g $C_6H_{12}O_6$.

For H_2O, $\quad n_{H_2O} = \dfrac{90 \text{ g}}{18.0 \text{ g} \cdot \text{mol}^{-1}} = 5.0 \text{ mol}$

For $C_6H_{12}O_6$, $\quad n_{C_6H_{12}O_6} = \dfrac{10 \text{ g}}{180 \text{ g} \cdot \text{mol}^{-1}} = 5.6 \times 10^{-2} \text{ mol}$

$x_{H_2O} = \dfrac{5.0 \text{ mol}}{5.0 \text{ mol} + 5.6 \times 10^{-2} \text{ mol}} = 0.98\overline{9}$

$P_{H_2O} = 0.98\overline{9} \times 1 \text{ atm} = 0.98\overline{9} \text{ atm}$

$\Delta G^\circ_{vap} = -RT \ln K_p = -RT \ln P$

$\qquad = -8.314 \text{ J} \cdot \text{K}^{-1} \cdot \text{mol}^{-1} \times 373 \text{ K} \times \ln(0.98\overline{9}) = +35 \text{ J} \cdot \text{mol}^{-1}$

Because $\Delta G^\circ_{vap} > 0$, this process is not spontaneous.

(c) The systems are different. The water is not pure in part (b). $\Delta G^\circ_{vap} = 0$, only for pure water at 100°C and 1 atm pressure. A nonvolatile solute depresses the vapor pressure.

16.105 $C_8H_{18}(\text{oct, l}) \rightleftharpoons C_8H_{18}(\text{iso, l})$

(a) $\Delta S^\circ_r = S^\circ_m(\text{iso}) - S^\circ_m(\text{oct}) = (+423.0 - 467.2) \text{ J} \cdot \text{K}^{-1} \cdot \text{mol}^{-1}$

$\qquad = -44.2 \text{ J} \cdot \text{K}^{-1} \cdot \text{mol}^{-1}$

$\Delta G^\circ_r = \Delta G^\circ_f(\text{iso}) - \Delta G^\circ_f(\text{oct}) = (+12.8 - 16.7) \text{ kJ} \cdot \text{mol}^{-1} = -3.9 \text{ kJ} \cdot \text{mol}^{-1}$

$\Delta G^\circ_r = -RT \ln K$

$\ln K = -\dfrac{\Delta G^\circ_r}{RT} = \dfrac{-(-3.9 \text{ kJ} \cdot \text{mol}^{-1})}{2.479 \text{ kJ} \cdot \text{mol}^{-1}} = 1.5\overline{7}$

$K = 5$

(b) Because ΔG°_r is negative, isooctane is favored under standard conditions.

(c) In each case, the products are the same. The enthalpy of combustion is then

$$\Delta H^\circ_c(\text{cmpd}) = \Delta H^\circ_f(\text{products}) - \Delta H^\circ_f(\text{cmpd})$$

and
$$\Delta H^\circ_c(\text{iso}) = \Delta H^\circ_f(\text{products}) - (-225.0 \text{ kJ} \cdot \text{mol}^{-1})$$
$$\Delta H^\circ_c(\text{oct}) = \Delta H^\circ_f(\text{products}) - (-208.2 \text{ kJ} \cdot \text{mol}^{-1})$$

Hence, for the conversion

$\Delta H^\circ_c(\text{iso}) - \Delta H^\circ_c(\text{oct}) = (225.0 - 208.2) \text{ kJ} \cdot \text{mol}^{-1} = +16.8 \text{ kJ} \cdot \text{mol}^{-1}$

So the amount of heat released is greater for octane than for isooctane (recall that the more positive ΔH_c°, the less heat released).

(d) The molecular structure of isooctane results in its being less flexible, with less freedom of movement; hence, its atomic arrangement is more ordered. So there is a decrease in entropy as octane is converted to isooctane.

CHAPTER 17
ELECTRONS IN TRANSITION: ELECTROCHEMISTRY

EXERCISES

Assume a temperature of 25°C (298 K) for the following exercises unless instructed otherwise.

Balancing Redox Equations

17.1   (a) $VO^{2+}(aq) + 2H^+(aq) + e^- \longrightarrow V^{3+}(aq) + H_2O(l)$
gain of electron; reduction
(b) $PbSO_4(s) + 2H_2O(l) \longrightarrow PbO_2(s) + SO_4^{2-}(aq) + 4H^+(aq) + 2e^-$
loss of electrons; oxidation
(c) $H_2O_2(aq) \longrightarrow O_2(g) + 2H^+(aq) + 2e^-$ loss of electrons; oxidation

17.3   (a) $ClO^-(aq) \longrightarrow Cl^-(aq) + H_2O(l)$ (balances O's); then,
$ClO^-(aq) + 2H_2O(l) \longrightarrow Cl^-(aq) + H_2O(l) + 2OH^-(aq)$ (balances H's); and,
$ClO^-(aq) + H_2O(l) + 2e^- \longrightarrow Cl^-(aq) + 2OH^-(aq)$ (balances charge)
(b) $IO_3^-(aq) \longrightarrow IO^-(aq) + 2H_2O(l)$ (balances O's); then,
$IO_3^-(aq) + 4H_2O(l) \longrightarrow IO^-(aq) + 2H_2O(l) + 4OH^-(aq)$ (balances H's); and,
$IO_3^-(aq) + 2H_2O(l) + 4e^- \longrightarrow IO^-(aq) + 4OH^-(aq)$ (balances charge)
(c) $2SO_3^{2-}(aq) \longrightarrow S_2O_4^{2-}(aq) + 2H_2O(l)$ (balances O's); then,
$2SO_3^{2-}(aq) + 4H_2O(l) \longrightarrow S_2O_4^{2-}(aq) + 2H_2O(l)$
$+ 4OH^-(aq)$ (balances H's); and,
$2SO_3^{2-}(aq) + 2H_2O(l) + 2e^- \longrightarrow S_2O_4^{2-}(aq) + 4OH^-(aq)$ (balances charge)
In each case, the reactants gain electrons, so all are reduction half-reactions.

17.5   In each case, first obtain the balanced half-reactions by using the methods employed in the solutions to Exercises 17.1 to 17.4. Then multiply the oxidation and reduction half-reactions by appropriate factors that will result in the same number of electrons being present in both half-reactions. Then add the half-reactions, canceling electrons in the process, to obtain the balanced equation for the whole reaction. Check to see that the final equation is balanced.

(a) $4[Cl_2(g) + 2e^- \longrightarrow 2Cl^-(aq)]$

$\underline{1[S_2O_3^{2-}(aq) + 5H_2O(l) \longrightarrow 2SO_4^{2-}(aq) + 10H^+(aq) + 8e^-]}$

$4Cl_2(g) + S_2O_3^{2-}(aq) + 5H_2O(l) + 8e^- \longrightarrow$

$8Cl^-(aq) + 2SO_4^{2-}(aq) + 10H^+(aq) + 8e^-$

$4Cl_2(g) + S_2O_3^{2-}(aq) + 5H_2O(l) \longrightarrow 8Cl^-(aq) + 2SO_4^{2-}(aq) + 10H^+(aq)$

Cl_2 is the oxidizing agent and $S_2O_3^{2-}$ is the reducing agent.

(b) $2[MnO_4^-(aq) + 8H^+(aq) + 5e^- \longrightarrow Mn^{2+}(aq) + 4H_2O(l)]$

$\underline{5[H_2SO_3(aq) + H_2O(l) \longrightarrow HSO_4^-(aq) + 3H^+(aq) + 2e^-]}$

$2MnO_4^-(aq) + 16H^+(aq) + 5H_2SO_3(aq) + 5H_2O(l) + 10e^- \longrightarrow$

$2Mn^{2+}(aq) + 8H_2O(l) + 5HSO_4^-(aq) + 15H^+(aq) + 10e^-$

$2MnO_4^-(aq) + H^+(aq) + 5H_2SO_3(aq) \longrightarrow 2Mn^{2+}(aq) + 3H_2O(l) + 5HSO_4^-(aq)$

MnO_4^- is the oxidizing agent and H_2SO_3 is the reducing agent.

(c) $Cl_2(g) + 2e^- \longrightarrow 2Cl^-(aq)$

$\underline{H_2S(aq) \longrightarrow S(s) + 2H^+(aq) + 2e^-}$

$Cl_2(g) + H_2S(aq) + 2e^- \longrightarrow 2Cl^-(aq) + S(s) + 2H^+(aq) + 2e^-$

$Cl_2(g) + H_2S(aq) \longrightarrow 2Cl^-(aq) + S(s) + 2H^+(aq)$

Cl_2 is the oxidizing agent and H_2S is the reducing agent.

(d) $Cl_2(g) + 2e^- \longrightarrow 2Cl^-(aq)$

$\underline{2H_2O(l) + Cl_2(g) \longrightarrow 2HOCl(aq) + 2H^+(aq) + 2e^-}$

$2H_2O(l) + Cl_2(g) + 2e^- \longrightarrow 2HOCl(aq) + 2H^+(aq) + 2Cl^-(aq) + 2e^-$

or $H_2O(l) + Cl_2(g) \longrightarrow HOCl(aq) + H^+(aq) + Cl^-(aq)$

Cl_2 is both the oxidizing and the reducing agent.

17.7 (a) $O_3(g) \longrightarrow O_2(g)$

$O_3(g) \longrightarrow O_2(g) + H_2O(l)$ (balances O's)

$2H_2O(l) + O_3(g) \longrightarrow O_2(g) + H_2O(l) + 2OH^-(aq)$ (balances H's)

$H_2O(l) + O_3(g) \longrightarrow O_2(g) + 2OH^-(aq)$ (cancels H_2O)

$H_2O(l) + O_3(g) + 2e^- \longrightarrow O_2(g) + 2OH^-(aq)$ (balances charge);

$Br^-(aq) \longrightarrow BrO_3^-(aq)$

$3H_2O(l) + Br^-(aq) \longrightarrow BrO_3^-(aq)$ (balances O's)

$6OH^-(aq) + 3H_2O(l) + Br^-(aq) \longrightarrow BrO_3^-(aq) + 6H_2O(l)$ (balances H's)

$6OH^-(aq) + 3H_2O(l) + Br^-(aq) \longrightarrow BrO^-(aq) + 6H_2O(l) + 6e^-$ (balances charge)

Combining half-reactions yields

$$3[H_2O(l) + O_3(g) + 2e^- \longrightarrow O_2(g) + 2OH^-(aq)]$$

$$\underline{6OH^-(aq) + 3H_2O(l) + Br^-(aq) \longrightarrow BrO_3^-(aq) + 6H_2O(l) + 6e^-}$$

$$2H_2O(l) + O_3(g) + 2OH^-(aq) + Br^-(aq) + 2e^- \longrightarrow$$
$$O_2(g) + 2OH^-(aq) + BrO_3^-(aq) + 2H_2O(l) + 2e^-$$

and, $3O_3(g) + Br^-(aq) \longrightarrow 3O_2(g) + BrO_3^-(aq)$

O_3 is the oxidizing agent and Br^- is the reducing agent.

(b) $Br_2(l) + 2e^- \longrightarrow 2Br^-(aq)$ (balanced reduction half-reaction)

$Br_2(l) + 6H_2O(l) \longrightarrow 2BrO_3^-(aq)$ (O's balanced); then,

$Br_2(l) + 6H_2O(l) + 12OH^-(aq) \longrightarrow 2BrO_3^-(aq) + 12H_2O(l)$ (H's balanced);

and,

$Br_2(l) + 12OH^-(aq) \longrightarrow 2BrO_3^-(aq) + 6H_2O(l) + 10e^-$ (electrons balanced)

Combining half-reactions yields

$$5[Br_2(l) + 2e^- \longrightarrow 2Br^-(aq)]$$

$$\underline{1[Br_2(l) + 12OH^-(aq) \longrightarrow 2BrO_3^-(aq) + 6H_2O(l) + 10e^-]}$$

$$6Br_2(l) + 12OH^-(aq) + 10e^- \longrightarrow 10Br^-(aq) + 2BrO_3^-(aq) + 6H_2O(l) + 10e^-$$

$$6Br_2(l) + 12OH^-(aq) \longrightarrow 10Br^-(aq) + 2BrO_3^-(aq) + 6H_2O(l)$$

Br_2 is both the oxidizing agent and the reducing agent.

(c) $Cr^{3+}(aq) + 4H_2O(l) \longrightarrow CrO_4^{2-}(aq)$ (O's balanced); then,

$Cr^{3+}(aq) + 4H_2O(l) + 8OH^-(aq) \longrightarrow CrO_4^{2-}(aq) + 8H_2O(l)$ (H's balanced);

and,

$Cr^{3+}(aq) + 8OH^-(aq) \longrightarrow CrO_4^{2-}(aq) + 4H_2O(l) + 3e^-$ (charge balanced)

$MnO_2(s) \longrightarrow Mn^{2+}(aq) + 2H_2O(l)$; then,

$MnO_2(s) + 4H_2O(l) \longrightarrow Mn^{2+}(aq) + 2H_2O(l) + 4OH^-(aq)$ (H's balanced);

and,

$MnO_2(s) + 2H_2O(l) + 2e^- \longrightarrow Mn^{2+}(aq) + 4OH^-(aq)$ (charge balanced)

Combining half-reactions yields

$$2[Cr^{3+}(aq) + 8OH^-(aq) \longrightarrow CrO_4^{2-}(aq) + 4H_2O(l) + 3e^-]$$

$$\underline{3[MnO_2(s) + 2H_2O(l) + 2e^- \longrightarrow Mn^{2+}(aq) + 4OH^-(aq)]}$$

$$2Cr^{3+}(aq) + 16OH^-(aq) + 3MnO_2(s) + 6H_2O(l) + 6e^- \longrightarrow$$
$$2CrO_4^{2-}(aq) + 8H_2O(l) + 3Mn^{2+}(aq) + 12OH^-(aq) + 6e^-$$

$$2Cr^{3+}(aq) + 4OH^-(aq) + 3MnO_2(s) \longrightarrow 2CrO_4^{2-}(aq) + 2H_2O(l) + 3Mn^{2+}(aq)$$

Cr^{3+} is the reducing agent and MnO_2 is the oxidizing agent.

(d) $3[P_4(s) + 8OH^-(aq) \longrightarrow 4H_2PO_2^-(aq) + 4e^-]$

$$\underline{P_4(s) + 12H_2O(l) + 12e^- \longrightarrow 4PH_3(g) + 12OH^-(aq)}$$

$$4P_4(s) + 12H_2O(l) + 24OH^-(aq) + 12e^- \longrightarrow$$
$$12H_2PO_2^-(aq) + 4PH_3(g) + 12OH^-(aq) + 12e^-$$

$$4P_4(s) + 12H_2O(l) + 12OH^-(aq) \longrightarrow 12H_2PO_2^-(aq) + 4PH_3(g)$$

or $P_4(s) + 3H_2O(l) + 3OH^-(aq) \longrightarrow 3H_2PO_2^-(aq) + PH_3(g)$

$P_4(s)$ is both the oxidizing and the reducing agent.

17.9 (a) $HSO_3^-(aq) + H_2O(l) \longrightarrow HSO_4^-(aq) + 2H^+(aq) + 2e^-$; and,

$2HSO_3^-(aq) \longrightarrow S_2O_6^{2-}(aq) + 2H^+(aq) + 2e^-$

(b) $I_2(aq) + 2e^- \longrightarrow 2I^-(aq)$

$\underline{HSO_3^-(aq) + H_2O(l) \longrightarrow HSO_4^-(aq) + 2H^+(aq) + 2e^-}$

$I_2(aq) + HSO_3^-(aq) + H_2O(l) + 2e^- \longrightarrow$

$2I^-(aq) + HSO_4^-(aq) + 2H^+(aq) + 2e^-$

$I_2(aq) + HSO_3^-(aq) + H_2O(l) \longrightarrow 2I^-(aq) + HSO_4^-(aq) + 2H^+(aq)$

17.11 The half-reactions are

$MnO_4^-(aq) \longrightarrow Mn^{2+}(aq) + 4H_2O(l)$ (O's balanced)

$MnO_4^-(aq) + 8H^+(aq) \longrightarrow Mn^{2+}(aq) + 4H_2O(l)$ (H's balanced)

$MnO_4^-(aq) + 8H^+(aq) + 5e^- \longrightarrow Mn^{2+}(aq) + 4H_2O(l)$ (charge balanced)

$C_6H_{12}O_6(aq) + 6H_2O(l) \longrightarrow 6CO_2(g)$ (O's balanced)

$C_6H_{12}O_6(aq) + 6H_2O(l) \longrightarrow 6CO_2(g) + 24H^+(aq)$ (H's balanced)

$C_6H_{12}O_6(aq) + 6H_2O(l) \longrightarrow 6CO_2(g) + 24H^+(aq) + 24e^-$ (charge balanced)

Adding half-reactions yields

$24[MnO_4^-(aq) + 8H^+(aq) + 5e^- \longrightarrow Mn^{2+}(aq) + 4H_2O(l)]$

$\underline{5[C_6H_{12}O_6(aq) + 6H_2O(l) \longrightarrow 6CO_2(g) + 24H^+(aq) + 24e^-]}$

$24MnO_4^-(aq) + 192H^+(aq) + 5C_6H_{12}O_6(aq) + 30H_2O(l) + 120e^- \longrightarrow$

$24Mn^{2+}(aq) + 96H_2O(l) + 30CO_2(g) + 120H^+(aq) + 120e^-$

$24MnO_4^-(aq) + 72H^+(aq) + 5C_6H_{12}O_6(aq) \longrightarrow 24Mn^{2+}(aq) + 66H_2O(l) + 30CO_2(g)$

Galvanic Cells

17.13 See Figs. 17.1 and 17.7

(a) anode   (b) positive

17.15 See Figs. 17.1 and 17.7

(a) electrons   (b) ions (cations and anions)

17.17 (a) $Zn^{2+}(aq) + 2e^- \longrightarrow Zn(s)$

(b) $Fe^{3+}(aq) + e^- \longrightarrow Fe^{2+}(aq)$ Platinum metal is an inert electrode and does not participate in the electrode reaction.

(c) $\frac{1}{2}Cl_2(g) + e^- \longrightarrow Cl^-(aq)$

(d) $Hg_2Cl_2(s) + 2e^- \longrightarrow 2Hg(l) + 2Cl^-(aq)$

17.19 (a) $Ag^+(aq) + e^- \longrightarrow Ag(s)$ $E°(cathode) = +0.80$ V

$Fe^{3+}(aq) + e^- \longrightarrow Fe^{2+}(aq)$ $E°(anode) = +0.77$ V

Reversing the anode half-reaction yields

$Fe^{2+}(aq) \longrightarrow Fe^{3+}(aq) + e^-$

and the cell reaction is, upon addition of the half-reactions,

$Ag^+(aq) + Fe^{2+}(aq) \longrightarrow Ag(s) + Fe^{3+}(aq)$ $E°_{cell} = +0.80$ V $- 0.77$ V

$\qquad\qquad\qquad\qquad\qquad\qquad\qquad\qquad\qquad = +0.03$ V

(b) $2H^+(aq) + 2e^- \longrightarrow H_2(g)$ $E°(anode) = 0.00$ V

$Cl_2(g) + 2e^- \longrightarrow 2Cl^-(aq)$ $E°(cathode) = +1.36$ V

Therefore, at the anode, after reversal,

$H_2(g) \longrightarrow 2H^+(aq) + 2e^-$

and, the cell reaction is, upon addition of the half-reactions,

$Cl_2(g) + H_2(g) \longrightarrow 2H^+(aq) + 2Cl^-(aq)$ $E°_{cell} = +1.36$ V $- 0.00$ V $= +1.36$ V

(c) $2[U^{3+}(aq) + 3e^- \longrightarrow U(s)]$ $E°(anode) = -1.79$ V

$3[V^{2+}(aq) + 2e^- \longrightarrow V(s)]$ $E°(cathode) = -1.19$ V

Therefore, at the anode, after reversal,

$2[U(s) \longrightarrow U^{3+}(aq) + 3e^-]$

and, the cell reaction is, upon addition of the half-reactions,

$3V^{2+}(aq) + 2U(s) \longrightarrow 2U^{3+}(aq) + 3V(s)$ $E°_{cell} = -1.19$ V $- (-1.79$V$)$

$\qquad\qquad\qquad\qquad\qquad\qquad\qquad\qquad\qquad = +0.60$ V

(d) $O_2(g) + 2H_2O(l) + 4e^- \longrightarrow 4OH^-(aq)$ $E°(cathode) = 0.40$ V

$O_2(g) + 4H^+(aq) + 4e^- \longrightarrow 2H_2O(l)$ $E°(anode) = 1.23$ V

Reversing the anode half-reaction yields

$2H_2O(l) \longrightarrow O_2(g) + 4H^+(aq) + 4e^-$

and the cell reaction is, upon addition of the half-reactions,

$4H_2O(l) \longrightarrow 4H^+(aq) + 4OH^-(aq)$ $E°_{cell} = 0.40$ V $- 1.23$ V $= -0.83$ V

or, $H_2O(l) \longrightarrow H^+(aq) + OH^-(aq)$

Note: This balanced equation corresponds to the cell notation given. The spontaneous process is the reverse of this reaction.

(e) $Sn^{4+}(aq) + 2e^- \longrightarrow Sn^{2+}(aq)$ $E°(anode) = +0.15$ V

$Hg_2Cl_2(s) + 2e^- \longrightarrow 2Hg(l) + 2Cl^-(aq)$ $E°(cathode) = +0.27$ V

Therefore, at the anode, after reversal,

$Sn^{2+}(aq) \longrightarrow Sn^{4+}(aq) + 2e^-$

and, the cell reaction is, upon addition of the half-reactions,

$Sn^{2+}(aq) + Hg_2Cl_2(s) \longrightarrow 2Hg(l) + 2Cl^-(aq) + Sn^{4+}(aq)$ $E°_{cell}$

$\qquad\qquad\qquad\qquad\qquad\qquad\qquad\qquad\qquad = 0.27$ V $- 0.15$ V $= 0.12$ V

17.21 (a) $Ni^{2+}(aq) + 2e^- \longrightarrow Ni(s)$ $E°(cathode) = -0.23$ V

$Zn^{2+}(aq) + 2e^- \longrightarrow Zn(s)$ $E°(anode) = -0.76$ V

Reversing the anode reaction yields

$Zn(s) \longrightarrow Zn^{2+}(aq) + 2e^-$ (at anode), then, upon addition,

$Ni^{2+}(aq) + Zn(s) \longrightarrow Ni(s) + Zn^{2+}(aq)$ (overall cell)

$$E°_{cell} = -0.23 \text{ V} - (-0.76 \text{ V}) = +0.53 \text{ V}$$

and $Zn(s) | Zn^{2+}(aq) || Ni^{2+}(aq) | Ni(s)$

(b) $2[Ce^{4+}(aq) + e^- \longrightarrow Ce^{3+}(aq)]$ $E°(cathode) = +1.61$ V

$I_2(s) + 2e^- \longrightarrow 2I^-(aq)$ $E°(anode) = +0.54$ V

Reversing the anode reaction yields

$2I^-(aq) \longrightarrow 2e^- + I_2(s)$ (at anode), then, upon addition,

$2I^-(aq) + 2Ce^{4+}(aq) \longrightarrow 2Ce^{3+}(aq) + I_2(s)$ (overall cell)

$$E°_{cell} = +1.61 \text{ V} - 0.54 \text{ V} = +1.07 \text{ V}$$

and $Pt | I^-(aq) | I_2(s) || Ce^{4+}(aq), Ce^{3+}(aq) | Pt$

An inert electrode such as Pt is necessary when both oxidized and reduced species are in the same solution.

(c) $Cl_2(g) + 2e^- \longrightarrow 2Cl^-(aq)$ $E°(cathode) = +1.36$ V

$2H^+(aq) + 2e^- \longrightarrow H_2(g)$ $E°(anode) = 0.00$ V

Reversing the anode reaction yields

$H_2(g) \longrightarrow 2H^+(aq) + 2e^-$ (at anode), then, upon addition,

$H_2(g) + Cl_2(g) \longrightarrow 2HCl(aq)$ (overall cell) $E°_{cell} = +1.36 \text{ V} - 0.00 \text{ V}$

$$= +1.36 \text{ V}$$

and $Pt | H_2(g) | H^+(aq) || Cl^-(aq) | Cl_2(g) | Pt$

An inert electrode such as Pt is necessary for gas/ion electrode reactions.

(d) $3[Au^+(aq) + e^- \longrightarrow Au(s)]$ $E°(cathode) = +1.69$ V

$Au^{3+}(aq) + 3e^- \longrightarrow Au(s)$ $E°(anode) = +1.40$ V

Reversing the anode reaction yields

$Au(s) \longrightarrow Au^{3+}(aq) + 3e^-$ then, upon addition, (anode),

$3Au^+(aq) \longrightarrow 2Au(s) + Au^{3+}(aq)$ (overall cell) $E°_{cell} = +1.69 \text{ V} - 1.40 \text{ V}$

$$= +0.29 \text{ V}$$

and $Au(s) | Au^{3+}(aq) || Au^+(aq) | Au(s)$

17.23 (a) $Ag^+(aq) + e^- \longrightarrow Ag(s)$ $E°(cathode) = +0.80$ V

$AgBr(s) + e^- \longrightarrow Ag(s) + Br^-(aq)$ $E°(anode) = +0.07$ V

Reversing the anode reaction yields

$Ag(s) + Br^-(aq) \longrightarrow AgBr(s) + e^-$ then, upon addition,

$Ag^+(aq) + Br^-(aq) \longrightarrow AgBr(s)$ (overall cell) $E°_{cell} = +0.80 \text{ V} - 0.07 \text{ V}$

$$= +0.73 \text{ V}$$

This is the direction of the spontaneous cell reaction that could be used to study the given solubility equilibrium. The reverse of this cell reaction corresponds to the reaction as given. It is not spontaneous. Thus,

$AgBr(s) \longrightarrow Ag^+(aq) + Br^-(aq)$ $E°_{cell} = -0.73$ V

For this, the cathode and anode reactions are reversed relative to those above. A cell diagram for the nonspontaneous process is

$Ag(s) | Ag^+(aq) || Br^-(aq) | AgBr(s) | Ag(s)$

(b) To conform to the notation of this chapter, the neutralization is rewritten as

$H^+(aq) + OH^- \longrightarrow H_2O(l)$

$O_2(g) + 4H^+(aq) + 4e^- \longrightarrow 2H_2O(l)$ $E°(\text{cathode}) = +1.23$ V

$O_2(g) + 2H_2O(l) + 4e^- \longrightarrow 4OH^-(aq)$ $E°(\text{anode}) = +0.40$ V

Reversing the anode reaction yields

$4OH^-(aq) \longrightarrow O_2(g) + 2H_2O(l) + 4e^-$, then, upon addition,

$4H^+(aq) + 4OH^-(aq) \longrightarrow 4H_2O(l)$

or $H^+(aq) + OH^-(aq) \longrightarrow H_2O(l)$ (overall cell) $E° = +1.23$ V $- 0.40$ V

$$= +0.83 \text{ V}$$

and $Pt | O_2(g) | OH^-(aq) || H^+(aq) | O_2(g) | Pt$

(c) $Cd(OH)_2(s) + 2e^- \longrightarrow Cd(s) + 2OH^-(aq)$ $E°(\text{anode}) = -0.81$ V

$Ni(OH)_3(s) + e^- \longrightarrow Ni(OH)_2(s) + OH^-(aq)$ $E°(\text{cathode}) = +0.49$ V

Reversing the anode reaction and multiplying the cathode reaction by 2 yields

$Cd(s) + 2OH^-(aq) \longrightarrow Cd(OH)_2(s) + 2e^-$

$2Ni(OH)_3 + 2e^- \longrightarrow 2Ni(OH)_2(s) + 2OH^-(aq)$ then, upon addition,

$2Ni(OH)_2(s) + Cd(s) \longrightarrow Cd(OH)_2(s) + 2Ni(OH)_2(s)$

and $Cd(s) | Cd(OH)_2(s) | KOH(aq) || Ni(OH)_3(s) | Ni(OH)_2(s) | Ni(s)$

17.25 (a) $MnO_4^-(aq) + 8H^+(aq) + 5e^- \longrightarrow Mn^{2+}(aq) + 4H_2O(l)$ (cathode half-reaction)

$5[Fe^{3+}(aq) + e^- \longrightarrow Fe^{2+}(aq)]$ (anode half-reaction)

(b) Reversing the anode reaction and adding the two equations yields

$MnO_4^-(aq) + 5Fe^{2+}(aq) + 8H^+(aq) \longrightarrow Mn^{2+}(aq) + 5Fe^{3+}(aq) + 4H_2O(l)$

The cell diagram is $Pt(s) | Fe^{2+}(aq), Fe^{3+}(aq) || MnO_4^-(aq), Mn^{2+}(aq), H^+(aq) | Pt(s)$

Cell Potential and Free Energy

17.27 Because the number of electrons lost by the reducing agent is the same as the number gained by the oxidizing agent, you can choose either the oxidizing agent or the reducing agent, whichever is easiest, to determine the number of electrons transferred. But first check to ensure that the equation is balanced.

(a) $6O_2(0) \longrightarrow 12O(-2)$, hence $n = 2 \times 12 = 24$

(b) $2B(0) \longrightarrow 2B(+3)$, hence $n = 2 \times 3 = 6$

(c) $Si(+4) \longrightarrow Si(0)$, hence $n = 4$

17.29 A galvanic cell has a positive potential difference; therefore identify as cathode and anode the electrodes that make $E°(cell)$ positive upon calculating

$$E°(cell) = E°(cathode) - E°(anode)$$

There are only two possibilities: If your first guess gives a negative $E°(cell)$, switch your identification.

(a) $Cu^{2+}(aq) + 2e^- \longrightarrow Cu(s)$ $E°(cathode) = +0.34$ V

$Cr^{3+}(aq) + 1e^- \longrightarrow Cr^{2+}(aq)$ $E°(anode) = -0.41$ V

$E°(cell) = +0.34$ V $- (-0.41$ V$) = +0.75$ V

(b) $AgCl(s) + e^- \longrightarrow Ag(s) + Cl^-(aq)$ $E°(cathode) = +0.22$ V

$AgI(s) + e^- \longrightarrow Ag(s) + I^-(aq)$ $E°(anode) = -0.15$ V

$E°(cell) = +0.22$V $- (-0.15$V$) = +0.37$ V

(c) $Hg_2^{2+}(aq) + 2e^- \longrightarrow 2Hg(l)$ $E°(cathode) = +0.79$ V

$Hg_2Cl_2(s) + 2e^- \longrightarrow 2Hg(l) + 2Cl^-(aq)$ $E°(anode) = +0.27$ V

$E°(cell) = +0.79$ V $- (+0.27$ V$) = +0.52$ V

(d) $Pb^{4+}(aq) + 2e^- \longrightarrow Pb^{2+}(aq)$ $E°(cathode) = +1.67$ V

$Sn^{4+}(aq) + 2e^- \longrightarrow Sn^{2+}(aq)$ $E°(anode) = +0.15$ V

$E°(cell) = +1.67$ V $- 0.15$ V $= +1.52$ V

17.31 See Exercise 17.29 solutions for $E°$ (cell) values. In each case, $\Delta G_r° = -nFE°$. 1 V $= 1$ J $\cdot$ C^{-1}. n is determined by balancing the equation for the cell reaction constructed from the half-reactions given in Exercise 17.29.

(a) $Cu^{2+}(aq) + 2Cr^{2+}(aq) \longrightarrow Cu(s) + 2Cr^{3+}(aq)$, $n = 2$

$E°_{cell} = +0.75$ V and $\Delta G_r° = -nFE° = -(2)(9.65 \times 10^4$ C $\cdot$ mol$^{-1})(0.75$ J $\cdot$ C$^{-1})$

$\qquad = -145$ kJ $\cdot$ mol^{-1}

(b) $AgCl(s) + I^-(aq) \longrightarrow AgI(s) + Cl^-(aq)$, $n = 1$

$E°_{cell} = +0.37$ V and $\Delta G_r° = -nFE° = -1 \times 9.65 \times 10^4$ C $\cdot$ mol$^{-1} \times 0.37$ J $\cdot$ C^{-1}

$\qquad = -36$ kJ $\cdot$ mol^{-1}

(c) $Hg_2^{2+}(aq) + 2Cl^-(aq) \longrightarrow Hg_2Cl_2(s)$, $n = 2$

$E°_{cell} = +0.52$ V and $\Delta G_r° = -nFE° = -(2)(9.65 \times 10^4$ C $\cdot$ mol$^{-1})(0.52$ J $\cdot$ C$^{-1})$

$\qquad = -100$ kJ $\cdot$ mol^{-1}

(d) $Pb^{4+}(aq) + Sn^{2+}(aq) \longrightarrow Pb^{2+}(aq) + Sn^{4+}(aq)$, $n = 2$

$E°_{cell} = +1.52$ V and $\Delta G°_r = -nFE° = -(2)(9.65 \times 10^4 \text{ C} \cdot \text{mol}^{-1})(1.52 \text{ J} \cdot \text{C}^{-1})$
$= -293 \text{ kJ} \cdot \text{mol}^{-1}$

The Electrochemical Series

17.33 Refer to Appendix 2B. The more negative (less positive) the standard reduction potential, the stronger the metal is as a reducing agent.

(a) Cu < Fe < Zn < Cr

(b) Mg < Na < K < Li

(c) V < Ti < Al < U

(d) Au < Ag < Sn < Ni

17.35 In each case, identify the couple with the more positive reduction potential. This will be the couple at which reduction occurs, and hence contains the oxidizing agent. The other couple contains the reducing agent.

(a) Co^{2+}/Co $E° = -0.28$ V, Co^{2+} is the oxidizing agent (cathode)
Ti^{3+}/Ti^{2+} $E° = -0.37$ V, Ti^{2+} is the reducing agent (anode)
$Pt \mid Ti^{2+}(aq), Ti^{3+}(aq) \parallel Co^{2+}(aq) \mid Co(s)$
$E°_{cell} = E°(\text{cathode}) - E°(\text{anode}) = -0.28 \text{ V} - (-0.37 \text{ V}) = +0.09$ V
(b) U^{3+}/U $E° = -1.79$ V, U^{3+} is the oxidizing agent (cathode)
La^{3+}/La $E° = -2.52$ V,   La is the reducing agent (anode)
$La(s) \mid La^{3+}(aq) \parallel U^{3+}(aq) \mid U(s)$
$E°_{cell} = -1.79 \text{ V} - (-2.52 \text{ V}) = +0.73$ V
(c) Fe^{3+}/Fe^{2+} $E° = +0.77$ V, Fe^{3+} is the oxidizing agent (cathode)
H^+/H_2 $E° = 0.00$ V, H_2 is the reducing agent (anode)
$Pt(s) \mid H_2(g) \mid H^+(aq) \parallel Fe^{2+}(aq), Fe^{3+}(aq) \mid Pt(s)$
$E°_{cell} = +0.77 \text{ V} - 0.00 \text{ V} = +0.77$ V
(d) $O_3/O_2, OH^-$ $E° = +1.24$ V, O_3 is the oxidizing agent (cathode)
Ag^+/Ag $E° = +0.80$ V,   Ag is the reducing agent (anode)
$Ag \mid Ag^+(aq) \parallel OH^-(aq) \mid O_3(g), O_2(g) \mid Pt$
$E°_{cell} = +1.24 \text{ V} - 0.80 \text{ V} = +0.44$ V

17.37 (a) H_2/H^+ $E° = 0.00$ V; Ni^{2+}/Ni $E° = -0.23$ V
No, Ni is the better reducing agent; its couple has a more negative $E°$.
(b) Cr^{3+}/Cr $E° = -0.74$ V; Pb^{2+}/Pb $E° = -0.13$ V
Yes, Cr is the better reducing agent; its couple has a more negative $E°$.

$$2[Cr(s) \longrightarrow Cr^{3+}(aq) + 3e^-] \quad \text{(anode)}$$
$$\underline{3[Pb^{2+}(aq) + 2e^- \longrightarrow Pb(s)] \quad \text{(cathode)}}$$
$$3Pb^{2+}(aq) + 2Cr(s) \longrightarrow 3Pb(s) + 2Cr^{3+}(aq)$$

$E^\circ_{cell} = E^\circ(\text{cathode}) - E^\circ(\text{anode}) = -0.13 \text{ V} - (-0.74 \text{ V}) = +0.61 \text{ V}$

(c) $MnO_4^-, H^+/Mn^{2+} \quad E^\circ = +1.51 \text{ V}; \quad Cu^{2+}/Cu \quad E^\circ = +0.34 \text{ V}$

Yes, MnO_4^- is the better oxidizing agent; its couple has a more positive E°.

$$5[Cu(s) \longrightarrow Cu^{2+}(aq) + 2e^-] \quad \text{(anode)}$$
$$\underline{2[MnO_4^-(aq) + 8H^+(aq) + 5e^- \longrightarrow Mn^{2+}(aq) + 4H_2O(l)] \quad \text{(cathode)}}$$
$$5Cu(s) + 2MnO_4^-(aq) + 16H^+(aq) \longrightarrow 5Cu^{2+}(aq) + 2Mn^{2+}(aq) + 8H_2O(l)$$

$E^\circ_{cell} = 1.51 \text{ V} - 0.34 \text{ V} = 1.17 \text{ V}$

(d) $Fe^{3+}/Fe^{2+} \quad E^\circ = +0.77 \text{ V}; \quad Hg_2^{2+}/Hg \quad E^\circ = +0.79 \text{ V}$

No, Hg_2^{2+} is the better oxidizing agent; its couple has the more positive E°.

17.39 (a) $I_2 + H_2 \longrightarrow 2I^- + 2H^+$

$I_2 + 2e^- \longrightarrow 2I^- \quad \text{reduction (cathode)} \quad E^\circ = +0.54 \text{ V}$

$H_2 \longrightarrow 2H^+ + 2e^- \quad \text{oxidation (anode)} \quad E^\circ = 0.00 \text{ V}$

$E^\circ_{cell} = E^\circ(\text{cathode}) - E^\circ(\text{anode}) = +0.54 \text{ V} - 0.00 \text{ V} = +0.54 \text{ V}$

$\Delta G^\circ_r = -nFE^\circ = -(2)(9.65 \times 10^4 \text{ C} \cdot \text{mol}^{-1})(0.54 \text{ J} \cdot \text{C}^{-1}) = -104 \text{ kJ} \cdot \text{mol}^{-1}$; therefore, spontaneous

(b) $Mg^{2+} + Cu \longrightarrow$ no reaction; E° for $Cu^{2+}/Cu > E^\circ$ for Mg^{2+}/Mg

(c) $2Al + 3Pb^{2+} \longrightarrow 2Al^{3+} + 3Pb$

$Pb^{2+} + 2e^- \longrightarrow Pb \quad \text{reduction (cathode)} \quad E^\circ = -0.13 \text{ V}$

$Al \longrightarrow Al^{3+} + 3e^- \quad \text{oxidation (anode)} \quad E^\circ = -1.66 \text{ V}$

$E^\circ_{cell} = E^\circ(\text{cathode}) - E^\circ(\text{anode}) = -0.13 \text{ V} - (-1.66 \text{ V}) = +1.53 \text{ V}$

$\Delta G^\circ_r = -nFE^\circ = -(6)(9.65 \times 10^4 \text{ C} \cdot \text{mol}^{-1})(+1.53 \text{ J} \cdot \text{C}^{-1}) =$
$-886 \text{ kJ} \cdot \text{mol}^{-1}$; therefore, spontaneous

17.41 $E^\circ (Br_2, Br^-) = +1.09 \text{ V} \quad E^\circ (Cl_2, Cl^-) = +1.36 \text{ V} \quad E^\circ (O_2, H^+, H_2O)$
$$= +1.23 \text{ V}$$

O_2 could be used because $E^\circ (O_2, H^+, H_2O) > E^\circ (Br_2, Br^-)$. It is not used because that reaction is so much slower than the one with Cl_2.

Equilibrium Constants

17.43 (a) From the cell diagram,

cathode, reduction $2[AgCl + e^- \longrightarrow Ag + Cl^-]$

anode, oxidation $H_2 \longrightarrow 2H^+ - 2e^-$

overall $2AgCl(s) + H_2(g) \longrightarrow 2Ag(s) + 2Cl^-(aq) + 2H^+(aq)$

$$K_c = \frac{[H^+]^2[Cl^-]^2}{[H_2]}$$

(b) From the cell diagram,

cathode, reduction $NO_3^- + 4H^+ + 3e^- \longrightarrow NO + 2H_2O$

anode, oxidation $Fe^{2+} \longrightarrow Fe^{3+} + e^-$

overall $NO_3^-(aq) + 4H^+(aq) + 3Fe^{2+}(aq) \longrightarrow NO(g) + 3Fe^{3+}(aq) + 2H_2O(l)$

$$K_c = \frac{[NO][Fe^{3+}]^3}{[Fe^{2+}]^3[H^+]^4[NO_3^-]}$$

17.45 (a) $E^\circ_{cell} = E^\circ(\text{cathode}) - E^\circ(\text{anode}) = 0.34\ V - (-0.41\ V) = 0.75\ V$, and

$\ln K = \dfrac{nFE^\circ}{RT}$ at $25°C = \dfrac{nE^\circ}{0.025\ 69\ V}$ $\ln K = \dfrac{(2)(0.75\ V)}{0.025\ 69\ V} = 58.\overline{3}$ and

$$K = \overline{2} \times 10^{25}$$

(b) $Ti^{2+}(aq) + 2e^- \longrightarrow Ti(s)$ $E^\circ(\text{cathode}) = -1.63\ V$

$Mn^{2+}(aq) + 2e^- \longrightarrow Mn(s)$ $E^\circ(\text{anode}) = -1.18\ V$

Note: These equations represent the cathode and anode half-reactions for the overall reaction as written. The spontaneous direction of this reaction under standard conditions is the opposite of that given.

$E^\circ_{cell} = E^\circ(\text{cathode}) - E^\circ(\text{anode}) = -1.63\ V - (-1.18\ V) = -0.45\ V$, and

$\ln K = \dfrac{nFE^\circ}{RT}$ at $25°C = \dfrac{nE^\circ}{0.025\ 69\ V}$ $\ln K = \dfrac{(2)(-0.45\ V)}{0.025\ 69\ V} = -35.\overline{0}$ and

$$K = \overline{6} \times 10^{-16} = 10^{-15}$$

(c) E° for $Hg_2^{2+}/Hg = +0.79\ V > E^\circ$ for $Pb^{2+}/Pb = -0.13\ V$

Therefore, Hg_2^{2+} is reduced and Pb is oxidized.

$Hg_2^{2+}(aq) + Pb(s) \longrightarrow Pb^{2+}(aq) + 2Hg(l)$

$Hg_2^{2+} + 2e^- \longrightarrow 2Hg(l)$ $E^\circ(\text{cathode}) = 0.79\ V$

$Pb^{2+} + 2e^- \longrightarrow Pb(s)$ $E^\circ(\text{anode}) = -0.13\ V$

$E^\circ_{cell} = E^\circ(\text{cathode}) - E^\circ(\text{anode}) = 0.79\ V - (-0.13\ V) = 0.92\ V$, and

$\ln K = \dfrac{nFE^\circ}{RT}$ at $25°C = \dfrac{nE^\circ}{0.025\ 69\ V}$ $\ln K = \dfrac{(2)(0.92\ V)}{0.025\ 69\ V} = +71.\overline{6}$ and

$$K = \overline{1} \times 10^{31} = 10^{31}$$

(d) $In^{3+}(aq) + e^- \longrightarrow In^{2+}(aq)$ $E^\circ(\text{cathode}) = -0.49\ V$

$U^{4+}(aq) + e^- \longrightarrow U^{3+}(aq)$ $E^\circ(\text{anode}) = -0.61\ V$

$E^\circ_{cell} = E^\circ(\text{cathode}) - E^\circ(\text{anode}) = -0.49\ V - (-0.61\ V) = +0.12\ V$

$$\ln K = \frac{nFE°}{RT} = \frac{nE°}{0.025\ 69\ \text{V}} \text{ at } 25°\text{C} \quad \ln K = \frac{1 \times (+0.12\ \text{V})}{0.025\ 69\ \text{V}} = 4.7 \quad K = 1 \times 10^2$$

17.47 Consider the half-reactions involved. Construct a cell reaction from them and calculate its standard potential. If positive, the oxidation will occur.

$S_2O_8^{2-}(aq) + 2e^- \longrightarrow 2SO_4^{2-}(aq) \quad E°(\text{cathode}) = +2.05\ \text{V}$

$Ag^{2+}(aq) + e^- \longrightarrow Ag^+(aq) \quad E°(\text{anode}) = +1.98\ \text{V}$

Reverse the anode reaction and multiply by 2.

$S_2O_8^{2-} + 2e^- \longrightarrow 2SO_4^{2-}$

$\underline{2[Ag^+ \longrightarrow Ag^{2+} + e^-]}$

$S_2O_8^{2-}(aq) + Ag^+(aq) \longrightarrow 2Ag^{2+}(aq) + 2SO_4^{2-}(aq) \quad E°_{\text{cell}} = 2.05\ \text{V} - (+1.98\ \text{V})$
$$= +0.07\ \text{V}$$

Yes, the oxidation will work.

$$\ln K = \frac{nFE°}{RT}, \text{ at } 25°\text{C} = \frac{nE°}{0.025\ 69\ \text{V}} = \frac{(2)(0.07\ \text{V})}{0.025\ 69\ \text{V}} = 5.\overline{45} \quad \text{and } K = \overline{2} \times 10^2 = 10^2$$

The Nernst Equation

17.49 (a) $Pb^{4+}(aq) + 2e^- \longrightarrow Pb^{2+}(aq) \quad E°(\text{cathode}) = +1.67\ \text{V}$

$\underline{Sn^{2+}(aq) \longrightarrow Sn^{4+}(aq) + 2e^- \quad E°(\text{anode}) = +0.15\ \text{V}}$

$Pb^{4+}(aq) + Sn^{2+}(aq) \longrightarrow Pb^{2+}(aq) + Sn^{4+}(aq) \quad E°_{\text{cell}} = 1.67\ \text{V} - (0.15\ \text{V})$
$$= +1.52\ \text{V}$$

Then, $E = E° - \left(\dfrac{0.0257\ \text{V}}{n}\right) \ln Q; \quad 1.33\ \text{V} = 1.52\ \text{V} - \left(\dfrac{0.0257\ \text{V}}{2}\right) \ln Q$

$\ln Q = \dfrac{1.52\ \text{V} - 1.33\ \text{V}}{0.0129\ \text{V}} = \dfrac{0.19\ \text{V}}{0.0129\ \text{V}} = 15 \quad Q = \overline{3} \times 10^6 = 10^6$

(b) $2[Cr_2O_7^{2-}(aq) + 14\ H^+(aq) + 6e^- \longrightarrow 2Cr^{3+}(aq) + 7\ H_2O(l)] \quad E°(\text{cathode})$
$$= 1.33\ \text{V}$$

$\underline{3[2\ H_2O(l) \longrightarrow O_2(g) + 4H^+(aq) + 4e^-] \quad E°(\text{anode}) = +1.23\ \text{V}}$

$2Cr_2O_7^{2-}(aq) + 16H^+(aq) \longrightarrow 4Cr^{3+}(aq) + 8H_2O(l) + 3O_2(g) \quad E°_{\text{cell}}$
$$= 0.10\ \text{V}$$

Then, $E = E° - \left(\dfrac{0.0257\ \text{V}}{n}\right) \ln Q; \quad 0.10\ \text{V} = +0.10\ \text{V} - \left(\dfrac{0.0257\ \text{V}}{12}\right) \ln Q$
$$\ln Q = 0.00 \quad Q = 1.0$$

17.51 (a) $Cu^{2+}(aq, 0.010\ \text{M}) + 2e^- \longrightarrow Cu(s) \quad (\text{cathode})$

$\underline{Cu^{2+}(aq, 0.0010\ \text{M}) + 2e^- \longrightarrow Cu(s) \quad (\text{anode})}$

$Cu^{2+}(aq, 0.010\ \text{M}) \longrightarrow Cu^{2+}(aq, 0.0010\ \text{M}), \ n = 2$

$$E_{cell}^{\circ} = E^{\circ}(\text{cathode}) - E^{\circ}(\text{anode}) = 0 \text{ V}$$

$$E_{cell} = E_{cell}^{\circ} - \left(\frac{RT}{nF}\right) \ln Q = -\left(\frac{0.0257 \text{ V}}{2}\right) \ln Q \text{ at } 25°C$$

$$E_{cell} = -\left(\frac{0.0257 \text{ V}}{2}\right) \ln \left(\frac{0.0010 \text{ M}}{0.010 \text{ M}}\right) = +0.030 \text{ V}$$

(b) at pH = 3.0, $[H^+] = 1 \times 10^{-3}$ M

at pH = 4.0, $[H^+] = 1 \times 10^{-4}$ M

Cell reaction is $H^+(\text{aq}, 1 \times 10^{-3} \text{ M}) \longrightarrow H^+(\text{aq}, 1 \times 10^{-4} \text{ M})$, $n = 1$

$$E_{cell}^{\circ} = 0 \text{ V} \quad E_{cell} = E_{cell}^{\circ} - \left(\frac{RT}{nF}\right) \ln Q = -\left(\frac{0.0257 \text{ V}}{1}\right) \ln \left(\frac{1 \times 10^{-4}}{1 \times 10^{-3}}\right)$$

$$= +6 \times 10^{-2} \text{ V}$$

17.53 In each case, $E_{cell}^{\circ} = E^{\circ}(\text{cathode}) - E^{\circ}(\text{anode})$. Recall that the values for E° at the electrodes refer to the electrode potential for the half-reaction written as a reduction reaction. In balancing the cell reaction, the half-reaction at the anode is reversed. However, this does not reverse the sign of electrode potential used at the anode, as the value always refers to the reduction potential.

(a) $2H^+(\text{aq}, 1.0 \text{ M}) + 2e^- \longrightarrow H_2(g, 1 \text{ atm}) \quad E^{\circ}(\text{cathode}) = 0.00 \text{ V}$

$\underline{H_2(g, 1 \text{ atm}) \longrightarrow 2H^+(\text{aq}, 0.0010 \text{ M}) + 2e^- \quad E^{\circ}(\text{anode}) = 0.00 \text{ V}}$

$2H^+(\text{aq}, 1.0 \text{ M}) + H_2(g, 1 \text{ atm}) \longrightarrow 2H^+(\text{aq}, 0.0010 \text{ M}) + H_2(g, 1 \text{ atm}) \quad E_{cell}^{\circ}$

$$= 0.00 \text{ V}$$

Then, $E = E^{\circ} - \left(\frac{0.0257 \text{ V}}{n}\right) \ln \left(\frac{[H^+, 0.0010 \text{ M}]^2 P_{H_2}}{[H^+, 1.0 \text{ M}]^2 P_{H_2}}\right)$

$E = 0.00 \text{ V} - \left(\frac{0.0257 \text{ V}}{2}\right) \ln \left(\frac{(0.0010 \text{ M})^2 \times 1 \text{ atm}}{(1.0 \text{ M})^2 \times 1 \text{ atm}}\right)$

$E = -0.0129 \text{ V} \ln(1.0 \times 10^{-3})^2 = +0.18 \text{ V}$

(b) $Ni^{2+}(\text{aq}) + 2e^- \longrightarrow Ni(s) \quad E^{\circ}(\text{cathode}) = -0.23 \text{ V}$

$\underline{Zn(s) \longrightarrow Zn^{2+}(\text{aq}) + 2e^- \quad E^{\circ}(\text{anode}) = -0.76 \text{ V}}$

$Ni^{2+}(\text{aq}) + Zn(s) \longrightarrow Ni(s) + Zn^{2+}(\text{aq}) \quad E_{cell}^{\circ} = +0.53 \text{ V}$

Then, $E = E^{\circ} - \left(\frac{0.0257 \text{ V}}{n}\right) \ln \left(\frac{[Zn^{2+}]}{[Ni^{2+}]}\right)$

$E = 0.53 \text{ V} - \left(\frac{0.0257 \text{ V}}{2}\right) \ln \left(\frac{0.10}{0.001}\right) = 0.53 \text{ V} - 0.06 \text{ V} = 0.47 \text{ V}$

(c) $2H^+(\text{aq}) + 2e^- \longrightarrow H_2(g) \quad E^{\circ}(\text{cathode}) = 0.00 \text{ V}$

$\underline{2Cl^-(\text{aq}) \longrightarrow Cl_2(g) + 2e^- \quad E^{\circ}(\text{anode}) = +1.36 \text{ V}}$

$2H^+(\text{aq}) + 2Cl^-(\text{aq}) \longrightarrow H_2(g) + Cl_2(g) \quad E_{cell}^{\circ} = -1.36 \text{ V}$

Then,

$$E = E^{\circ} - \left(\frac{0.0257 \text{ V}}{n}\right) \ln \left(\frac{P_{H_2} P_{Cl_2}}{[H^+]^2 [Cl^-]^2}\right)$$

$$E = -1.36 \text{ V} - \left(\frac{0.0257 \text{ V}}{2}\right) \ln\left(\frac{\left(\frac{450}{760}\right)\left(\frac{100}{760}\right)}{(0.010)^2(1.0)^2}\right)$$

$$E = -1.36 \text{ V} - (0.0129 \text{ V})\ln\left(\frac{(0.592)(0.132)}{(1.0 \times 10^{-4})(1)}\right) = -1.36 \text{ V} - 0.09 \text{ V}$$

$$= -1.45 \text{ V}$$

(d) Sn^{4+}(aq, 0.060 M) + 2e$^-$ $\longrightarrow$ Sn^{2+}(aq, 1.0 M) $E°$(cathode) = +0.15 V

$\underline{\qquad Sn(s) \longrightarrow Sn^{2+}(aq, 0.020 \text{ M}) + 2e^-   E°(anode) = -0.14 \text{ V} \qquad}$

Sn^{4+}(aq, 0.060 M) + Sn(s) $\longrightarrow$ Sn^{2+}(aq, 1.0 M) + Sn^{2+}(aq, 0.020 M)

$$E°_{cell} = 0.29 \text{ V}$$

$$E = E° - \left(\frac{0.0257 \text{ V}}{n}\right) \ln\left(\frac{[Sn^{2+}, 1.0 \text{ M}][Sn^{2+}, 0.020 \text{ M}]}{[Sn^{4+}, 0.060 \text{ M}]}\right)$$

$$E = 0.29 \text{ V} - \left(\frac{0.0257 \text{ V}}{2}\right) \ln\left(\frac{(1)(0.020)}{(0.060)}\right) = 0.30 \text{ V}$$

17.55   In each case, obtain the balanced equation for the cell reaction from the half-cell reactions at the electrodes by reversing the reduction equation for the half-reaction at the anode, multiplying the half-reaction equations by an appropriate factor to balance the number of electrons, and then adding the half-reactions. Calculate $E°_{cell} = E°$(cathode) − $E°$(anode). Then write the Nernst equation for the cell reaction and solve for the unknown.

(a) Hg_2Cl_2(s) + 2e$^-$ $\longrightarrow$ 2Hg(l) + 2Cl$^-$(aq) $E°$(cathode) = +0.27 V

$\underline{\qquad H_2(g) \longrightarrow 2H^+(aq) + 2e^-   E°(anode) = 0.00 \text{ V} \qquad}$

H_2(g) + Hg_2Cl_2(s) $\longrightarrow$ 2H$^+$(aq) + 2Hg(l) + 2Cl$^-$(aq) $E°_{cell}$ = +0.27 V

$$E = E° - \left(\frac{0.0257 \text{ V}}{n}\right) \ln\left(\frac{[H^+]^2[Cl^-]^2}{[H_2]}\right)$$

$$0.33 \text{ V} = 0.27 \text{ V} - \left(\frac{0.0257 \text{ V}}{2}\right) \ln\left(\frac{[H^+]^2(1)^2}{(1)}\right)$$

$$= 0.27 \text{ V} - (0.0129 \text{ V})\ln[H^+]^2$$

$$0.06 \text{ V} = -0.0257 \text{ V} \ln[H^+] = -0.0257 \text{ V} \times (2.303 \log [H^+])$$

$$pH = \frac{0.06 \text{ V}}{(2.303) \times (0.0257 \text{ V})} = 1$$

(b) 2[MnO_4^-(aq) + 8H$^+$(aq) + 5e$^-$ $\longrightarrow$ Mn^{2+}(aq) + 4H$_2$O(l)] $E°$(cathode)

$$= +1.51 \text{ V}$$

$\underline{\qquad 5[2Cl^-(aq) \longrightarrow Cl_2(g) + 2e^-]   E°(anode) = +1.36 \text{ V} \qquad}$

2MnO_4^-(aq) + 16H$^+$(aq) + 10Cl$^-$(aq) $\longrightarrow$ 5Cl$_2$(g) + 2Mn^{2+}(aq)

$$+ 8H_2O(l)   E°_{cell} = +0.15 \text{ V}$$

$$E = E° - \left(\frac{0.0257 \text{ V}}{n}\right) \ln \left(\frac{[\text{Cl}_2]^5[\text{Mn}^{2+}]^2}{[\text{MnO}_4]^2[\text{H}^+]^{16}[\text{Cl}^-]^{10}}\right)$$

$$-0.30 \text{ V} = +0.15 \text{ V} - \left(\frac{0.0257 \text{ V}}{10}\right) \ln \left(\frac{(1)^5 \times (0.10)^2}{(0.010)^2(1 \times 10^{-4})^{16}(\text{Cl}^-)^{10}}\right)$$

$$-0.45 \text{ V} = -(0.002\ 57 \text{ V})\log\left(\frac{1 \times 10^{-2}}{(1 \times 10^{-4}) \times (1 \times 10^{-64})[\text{Cl}^-]^{10}}\right)$$

$$= -0.002\ 57 \text{ V}\left[\ln(1 \times 10^{66}) + \ln\left(\frac{1}{[\text{Cl}^-]^{10}}\right)\right]$$

$$= -0.3906 \text{ V} + (0.002\ 57 \text{ V})\ln[\text{Cl}^-]^{10}$$

$$-0.0594 \text{ V} = 0.002\ 57 \text{ V} \ln[\text{Cl}^-]^{10}$$

$$= (0.0257 \text{ V})\ln[\text{Cl}^-]$$

$$\ln[\text{Cl}^-] = \frac{-0.0594 \text{ V}}{0.0257 \text{ V}} = -2.31$$

$$[\text{Cl}^-] = 9.9 \times 10^{-2} \text{ mol} \cdot \text{L}^{-1}$$

Practical Cells

17.57 A primary cell is the primary source of the electrical energy produced by its operation. A secondary cell is an energy storage device that stores electrical energy produced elsewhere and releases it upon operation (discharge). It is the secondary source of the electrical energy. Most primary cells produce electricity from chemicals that were sealed into them when they were made. They are not normally rechargeable. A secondary cell is one that must be charged from some other electrical supply before use. It is normally rechargeable.

17.59 See Table 17.2

(a) The electrolyte is KOH(aq)/HgO(s), which will have the consistency of a moist paste.

(b) The oxidizing agent is HgO(s). See the cathode reaction given in Table 17.2.

(c) $\text{HgO}(s) + \text{Zn}(s) \longrightarrow \text{Hg}(l) + \text{ZnO}(s)$

17.61 See Table 17.2.
The anode reaction is $\text{Zn}(s) \longrightarrow \text{Zn}^{2+}(aq) + 2e^-$; this reaction supplies the electrons to the external circuit. The cathode reaction is $\text{MnO}_2(s) + \text{H}_2\text{O}(l) + e^- \longrightarrow \text{MnO(OH)}_2(s) + \text{OH}^-(aq)$. The OH$^-$(aq) produced reacts with NH$_4^+$(aq) from the NH$_4$Cl(aq) present: $\text{NH}_4^+(aq) + \text{OH}^-(aq) \longrightarrow \text{H}_2\text{O}(l) + \text{NH}_3(g)$. The NH$_3$(g) produced complexes with the Zn^{2+}(aq) produced in the anode reaction: $\text{Zn}^{2+}(aq) + 4\text{NH}_3(g) \longrightarrow [\text{Zn(NH}_3)_4]^{2+}(aq)$. The overall reaction is complicated.

17.63 See Table 17.2. (a) KOH(aq) (b) In the charging process, the cell reaction is the reverse of what occurs in discharge. Therefore, at the anode, $2Ni(OH)_2(s) + 2OH^-(aq) \longrightarrow 2Ni(OH)_3 + 2e^-$.

Corrosion

17.65
$$Fe^{3+}(aq) + 3e^- \longrightarrow Fe(s) \quad E° = -0.04 \text{ V}$$
$$Cr^{3+}(aq) + 3e^- \longrightarrow Cr(s) \quad E° = -0.74 \text{ V}$$
$$Fe^{2+}(aq) + 2e^- \longrightarrow Fe(s) \quad E° = -0.44 \text{ V}$$
$$Cr^{2+}(aq) + 2e^- \longrightarrow Cr(s) \quad E° = -0.91 \text{ V}$$

Comparison of the reduction potentials shows that Cr is more easily oxidized than Fe, so the presence of Cr retards the rusting of Fe. At the position of the scratch, the gap is filled with oxidation products of Cr, thereby preventing contact of air and water with the iron.

17.67 (a) $Fe_2O_3 \cdot H_2O$ (b) H_2O and O_2 jointly oxidize iron. (c) Water is more highly conducting if it contains dissolved ions, so the rate of rusting is increased.

17.69 (a) aluminum or magnesium; both are below titanium in the electrochemical series.

(b) cost, availability, and toxicity of products in the environment

(c) $Cu^{2+} + 2e^- \longrightarrow Cu(s) \quad E° = +0.34 \text{ V}$
$Cu^+ + e^- \longrightarrow Cu(s) \quad E° = +0.52 \text{ V}$
$Fe^{3+} + 3e^- \longrightarrow Fe(s) \quad E° = -0.04 \text{ V}$
$Fe^{2+} + 2e^- \longrightarrow Fe(s) \quad E° = -0.44 \text{ V}$

Fe could act as the anode of an electrochemical cell if Cu^{2+} or Cu^+ are present; hence it could be oxidized at the point of contact. Water with dissolved ions acts as the electrolyte.

Electrolysis

17.71 See Figs. 17.22 and 17.23. (a) anode (same as galvanic cell) (b) positive (opposite of galvanic cell)

17.73 The strategy is to consider the possible competing cathode and anode reactions. At the cathode, choose the reduction reaction with the most positive (least negative) standard reduction potential ($E°$ value). At the anode, choose the oxidation reaction with the least positive (most negative) standard reduction potential ($E°$ value, as given in the table). Then calculate $E°_{cell} = E°(\text{cathode}) - E°(\text{anode})$. The negative of this value is the minimum potential that must be supplied.

(a) cathode: $Co^{2+}(aq) + 2e^- \longrightarrow Co(s)$ $E° = -0.28$ V

(rather than $2H_2O(l) + 2e^- \longrightarrow H_2(g) + 2OH^-(aq)$ $E° = -0.83$ V)

(b) anode: $2H_2O(l) \longrightarrow O_2(g) + 4H^+(aq) + 4e^-$ $E° = +1.23$ V

(the SO_4^{2-} ion will not oxidize)

(c) $E°_{cell} = E°(\text{cathode}) - E°(\text{anode}) = -0.28$ V $- (+0.81$ V$) = -1.09$ V

Therefore E (supplied) must be $> +1.09$ V (1.09 V is the minimum).

17.75 (a) $Cu^{2+}(aq) + 2e^- \longrightarrow Cu(s)$ reduction, cathode

(b) $Na^+(l) + e^- \longrightarrow Na(l)$ reduction, cathode

(c) $2Cl^-(l) \longrightarrow Cl_2(g) + 2e^-$ oxidation, anode

(d) $2H_2O(l) + 2e^- \longrightarrow H_2(g) + 2OH^-(aq)$ reduction, cathode

17.77 In each case, compare the reduction potential of the ion to the reduction potential of water ($E° = -0.42$ V) and choose the process with the least negative $E°$ value.

(a) $Mn^{2+}(aq) + 2e^- \longrightarrow Mn(s)$ $E° = -1.18$ V

(b) $Al^{3+}(aq) + 3e^- \longrightarrow Al(s)$ $E° = -1.66$ V

The reactions in (a) and (b) evolve hydrogen rather than yield a metallic deposit because water is reduced according to $2H_2O(l) + 2e^- \longrightarrow H_2(g) + 2OH^-(aq)$

($E° = -0.42$ V, at pH $= 7$)

(c) $Ni^{2+}(aq) + 2e^- \longrightarrow Ni(s)$ $E° = -0.23$ V

(d) $Au^{3+}(aq) + 3e^- \longrightarrow Au(s)$ $E° = +1.69$ V

In (c) and (d) the metal ion will be reduced.

17.79 moles of $e^- = \dfrac{\text{current} \times \text{time}}{F}$

$= \dfrac{18 \text{ A} \times 1.0 \text{ h} \times 3600 \text{ s} \cdot \text{h}^{-1}}{9.65 \times 10^4 \text{ C} \cdot \text{mol}^{-1}}$ ($1A = 1 \text{ C} \cdot \text{s}^{-1}$)

$= 0.67$ mol e^-

17.81 (a) $Cu^{2+} + 2e^- \longrightarrow Cu$

amount (moles) of $e^- = (5.12 \text{ g Cu}) \times \left(\dfrac{1 \text{ mol Cu}}{63.5 \text{ g Cu}}\right) \times \left(\dfrac{2 \text{ mol } e^-}{1 \text{ mol Cu}}\right)$

$= 0.161$ mol e^-

(b) $Al^{3+} + 3e^- \longrightarrow Al$

amount (moles) of $e^- = (200 \text{ g Al}) \times \left(\dfrac{1 \text{ mol Al}}{27.0 \text{ g Al}}\right) \times \left(\dfrac{3 \text{ mol } e^-}{1 \text{ mol Al}}\right)$

$= 22.2$ mol e^-

(c) $2H_2O \longrightarrow O_2 + 4H^+ + 4e^-$

amount (moles) of $e^- = (200 \text{ L } O_2) \times \left(\dfrac{1 \text{ mol } O_2}{22.4 \text{ L } O_2}\right) \times \left(\dfrac{4 \text{ mol } e^-}{1 \text{ mol } O_2}\right)$

$= 35.7 \text{ mol } e^-$

Note: 22.4 L is the volume of 1 mole of a perfect gas at 273 K and 1 atm.

17.83 (a) $Ag^+(aq) + e^- \longrightarrow Ag(s)$

time $= (4.4 \text{ mg Ag}) \times \left(\dfrac{10^{-3} \text{ g}}{1 \text{ mg}}\right) \times \left(\dfrac{1 \text{ mol Ag}}{108 \text{ g Ag}}\right) \times \left(\dfrac{1 \text{ mol } e^-}{1 \text{ mol Ag}}\right)$

$\times \left(\dfrac{9.65 \times 10^4 \text{ C}}{1 \text{ mol } e^-}\right) \times \left(\dfrac{1 \text{ A} \cdot \text{s}}{1 \text{ C}}\right) \times \left(\dfrac{1}{0.50 \text{ A}}\right) = 7.86 \text{ s}$

(b) $Cu^{2+}(aq) + 2e^- \longrightarrow Cu(s)$

mass Cu $= (7.86 \text{ s}) \times (0.5 \text{ A}) \times \left(\dfrac{1 \text{ C}}{1 \text{ A} \cdot \text{s}}\right) \times \left(\dfrac{1 \text{ mol } e^-}{9.65 \times 10^4 \text{ C}}\right)$

$\times \left(\dfrac{0.50 \text{ mol Cu}}{1 \text{ mol } e^-}\right) \times \left(\dfrac{63.5 \text{ g Cu}}{1 \text{ mol Cu}}\right) = 1.29 \text{ mg Cu}$

17.85 (a) $Cr(VI) + 6e^- \longrightarrow Cr(s)$

current $= \dfrac{\text{charge}}{\text{time}}$

$= \dfrac{4.0 \text{ g Cr} \times \left(\dfrac{1 \text{ mol Cr}}{52.00 \text{ g Cr}}\right) \times \left(\dfrac{6 \text{ mol } e^-}{1 \text{ mol Cr}}\right) \times \left(\dfrac{9.65 \times 10^4 \text{ C}}{1 \text{ mol } e^-}\right)}{24 \text{ h} \times 3600 \text{ s} \cdot \text{h}^{-1}}$

$= 0.52 \text{ C} \cdot \text{s}^{-1} = 0.52 \text{ A}$

(b) $Na^+ + e^- \longrightarrow Na(s)$

current $= \dfrac{4.0 \text{ g Na} \times \left(\dfrac{1 \text{ mol Na}}{22.99 \text{ g Na}}\right) \times \left(\dfrac{1 \text{ mol } e^-}{1 \text{ mol Na}}\right) \times \left(\dfrac{9.65 \times 10^4 \text{ C}}{1 \text{ mol } e^-}\right)}{24 \text{ h} \times 3600 \text{ s} \cdot \text{h}^{-1}}$

$= 0.19 \text{ C} \cdot \text{s}^{-1} = 0.19 \text{ A}$

17.87 $Ti^{n+}(aq) + ne^- \longrightarrow Ti(s)$; solve for n

moles of Ti $= (0.015 \text{ g Ti}) \times \left(\dfrac{1 \text{ mol Ti}}{47.9 \text{ g Ti}}\right) = 3.1 \times 10^{-4} \text{ mol Ti}$

total charge $= (500 \text{ s}) \times (120 \text{ mA}) \times \left(\dfrac{10^{-3} \text{ A}}{1 \text{ mA}}\right) \times \left(\dfrac{1 \text{ C} \cdot \text{s}^{-1}}{1 \text{ A}}\right) = 60 \text{ C}$

moles of $e^- = (60 \text{ C}) \times \left(\dfrac{1 \text{ mol } e^-}{96,500 \text{ C}}\right) = 6.2 \times 10^{-4} \text{ mol } e^-$

$$n = \frac{6.2 \times 10^{-4} \text{ mol e}^-}{3.1 \times 10^{-4} \text{ mol Ti}} = \frac{2 \text{ mol charge}}{1 \text{ mol Ti}}; \text{ therefore, Ti}^{2+}, \text{ oxidation number of } +2$$

17.89 $P_{O_2}V = n_{O_2}RT$, $P_{O_2} = P_{tot} - P_{H_2O} = (722 - 20)$ Torr $= 702$ Torr

$$n_{O_2} = \frac{(702 \text{ Torr}) \times \left(\dfrac{1 \text{ atm}}{760 \text{ Torr}}\right) \times (25.0 \text{ mL}) \times \left(\dfrac{10^{-3} \text{ L}}{1 \text{ mL}}\right)}{0.0821 \text{ L} \cdot \text{atm} \cdot \text{K}^{-1} \cdot \text{mol}^{-1} \times 295 \text{ K}} = 9.54 \times 10^{-4} \text{ mol}$$

$$\text{moles e}^- = 9.54 \times 10^{-4} \text{ mol O}_2 \times \frac{4 \text{ mol e}^-}{1 \text{ mol O}_2} = 3.81 \times 10^{-3} \text{ mol e}^-$$

$$\text{current} = (3.81 \times 10^{-3} \text{ mol e}^-) \times \left(\frac{9.65 \times 10^4 \text{ C}}{1 \text{ mol e}^-}\right) \times \left(\frac{1 \text{ A} \cdot \text{s}}{1 \text{ C}}\right) \times \left(\frac{1}{1800 \text{ s}}\right) = 0.20 \text{ A}$$

17.91 $Zn^{2+} + 2 \text{ e}^- \longrightarrow Zn$ (2 mol e$^-$/1 mol Zn)

$$\text{charge used} = (1.0 \text{ mA}) \times \left(\frac{10^{-3} \text{ A}}{1 \text{ mA}}\right) \times (31 \text{ d}) \times \left(\frac{24 \text{ h}}{1 \text{ d}}\right) \times \left(\frac{3600 \text{ s}}{1 \text{ h}}\right) = 2.\overline{68} \times 10^3 \text{ C}$$

$$\text{moles of e}^- \text{ used} = (2.\overline{68} \times 10^3 \text{ C}) \times \left(\frac{1 \text{ mol e}^-}{96,500 \text{ C}}\right) = 2.8 \times 10^{-2} \text{ mol e}^-$$

$$\text{moles of Zn} = (2.8 \times 10^{-2} \text{ mol e}^-) \times \left(\frac{1 \text{ mol Zn}}{2 \text{ mol e}^-}\right) = 1.4 \times 10^{-2} \text{ mol Zn}$$

$$\text{mass of Zn} = (1.4 \times 10^{-2} \text{ mol Zn}) \times \left(\frac{65.4 \text{ g Zn}}{1 \text{ mol Zn}}\right) = 0.92 \text{ g Zn}$$

SUPPLEMENTARY EXERCISES

17.93 (a) $3I^-(aq) \longrightarrow I_3^-(aq) + 2e^-$; electron loss; hence, oxidation

(b) $SeO_4^{2-}(aq) \longrightarrow SeO_3^{2-}(aq) + H_2O(l)$ (O's balanced)

$SeO_4^{2-}(aq) + 2H_2O(l) \longrightarrow SeO_3^{2-}(aq) + H_2O(l) + 2OH^-(aq)$ (H's balanced)

$SeO_4^{2-}(aq) + H_2O(l) + 2e^- \longrightarrow SeO_3^{2-}(aq) + 2OH^-(aq)$ (charge balanced)

electron gain; hence, reduction

17.95 (a) $O_2 + 4H^+ + 4e^- \longrightarrow 2H_2O$ $E°(\text{cathode}) = +1.23$ V

$Fe^{2+} + 2e^- \longrightarrow Fe$ $E°(\text{anode}) = -0.44$ V

Therefore, $Fe \longrightarrow Fe^{2+} + 2e^-$

(b) $Fe(s) \,|\, Fe^{2+}(aq) \,\|\, O_2(g) \,|\, H^+(aq), H_2O(l) \,|\, Pt(s)$

(c) $E°_{cell} = E°(\text{cathode}) - E°(\text{anode})$

$E°_{cell} = +1.23$ V $- (-0.44$ V$) = +1.67$ V

(d) Overall reaction: $2Fe(s) + O_2(g) + 4H^+(aq) \longrightarrow 2H_2O(l) + 2FeO(s)$

$$E_{cell} = E°_{cell} - \left(\frac{0.0257 \text{ V}}{n}\right) \ln \left(\frac{1}{[H^+]^4}\right)$$

$$pH = 6.00 = -\log[H^+]; \text{ therefore, } [H^+] = 1.0 \times 10^{-6} \text{ mol} \cdot L^{-1}$$

$$E_{cell} = 1.67 \text{ V} - \left(\frac{0.0257 \text{ V}}{4}\right) \ln\left(\frac{1}{(1.0 \times 10^{-6})^4}\right) = 1.67 \text{ V} - 0.36 \text{ V}$$

$$= +1.31 \text{ V}$$

17.97 For the standard calomel electrode, $E° = +0.27$ V. If this were set equal to 0, all other potentials would also be decreased by 0.27 V. (a) Therefore, the standard hydrogen electrode's standard reduction potential would be 0.00 V $-$ 0.27 V or -0.27 V. (b) The standard reduction potential for Cu^{2+}/Cu would be 0.34 V $-$ 0.27 V or $+0.07$ V.

17.99 $Au \longrightarrow Au^{3+} + 3e^-$ $E°(\text{anode}) = +1.40$ V
$MnO_4^- + 8H^+ + 5e^- \longrightarrow Mn^{2+} + 4H_2O$ $E°(\text{cathode}) = +1.51$ V
$E°_{cell} = E°(\text{cathode}) - E°(\text{anode}) = 1.51 \text{ V} - (+1.40 \text{ V}) = +0.11$ V
therefore, spontaneous; so gold will be oxidized
however, $Au \longrightarrow Au^{3+} + 3e^-$ $E°(\text{anode}) = +1.40$ V
$Cr_2O_7^{2-} + 14H^+ + 6e^- \longrightarrow 2Cr^{3+} + 7H_2O$ $E°(\text{cathode}) = 1.33$ V
$E°_{cell} = E°(\text{cathode}) - E°(\text{anode}) = 1.33 \text{ V} - (+1.40 \text{ V}) = -0.07$ V
therefore, not spontaneous; so gold will not be oxidized

17.101 In each case, determine the cathode and anode half-reactions corresponding to the reaction *as written*. Look up the standard reduction potentials for these half-reactions and then calculate $E°_{cell} = E°(\text{cathode}) - E°(\text{anode})$. If $E°_{cell}$ is negative, the reaction is spontaneous under standard conditions.

(a) $E°_{cell} = E°(\text{cathode}) - E°(\text{anode}) = +0.96 \text{ V} - (+0.79 \text{ V}) = +0.17$ V
therefore, spontaneous galvanic cell
$Hg(l) \,|\, Hg_2^{2+}(aq) \,\|\, NO_3^-(aq), H^+(aq) \,|\, NO(g) \,|\, Pt$
$\Delta G_r° = -nFE° = -(6)(9.65 \times 10^4 \text{ C} \cdot \text{mol}^{-1})(+0.17 \text{ J} \cdot \text{C}^{-1}) = -98 \text{ kJ} \cdot \text{mol}^{-1}$
(b) $E°_{cell} = E°(\text{cathode}) - E°(\text{anode}) = +0.92 \text{ V} - (+1.09 \text{ V}) = -0.17$ V
therefore, not spontaneous
(c) $E°_{cell} = E°(\text{cathode}) - E°(\text{anode}) = +1.33 \text{ V} - (+0.97 \text{ V}) = +0.36$ V
therefore, spontaneous galvanic cell
$Pt \,|\, Pu^{3+}(aq), Pu^{4+}(aq) \,\|\, Cr_2O_7^{2-}(aq), Cr^{3+}(aq), H^+(aq) \,|\, Pt$
$\Delta G_r° = -nFE° = -(6)(9.65 \times 10^4 \text{ C} \cdot \text{mol}^{-1})(0.36 \text{ J} \cdot \text{C}^{-1}) = -208 \text{ kJ} \cdot \text{mol}^{-1}$

17.103 In each case, break down the solution equilibrium reaction into two half-reactions and identify the cathode and anode half-reaction corresponding to the dissolution reaction. Then calculate $E°_{cell} = E°(\text{cathode}) - E°(\text{anode})$. From this, calculate K_{sp} and, finally, the solubility.

(a) $AgCl(s) + e^- \longrightarrow Ag(s) + Cl^-(aq)$ $E°(\text{cathode}) = +0.22$ V

$\underline{Ag(s) \longrightarrow Ag^+(aq) + e^- \quad E°(\text{anode}) = +0.80 \text{ V}}$

$AgCl(s) \longrightarrow Ag^+(aq) + Cl^-(aq) \quad E°_{\text{cell}} = -0.58$ V

$\ln K_{sp} = \dfrac{n(E°_{\text{cell}})}{0.0257 \text{ V}} = \dfrac{(1)(-0.58)}{0.0257} = -22.\overline{6}$

$K_{sp} = \overline{2} \times 10^{-10}$

Because the solubility of $AgCl = \sqrt{K_{sp}}$, the solubility of $AgCl = \overline{1} \times 10^{-5} \text{ mol} \cdot L^{-1} = 10^{-5} \text{ mol} \cdot L^{-1}$.

(b) $Hg_2Cl_2(s) + 2e^- \longrightarrow 2Hg(l) + 2Cl^-(aq)$ $E°(\text{cathode}) = +0.27$ V

$\underline{Hg^0(l) \longrightarrow Hg_2^{2+}(aq) + 2e^- \quad E°(\text{anode}) = +0.79 \text{ V}}$

$Hg_2Cl_2(s) \longrightarrow Hg_2^{2+}(aq) + 2Cl^-(aq) \quad E°_{\text{cell}} = -0.52$ V

$\ln K_{sp} = \dfrac{n(E°_{\text{cell}})}{0.0257 \text{ V}} = \dfrac{(2)(-0.52)}{0.0257} = -40.\overline{5}$

$K_{sp} = \overline{3} \times 10^{-18} = 10^{-18}$

For Hg_2Cl_2, $K_{sp} = \overline{3} \times 10^{-18} = (S)(2S)^2 = 4S^3$. $S = \overline{1} \times 10^{-6} \text{ mol} \cdot L^{-1}$
$= 10^{-6} \text{ mol} \cdot L^{-1}$.

(c) $PbSO_4(s) + 2e^- \longrightarrow Pb + SO_4^{2-}(aq)$ $E°(\text{cathode}) = -0.36$ V

$\underline{Pb \longrightarrow Pb^{2+}(aq) + 2e^- \quad E°(\text{anode}) = -0.13 \text{ V}}$

$PbSO_4(s) \longrightarrow Pb^{2+}(aq) + SO_4^{2-}(aq) \quad E°_{\text{cell}} = -0.23$ V

$\ln K_{sp} = \dfrac{n(E°_{\text{cell}})}{0.0257 \text{ V}} = \dfrac{(2)(-0.23)}{0.0257 \text{ V}} = -17.\overline{9}$

$K_{sp} = \overline{2} \times 10^{-8}$

Solving the K_{sp} expression for $PbSO_4$ yields the solubility of
$PbSO_4 = \sqrt{\overline{2} \times 10^{-8}} = \overline{1} \times 10^{-4} \text{ mol} \cdot L^{-1} = 10^{-4} \text{ mol}$.

17.105 $F_2(g) + 2e^- \longrightarrow 2F^-(aq)$ $E°(\text{cathode}) = +2.87$ V

$\underline{2HF(aq) \longrightarrow F_2(g) + 2H^+(aq) + 2e^- \quad E°(\text{anode}) = +3.03 \text{ V}}$

$2HF(aq) \longrightarrow 2H^+(aq) + 2F^-(aq) \quad E°_{\text{cell}} = -0.16$ V

For the above reaction, $K = \dfrac{[H^+]^2[F^-]^2}{[HF]^2}$ and $\ln K = \dfrac{nFE°}{RT}$ at 25°C $= \dfrac{nE°}{0.025\,69 \text{ V}}$

$= \dfrac{(2)(-0.16 \text{ V})}{0.025\,69 \text{ V}} = -12.\overline{46}$

$K = 4 \times 10^{-6}$

$K_a = \sqrt{K} = \sqrt{4 \times 10^{-6}} = 2 \times 10^{-3}$

17.107 $Ag^+(aq) + e^- \longrightarrow Ag$ $E°(\text{cathode}) = +0.80$ V

$\underline{Fe^{2+}(aq) \longrightarrow Fe^{3+}(aq) + e^- \quad E°(\text{anode}) = +0.77 \text{ V}}$

$Ag^+(aq) + Fe^{2+}(aq) \longrightarrow Fe^{3+}(aq) + Ag(s) \quad E°_{\text{cell}} = +0.03$ V

$$E_{cell} = E^{\circ}_{cell} - \left(\frac{0.0257 \text{ V}}{n}\right) \ln \left(\frac{[Fe^{3+}]}{[Ag^+][Fe^{2+}]}\right)$$

$$= 0.03 \text{ V} - (0.0257 \text{ V})\ln \left(\frac{1}{(0.010)(0.0010)}\right) = 0.03 \text{ V} - 0.30 \text{ V} = -0.27 \text{ V}$$

Comment: The cell changes from spontaneous to nonspontaneous as a function of concentration.

17.109 The wording of this exercise suggests that K^+ ions participate in an electrolyte concentration cell reaction. Therefore, $E^{\circ}_{cell} = 0.00$ V, because the two half cells would be identical under standard conditions.
Then,

$$E = E^{\circ} - \left(\frac{0.0257 \text{ V}}{n}\right) \ln \left(\frac{[K^+_{out}]}{[K^+_{in}]}\right) = 0.00 \text{ V} - \left(\frac{0.0257 \text{ V}}{1}\right) \ln \left(\frac{1}{30}\right) = +0.09 \text{ V}$$

$$\text{and} \quad E = 0.00 \text{ V} - \left(\frac{0.0257 \text{ V}}{1}\right) \ln \left(\frac{1}{20}\right) = +0.08 \text{ V}$$

The range of potentials is 0.08 V to 0.09 V.

17.111 $Pb^{2+}(aq) + 2e^- \longrightarrow Pb(s) \quad E^{\circ}(\text{cathode}) = -0.13 \text{ V}$
$\underline{Zn(s) \longrightarrow Zn^{2+}(aq) + 2e^- \quad E^{\circ}(\text{anode}) = -0.76 \text{ V}}$
$Pb^{2+}(aq) + Zn(s) \longrightarrow Zn^{2+}(aq) + Pb(s) \quad E^{\circ}_{cell} = +0.63 \text{ V}$

$$E_{cell} = E^{\circ}_{cell} - \left(\frac{0.0257 \text{ V}}{n}\right) \ln \left(\frac{[Zn^{2+}]}{[Pb^{2+}]}\right)$$

$$0.66 \text{ V} = 0.63 \text{ V} - \left(\frac{0.0257 \text{ V}}{2}\right) \ln \left(\frac{[Zn^{2+}]}{0.10}\right)$$

$$-2.33 = \ln \left(\frac{[Zn^{2+}]}{0.10}\right)$$

$$[Zn^{2+}] = 9.8 \times 10^{-3} \text{ mol} \cdot L^{-1}$$

17.113 In this reaction, $O_2(0) \longrightarrow 2O(-2)$. Thus, there is a transfer of $4e^-$ for each O_2, or $6 \times 4e^- = 24e^-$ for each glucose molecule oxidized. For the reaction: $\Delta G^{\circ}_r = (6)(-394.36) + (6)(-237.13) - (-910) = -2879 \text{ kJ} \cdot \text{mol}^{-1}$

Then, current $= \left(\frac{1.0 \times 10^7 \text{ J}}{1 \text{ day}}\right) \times \left(\frac{1 \text{ mol glucose}}{2.88 \times 10^6 \text{ J}}\right) \times \left(\frac{24 \text{ mol e}^-}{1 \text{ mol glucose}}\right)$

$$\times \left(\frac{9.65 \times 10^4 \text{ C}}{1 \text{ mol e}^-}\right) \times \left(\frac{1 \text{ day}}{86,400 \text{ s}}\right) = 93 \text{ C} \cdot \text{s}^{-1} \, (= 93 \text{ A})$$

17.115 $2Cl^- \longrightarrow Cl_2(g) + 2e^-$ At STP, 1.00 mol of Cl_2 occupies 22.4 L.

current $= (15.0 \text{ L Cl}_2) \times \left(\frac{1 \text{ mol Cl}_2}{22.4 \text{ L Cl}_2}\right) \times \left(\frac{2 \text{ mol e}^-}{1 \text{ mol Cl}_2}\right) \times \left(\frac{9.65 \times 10^4 \text{ C}}{1 \text{ mol e}^-}\right)$

$$\times \left(\frac{1 \text{ A} \cdot \text{s}}{1 \text{ C}}\right) \times \left(\frac{1}{3600 \text{ s}}\right) = 35.9 \text{ A}$$

17.117 $Hf^{n+} + ne^- \longrightarrow Hf(s)$; solve for n.

charge consumed = $15.0 \text{ C} \cdot \text{s}^{-1} \times 2.00 \text{ h} \times 3600 \text{ s} \cdot \text{h}^{-1} = 1.08 \times 10^5 \text{ C}$

moles of charge consumed = $(1.08 \times 10^5 \text{ C}) \times \left(\dfrac{1 \text{ mol e}^-}{9.65 \times 10^4 \text{ C}} \right) = 1.12 \text{ mol e}^-$

moles of Hf plated = $(50.0 \text{ g Hf}) \times \left(\dfrac{1 \text{ mol Hf}}{178 \text{ g Hf}} \right) = 0.281 \text{ mol Hf}$

Then, $n = \dfrac{1.12 \text{ mol e}^-}{0.281 \text{ mol Hf}} = 4.0 \text{ mol e}^-/\text{mol Hf}$

Therefore, the oxidation number is 4, that is, Hf^{4+}.

17.119 First calculate the volume of Ag(s) to be plated on the surface of the copper metal; then determine its mass and the number of moles.

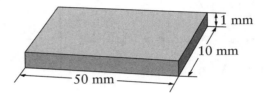

Calculate the surface area: $2(50 \text{ mm} \times 10 \text{ mm}) + 2(10 \text{ mm} \times 1 \text{ mm})$
$+ 2(50 \text{ mm} \times 1 \text{ mm}) = 2(500 \text{ mm}^2) + 2(10 \text{ mm}^2) + 2(50 \text{ mm}^2) = 1120 \text{ mm}^2$.

Then, $1120 \text{ mm}^2 \times 1 \text{ } \mu m \times \left(\dfrac{10^{-3} \text{ mm}}{1 \text{ } \mu m} \right) = 1.120 \text{ mm}^3 = $ volume of Ag(s)

For $Ag^+ + e^- \longrightarrow Ag$, we require $(1 \text{ mol e}^-/1 \text{ mol Ag})$.

mass of Ag = volume $\times$ density = $(1.120 \text{ mm}^3) \times \left(\dfrac{10^{-3} \text{ m}}{1 \text{ mm}} \right)^3$

$\times \left(\dfrac{1 \text{ cm}}{10^{-2} \text{ m}} \right)^3 \times \left(\dfrac{10.5 \text{ g}}{1 \text{ cm}^3} \right) = 1.17\overline{6} \text{ g}$

moles of e^- = $1.17\overline{6} \times 10^{-2} \text{ g} \times \left(\dfrac{1 \text{ mol Ag}}{108 \text{ g Ag}} \right) \times \left(\dfrac{1 \text{ mol e}^-}{1 \text{ mol Ag}} \right) = 1.09 \times 10^{-4} \text{ mol e}^-$

charge required = $(1.09 \times 10^{-4} \text{ mol e}^-) \times \left(\dfrac{9.65 \times 10^4 \text{ C}}{1 \text{ mol e}^-} \right) = 10.5 \text{ C}$

charge = current $\times$ time

time = $\dfrac{\text{charge}}{\text{current}} = \dfrac{10.5 \text{ C}}{0.100 \text{ C} \cdot \text{s}^{-1}} = 105 \text{ s}$

17.121 $MCl_3 \longrightarrow M^{3+} + 3Cl^- \qquad M^{3+} + 3e^- \longrightarrow M(s)$

First determine the number of moles of electrons consumed; the number of moles of M^{3+} reduced is then three times this number.

charge used = $(6.63 \text{ h}) \times \left(\dfrac{3600 \text{ s}}{1 \text{ h}} \right) \times \left(\dfrac{0.70 \text{ C}}{1 \text{ s}} \right) = 1.6\overline{7} \times 10^4 \text{ C}$

number of moles of $e^- = (1.6\overline{7} \times 10^4 \text{ C}) \times \left(\dfrac{1 \text{ mol } e^-}{9.65 \times 10^4 \text{ C}}\right) = 0.17\overline{3} \text{ mol } e^-$

number of moles of M^{3+} (and M) $= 0.17\overline{3} \text{ mol } e^- \times \dfrac{1 \text{ mol } M^{3+}}{3 \text{ mol } e^-} = 0.057\overline{7} \text{ mol } M^{3+}$

molar mass $M = \dfrac{3.00 \text{ g}}{0.057\overline{7} \text{ mol}} = 52 \text{ g} \cdot \text{mol}^{-1}$ (Cr)

CHALLENGING EXERCISES

17.123 (a) $Cu^{2+} + 2e^- \longrightarrow Cu \quad E^\circ = +0.34 \text{ V}$

$Cu^{2+} + e^- \longrightarrow Cu^+ \quad E^\circ = +0.15 \text{ V}$

Here we do not combine the half-reactions to obtain an overall cell reaction; instead, we combine them to obtain a new half-reaction. Therefore the procedure $E^\circ = E^\circ(\text{cathode}) - E^\circ(\text{anode})$ **cannot** be used here to obtain $E^\circ_{Cu^+/Cu}$. Reduction potentials are not extensive physical properties and therefore cannot be directly added or subtracted to obtain a third reduction potential. However, the related ΔG°_r value for the half-reactions is an extensive property, so we first calculate $\Delta G^\circ_{r,Cu^+/Cu}$ and from it obtain $E^\circ_{Cu^+/Cu^\circ}$. Then,

$Cu^{2+} + 2e^- \longrightarrow Cu$

$Cu^+ \longrightarrow Cu^{2+} + e^-$

$\overline{Cu^+ + e^- \longrightarrow Cu}$ (new half-reaction)

$Cu^{2+}/Cu^+ \quad \Delta G^\circ_r = -nFE^\circ = -(2)(9.65 \times 10^4 \text{ C} \cdot \text{mol}^{-1})(+0.34 \text{ J} \cdot \text{C}^{-1})$
$= -65.\overline{6} \text{ kJ} \cdot \text{mol}^{-1}$

$Cu^+/Cu \quad \Delta G^\circ_r = -nFE^\circ = -(1)(9.65 \times 10^4 \text{ C} \cdot \text{mol}^{-1})(-0.15 \text{ J} \cdot \text{C}^{-1})$
$= +14.\overline{5} \text{ kJ} \cdot \text{mol}^{-1}$

$\Delta G^\circ_{r,Cu^+/Cu} = \Delta G^\circ_{r,Cu^{2+}/Cu} + \Delta G^\circ_{r,Cu^{2+}/Cu^+} = -65.\overline{6} \text{ kJ} + 14.\overline{5} \text{ kJ}$
$= -51.\overline{1} \text{ kJ} \cdot \text{mol}^{-1}$

Then, $E^\circ_{Cu^+/Cu} = \dfrac{\Delta G^\circ_{r,Cu^+/Cu}}{-nF} = \dfrac{-51.\overline{1} \times 10^3 \text{ J}}{-(1)(9.65 \times 10^4 \text{ C} \cdot \text{mol}^{-1})} = +0.52 \text{ V}$

(b) $Fe^{3+} + e^- \longrightarrow Fe^{2+} \quad E^\circ = +0.77 \text{ V}$

$\dfrac{Fe^{2+} + 2e^- \longrightarrow Fe \quad E^\circ = -0.44 \text{ V}}{Fe^{3+} + 3e^- \longrightarrow Fe}$

$Fe^{3+} | Fe^{2+} \quad \Delta G^\circ_r = -nFE^\circ = -(1e^-)(9.65 \times 10^4 \text{ C} \cdot \text{mol}^{-1})(+0.77 \text{ J} \cdot \text{C}^{-1})$
$= -74.\overline{3} \text{ kJ} \cdot \text{mol}^{-1}$

$Fe^{2+} | Fe \quad \Delta G^\circ_r = -nFE^\circ = -(2e^-)(9.65 \times 10^4 \text{ C} \cdot \text{mol}^{-1})(-0.44 \text{ J} \cdot \text{C}^{-1})$
$= +84.\overline{9} \text{ kJ} \cdot \text{mol}^{-1}$

$\Delta G^\circ_{r,Fe^{3+}|Fe} = \Delta G^\circ_{r,Fe^{3+}|Fe^{2+}} + \Delta G^\circ_{r,Fe^{2+}|Fe} = -74.\overline{3} \text{ kJ} + 84.\overline{9} \text{ kJ} = 10.\overline{6} \text{ kJ} \cdot \text{mol}^{-1}$

Then, $E^{\circ}_{Fe^{3+}|Fe} = \dfrac{\Delta G^{\circ}_{r,Fe^{3+}|Fe}}{-nF} = \dfrac{10.\overline{6} \times 10^3 \text{ J}}{-(3)(9.65 \times 10^4 \text{ C} \cdot \text{mol}^{-1})} = -0.037 \text{ V}$

17.125 Set up a cell in which one electrode is the silver-silver chloride electrode and the other is the hydrogen electrode. The E of this cell will be sensitive to $[H^+]$ and hence can be used to obtain pH.

$2H^+(aq) + 2e^- \longrightarrow H_2(g) \quad E^{\circ}(\text{cathode}) = 0.00 \text{ V}$

$\underline{2AgCl(s) + 2e^- \longrightarrow 2Ag(s) + 2Cl^-(aq) \quad E^{\circ}(\text{anode}) = -0.22 \text{ V}}$

$2AgCl(s) + H_2(g, 1 \text{ atm}) \longrightarrow 2Ag(s) + 2Cl^-(aq) + 2H^+(aq) \quad E^{\circ}_{cell} = 0.22 \text{ V}$

If $[Cl^-] = 1.0 \text{ mol} \cdot L^{-1}$.

(a) $E = E^{\circ} - \left(\dfrac{0.0257 \text{ V}}{2}\right) \ln([H^+]^2) = 0.22 \text{ V} - (0.0257) \ln[H^+]$

$\ln[H^+] = 2.303 \log[H^+] = -2.303(\text{pH})$, so $E = 0.22 \text{ V} + 0.0592 \text{ V} \times \text{pH}$, and

$\text{pH} = \dfrac{E - 0.22 \text{ V}}{0.0592 \text{ V}}$

So, by measuring E of this cell, pH can be obtained.

(b) $\text{pOH} = 14.00 - \text{pH}$

17.127 charge consumed = $4.00 \text{ A} \times 1800 \text{ s} = 7.20 \times 10^3 \text{ C}$

moles of $e^- = (7.20 \times 10^3 \text{ C}) \times \left(\dfrac{1 \text{ mol } e^-}{9.65 \times 10^4 \text{ C}}\right) = 7.46 \times 10^{-2} \text{ mol } e^-$

The reaction at the platinum anode is

$$2H_2O \longrightarrow O_2 + 4H^+ + 4e^-$$

and the ratio of $H^+(H_3O^+)$ to e^- is

$$\dfrac{1 \text{ mol } H_3O^+}{1 \text{ mol } e^-}$$

Therefore, amount (moles) of $H_3O^+ = 7.46 \times 10^{-2} \text{ mol } H_3O^+$

(b) $[H_3O^+] = \dfrac{7.46 \times 10^{-2} \text{ mol } H_3O^+}{0.200 \text{ L}} = 0.373 \text{ mol} \cdot L^{-1}$

$\text{pH} = -\log(0.373) = 0.428$ (very acidic!)

CHAPTER 18
KINETICS: THE RATES
OF REACTIONS

EXERCISES

Reaction Rates

18.1 (a) $\text{rate}(N_2) = \text{rate}(H_2) \times \left(\dfrac{1 \text{ mol } N_2}{3 \text{ mol } H_2}\right) = \dfrac{1}{3} \times \text{rate}(H_2)$

(b) $\text{rate }(NH_3) = \text{rate}(H_2) \times \left(\dfrac{2 \text{ mol } NH_3}{3 \text{ mol } H_2}\right) = \dfrac{2}{3} \times \text{rate}(H_2)$

(c) $\text{rate}(NH_3) = \text{rate}(N_2) \times \left(\dfrac{2 \text{ mol } NH_3}{1 \text{ mol } N_2}\right) = 2 \times \text{rate}(N_2)$

18.3 (a) $\text{rate of decomposition of ozone} = \left(1.5 \times 10^{-3}\,\dfrac{\text{mol } O_2}{L \cdot s}\right) \times \left(\dfrac{2 \text{ mol } O_3}{3 \text{ mol } O_2}\right)$

$\qquad\qquad = 1.0 \times 10^{-3}\,(\text{mol } O_3) \cdot L^{-1} \cdot s^{-1}$

(b) $\text{rate of formation of dichromate ions} = \left(0.14\,\dfrac{\text{mol } Cr_2O_7^{2-}}{L \cdot s}\right)$

$\qquad\qquad \times \left(\dfrac{2 \text{ mol } CrO_4^{2-}}{1 \text{ mol } Cr_2O_7^{2-}}\right) = 0.28\,(\text{mol } Cr_2O_4^{2-}) \cdot L^{-1} \cdot s^{-1}$

Rate Laws

18.5 The concentrations of NO_2 and O_2 at time t, $[NO_2]_t$ and $[O_2]_t$, are related to the amount of N_2O_5 decomposed by the stoichiometry of the reaction; that is,

$$[NO_2]_t \left(\dfrac{\text{mol } NO_2}{L}\right) = ([N_2O_5]_{t=0} - [N_2O_5]_t) \times \left(\dfrac{\text{mol } N_2O_5}{L}\right) \times \left(\dfrac{4 \text{ mol } NO_2}{2 \text{ mol } N_2O_5}\right) \text{ and}$$

$$[O_2]_t \left(\dfrac{\text{mol } O_2}{L}\right) = ([N_2O_5]_{t=0} - [N_2O_5]_t) \times \left(\dfrac{\text{mol } N_2O_5}{L}\right) \times \left(\dfrac{1 \text{ mol } O_2}{2 \text{ mol } N_2O_5}\right)$$

Thus, for example, after 1.11 h,

$$[NO_2]\left(\dfrac{\text{mol } NO_2}{L}\right) = (2.15 - 1.88) \times 10^{-3} \times 2\left(\dfrac{\text{mol } NO_2}{L}\right)$$

$$= 0.54 \times 10^{-4}\,(\text{mol } NO_2) \cdot L^{-1}$$

All other values in the table below are obtained in a similar manner. The concentrations are plotted as a function of time in the following figure. The rates at a time t can be found by determining the slope of the concentration versus time curve at time t. Methods of determining the slope are discussed in Section 18.2 and in more detail in Appendix 1E. Here we adopt the two-point method described in the appendix because it is likely to be more accurate than a strictly graphical method based on drawing tangents to the curve. The tangent method would work well if a very accurate curve with many data points could be constructed.

(b) Time, h	$[N_2O_5]^a$	$[NO_2]^a$	$[O_2]^a$	Rate, $\dfrac{\Delta[N_2O_5]}{\Delta t}^b$
0	2.15	0.00	0.00	2.6
1.11	1.88	0.54	0.14	2.3
2.22	1.64	1.02	0.26	2.0
3.33	1.43	1.44	0.36	1.8
4.44	1.25	1.80	0.45	1.6

a. Units $= 10^{-3}$ mol $\cdot$ L^{-1}.   b. Units $= 10^{-4}$ mol $\cdot$ L^{-1} $\cdot$ h^{-1}.

(a, c)

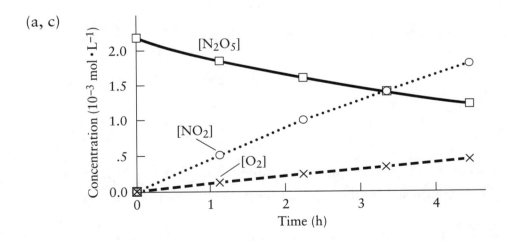

The rate at time t is found from the two closest values of $[N_2O_5]$ at time t_2 and t_1, such that t lies between t_2 and t_1; that is,

$$\text{Rate at } t = \frac{\Delta[N_2O_5]_t}{\Delta t} = \frac{[N_2O_5]_{t_1} - [N_2O_5]_{t_2}}{t_2 - t_1}$$

Thus, for example, the rate at 1.11 h $= \dfrac{(2.15 - 1.64) \times 10^{-3} \text{ mol} \cdot \text{L}^{-1}}{(2.22 - 0) \text{ h}}$

$$= 2.3 \times 10^{-4} \text{ mol} \cdot \text{L}^{-1} \cdot \text{h}^{-1}$$

In the table above, the rates at times 1.11 h, 2.22 h, and 3.33 h are determined in this manner. The rates at times 0 h and 4.44 h are estimated by extrapolation.

18.7 (a) rate $= k[\text{X}]^2[\text{Y}]^{1/2}$

(b) rate $= k[\text{A}][\text{B}][\text{C}]^x$

sum of orders $= 1 + 1 + x = \frac{3}{2}$, thus $x = -\frac{1}{2}$. The rate law is then, rate $= k[\text{A}][\text{B}][\text{C}]^{-1/2}$.

18.9 For A $\longrightarrow$ products, rate $= (\text{mol A}) \cdot \text{L}^{-1} \cdot \text{s}^{-1}$.

(a) rate $(\text{mol A} \cdot \text{L}^{-1} \cdot \text{s}^{-1}) = k_0[\text{A}]^0 = k_0$, so units of k_0 are $(\text{mol A}) \cdot \text{L}^{-1} \cdot \text{s}^{-1}$ (same as the units for the rate in this case)

(b) rate $(\text{mol A} \cdot \text{L}^{-1} \cdot \text{s}^{-1}) = k_1[\text{A}]$, so units of k_1 are $\dfrac{(\text{mol A}) \cdot \text{L}^{-1} \cdot \text{s}^{-1}}{(\text{mol A}) \cdot \text{L}^{-1}} = \text{s}^{-1}$

(c) rate $(\text{mol A} \cdot \text{L}^{-1} \cdot \text{s}^{-1}) = k_2[\text{A}]^2$, so units of k_2 are $\dfrac{(\text{mol A}) \cdot \text{L}^{-1} \cdot \text{s}^{-1}}{[(\text{mol A}) \cdot \text{L}^{-1}]^2} =$

$$\text{L} \cdot (\text{mol A})^{-1} \cdot \text{s}^{-1}$$

18.11 In general, we can write

$$\text{rate } [\text{mol} \cdot \text{L}^{-1} \cdot (\text{unit of time})^{-1}] = k \, (\text{mol} \cdot \text{L}^{-1})^n, \quad \text{or}$$

$$k = \frac{[\text{mol} \cdot \text{L}^{-1} \cdot (\text{unit of time})^{-1}]}{(\text{mol} \cdot \text{L}^{-1})^n} = (\text{L} \cdot \text{mol}^{-1})^{n-1} \cdot (\text{unit of time})^{-1}$$

where $n = $ order. In this case, $n - 1 = 2$, so $n = 3$.

18.13 From the units of the rate constant, k, and the solution of Exercise 18.11, it follows that the reaction is first order, thus rate $= k[\text{N}_2\text{O}_5]$.

$$[\text{N}_2\text{O}_5] = \left(\frac{2.0 \text{ g N}_2\text{O}_5}{1.0 \text{ L}}\right) \times \left(\frac{1 \text{ mol N}_2\text{O}_5}{108.02 \text{ g N}_2\text{O}_5}\right) = 0.018\overline{5} \text{ mol} \cdot \text{L}^{-1}$$

rate $= 5.2 \times 10^{-3} \text{ s}^{-1} \times 0.018\overline{5} \text{ mol} \cdot \text{L}^{-1} = 9.6 \times 10^{-5} \, (\text{mol N}_2\text{O}_5) \cdot \text{L}^{-1} \cdot \text{s}^{-1}$

18.15 From the units of the rate constant and the solution to Exercise 18.11, it follows that the reaction is second order, thus

$$\text{rate} = k[H_2][I_2] = 0.063 \ \text{L} \cdot \text{mol}^{-1} \cdot \text{s}^{-1} \times \left(\frac{0.15 \ \text{g H}_2}{0.500 \ \text{L}} \right) \times \left(\frac{1 \ \text{mol H}_2}{2.016 \ \text{g H}_2} \right)$$

$$\times \left(\frac{0.32 \ \text{g I}_2}{0.500 \ \text{L}} \right) \times \left(\frac{1 \ \text{mol I}_2}{253.8 \ \text{g I}_2} \right) = 2.4 \times 10^{-5} \ \text{mol} \cdot \text{L}^{-1} \cdot \text{s}^{-1}$$

(b) $\text{rate(new)} = k \times 2 \times [H_2]_{\text{initial}}[I_2] = 2 \times \text{rate(initial)}$, so, by a factor of 2.

18.17 (a) first order in H_2; first order in T_2; second order overall

(b) first order in SO_2; zero order in O_2; negative one-half order in SO_3; one-half order overall

(c) second order in A; zero order in B; first order in C; third order overall

18.19 Because the rate increased in direct proportion to the concentrations of both reactants, the rate is first order in both reactants. $\text{rate} = k[\text{CH}_3\text{Br}][\text{OH}^-]$

18.21 (a) $\text{rate} = k[A]^a[B]^b$, where the orders a and b are to be determined. When the concentration of A was decreased by a factor of 3, the rate decreased by a factor of 9; thus $(\frac{1}{3})^a = (\frac{1}{9})$, giving $a = 2$, and the reaction is second order in A. When the concentration of B was decreased by a factor of 3, the rate decreased by a factor of 3; thus $(\frac{1}{3})^b = (\frac{1}{3})$, giving $b = 1$, and the reaction is first order in B. The overall order $= 2 + 1 = 3$.

(b) $\text{rate} = k[A]^2[B]$

(c) $k = \dfrac{\text{rate}}{[A]^2[B]} = \left(\dfrac{12.6 \ \text{mol}}{\text{L} \cdot \text{s}} \right) \times \left(\dfrac{\text{L}}{0.60 \ \text{mol}} \right)^2 \times \left(\dfrac{\text{L}}{0.30 \ \text{mol}} \right)$

$= 1.1\overline{7} \times 10^2 \ \text{L}^2 \cdot \text{mol}^{-2} \cdot \text{s}^{-1} = 1.2 \times 10^2 \ \text{L}^2 \cdot \text{mol}^{-2} \cdot \text{s}^{-1}$

The data from any of the experiments 1, 2, or 3 could have been used.

(d) $\text{rate} = \left(\dfrac{1.1\overline{7} \times 10^2 \ \text{L}^2}{\text{mol}^2 \cdot \text{s}} \right) \times \left(\dfrac{0.17 \ \text{mol}}{\text{L}} \right)^2 \times \left(\dfrac{0.25 \ \text{mol}}{\text{L}} \right)$

$= 0.85 \ \text{mol} \cdot \text{L}^{-1} \cdot \text{s}^{-1}$

18.23 When the concentration of ICl was doubled, the rate doubled (experiments 1 and 2). Hence, the reaction is first order in ICl. When the concentration of H_2 was tripled, the rate tripled (experiments 2 and 3); Hence, the reaction is first order in H_2.

(a) $\text{rate} = k[\text{ICl}][H_2]$

(b) $k = \left(\dfrac{22 \times 10^{-7} \ \text{mol}}{\text{L} \cdot \text{s}} \right) \times \left(\dfrac{\text{L}}{3.0 \times 10^{-3} \ \text{mol}} \right) \times \left(\dfrac{\text{L}}{4.5 \times 10^{-3} \ \text{mol}} \right)$

$= 0.16\overline{3} \ \text{L} \cdot \text{mol}^{-1} \cdot \text{s}^{-1} = 0.16 \ \text{L} \cdot \text{mol}^{-1} \cdot \text{s}^{-1}$

(c) $\text{rate} = \left(\dfrac{0.16\overline{3}\ \text{L}}{\text{mol} \cdot \text{s}}\right) \times \left(\dfrac{4.7 \times 10^{-3}\ \text{mol}}{\text{L}}\right) \times \left(\dfrac{2.7 \times 10^{-3}\ \text{mol}}{\text{L}}\right)$

$= 2.1 \times 10^{-6}\ \text{mol} \cdot \text{L}^{-1} \cdot \text{s}^{-1}$

18.25 (a) Doubling the concentration of A (experiments 1 and 2) doubled the rate; hence, the reaction is first order in A. Increasing the concentration of B by the ratio 3.02/1.25 (experiments 2 and 3) increased the rate by $(3.02/1.25)^2$; hence, the reaction is second order in B. Tripling the concentration of C (experiment 3 and 4) increased the rate by $3^2 = 9$; hence, the reaction is second order in C. Therefore, $\text{rate} = k[\text{A}][\text{B}]^2[\text{C}]^2$.

(b) overall order $= 5$

(c) $k = \dfrac{\text{rate}}{[\text{A}][\text{B}]^2[\text{C}]^2}$

Using the data from experiment 4, we get

$k = \left(\dfrac{0.457\ \text{mol}}{\text{L} \cdot \text{s}}\right) \times \left(\dfrac{\text{L}}{1.25 \times 10^{-3}\ \text{mol}}\right) \times \left(\dfrac{\text{L}}{3.02 \times 10^{-3}\ \text{mol}}\right)^2$

$\times \left(\dfrac{\text{L}}{3.75 \times 10^{-3}\ \text{mol}}\right)^2 = 2.85 \times 10^{12}\ \text{L}^4 \cdot \text{mol}^{-4} \cdot \text{s}^{-1}$

From experiment 3, we get

$k = \left(\dfrac{5.08 \times 10^{-2}\ \text{mol}}{\text{L} \cdot \text{s}}\right) \times \left(\dfrac{\text{L}}{1.25 \times 10^{-3}\ \text{mol}}\right) \times \left(\dfrac{\text{L}}{3.02 \times 10^{-3}\ \text{mol}}\right)^2$

$\times \left(\dfrac{\text{L}}{1.25 \times 10^{-3}\ \text{mol}}\right)^2 = 2.85 \times 10^{12}\ \text{L}^4 \cdot \text{mol}^{-4} \cdot \text{s}^{-1}$ (Checks!)

(d) $\text{rate} = \left(\dfrac{2.85 \times 10^{12}\ \text{L}^4}{\text{mol}^4 \cdot \text{s}}\right) \times \left(\dfrac{3.01 \times 10^{-3}\ \text{mol}}{\text{L}}\right) \times \left(\dfrac{1.00 \times 10^{-3}\ \text{mol}}{\text{L}}\right)^2$

$\times \left(\dfrac{1.15 \times 10^{-3}\ \text{mol}}{\text{L}}\right)^2 = 1.13 \times 10^{-2}\ \text{mol} \cdot \text{L}^{-1} \cdot \text{s}^{-1}$

Integrated Rate Laws

18.27 (a) $k = \dfrac{0.693}{t_{1/2}} = \dfrac{0.693}{1000\ \text{s}} = 6.93 \times 10^{-4}\ \text{s}^{-1}$

(b) We use $\ln\left(\dfrac{[\text{A}]_0}{[\text{A}]_t}\right) = kt$ and solve for k.

$k = \dfrac{\ln([\text{A}]_0/[\text{A}]_t)}{t} = \dfrac{\ln\left(\dfrac{0.33\ \text{mol} \cdot \text{L}^{-1}}{0.14\ \text{mol} \cdot \text{L}^{-1}}\right)}{47\ \text{s}} = 1.8 \times 10^{-2}\ \text{s}^{-1}$

(c) $[A]_t = \left(\dfrac{0.050 \text{ mol A}}{L}\right) - \left[\left(\dfrac{2 \text{ mol A}}{1 \text{ mol B}}\right) \times \left(\dfrac{0.015 \text{ mol B}}{L}\right)\right]$

$= 0.020 \text{ (mol A)} \cdot L^{-1}$

$k = \dfrac{\ln\left(\dfrac{0.050 \text{ mol} \cdot L^{-1}}{0.020 \text{ mol} \cdot L^{-1}}\right)}{120 \text{ s}} = 7.6 \times 10^{-3} \text{ s}^{-1}$

18.29 (a) $t_{1/2} = \dfrac{0.693}{k} = \left(\dfrac{0.693 \text{ s}}{3.7 \times 10^{-5}}\right) \times \left(\dfrac{1 \text{ min}}{60 \text{ s}}\right) \times \left(\dfrac{1 \text{ h}}{60 \text{ min}}\right) = 5.2 \text{ h}$

(b) $[A]_t = [A]_0\, e^{-kt}$

$t = 2.0 \text{ h} = 2.0 \text{ h} \times 3600 \text{ s} \cdot \text{h}^{-1} = 7.2 \times 10^3 \text{ s}$

$[N_2O_5] = 2.33 \times 10^{-2} \text{ mol} \cdot L^{-1} \times e^{-(3.7 \times 10^{-5} \text{ s}^{-1} \times 7.2 \times 10^3 \text{ s})} = 1.79 \times 10^{-2} \text{ mol} \cdot L^{-1}$

(c) Solve for t from $\ln\left(\dfrac{[A]_0}{[A]_t}\right) = kt$, which gives

$t = \dfrac{\ln\left(\dfrac{[A]_0}{[A]_t}\right)}{k} = \dfrac{\ln\left(\dfrac{[N_2O_5]_0}{[N_2O_5]_t}\right)}{k} = \dfrac{\ln\left(\dfrac{2.33}{1.76}\right)}{3.7 \times 10^{-5} \text{ s}^{-1}} = 7.5\overline{8} \times 10^3 \text{ s}$

$= 7.5\overline{8} \times 10^3 \text{ s} \times \left(\dfrac{1 \text{ min}}{60 \text{ s}}\right) = 1.3 \times 10^2 \text{ min}$

18.31 (a) This is the half-life itself, 200 s.

(b) $\dfrac{[A]}{[A]_0} = \dfrac{1}{16} = \left(\dfrac{1}{2}\right)^4$; so the time elapsed is 4 half-lives.

$t = 4 \times 200 \text{ s} = 800 \text{ s}$

(c) Because $\frac{1}{9}$ is not a multiple of $\frac{1}{2}$, we cannot work directly from the half-life. But $k = 0.693/t_{1/2}$,

so $k = \dfrac{0.693}{200 \text{ s}} = 3.46\overline{5} \times 10^{-3} \text{ s}^{-1}$.

Then [see the solution to Exercise 18.29(c)],

$t = \dfrac{\ln\left(\dfrac{[A]_0}{[A]_t}\right)}{k} = \dfrac{\ln\left(\dfrac{9}{1}\right)}{3.46\overline{5} \times 10^{-3} \text{ s}^{-1}} = 634 \text{ s}$

18.33 (a) $t_{1/2} = \dfrac{0.693}{k} = \dfrac{0.693}{2.81 \times 10^{-3} \text{ min}^{-1}} = 247 \text{ min}$

(b) See the solutions to Exercises 10.29(c) and 10.31(c).

$t = \dfrac{\ln\left(\dfrac{[SO_2Cl_2]_0}{[SO_2Cl_2]_t}\right)}{k} = \dfrac{\ln 10}{2.81 \times 10^{-3} \text{ min}^{-1}} = 819 \text{ min}$

(c) $[A]_t = [A]_0\, e^{-kt}$

Because the vessel is sealed, masses and concentrations are proportional and we write

$$\text{(mass left)}_t = \text{(mass)}_0\, e^{-kt}$$
$$= 14.0\ \text{g} \times e^{-(2.81 \times 10^{-3}\ \text{min}^{-1} \times 60\ \text{min} \cdot \text{h}^{-1} \times 1.5\ \text{h})}$$
$$= 10.9\ \text{g}$$

Note: Knowledge of the volume of the vessel is not required. However, one could have converted mass to concentration, solved for the new concentration at 1.5 h, and finally converted back to the new (remaining) mass. But this is not necessary.

18.35 (a) $\ln\left(\dfrac{[A]_0}{[A]_t}\right) = kt$

$\ln\left(\dfrac{100\%}{20\%}\right) = k \times 120\ \text{s}$

$k = \dfrac{\ln 5.0}{120\ \text{s}} = 0.0134\ \text{s}^{-1}$

(b) Solving for t as we did in Exercise 18.29(c), we get

$$t = \frac{\ln\left(\dfrac{[A]_0}{[A]_t}\right)}{k} = \frac{\ln\left(\dfrac{100\%}{10\%}\right)}{0.013\overline{4}\ \text{s}^{-1}} = 1.7 \times 10^2\ \text{s}$$

18.37 (a) We first calculate the concentration of A at 3.0 min.

$[A]_t = [A]_0 - \left(\dfrac{1\ \text{mol A}}{3\ \text{mol B}}\right) \times [B]_t$

$= 0.015\ \text{mol} \cdot \text{L}^{-1} - \left(\dfrac{1\ \text{mol A}}{3\ \text{mol B}}\right) \times 0.020\ (\text{mol B}) \cdot \text{L}^{-1}$

$= 0.0083\ \text{mol} \cdot \text{L}^{-1}$

The rate constant is then determined from the first-order integrated rate law.

$$k = \frac{\ln\left(\dfrac{[A]_0}{[A]_t}\right)}{t} = \frac{\ln\left(\dfrac{0.015}{0.0083}\right)}{3.0\ \text{min}} = 0.19\overline{7}\ \text{min}^{-1} = 0.20\ \text{min}^{-1}$$

(b) $[A]_t = 0.015\ \text{mol} \cdot \text{L}^{-1} - \left(\dfrac{1\ \text{mol A}}{3\ \text{mol B}}\right) \times 0.040\ (\text{mol B}) \cdot \text{L}^{-1}$

$= 0.001\ 6\overline{7}\ \text{mol} \cdot \text{L}^{-1}$

$$t = \frac{\ln\left(\dfrac{[A]_0}{[A]_t}\right)}{k} = \frac{\ln\left(\dfrac{0.015}{0.001\ 67}\right)}{0.19\overline{7}\ \text{min}^{-1}} = 11.\overline{1}\ \text{min}$$

additional time $= 11.\overline{1}\ \text{min} - 3.0\ \text{min} = 8\ \text{min}$

18.39 For a first-order reaction, $\ln[A]_t = \ln[A]_0 - kt$ [Eq. 2]
The description of the kinetic data fits this equation, which is the equation of a straight line with a negative slope, $-k$. Therefore, the reaction is first order.

18.41 We draw up the following table:

Time, s	$[N_2O_5]$, 10^{-3} mol · L^{-1}	$[A]_0/[A]$	$\ln([A]_0/[A])$
0	2.15	1.00	0.000
4000	1.88	1.14	0.134
8000	1.64	1.31	0.270
12000	1.43	1.50	0.405
16000	1.25	1.72	0.542

(a) The integrated rate equation for a first-order reaction is

$$\ln[A]_t = \ln[A]_0 - kt \quad \text{or} \quad \ln\left(\frac{[A]_0}{[A]_t}\right) = kt$$

We then plot $\ln([A]_0/[A]_t)$ versus t and see whether a straight line through the origin results.

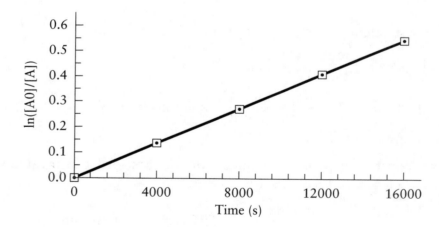

The data fit the first-order equation well.
(b) The rate constant is the slope of this line. It is easily determined with plotting software, with a graphing calculator, or by the methods of Appendix 1E and Example 18.5. Using first and last points in the graph yields

$$\text{slope} = \frac{0.542 - 0.000}{(16000 - 0)\text{ s}} = 3.39 \times 10^{-5}\text{ s}^{-1} = k$$

18.43 (a) Draw up the following table and plot 1/[HI] against time.

Time, s	[HI], 10^{-3} mol·L^{-1}	1/[HI], 10^3 L·mol^{-1}
0	1000	0.001 00
1000	112	0.008 93
2000	61	0.016 $\overline{4}$
3000	41	0.024 $\overline{4}$
4000	31	0.032 $\overline{3}$

Equation 4 in the text can be rearranged as

$$\frac{1}{[A]_t} = \frac{1 + [A]_0\, kt}{[A]_0} = \frac{1}{[A]_0} + kt$$

Thus, if the reaction is second order, a plot of 1/[HI] against time should give a straight line of slope k.

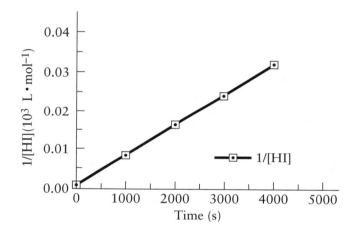

As can be seen from the graph, the data fit the equation for a second-order reaction quite well. The slope can be determined from any pair of data points, but we choose the points at 4000 and 1000 s.

(b) $\text{slope} = \dfrac{(0.032\overline{3} - 0.008\ 93) \times 10^3\ \text{L·mol}^{-1}}{(4000 - 1000)\ \text{s}}$

$= 7.8 \times 10^{-3}\ \text{L·mol}^{-1}\cdot\text{s}^{-1} = k$

Collision Theory and Arrhenius Behavior

18.45 As temperature increases, the average speed of the reacting molecules also increases; therefore, the number of collisions between molecules increases as well. The rate of reaction is proportional to the number of collisions between molecules; hence the rate increases in proportion to this factor. This collision frequency factor is contained within the preexponential factor, A, in the Arrhenius equation.

Not all molecules that collide will react; only those having sufficient collision energy to surmount the energy barrier, E_a, between reactants and products will react. This fraction of molecules having the necessary energy increases with temperature in a manner governed by the Maxwell distribution of speeds. It turns out that this fraction is proportional to $e^{-E_a/RT}$. Therefore, we can write

$$k \propto \text{collision frequency} \times e^{-E_a/RT} \quad \text{or} \quad k = Ae^{-E_aRT}$$

18.47 (a) Make the following table and graph.

T, K	$1/T$, K^{-1}	k, s^{-1}	$\ln k$
750	0.001 33	1.8×10^{-4}	-8.62
800	0.001 25	2.7×10^{-3}	-5.91
850	0.001 18	3.0×10^{-2}	-3.51
900	0.001 11	2.6×10^{-1}	-1.35

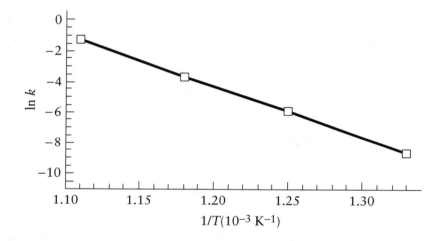

$$\ln k = \ln(A - E_a/RT)$$

$$\text{slope of plot} = -E_a/R = \frac{[-1.35 - (-8.62)]\ \text{K}}{0.001\ 11 - 0.001\ 33} = 3.3 \times 10^4\ \text{K}$$

$$E_a = (3.3 \times 10^4\ \text{K}) \times (8.31 \times 10^{-3}\ \text{kJ} \cdot \text{mol}^{-1} \cdot \text{K}^{-1}) = 2.74 \times 10^2\ \text{kJ} \cdot \text{mol}^{-1}$$

(b) $\ln\left(\dfrac{k'}{k}\right) = \dfrac{E_a}{R}\left(\dfrac{1}{T} - \dfrac{1}{T'}\right) = \left(\dfrac{2.74 \times 10^2\ \text{kJ} \cdot \text{mol}^{-1}}{8.31 \times 10^{-3}\ \text{kJ} \cdot \text{K}^{-1} \cdot \text{mol}^{-1}}\right)$

$$\times \left(\frac{1}{750\ \text{K}} - \frac{1}{873\ \text{K}}\right) = 6.19$$

$$\frac{k'}{k} = 48\overline{8}$$

$$k' = 48\overline{8} \times (1.8 \times 10^{-4}\ \text{s}^{-1}) = 8.8 \times 10^{-2}\ \text{s}^{-1}$$

An approximate value of k' can also be obtained from the plot itself and yields the same value.

18.49 We use $\ln\left(\dfrac{k'}{k}\right) = \dfrac{E_a}{R}\left(\dfrac{1}{T} - \dfrac{1}{T'}\right) = \dfrac{E_a}{R}\left(\dfrac{T'-T}{T'T}\right)$

$\ln\left(\dfrac{k'}{k}\right) = \ln\left(\dfrac{0.87\ \text{s}^{-1}}{0.38\ \text{s}^{-1}}\right) = \left(\dfrac{E_a}{8.31 \times 10^{-3}\ \text{kJ}\cdot\text{K}^{-1}\cdot\text{mol}^{-1}}\right) \times \left(\dfrac{1030\ \text{K} - 1000\ \text{K}}{1030\ \text{K} \times 1000\ \text{K}}\right)$

$E_a = \dfrac{(8.31 \times 10^{-3}\ \text{kJ}\cdot\text{K}^{-1}\cdot\text{mol}^{-1})(1000\ \text{K})(1030\ \text{K})(0.83)}{30\ \text{K}} = 2.4 \times 10^2\ \text{kJ}\cdot\text{mol}^{-1}$

18.51 We use $\ln\left(\dfrac{k'}{k}\right) = \dfrac{E_a}{R}\left(\dfrac{1}{T} - \dfrac{1}{T'}\right) = \dfrac{E_a}{R}\left(\dfrac{T'-T}{TT'}\right)$

$k' = $ rate constant at 700°C, $T' = (700 + 273)\ \text{K} = 973\ \text{K}$

$\ln\left(\dfrac{k'}{k}\right) = \left(\dfrac{315\ \text{kJ}\cdot\text{mol}^{-1}}{8.31 \times 10^{-3}\ \text{kJ}\cdot\text{K}^{-1}\cdot\text{mol}^{-1}}\right) \times \left(\dfrac{973\ \text{K} - 1073\ \text{K}}{973\ \text{K} \times 1073\ \text{K}}\right)$

$\qquad = -3.63;\quad \dfrac{k'}{k} = 0.026\overline{5}$

$k' = 0.026\overline{5} \times 9.7 \times 10^{10}\ \text{L}\cdot\text{mol}^{-1}\cdot\text{s}^{-1} = 2.6 \times 10^9\ \text{L}\cdot\text{mol}^{-1}\cdot\text{s}^{-1}$

18.53 $\ln\left(\dfrac{k'}{k}\right) = \dfrac{E_a}{R}\left(\dfrac{1}{T} - \dfrac{1}{T'}\right) = \dfrac{E_a}{R}\left(\dfrac{T'-T}{TT'}\right)$

$\qquad = \left(\dfrac{103\ \text{kJ}\cdot\text{mol}^{-1}}{8.31 \times 10^{-3}\ \text{kJ}\cdot\text{K}^{-1}\cdot\text{mol}^{-1}}\right) \times \left(\dfrac{323\ \text{K} - 318\ \text{K}}{318\ \text{K} \times 323\ \text{K}}\right) = 0.603$

$\dfrac{k'}{k} = 1.82\overline{8}$

$k' = 1.82\overline{8} \times 5.1 \times 10^{-4}\ \text{s}^{-1} = 9.3 \times 10^{-4}\ \text{s}^{-1}$

Catalysis

18.55 cat = catalyzed,   uncat = uncatalyzed $E_{a,\text{cat}} = \frac{1}{2} E_a = \frac{1}{2} E_{a,\text{uncat}}$

$\dfrac{\text{rate(cat)}}{\text{rate(uncat)}} = \dfrac{k_{\text{cat}}}{k_{\text{uncat}}} = \dfrac{Ae^{-E_{a,\text{cat}}/RT}}{Ae^{-E_a/RT}} = \dfrac{e^{-(1/2)E_a/RT}}{e^{-E_a/RT}} = e^{(1/2)E_a/RT}$

$e^{[(100\ \text{kJ}\cdot\text{mol}^{-1})/(8.31 \times 10^{-3}\ \text{kJ}\cdot\text{K}^{-1}\cdot\text{mol}^{-1} \times 400\ \text{K})]} = e^{15.0} = 3.4 \times 10^6$

18.57 cat = catalyzed,   uncat = uncatalyzed

$\dfrac{\text{rate(cat)}}{\text{rate(uncat)}} = \dfrac{k_{\text{cat}}}{k_{\text{uncat}}} = 1000 = \dfrac{Ae^{-E_{a,\text{cat}}/RT}}{Ae^{-E_a/RT}} = \dfrac{e^{-E_{a,\text{cat}}/RT}}{e^{-E_a/RT}}$

$\ln 1000 = \dfrac{-E_{a,\text{cat}}}{RT} + \dfrac{E_a}{RT}$

$E_{a,\text{cat}} = E_a - RT\ln 1000 = 98\ \text{kJ}\cdot\text{mol}^{-1} - (8.31$

$\qquad\qquad\qquad \times 10^{-3}\ \text{kJ}\cdot\text{K}^{-1}\cdot\text{mol}^{-1})(298\ \text{K})(\ln 1000) = 80.9\ \text{kJ}\cdot\text{mol}^{-1}$

18.59 (a) rate $= k[NO]^2$, bimolecular

(b) rate $= k[Cl_2]$, unimolecular

(c) rate $= k[NO_2]^2$, bimolecular

(d) (b) and (c), because Cl and NO are radicals

18.61 NO_2, because it appears only in the course of the reaction and is neither a reactant nor a product. NO would not be considered an intermediate; rather, it is a catalyst, because it enables the reaction but is not consumed in the reaction.

18.63 $2ICl + H_2 \longrightarrow 2HCl + I_2$

HI is the only intermediate. It is the only species that does not appear as either a reactant or a product.

18.65 The first elementary reaction is the rate-controlling step, because it is the slow step. The second elementary reaction is fast and does not affect the overall reaction order, which is second order as a result of the fact that the rate-controlling step is bimolecular.

$$\text{rate} = k[NO][Br_2]$$

18.67 The overall rate is determined by the slow step. rate $= k_3[COCl][Cl_2]$. But COCl is an intermediate and its concentration has to be eliminated.

$k_1[Cl_2] = k_1'[Cl]^2$, giving $[Cl] = \sqrt{\dfrac{k_1}{k_1'}} [Cl_2]$

and $k_2 = [Cl][CO] = k_2'[COCl]$; substituting for [Cl] gives

$[COCl] = \left(\dfrac{k_2}{k_2'}\right) \sqrt{\dfrac{k_1}{k_1'}} [Cl_2]^{1/2}[CO]$, hence

rate $= k_3(k_2/k_2')(k_1/k_1')^{1/2}[CO][Cl_2]^{3/2} = k[CO][Cl_2]^{3/2}$

18.69 If mechanism (a) were correct, the rate law would be rate $= k_2[NO_2][CO]$. But this expression does not agree with the experimental result and can be eliminated as a possibility. Mechanism (b) has rate $= k_2[NO_2]^2$ from the slow step. Step 2 does not influence the overall rate, but it is necessary to achieve the correct overall reaction; thus this mechanism agrees with the experimental data $k = k_2$. Mechanism (c) is not correct, which can be seen from the rate expression for the slow step, rate $= k_2[NO_3][CO]$. [CO] cannot be eliminated from this expression to yield the experimental result, which does not contain [CO].

18.71 (a) All chemical reactions involve a change in enthalpy, ΔH. As a consequence, the products are not at the same energy level as the reactants, and activation energies for the forward and backward reactions are different. Therefore, the rate constants will be different, because $k = Ae^{-E_a/RT}$, and they depend on E_a. However, at equilibrium, the *rates* of the forward and reverse reactions are equal.

(b) For a reversible reaction,

$$K_c = \frac{k(\text{forward})}{k(\text{reverse})} = \frac{k}{k'} \qquad \text{Eq. 7}$$

Therefore, if K_c is very large, k (forward) $\gg k$ (reverse).

SUPPLEMENTARY EXERCISES

18.73 $\text{Rate(HCl)} = \text{rate(C}_4\text{H}_9\text{Cl)} \times \left(\dfrac{1 \text{ mol HCl}}{1 \text{ mol C}_4\text{H}_9\text{Cl}} \right)$

$\qquad = 1.90 \times 10^{-4} \text{ (mol C}_4\text{H}_9\text{Cl)} \cdot \text{L}^{-1} \cdot \text{s}^{-1} \times \left(\dfrac{1 \text{ mol HCl}}{1 \text{ mol C}_4\text{H}_9\text{Cl}} \right)$

$\qquad = 1.90 \times 10^{-4} \text{ (mol HCl)} \cdot \text{L}^{-1} \cdot \text{s}^{-1}$

18.75 (a, c)

(b) $\text{rate(4000 s)} = \dfrac{(2.57 - 0.87) \times 10^{-3} \text{ mol} \cdot \text{L}^{-1}}{8.0 \times 10^3 \text{ s}} = 2.1 \times 10^{-7} \text{ mol} \cdot \text{L}^{-1} \cdot \text{s}^{-1}$

$\text{rate(8000 s)} = \dfrac{(1.50 - 0.51) \times 10^{-3} \text{ mol} \cdot \text{L}^{-1}}{8.0 \times 10^3 \text{ s}} = 1.2 \times 10^{-7} \text{ mol} \cdot \text{L}^{-1} \cdot \text{s}^{-1}$

$\text{rate(12000 s)} = \dfrac{(0.87 - 0.30) \times 10^{-3} \text{ mol} \cdot \text{L}^{-1}}{8.0 \times 10^3 \text{ s}} = 7.1 \times 10^{-8} \text{ mol} \cdot \text{L}^{-1} \cdot \text{s}^{-1}$

The rates at 1.60×10^4 s and at the start (0 s) can be estimated from the slope of the plot of $[N_2O_5]$ vs time. These rates, as well as those calculated above, are most easily determined from readily available plotting software or from a graphing calculator. One may also obtain them from tangents drawn to the curve at the various times. Approximate values are

$$\text{rate (0 s)} = 3.\overline{1} \times 10^{-7} \text{ mol} \cdot \text{L}^{-1} \cdot \text{s}^{-1}$$
$$\text{rate (16000 s)} = 4 \times 10^{-8} \text{ mol} \cdot \text{L}^{-1} \cdot \text{s}^{-1}$$

(c) at time t,

$$[NO_2]_t = ([N_2O_5]_0 - [N_2O_5]) \times \left(\frac{4 \text{ mol NO}_2}{2 \text{ mol N}_2O_5}\right)$$

$$[O_2]_t = [NO_2]_t \times \left(\frac{1 \text{ mol O}_2}{4 \text{ mol NO}_2}\right)$$

These expressions give the following table:

t, 10^3 s	$[N_2O_5]$, 10^{-3} mol $\cdot$ L^{-1}	$[NO_2]$, 10^{-3} mol $\cdot$ L^{-1}	$[O_2]$, 10^{-3} mol $\cdot$ L^{-1}
0	2.57	0	0
4.0	1.50	2.14	0.535
8.0	0.87	3.40	0.850
12.0	0.51	4.12	1.03
16.0	0.30	4.54	1.14

These values are plotted in the figure above.

18.77 (a) rate $= k[A][B]^{1/2}$

(b) $k = \dfrac{\text{units of rate}}{\text{units of } ([A][B]^{1/2})} = \dfrac{\text{mol} \cdot \text{L}^{-1} \cdot \text{min}^{-1}}{(\text{mol} \cdot \text{L}^{-1}) \cdot (\text{mol} \cdot \text{L}^{-1})^{1/2}}$

$\quad = \text{L}^{1/2} \cdot \text{mol}^{-1/2} \cdot \text{min}^{-1}$

18.79 (a) rate $= k[A]^a[B]^b[C]^c$

Comparing experiments 1 and 4, we see that changing [C] has no effect on the rate; thus, $c = 0$ and we can write rate $= k[A]^a[B]^b$.

Comparing experiments 1 and 2, we see that doubling [A] doubles the rate; thus, $a = 1$. Comparing experiments 2 and 3, we see that doubling [B] quadruples the rate; thus, $2^b = 4$; hence $b = 2$.

The overall order is then $a + b + c = 1 + 2 + 0 = 3$

(b) rate $= k[A][B]^2$

(c) $k = \dfrac{2.0 \times 10^{-3} \text{ mol} \cdot \text{L}^{-1} \cdot \text{s}^{-1}}{(10 \times 10^{-3} \text{ mol} \cdot \text{L}^{-1}) \times (100 \times 10^{-3} \text{ mol} \cdot \text{L}^{-1})^2} = 20 \text{ L}^2 \cdot \text{mol}^{-2} \cdot \text{s}^{-1}$

(d) $\text{rate} = \left(20\ \dfrac{\text{L}^2}{\text{mol}^2 \cdot \text{s}}\right) \times (4.62 \times 10^{-3}\ \text{mol} \cdot \text{L}^{-1}) \times \left(0.177 \times 10^{-3}\ \dfrac{\text{mol}}{\text{L}}\right)^2$

$= 2.9 \times 10^{-9}\ \text{mol} \cdot \text{L}^{-1} \cdot \text{s}^{-1}$

18.81 (a) $[A]_t = [A]_0 e^{-kt}$

$[H_2O_2]_t = [H_2O_2]_0 e^{-kt}$

$[H_2O_2]_t = 0.20\ \text{mol} \cdot \text{L}^{-1} \times e^{-0.0410\ \text{min}^{-1} \times 10\ \text{min}}$

$= 0.13\ \text{mol} \cdot \text{L}^{-1}$

(b) $\ln\left(\dfrac{[A]_t}{[A]_0}\right) = kt$

$\ln\left(\dfrac{0.50}{0.10}\right) = 0.0410\ \text{min}^{-1} \times t$

$t = \dfrac{\ln 5}{0.0410\ \text{min}^{-1}} = 39\ \text{min}$

(c) A reduction of $\frac{1}{4}$, means $\frac{3}{4}$ remains.

$t = \dfrac{\ln\left(\dfrac{[H_2O_2]_0}{[H_2O_2]}\right)}{k} = \dfrac{\ln\left(\dfrac{4}{3}\right)}{0.0410\ \text{min}^{-1}} = 7.0\ \text{min}$

(d) A reduction of 75%, means 25% or $\frac{1}{4}$ remains.

$t = \dfrac{\ln\left(\dfrac{[H_2O_2]_0}{[H_2O_2]}\right)}{k} = \dfrac{\ln\left(\dfrac{4}{1}\right)}{k} = \dfrac{1.39}{0.0410\ \text{min}^{-1}} = 34\ \text{min}$

18.83 (a) $k = \dfrac{0.693}{t_{1/2}} = \dfrac{0.693}{1.02\ \text{s}} = 0.679\ \text{s}^{-1}$

Because volume is a constant, $P_{CH_3N=NCH_3} \propto \text{mass} \propto [CH_3N=NCH_3]$; therefore,

$\ln\left(\dfrac{P_0}{P_t}\right) = \ln\left(\dfrac{[CH_3N=NCH_3]_0}{[CH_3N=NCH_3]_t}\right) = \ln\left(\dfrac{\text{mass}_0}{\text{mass}_t}\right) = kt$

$\ln\left(\dfrac{\text{mass}_0}{\text{mass}_t}\right) = 0.679\ \text{s}^{-1} \times 10\ \text{s} = 6.79$

$\dfrac{\text{mass}_0}{\text{mass}_t} = 889, \quad \text{mass} = \dfrac{45.0\ \text{mg}}{889} = 0.0506\ \text{mg}$

(b) $\ln\left(\dfrac{\text{mass}_0}{\text{mass}_t}\right) = 0.679\ \text{s}^{-1} \times 3.0\ \text{s} = 2.04$

$\dfrac{\text{mass}_0}{\text{mass}_t} = 7.67, \quad \text{mass} = \dfrac{45.0\ \text{mg}}{7.67} = 5.87\ \text{mg}\ CH_3N=NCH_3$

$$n_{N_2} = \text{amount of } N_2(g) = [(45.0 - 5.9) \times 10^{-3} \text{ g CH}_3\text{N}{=}\text{NCH}_3]$$

$$\times \left(\frac{1 \text{ mol CH}_3\text{N}{=}\text{NCH}_3}{58.09 \text{ g CH}_3\text{N}{=}\text{NCH}_3} \right) \times \left(\frac{1 \text{ mol N}_2}{1 \text{ mol CH}_3\text{N}{=}\text{NCH}_3} \right)$$

$$= 6.73 \times 10^{-4} \text{ mol N}_2(g)$$

$$P_{N_2} = \frac{n_{N_2}RT}{V} = \frac{(6.73 \times 10^{-4} \text{ mol})(0.0821 \text{ L} \cdot \text{atm} \cdot \text{K}^{-1} \cdot \text{mol}^{-1})(573 \text{ K})}{0.300 \text{ L}}$$

$$= 0.106 \text{ atm}$$

18.85 Refer to Figure 18.35b. For an exothermic reaction, the activation energy for the reverse reaction is greater than that for the forward reaction.

$$E_{a,\text{reverse}} = E_{a,\text{forward}} - \Delta H = 100 \text{ kJ} \cdot \text{mol}^{-1} - (-200 \text{ kJ} \cdot \text{mol}^{-1}) = 300 \text{ kJ} \cdot \text{mol}^{-1}$$

18.87 For a first-order reaction, the concentration falls by $(\frac{1}{2})^n$ after n half-lives.
   (a) The half-life is 100 s. $\frac{1}{8}$ corresponds to 3 half-lives, because $\frac{1}{8} = (\frac{1}{2})^3$. Thus, it would take $3 \times 100 \text{ s} = 300 \text{ s}$.
   (b) $\frac{1}{32} = (\frac{1}{2})^5$. Thus, 5 half-lives: $5 \times 100 \text{ s} = 500 \text{ s}$.

18.89 Solid catalysts provide surface sites at which the reaction occurs. A finely divided solid catalyst has a greater surface area, hence more surface sites; and, consequently, it is more effective.

18.91 (a) bimolecular (b) unimolecular (c) termolecular. Argon atoms provide a spot for the O atoms to come together for a sufficiently long time for their reaction to occur.

18.93 The overall reaction is $2SO_2 + O_2 \longrightarrow 2SO_3$. The complete mechanism is complicated. For the mechanism given, NO is the catalyst and NO_2 the intermediate.

18.95 cat = catalyzed, uncat = uncatalyzed
The rates are proportional to the rate constants.

$$\frac{\text{rate (cat)}}{\text{rate (uncat)}} = \frac{k_{\text{cat}}}{k_{\text{uncat}}} = \frac{Ae^{-E_{a(\text{cat})}/RT}}{Ae^{-E_{a(\text{uncat})}/RT}} = e^{-[E_{a(\text{cat})} - E_{a(\text{uncat})}]/RT}$$

$$\frac{E_{a(\text{cat})} - E_{a(\text{uncat})}}{RT} = \frac{(162 - 350) \text{ kJ} \cdot \text{mol}^{-1}}{8.314 \times 10^{-3} \text{ kJ} \cdot \text{K}^{-1} \cdot \text{mol}^{-1} \times 973 \text{ K}} = -23.2\overline{4}$$

$$\frac{\text{rate(cat)}}{\text{rate(uncat)}} = e^{-(-23.2\overline{4})} = 1.2 \times 10^{10}$$

$$= \text{factor by which reaction rate is increased}$$

18.97 (a) Make the following table and graph.

T, K	$1/T$, K^{-1}	$(k \times 10^3)$ $L \cdot mol^{-1} \cdot s^{-1}$	$\ln(k \times 10^3)$
297	0.003 37	1.3	$0.26\overline{2}$
301	0.003 32	2.0	$0.69\overline{3}$
305	0.003 28	3.0	$1.1\overline{0}$
309	0.003 24	4.4	$1.4\overline{8}$
313	0.003 19	6.4	$1.8\overline{6}$

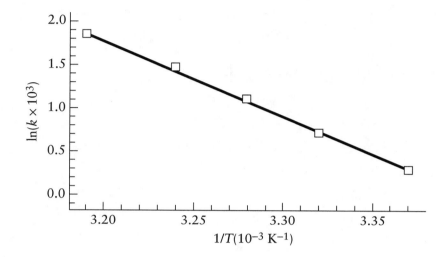

slope of straight line $= -\left(\dfrac{E_a}{R}\right) = \dfrac{(1.8\overline{6} - 0.26)\ K}{0.003\ 19 - 0.003\ 37} = -8.9 \times 10^3\ K$

$E_a = (8.9 \times 10^3\ K)(8.31 \times 10^{-3}\ kJ \cdot K^{-1} \cdot mol^{-1}) = 74\ kJ \cdot mol^{-1}$

(b) $T = 298\ K$, $1/T = 3.36 \times 10^{-3}\ K^{-1}$

From the plot, $\ln(k \times 10^3) \approx 0.37$, $k = 1.4 \times 10^{-3}\ L \cdot mol^{-1} \cdot s^{-1}$

18.99 (a) ClO is the reaction intermediate; Cl is the catalyst.

(b) Cl, ClO, O, O_2

(c) Step 1 is initiating; step 2 is propagating.

(d) $Cl + Cl \longrightarrow Cl_2$

CHALLENGING EXERCISES

18.101

Concentration	$2N_2O_5 \longrightarrow$	$4NO_2$ +	O_2
initial $(mol \cdot L^{-1})$	P_0	0	0
change $(mol \cdot L^{-1})$	$-x$	$+2x$	$+0.5x$
at time t $(mol \cdot L^{-1})$	$P_0 - x$	$2x$	$0.5x$

Therefore, P_{total} at time $t = P_0 + 1.5x$. This allows calculation of x at each time, which in turn allows calculation of $P_{N_2O_5}(= P_0 - x)$ at these times. Converting the units to atmospheres by dividing by 101.325 kPa · atm^{-1} and to [N_2O_5] by dividing by RT allows us to make the following table:

t, min	x, kPa	$P_{N_2O_5}$, kPa	$P_{N_2O_5}$, atm	[N_2O_5], mol · L^{-1}
0	0	27.3	0.269	0.0100
5	10.9	16.4	0.162	6.01×10^{-3}
10	17.5	9.85	0.0972	3.61×10^{-3}
15	21.4	5.9	0.058	2.2×10^{-3}
20	23.8	3.5	0.035	1.3×10^{-3}
30	26.0	1.3	0.013	4.8×10^{-4}

t, min	ln[N_2O_5]	Rate, mol · L^{-1} · min^{-1}
0	-4.605	1.01×10^{-3}
5	-5.114	6.07×10^{-4}
10	-5.624	3.65×10^{-4}
15	-6.12	2.2×10^{-4}
20	-6.65	1.3×10^{-4}
30	-7.64	4.8×10^{-5}

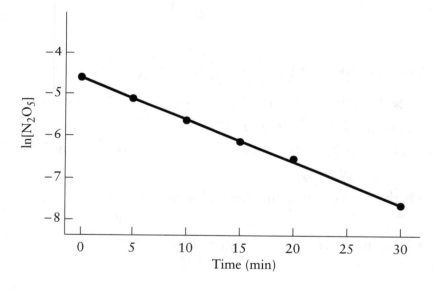

The data fit closely to a straight line; therefore, this is a first-order reaction. The rate constant can be obtained from the slope, which is

$$\frac{-4.605 - (-7.64)}{30 \text{ min}} = 0.101 \text{ min}^{-1} = k$$

Rate = $k[N_2O_5]$ = 0.101 min^{-1}[N_2O_5], which gives the results in the table above.

18.103 It is convenient to obtain an expression for the half-life of a second-order reaction. We work with Eq. 4.

$$[A]_t = \frac{[A]_0}{1 + [A]_0 kt} \qquad (4)$$

$$\frac{[A]_{t_{1/2}}}{[A]_0} = \frac{1}{2} = \frac{1}{1 + [A]_0 kt_{1/2}}$$

Therefore, $1 + [A]_0 kt_{1/2} = 2$, or $[A]_0 kt_{1/2} = 1$, or

$$t_{1/2} = \frac{1}{k[A]_0} \quad \text{and} \quad k = \frac{1}{t_{1/2}[A]_0}$$

It is also convenient to rewrite Eq. 4 to solve for t. We take reciprocals:

$$\frac{1}{[A]_t} = \frac{1}{[A]_0} + kt$$

giving

$$t = \frac{\dfrac{1}{[A]_t} - \dfrac{1}{[A]_0}}{k}$$

(a) $k = \dfrac{1}{t_{1/2}[A]_0} = \dfrac{1}{(50.5 \text{ s}) \times (0.84 \text{ mol} \cdot \text{L}^{-1})} = 0.023\overline{6} \text{ L} \cdot \text{mol}^{-1} \cdot \text{s}^{-1}$

$$t = \frac{\dfrac{1}{[A]} - \dfrac{1}{[A]_0}}{k} = \frac{\dfrac{16}{[A]_0} - \dfrac{1}{[A]_0}}{k} = \frac{15}{k[A]_0}$$

$$= \frac{15}{(0.023\overline{6} \text{ L} \cdot \text{mol}^{-1} \cdot \text{s}^{-1}) \times (0.84 \text{ mol} \cdot \text{L}^{-1})} = 7.6 \times 10^2 \text{ s}$$

(b) $t = \dfrac{\dfrac{4}{[A]_0} - \dfrac{1}{[A]_0}}{k} = \dfrac{3}{k[A]_0}$

$$= \frac{3}{(0.023\overline{6} \text{ L} \cdot \text{mol}^{-1} \cdot \text{s}^{-1}) \times (0.84 \text{ mol} \cdot \text{L}^{-1})} = 1.5 \times 10^2 \text{ s}$$

(c) $t = \dfrac{\dfrac{5}{[A]_0} - \dfrac{1}{[A]_0}}{k} = \dfrac{4}{k[A]_0}$

$$= \frac{4}{(0.023\overline{6} \text{ L} \cdot \text{mol}^{-1} \cdot \text{s}^{-1}) \times (0.84 \text{ mol} \cdot \text{L}^{-1})} = 2.0 \times 10^2 \text{ s}$$

18.105 See the solution to Exercise 18.103 for the derivation of the formulas needed here.

(a) $t = \dfrac{\dfrac{1}{[A]} - \dfrac{1}{[A]_0}}{k} = \dfrac{\dfrac{1\ L}{0.080\ mol} - \dfrac{1\ L}{0.10\ mol}}{0.010\ L \cdot mol^{-1} \cdot min^{-1}} = 2.5 \times 10^2\ min$

(b) $[A] = \dfrac{0.45\ mol\ A}{L} - \left[\left(\dfrac{0.45\ mol\ B}{L} \right) \times \left(\dfrac{1\ mol\ A}{2\ mol\ B} \right) \right]$

$\qquad = 0.22\overline{5}(mol\ A) \cdot L^{-1} = \tfrac{1}{2}[A]_0$

$t = t_{1/2} = \dfrac{1}{k[A]_0} = \dfrac{1}{(0.0045\ L \cdot mol^{-1} \cdot min^{-1}) \times (0.45\ mol \cdot L^{-1})}$

$\qquad = 4.9 \times 10^2\ min$

18.107 (a) A reasonable approach is to assume that the reaction is either first or second order. First attempt to fit the data to the first-order case. If the fit is good, the reaction is first order. If not, try second order and see if the fit is good. If the data do not fit either the first- or second-order integrated rate equations, then other orders have to be tried.

Make the following table and graph.

Time, s	[A], $10^{-3}\ mol \cdot L^{-1}$	$\ln([A] \times 10^3)$
0	250	5.521
100	143	4.963
200	81	4.39
300	45	3.81
400	25	3.22

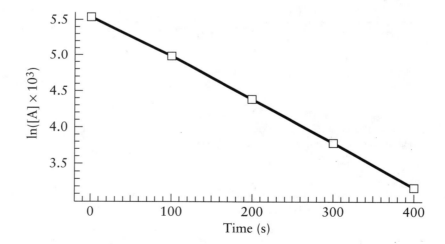

The plot is linear, thus confirming that the reaction is first order. The slope is

$$\text{slope} = \dfrac{\ln([A] \times 10^3)_{400} - \ln([A] \times 10^3)_0}{400\ s} = \dfrac{3.22 - 5.52}{400\ S} = -5.75 \times 10^{-3}\ s^{-1}$$

(b) slope $= -k = -5.75 \times 10^{-3}\ s^{-1}$; hence, $k = 5.75 \times 10^{-3}\ s^{-1}$

18.109 For a third-order reaction,

$$t_{1/2} \propto \frac{1}{[A_0]^2} \quad \text{or} \quad t_{1/2} = \frac{\text{constant}}{[A_0]^2}$$

(a) The time necessary for the concentration to fall to one-half of the initial concentration is one half-life:

$$\text{first half-life} = t_1 = t_{1/2} = \frac{\text{constant}}{[A_0]^2}$$

(b) This time, $t_{1/4}$, is two half-lives, but because of different starting concentrations, the half-lives are not the same:

$$\text{second half-life} = t_2 = \frac{\text{constant}}{(\frac{1}{2}[A_0])^2} = \frac{4(\text{constant})}{[A_0]^2} = 4t_1$$

$$\text{total time} = t_1 + t_2 = t_1 + 4t_1 = 5t_1 = t_{1/4}$$

(c) This time, $t_{1/16}$, is four half-lives, again the half-lives are not the same:

$$\text{third half-life} = t_3 = \frac{\text{constant}}{(\frac{1}{4}[A_0])^2} = \frac{16(\text{constant})}{[A_0]^2} = 16t_1$$

$$\text{fourth half-life} = t_4 = \frac{\text{constant}}{(\frac{1}{8}[A_0])^2} = \frac{64(\text{constant})}{[A_0]^2} = 64t_1$$

$$\text{total time} = t_1 + t_2 + t_3 + t_4 = t_1 + 4t_1 + 16t_1 + 64t_1 = 85t_1 = t_{1/16}$$

If t_1 is known, the times $t_{1/4}$ and $t_{1/16}$ can be calculated easily.

18.111 Consider for example, $A \rightleftharpoons B$. Assume that the reaction is first order in both directions:

$$\text{rate(forward)} = k[A]$$
$$\text{rate(reverse)} = k'[B]$$

At equilibrium, rate(forward) = rate(reverse), so
rate $= 0 = $ rate(forward) $-$ rate(reverse),
or $k[A] - k'[B] = 0$,
or $k[A] - k'([A]_0 - [A]) = 0$,
or $(k + k')[A] = k'[A]_0$,
or $[A] = \dfrac{k'}{(k + k')} [A]_0$, which is not zero.

18.113 Let P = pollutant.

(a) rate $= R - k[P]_{eq} = 0$ at equilibrium

$$[P]_{eq} = + \left(\frac{R}{k} \right)$$

(b) Because $[P]_{eq}$ = constant, there is no overall half-life, but on average, for an individual molecule, there is a 50% probability that it will have decayed after

$$t_{1/2} = \frac{0.693}{k}$$

18.115 (a) If the forward reaction is exothermic, then increasing the temperature will drive the reaction in the direction of reactants; the reverse is true if the temperature is decreased.

(b) If the forward reaction is endothermic, then increasing the temperature will drive the reaction in the direction of products; the reverse is true if the temperature is decreased.

(c) $\ln(k'/k) = E_a/R(1/T - 1/T') = E_a/R(T' - T/TT')$ [Example 18.8]

For (a), $E_a(\text{reverse}) > E_a(\text{forward})$. From the equation above for $\ln(k'/k)$, we see that for a given $\Delta T = (T' - T) > 0$, $\ln(k'/k)(\text{reverse}) > \ln(k'/k)(\text{forward})$ and $(k'/k)(\text{reverse}) > (k'/k)(\text{forward})$. The rate of the reverse reaction increases more rapidly with increasing T than the forward reaction does. Hence, the equilibrium is shifted in the direction of reactants.

For (b), because $E_a(\text{forward}) > E_a(\text{reverse})$, the opposite is true. The rate of the forward reaction will increase relatively more than that of the reverse reaction, and products will be favored.

CHAPTER 19
THE MAIN-GROUP ELEMENTS:
I. THE FIRST FOUR FAMILIES

EXERCISES

Hydrogen

19.1 In the majority of its reactions, hydrogen acts as a reducing agent. Examples are $2H_2(g) + O_2(g) \longrightarrow 2H_2O(l)$ and various ore reduction processes, such as $NiO(s) + H_2(g) \xrightarrow{\Delta} Ni(s) + H_2O(g)$. With highly electropositive elements, such as the alkali metals, $H_2(g)$ acts as an oxidizing agent and forms metal hydrides, for example, $2K(s) + H_2(g) \longrightarrow 2KH(s)$.

19.3 (a) $CO(g) + H_2O(g) \xrightarrow{400\ °C,\ Fe/Cu} CO_2(g) + H_2(g)$

(b) $2Li(s) + 2H_2O(l) \longrightarrow 2LiOH(aq) + H_2(g)$

(c) $Mg(s) + 2H_2O(l) \longrightarrow Mg(OH)_2(aq) + H_2(g)$

(d) $2K(s) + H_2(g) \longrightarrow 2KH(s)$

19.5 (a) saline (b) molecular (c) molecular (d) metallic

19.7 (a) $CH_4(g) + H_2O(g) \longrightarrow CO(g) + 3H_2(g)$

$\Delta H_r^° = 1 \times \Delta H_f^°(CO, g) - [1 \times \Delta H_f^°(CH_4, g) + 1 \times \Delta H_f^°(H_2O, g)]$
$= 1 \times (-110.53\ \text{kJ} \cdot \text{mol}^{-1}) - [1 \times (-74.81\ \text{kJ} \cdot \text{mol}^{-1})$
$+ 1 \times (-241.82\ \text{kJ} \cdot \text{mol}^{-1})] = +206.10\ \text{kJ} \cdot \text{mol}^{-1}$

(b) $CO(g) + H_2O(g) \longrightarrow CO_2(g) + H_2(g)$

$\Delta H_r^° = 1 \times \Delta H_f^°(CO_2, g) - [1 \times \Delta H_f^°(CO, g) + 1 \times \Delta H_f^°(H_2O, g)]$
$= 1 \times (-393.51\ \text{kJ} \cdot \text{mol}^{-1}) - [1 \times (-110.53\ \text{kJ} \cdot \text{mol}^{-1})$
$+ 1 \times (-241.82\ \text{kJ} \cdot \text{mol}^{-1})] = -41.16\ \text{kJ} \cdot \text{mol}^{-1}$

(c) $CH_4(g) + 2H_2O(g) \rightleftharpoons CO_2(g) + 4H_2(g)$

$\Delta H_r^°(c) = \Delta H_r^°(a) + \Delta H_r^°(b) = (206.10 - 41.16)\ \text{kJ} \cdot \text{mol}^{-1} = +164.94\ \text{kJ} \cdot \text{mol}^{-1}$

19.9 (a) At STP, 273 K and 1.00 atm, 1.00 mol of $H_2(g)$, assumed to be ideal, occupies 22.4 L. Then, for

$$CaH_2(s) + 2H_2O(l) \longrightarrow Ca(OH)_2(s) + H_2(g)$$

$$\text{volume of } H_2(g) = (500 \text{ g } CaH_2) \times \left(\frac{1 \text{ mol } CaH_2}{42.1 \text{ g } CaH_2}\right)$$

$$\times \left(\frac{2 \text{ mol } H_2}{1 \text{ mol } CaH_2}\right) \times \left(\frac{22.4 \text{ L } H_2}{1 \text{ mol } H_2}\right) = 532 \text{ L } H_2$$

(b) $\text{volume of } H_2O(l) = (500 \text{ g } CaH_2) \times \left(\frac{1 \text{ mol } CaH_2}{42.1 \text{ g } CaH_2}\right) \times \left(\frac{2 \text{ mol } H_2O}{1 \text{ mol } CaH_2}\right)$

$$\times \left(\frac{18.02 \text{ g } H_2O}{1 \text{ mol } H_2O}\right) \times \left(\frac{1.0 \text{ mL } H_2O}{1.0 \text{ g } H_2O}\right) = 428 \text{ mL } H_2O$$

19.11 $\quad N_2(g) + 3H_2(g) \longrightarrow 2NH_3(g)$

$\text{amount (moles) of } H_2 \text{ used} = (1.5 \times 10^9 \text{ kg } NH_3) \times \left(\frac{1 \text{ mol } NH_3}{0.017 \text{ kg } NH_3}\right) \times \left(\frac{3 \text{ mol } H_2}{2 \text{ mol } NH_3}\right)$

$$= 1.3 \times 10^{11} \text{ mol } H_2$$

$\text{amount (moles) of } H_2 \text{ produced} = (3 \times 10^8 \text{ kg } H_2) \times \left(\frac{1 \text{ mol } H_2}{0.002 \text{ kg } H_2}\right)$

$$= 1.\overline{5} \times 10^{11} \text{ mol } H_2$$

$\text{fraction used} = \dfrac{1.3 \times 10^{11} \text{ mol } H_2}{1.\overline{5} \times 10^{11} \text{ mol } H_2} = 0.9$

19.13 (a) $H_2(g) + Cl_2(g) \xrightarrow{\text{light}} 2HCl(g)$

(b) $H_2(g) + 2Na(l) \xrightarrow{\Delta} 2NaH(s)$

(c) $P_4(s) + 6H_2(g) \longrightarrow 4PH_3(g)$

19.15 (a) $Li^+[H\colon]^-$ (b) H—Si—H (with H above and below)   (c) H—S̈b—H (with H below)

Group 1: The Alkali Metals

19.17 (a) red (b) violet (c) yellow (d) violet

19.19 (a) $4\,Li(s) + O_2(g) \longrightarrow 2Li_2O(s)$

(b) $6Li(s) + N_2(g) \xrightarrow{\Delta} 2Li_3N(s)$

(c) $2Na(s) + 2H_2O(l) \longrightarrow 2NaOH(aq) + H_2(g)$

(d) $4KO_2(s) + 2H_2O(g) \longrightarrow 4KOH(s) + 3O_2(g)$

19.21 (a) $Ca(s) + H_2(g) \xrightarrow{\Delta} CaH_2(s)$

(b) $2KNO_3(s) \xrightarrow{\Delta} 2KNO_2(s) + O_2(g)$

19.23 (a) sodium chloride, $NaCl$

(b) potassium chloride, KCl

(c) potassium magnesium chloride hexahydrate, $KCl \cdot MgCl_2 \cdot 6H_2O$

19.25 1 mol $Na_2CO_3 \cdot 10H_2O$ yields 1 mol Na_2CO_3 in water.

mass of $Na_2CO_3 \cdot 10H_2O = 0.250$ L $\times$ 0.100 mol $\cdot$ L^{-1} $\times$ 286 g $Na_2CO_3 \cdot 10H_2O \cdot$ mol^{-1}
$$= 7.15 \text{ g } Na_2CO_3 \cdot 10H_2O$$

Group 2: The Alkaline Earth Metals

19.27 Be is the weakest reducing agent, Mg is stronger, but weaker than the remaining members of the group, all of which have approximately the same reducing strength. This effect is related to the very small radius of the Be^{2+} ion, 27 pm; its strong polarizing power introduces much covalent character into its compounds. Thus, Be attracts electrons more strongly and does not release them as readily as other members of the group. Mg^{2+} is also a small ion, 58 pm, so the same reasoning applies to it also, but to a lesser extent. The remaining ions of the group are considerably larger, release electrons more readily, and are better reducing agents.

19.29 (a) magnesium sulfate heptahydrate, $MgSO_4 \cdot 7H_2O$

(b) calcium carbonate, $CaCO_3$

(c) magnesium hydroxide, $Mg(OH)_2$

19.31 (a) $2Al(s) + 2OH^-(aq) + 6H_2O(l) \longrightarrow 2[Al(OH)_4]^-(aq) + 3H_2(g)$

(b) $Be(s) + 2OH^-(aq) + 2H_2O(l) \longrightarrow [Be(OH)_4]^{2-}(aq) + H_2(g)$

The similarity of Be and Al in chemical reactions is an example of the diagonal relationship in the periodic table; namely, the similar chemical behavior of elements that are diagonal neighbors of each other, such as Be and Al.

19.33 (a) $Mg(OH)_2(s) + 2HCl(aq) \longrightarrow MgCl_2(aq) + 2H_2O(l)$

(b) $Ca(s) + 2H_2O(l) \longrightarrow Ca(OH)_2(aq) + H_2(g)$

(c) $BaCO_3(s) \xrightarrow{\Delta} BaO(s) + CO_2(g)$

19.35 (a) $:\ddot{C}l\!-\!Be\!-\!\ddot{C}l:$ (b) 180° (c) *sp*

19.37 (a) $\Delta H_r^\circ = 1 \times (-986.09 \text{ kJ} \cdot \text{mol}^{-1}) - [1 \times (-635.09 \text{ kJ} \cdot \text{mol}^{-1})$
$+ 1 \times (-285.83 \text{ kJ} \cdot \text{mol}^{-1})] = -65.17 \text{ kJ} \cdot \text{mol}^{-1} = -6.517 \times 10^4 \text{ J} \cdot \text{mol}^{-1}$

(b) The heat absorbed by the water is

$+6.517 \times 10^4 \text{ J} = \text{mass} \times c \times (t_{\text{final}} - t_{\text{initial}})$
$= 250 \text{ g} \times 4.184 \text{ J} \cdot \text{g}^{-1} \cdot (^\circ\text{C})^{-1} \times \Delta t$

Solving for Δt, we get

$$\Delta t = \frac{6.517 \times 10^4 \text{ J}}{250 \text{ g} \times 4.184 \text{ J} \cdot \text{g}^{-1} \cdot (^\circ\text{C})^{-1}} = 62.3 \,^\circ\text{C}$$

19.39 (a) $CaCO_3(s) \xrightarrow{\Delta} CaO(s) + CO_2(g)$
$\Delta H_r^\circ = 1 \times (-635.09 \text{ kJ} \cdot \text{mol}^{-1}) + 1 \times (-393.51 \text{ kJ} \cdot \text{mol}^{-1})$
$- 1 \times (-1206.9 \text{ kJ} \cdot \text{mol}^{-1}) = +178.3 \text{ kJ} \cdot \text{mol}^{-1}$
$\Delta S_r^\circ = 1 \times (39.75 \text{ J} \cdot \text{K}^{-1} \cdot \text{mol}^{-1}) + 1 \times (213.75 \text{ J} \cdot \text{K}^{-1} \cdot \text{mol}^{-1})$
$- 1 \times (92.9 \text{ J} \cdot \text{K}^{-1} \cdot \text{mol}^{-1}) = +160.6 \text{ J} \cdot \text{K}^{-1} \cdot \text{mol}^{-1}$

(b) The temperature at which the equilibrium constant becomes greater than 1 is the temperature at which ΔG_r° crosses over between positive and negative values. Therefore, it is the temperature at which $\Delta G_r^\circ = 0$.
$\Delta G_r^\circ = 0 = \Delta H_r^\circ - T\Delta S_r^\circ = -RT \ln K$ (for $K = 1$, $\ln K = 0$)

$$T = \frac{\Delta H_r^\circ}{\Delta S_r^\circ} = \frac{178,300 \text{ J} \cdot \text{mol}^{-1}}{160.6 \text{ J} \cdot \text{K}^{-1} \cdot \text{mol}^{-1}} = 1110 \text{ K} = 837\,^\circ\text{C}$$

Consequently, at temperatures above 1110 K, $\ln K > 0$ and K becomes greater than 1.

19.41 Epsom salts = $MgSO_4 \cdot 7H_2O$; molar mass = $246.43 \text{ g} \cdot \text{mol}^{-1}$

$$\text{mass \% } H_2O = \frac{7 \times 18.02 \text{ g} \cdot \text{mol}^{-1}}{246.43 \text{ g} \cdot \text{mol}^{-1}} \times 100\% = 51.19\%$$

Group 13: The Boron Family

19.43 The overall equation for the electrolytic reduction in the Hall process is
$4Al^{3+}(\text{melt}) + 6O^{2-}(\text{melt}) + 3C(s, gr) \longrightarrow 4Al(s) + 3CO_2(g)$

19.45 (a) boric acid, $B(OH)_3$
(b) alumina, Al_2O_3
(c) borax, $Na_2B_4O_7 \cdot 10H_2O$
(d) boron oxide, B_2O_3

19.47 (a) $B_2O_3(s) + 3Mg(l) \xrightarrow{\Delta} 2B(s) + 3MgO(s)$

(b) $2Al(s) + 3Cl_2(g) \longrightarrow 2AlCl_3(s)$

(c) $4Al(s) + 3O_2(g) \longrightarrow 2Al_2O_3(s)$

19.49 (a) The hydrate of $AlCl_3$, that is, $AlCl_3 \cdot 6H_2O$, functions as a deodorant and antiperspirant.

(b) α-Alumina is corundum. It is used as an abrasive in sandpaper.

(c) $B(OH)_3$ is an antiseptic and insecticide.

19.51 (a) $B_2H_6(g) + 6H_2O(l) \longrightarrow 2B(OH)_3(aq) + 6H_2(g)$

(b) $B_2H_6(g) + 3O_2(g) \longrightarrow B_2O_3(g) + 3H_2O(l)$

19.53 The cathode reaction is $Al^{3+}(melt) + 3e^- \longrightarrow Al(l)$

charge consumed $= (8.0\ h) \times \left(\dfrac{3600\ s}{1\ h}\right) \times (1.0 \times 10^5\ C \cdot s^{-1}) = 2.88 \times 10^9 C$

mass of Al produced $= (2.88 \times 10^9\ C) \times \left(\dfrac{1\ mol\ e^-}{9.65 \times 10^4\ C}\right) \times \left(\dfrac{1\ mol\ Al}{3\ mol\ e^-}\right)$

$$\times \left(\dfrac{27\ g\ Al}{1\ mol\ Al}\right) = 2.7 \times 10^5\ g\ Al$$

19.55 We want E° for $Tl^{3+}(aq) + 3e^- \longrightarrow Tl(s)$, $n = 3$.

This reaction is the reverse of the formation reaction

$$Tl(s) \longrightarrow Tl^{3+}(aq) + 3e^-$$

Therefore, for the Tl^{3+}/Tl couple, $\Delta G_r^\circ = -215\ kJ \cdot mol^{-1}$.

$\Delta G_r^\circ = -nFE^\circ = -215\ kJ \cdot mol^{-1}$

$E^\circ = \dfrac{\Delta G_r^\circ}{-nF} = \dfrac{-2.15 \times 10^5\ J \cdot mol^{-1}}{-3 \times 9.65 \times 10^4\ C \cdot mol^{-1}} = +0.743\ V$

Group 14: The Carbon Family

19.57 Silicon occurs widely in the Earth's crust in the form of silicates in rocks and as silicon dioxide in sand. It is obtained from quartzite, a form of quartz (SiO_2), by the following processes:

(1) reduction in an electric arc furnace

$$SiO_2(s) + 2C(s) \longrightarrow Si(s, crude) + 2CO(g)$$

(2) purification of the crude product in two steps

$$Si(s, crude) + 2Cl_2(g) \longrightarrow SiCl_4(l)$$

followed by reduction with hydrogen to the pure element

$$SiCl_4(l) + 2H_2(g) \longrightarrow Si(s, pure) + 4HCl(g)$$

19.59 In diamond, carbon is sp^3 hybridized and forms a tetrahedral, three-dimensional network structure, which is extremely rigid. Graphite carbon is sp^2 hybridized and planar, and its application as a lubricant results from the fact that the two-dimensional sheets can "slide" across one another, thereby reducing friction. In graphite, the unhybridized p-electrons are free to move from one carbon atom to another, which results in its high electrical conductivity. In diamond, all electrons are localized in sp^3 hybridized C—C σ-bonds, so diamond is a poor conductor of electricity.

19.61 (a) carborundum, SiC
(b) silica, SiO_2
(c) zircon, $ZrSiO_4$

19.63 (a) $MgC_2(s) + 2H_2O(l) \longrightarrow C_2H_2(g) + Mg(OH)_2(aq)$
(acid-base; carbide ion is the base, water is the acid)
(b) $2Pb(NO_3)_2(s) \longrightarrow 2PbO(s) + 4NO_2(g) + O_2(g)$
(redox; N is reduced, O is oxidized)

19.65 (a) $SiCl_4(l) + 2H_2(g) \longrightarrow Si(s) + 4HCl(g)$
(b) $SiO_2(s) + 3C(s) \xrightarrow{2000°C} SiC(s) + 2CO(g)$
(c) $Ge(s) + 2F_2(g) \longrightarrow GeF_4(s)$
(d) $CaC_2(s) + 2H_2O(l) \longrightarrow Ca(OH)_2(s) + C_2H_2(g)$

19.67

$$\left[\ddot{\underset{..}{O}}-Si-\ddot{\underset{..}{O}} \atop \begin{array}{c} :\ddot{O}: \\ | \\ | \\ :\underset{..}{O}: \end{array} \right]^{4-}$$

Formal charges: Si = 0, O = −1
oxidation numbers: Si = +4, O = −2
This is an AX_4 VSEPR structure; therefore the shape is tetrahedral.

19.69   Silica is SiO_2

$$\text{mass percentage Si} = \frac{\text{molar mass Si}}{\text{molar mass } SiO_2} \times 100\%$$

$$= \frac{28.09 \text{ g} \cdot \text{mol}^{-1}}{60.09 \text{ g} \cdot \text{mol}^{-1}} \times 100\%$$

$$= 46.74\%$$

19.71 $SiO_2(s) + 2C(s) \longrightarrow Si(s) + 2CO(g)$

$\Delta H_r^\circ = \Delta H_f^\circ(\text{products}) - \Delta H_f^\circ(\text{reactants})$

$\quad = [0 + (2)(-110.53 \text{ kJ} \cdot \text{mol}^{-1})] - [-910.54 \text{ kJ} \cdot \text{mol}^{-1} + (2)(0 \text{ kJ} \cdot \text{mol}^{-1})]$

$\quad = -221.06 + 910.94 = +689.88 \text{ kJ} \cdot \text{mol}^{-1}(\text{or} +689.88 \times 10^3 \text{ J} \cdot \text{mol}^{-1})$

$\Delta S_r^\circ = S^\circ(\text{products}) - S^\circ(\text{reactants})$

$\quad = [18.83 \text{ J} \cdot \text{K}^{-1} \cdot \text{mol}^{-1} + (2)(197.67 \text{ J} \cdot \text{K}^{-1} \cdot \text{mol}^{-1})]$

$\qquad\qquad\qquad\qquad - [41.84 \text{ J} \cdot \text{K}^{-1} \cdot \text{mol}^{-1} + (2)(5.740 \text{ J} \cdot \text{K}^{-1} \cdot \text{mol}^{-1})]$

$\quad = 414.17 - 53.32 = +360.85 \text{ J} \cdot \text{K}^{-1} \cdot \text{mol}^{-1}$

$\Delta G_r^\circ = \Delta H_r^\circ - T\Delta S_r^\circ$

$\quad = 689.88 \times 10^3 \text{ J} - (298.15 \text{ K})(360.85 \text{ J} \cdot \text{K}^{-1} \cdot \text{mol}^{-1})$

$\quad = +5.8229 \times 10^5 \text{ J} \cdot \text{mol}^{-1} = +5.8229 \times 10^2 \text{ kJ} \cdot \text{mol}^{-1}$

The temperature at which the equilibrium constant becomes greater than 1 is the temperature at which $\Delta G_r^\circ = -RT \ln K = 0$, because $\ln 1 = 0$. Above this temperature, the equilibrium constant is greater than 1. $\Delta G_r^\circ = 0$ when $T\Delta S_r^\circ = \Delta H_r^\circ$, or

$$T = \frac{\Delta H_r^\circ}{\Delta S_r^\circ} = \frac{+689.88 \times 10^3 \text{ J} \cdot \text{mol}^{-1}}{+360.85 \text{ J} \cdot \text{K}^{-1} \cdot \text{mol}^{-1}} = 1912 \text{ K}$$

19.73 $\text{mass of HF required} = 2.00 \times 10^{-3} \text{ g} \times \left(\dfrac{1 \text{ mol } SiO_2}{60.1 \text{ g } SiO_2}\right) \times \left(\dfrac{6 \text{ mol HF}}{1 \text{ mol } SiO_2}\right)$

$\qquad\qquad\qquad\qquad \times \left(\dfrac{20.0 \text{ g HF}}{1 \text{ mol HF}}\right) = 3.99 \times 10^{-3} \text{ g HF} = 3.99 \text{ mg HF}$

19.75 $\text{surface area} = (1.00 \text{ mol C}) \times \left(\dfrac{12.0 \text{ g C}}{1 \text{ mol C}}\right) \times \left(\dfrac{2000 \text{ m}^2}{1 \text{ g}}\right) = 24.0 \times 10^3 \text{ m}^2$

19.77   (a) The $Si_2O_7^{6-}$ ion is built from two SiO_4^{4-} tetrahedral ions in which the silicate tetrahedra share one O atom. See Figs. 19.42 and 19.43a. This is the only case in which one O is shared.

(b) The pyroxenes, for example, jade, $NaAl(SiO_3)_2$, consist of chains of SiO_4 units in which two O atoms are shared by neighboring units. The repeating unit has the formula SiO_3^{2-}. See Fig. 19.45.

SUPPLEMENTARY EXERCISES

19.79 (a)

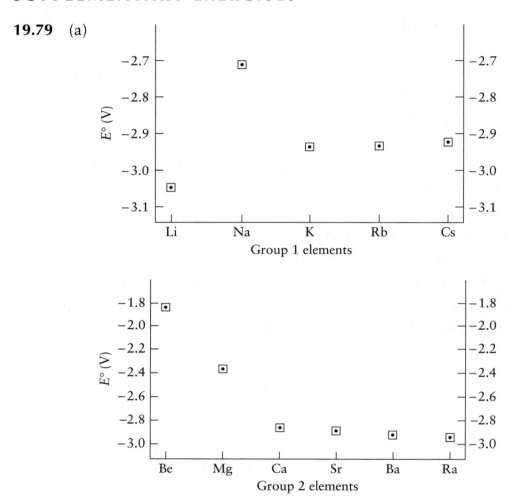

(b) For both groups, the trend in standard potentials with increasing atomic number is overall downward (they become more negative), but lithium is anomalous. This overall downward trend makes sense, because, we expect that it is easier to remove electrons that are farther away from the nuclei. However, because there are several factors that influence ease of removal, the trend is not smooth. The potentials are a net composite of the free energies of sublimation of solids, dissociation of gaseous molecules, ionization enthalpies, and enthalpies of hydration of gaseous ions. The origin of the anomalously strong reducing power of Li is the strongly exothermic energy of hydration of the very small Li^+ ion, which favors the ionization of the element in aqueous solution.

19.81 (a, b)

$$H_2(g) + F_2(g) \longrightarrow 2HF(g), \text{ explosive} \quad \Delta G_f^\circ = -273.2 \text{ kJ} \cdot \text{mol}^{-1}$$
$$H_2(g) + Cl_2(g) \longrightarrow 2HCl(g), \text{ explosive} \quad \Delta G_f^\circ = -95.30 \text{ kJ} \cdot \text{mol}^{-1}$$
$$H_2(g) + Br_2(g) \longrightarrow 2HBr(g), \text{ vigorous} \quad \Delta G_f^\circ = -53.45 \text{ kJ} \cdot \text{mol}^{-1}$$
$$H_2(g) + I_2(g) \longrightarrow 2HI(g), \text{ less vigorous} \quad \Delta G_f^\circ = +1.70 \text{ kJ} \cdot \text{mol}^{-1}$$

The word *vigor* as used here has two components, a thermodynamic one and a kinetic one. ΔG_f° is most negative for HF and becomes slightly positive for HI. So the formation of HF, HCl, and HBr are all thermodynamically spontaneous. The kinetics parallel in this case, the thermodynamic spontaneity, although this parallel behavior is not necessarily true in other systems.

(c) hydrofluoric acid

hydrochloric acid

hydrobromic acid

hydroiodic acid

19.83 (a) The oxide ion, O^{2-}, in CaO acts as a Lewis base and reacts with the Lewis acid SiO_2 in a Lewis acid-base reaction:

$$CaO(s) + SiO_2(s) \longrightarrow CaSiO_3(l)$$

SiO_2, which is an impurity in iron ore, is removed by this reaction. The calcium oxide in this reaction can be obtained from limestone [$CaCO_3(s) \xrightarrow{\Delta} CaO(s) + CO_2(g)$]. This is the reason that limestone is important in the iron industry.

(b) $CaO(s) + CO_2(g) \longrightarrow CaCO_3(s)$ (not an efficient preparation of $CaCO_3$, because of the weak Lewis acidity of CO_2)

19.85 (a) beryl (b) limestone or dolomite (c) dolomite

19.87 (a) The "hardness" of water is due to the presence of calcium and magnesium salts (particularly their hydrogen carbonates). In laundering and bathing, Ca^{2+} and Mg^{2+} cations convert soluble Na^+ soaps to insoluble Ca^{2+} and Mg^{2+} soaps (thereby reducing the detergent efficiency).

(b) Softening can be achieved by removing the Ca^{2+} and Mg^{2+} before they form these insoluble compounds with the use of lime.

$$Ca(HCO_3)_2(aq) + Ca(OH)_2(aq) \longrightarrow 2CaCO_3(s) + 2H_2O(l)$$
$$Mg(HCO_3)_2(aq) + Ca(OH_2)(aq) \longrightarrow Mg(OH)_2(s) + Ca(HCO_3)_2(aq)$$

19.89 The overall reaction is

$$MgCl_2(l) \longrightarrow Mg(l) + Cl_2(g)$$

hence the half-reaction involving Mg is

$$Mg^{2+}(l) + 2e^- \longrightarrow Mg(l)$$

(a) mass of Mg = $(100\ A) \times (1.5\ h) \times \left(\dfrac{3600\ s}{1\ h}\right) \times \left(\dfrac{1\ mol\ e^-}{96{,}500\ C}\right)$

$\times \left(\dfrac{1\ mol\ Mg}{2\ mol\ e^-}\right) \times \left(\dfrac{24.31\ g\ Mg}{1\ mol\ Mg}\right) = 68\ g\ Mg$

(b) At 273 K and 1.00 atm, 1 mol of gas occupies 22.4 L.

volume of Cl_2 = $(1.00 \times 10^6\ g\ Mg) \times \left(\dfrac{1\ mol\ Mg}{24.31\ g\ Mg}\right) \times \left(\dfrac{1\ mol\ Cl_2}{1\ mol\ Mg}\right)$

$\times \left(\dfrac{22.4\ L\ Cl_2}{1\ mol\ Cl_2}\right) = 9.21 \times 10^5\ L\ Cl_2$

19.91 Elemental boron exists in several allotropic forms. It is a gray-black nonmetallic, high-melting-point solid or a dark brown powder based on 12-atom clusters. When mixed with plastics, it produces a light, tough, stiff material. It is inert and resistant to oxidation. Aluminum is a light, strong metal and an excellent conductor of electricity. It is corrosion resistant as a result of the surface oxide layer. It has a low density.

19.93 (a) H_3BO_3, acid; $B(OH)_4^-$, conjugate base

(b) $B(OH)_3(aq) + 2H_2O(l) \rightleftharpoons H_3O^+(aq) + B(HO)_4^-$

19.95 (a) C, [He] $2s^2 2p^2$

(b) In, [Kr] $4d^{10} 5s^2 5p^1$

(c) Ba, [Xe] $6s^2$

(d) Rb, [Kr] $5s^1$

19.97 (a)

Element		Ionization energy, kJ·mol^{-1}	Atomic radius, pm
Group 13	B	799	88
	Al	577	143
	Ga	577	153
	In	556	167
	Tl	590	171
Group 14	C	1090	77
	Si	786	118
	Ge	784	122
	Sn	707	158
	Pb	716	175

Gen. decreasing (ionization energy); Increasing (atomic radius)

(b) The ionization energies generally decrease down a group. As the atomic number of an element increases, atomic shells and subshells that are farther from the nucleus are filled. The outermost valence electrons are consequently easier to remove. The radii increase down a group for the same reason. The radii are primarily determined by the outer shell electrons, which are farther from the nucleus in the heavy elements.

(c) The trends correlate well with elemental properties, for example, the greater ease of outermost electron removal correlates with increased metallic character, that is, ability to form positive ions by losing one or more electrons.

19.99 (a) $2AlCl_3(s) + 3H_2O(l) \longrightarrow 6HCl(g) + Al_2O_3(s)$

(b) $B_2H_6(g) \xrightarrow{\text{high temp.}} 2B(s) + 3H_2(g)$

(c) $4BF_3 + 3BH_4^- \xrightarrow{\text{organic solvent}} 3BF_4^- + 2B_2H_6$

19.101 (a) $2H_2O(l) + 2e^- \longrightarrow H_2(g) + 2OH^-(aq)$

(b) cathode, because this process is reduction

(c) At STP (273 K and 1 atm), 1 mol H_2 occupies 22.4 L.

$$\text{volume of } H_2(g) = (10.0 \text{ A}) \times (30 \text{ min}) \times \left(\frac{60 \text{ s}}{1 \text{ min}}\right) \times \left(\frac{1 \text{ mol } e^-}{9.65 \times 10^4 \text{ A} \cdot \text{s}}\right)$$
$$\times \left(\frac{1 \text{ mol } H_2}{2 \text{ mol } e^-}\right) \times \left(\frac{22.4 \text{ L } H_2}{1 \text{ mol } H_2}\right) = 2.1 \text{ L } H_2$$

CHALLENGING EXERCISES

19.103 In the majority of its reactions, hydrogen acts as a reducing agent, that is, $H_2(g) \longrightarrow 2H^+(aq) + 2e^-$, $E° = 0$ V. In these reactions, hydrogen resembles Group 1 elements, such as Na and K. However, as described in the text and in the answer to Exercise 19.1, it may also act as an oxidizing agent; that is, $H_2(g) + 2e^- \longrightarrow 2H^-(aq)$, $E° = -2.25$ V. In these reactions, hydrogen resembles Group 17 elements, such as Cl and Br. Consequently, H_2 will oxidize elements with standard reduction potentials more negative than -2.25 V, such as the alkali and alkaline earth metals (except Be). The compounds formed are hydrides and contain the H^- ion; the singly charged negative ion is reminiscent of the halide ions. Hydrogen also forms diatomic molecules and covalent bonds like the halogens.

The atomic radius of H is 78 pm, which compares rather well to that of F (64 pm) but not as well to that of Li (157 pm). The ionization energy of H is 1310 kJ · mol^{-1} which is similar to that of F (1680 kJ · mol^{-1}) but not similar to that of Li (519 kJ · mol^{-1}). The electron affinity of H is $+73$ kJ · mol^{-1}, that of F is $+328$ kJ · mol^{-1}, and that of Li is

$60 \text{ kJ} \cdot \text{mol}^{-1}$. So in its atomic radius and ionization energy H more closely resembles the Period 2 halogen, fluorine, in Group 17, than the Period 2 alkali metal, lithuim, in Group 1; whereas in electron affinity, it more closely resembles lithium, Group 1. In electronegativity, H does not resemble elements in either Group 1 or Group 17, although its electronegativity is somewhat closer to those of Group 1. Consequently, hydrogen could be placed in either Group 1 or Group 17. But it is probably best to think of hydrogen as a unique element that has properties in common with both metals and nonmetals; therefore, it should probably be centered in the periodic table, as it is shown in the table in the text.

19.105 (a)

Ion	Radius, pm	Polarizing ability (×1000)	Ion	Radius, pm	Polarizing ability (×1000)
Li^+	58	17	Be^{2+}	27	74
Na^+	102	10	Mg^{2+}	72	28
K^+	138	7.2	Ca^{2+}	100	20
Rb^+	149	6.7	Sr^{2+}	116	17
Cs^+	170	5.9	Ba^{2+}	136	15

(b) These data roughly support the diagonal relationship. Li^+ is more like Mg^{2+} than Be^{2+}, and Na^{2+} is more like Ca^{2+} than Mg^{2+}; but further down the group, the correlation fails. Charge divided by r^3 would be a better measure of polarizing ability.

19.107 $H_2(g) + Br_2(l) \longrightarrow 2HBr(g)$

$$\text{number of moles of HBr} = (0.120 \text{ L H}_2) \times \left(\frac{1 \text{ mol H}_2}{22.4 \text{ L H}_2} \right) \times \left(\frac{2 \text{ mol HBr}}{1 \text{ mol H}_2} \right)$$

$$= 0.0107 \text{ mol}$$

$$\text{molar concentration of HBr} = \frac{0.0107 \text{ mol}}{0.150 \text{ L}} = 0.0714 \text{ mol} \cdot \text{L}^{-1}$$

19.109 The smaller the cation, the greater is the ability of the cation to polarize and weaken the carbonate ion, CO_3^{2-}. On that basis, we would predict that within a group the carbonates of the first members of the group are less stable than those of the later members. Thus, $Li_2CO_3 < Na_2CO_3 < K_2CO_3 < Rb_2CO_3 < Cs_2CO_3$ and $BeCO_3 < MgCO_3 < CaCO_3 < SrCO_3 < BaCO_3$. Between groups, we would expect the stability of the carbonates in one period to decrease from Group 1 to Group 13 because of the smaller size of Group 13 ions. Thus, $Al_2(CO_3)_2 < MgCO_3 < Na_2CO_3$. Carbonates of Group 13 are, in fact, so unstable that they do not exist.

CHAPTER 20
THE MAIN GROUP ELEMENTS:
II. THE LAST FOUR FAMILIES

EXERCISES

Groups 15–18

20.1 (a) He, $1s^2$

(b) O, [He] $2s^2 2p^4$

(c) F, [He] $2s^2 2p^5$

(d) As, [Ar] $3d^{10} 4s^2 4p^3$

20.3 The larger the value of $E°$ for the reduction $X_2 + 2e^- \longrightarrow 2X^-$, the greater the oxidizing strength of the halogen X_2. From Appendix 2B,

$$F_2 + 2e^- \longrightarrow 2F^- \quad E° = +2.87 \text{ V}$$
$$Cl_2 + 2e^- \longrightarrow 2Cl^- \quad E° = +1.36 \text{ V}$$
$$Br_2 + 2e^- \longrightarrow 2Br^- \quad E° = +1.09 \text{ V}$$
$$I_2 + 2e^- \longrightarrow 2I^- \quad E° = +0.54 \text{ V}$$

Thus, $I_2 < Br_2 < Cl_2 < F_2$.

20.5 Refer to Appendix 2D.

Element	χ	
O	3.4	↑
S	2.6	Increasing electro-negativity
P	2.2	
As	2.2	

Thus, As $\approx$ P $<$ S $<$ O

Group 15

20.7 The first step is the liquefaction of air, which is 76% by mass nitrogen. Air is cooled to below its boiling point by a series of expansion and compression steps in a kind of refrigerator. Nitrogen gas is then obtained by distillation of liquid air. The nitrogen boils off at $-196°C$, but gases with higher boiling points, principally O_2, remain as a liquid. The pure nitrogen gas is then liquefied by repeating the process.

20.9   (a) HNO_2, nitrous acid

(b) NO, nitrogen oxide or nitric oxide

(c) H_3PO_4, phosphoric acid

(d) N_2O_3, dinitrogen trioxide

20.11   (a) ammonium nitrate, NH_4NO_3

(b) magnesium nitride, Mg_3N_2

(c) calcium phosphide, Ca_3P_2

(d) hydrazine, H_2NNH_2

20.13   (a) $2NH_3(g) + 3CuO(s) \longrightarrow N_2(g) + 3Cu(s) + 3H2O(l)$

(b) $4NH_3(g) + 3F_2(g) \longrightarrow NF_3(g) + 3NH_4F(s)$

(c) $4NH_3(g) + 5O_2(g) \longrightarrow 4NO(g) + 6H_2O(l)$

20.15   Let N_{ox} = oxidation number. The sum of the oxidation numbers must equal the charge on the species.

(a) $1 \times N_{ox}(N) + 1 \times N_{ox}(O) = 0$

$1 \times N_{ox}(N) + 1 \times (-2) = 0$

Therefore, $N_{ox}(N) = +2$

(b) $2 \times N_{ox}(N) + 1 \times N_{ox}(O) = 0$

$2 \times N_{ox}(N) + 1 \times (-2) = 0$

Therefore, $N_{ox}(N) = +1$

(c) $1 \times N_{ox}(H) + 1 \times N_{ox}(N) + 2 \times N_{ox}(O) = 0$

$1 \times (+1) + 1 \times N_{ox}(N) + 2 \times (-2) = 0$

Therefore, $N_{ox}(N) = -1 - (-4) = +3$

(d) $N_{ox}(N) = \frac{1}{3}(-1) = -\frac{1}{3}$

20.17 $CO(NH_2)_2 + 2H_2O \longrightarrow (NH_4)_2CO_3$

mass of $(NH_4)_2CO_3$ = $(5.0 \text{ kg urea}) \times \left(\dfrac{10^3 \text{ g urea}}{1 \text{ kg urea}}\right) \times \left(\dfrac{1 \text{ mol urea}}{60 \text{ g urea}}\right)$

$\times \left(\dfrac{1 \text{ mol } (NH_4)_2CO_3}{1 \text{ mol urea}}\right) \times \left(\dfrac{96 \text{ g } (NH_4)_2CO_3}{1 \text{ mol } (NH_4)_2CO_3}\right) = 8.0 \times 10^3 \text{ g (or 8.0 kg)}(NH_4)_2CO_3$

20.19   (a) 1 mol of $N_2(g)$ occupies 22.4 L at STP. For the reaction $Pb(N_3)_2 \longrightarrow Pb + 3N_2$, the volume of $N_2(g)$ produced is

$$(1.0 \text{ g Pb}(N_3)_2) \times \left(\frac{1 \text{ mol Pb}(N_3)_2}{291 \text{ g Pb}(N_3)_2}\right) \times \left(\frac{3 \text{ mol } N_2}{1 \text{ mol Pb}(N_3)_2}\right)$$

$$\times \left(\frac{22.4 \text{ L } N_2}{1 \text{ mol } N_2}\right) = 0.23 \text{ L } N_2(g)$$

(b) $Hg(N_3)_2$ would produce a larger volume, because its molar mass is less. Note that molar mass occurs in the denominator in this calculation.

20.21 N_2O: $H_2N_2O_2$; $N_2O(g) + H_2O(l) \longrightarrow H_2N_2O_2(aq)$

N_2O_3: HNO_2; $N_2O_3(g) + H_2O(l) \longrightarrow 2HNO_2(aq)$

N_2O_5: HNO_3; $N_2O_5(g) + H_2O(l) \longrightarrow 2HNO_3(aq)$

20.23

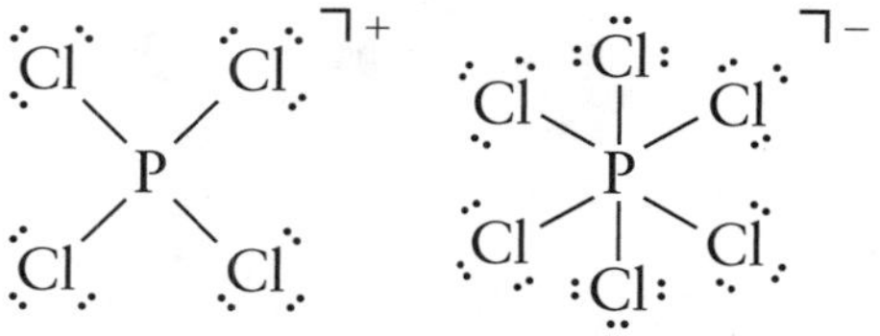

PCl$_4^+$, AX$_4$
tetrahedral

PCl$_6^-$, AX$_6$
octahedral

20.25 (a) superphosphate, $2CaSO_4 + Ca(H_2PO_4)_2$

$$\%P = \frac{2 \times \text{molar mass P}}{\left(\begin{array}{c}3 \times \text{molar mass Ca} + 2 \times \text{molar mass S} + 16 \times \text{molar mass O} \\ + 4 \times \text{molar mass H} + 2 \times \text{molar mass P}\end{array}\right)} \times 100\%$$

$$\%P = \frac{[2(30.97)] \text{ g} \cdot \text{mol}^{-1}}{[3(40.08) + 2(32.06) + 16(16.00) + 4(1.00) + 2(30.97)] \text{ g} \cdot \text{mol}^{-1}} \times 100\%$$

$$\%P = \frac{61.94}{(120.24 + 64.12 + 256.00 + 4.00 + 61.94)} \times 100\% = 12.23\%$$

(b) triple superphosphate, $Ca(H_2PO_4)_2$

$$\%P = \frac{2 \times \text{molar mass P}}{\left(\begin{array}{c}1 \times \text{molar mass Ca} + 4 \times \text{molar mass H} + 2 \times \text{molar mass P} \\ + 8 \times \text{molar mass O}\end{array}\right)} \times 100\%$$

$$\%P = \frac{[2(30.97)] \text{ g} \cdot \text{mol}^{-1}}{[1(40.80) + 4(1.00) + 2(30.97) + 8(16.00)] \text{ g} \cdot \text{mol}^{-1}} \times 100\% = 26.47\%$$

Group 16

20.27 (a) H_2SO_4 (b) $CaSO_3$ (c) O_3 (d) BaO_2

20.29 Underground deposits of elemental sulfur are recovered by the Frasch process. Steam and hot water are forced into the deposit, causing the sulfur to melt. The molten sulfur mixes with the water and the mixture is forced to the surface by compressed air.

20.31
(a) $4Li(s) + O_2(g) \xrightarrow{\Delta} 2Li_2O(s)$

(b) $2Na(s) + 2H_2O(l) \longrightarrow 2NaOH(aq) + H_2(g)$

(c) $2F_2(g) + 2H_2O(l) \longrightarrow 4HF(aq) + O_2(g)$

(d) $2H_2O(l) \longrightarrow O_2(g) + 4H^+(aq) + 4e^-$

20.33
(a) $2H_2S(g) + 3O_2(g) \longrightarrow 2SO_2(g) + 2H_2O(g)$

(b) $CaO(s) + H_2O(l) \longrightarrow Ca(OH)_2(aq)$

(c) $PCl_5(s) + 4H_2O(l) \longrightarrow H_3PO_4(aq) + 5HCl(g)$

20.35

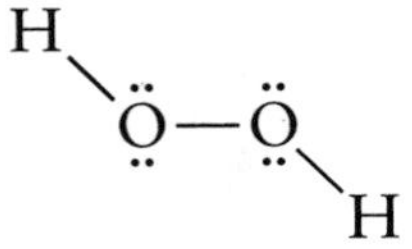

Each O in H_2O_2 is an AX_2E_2 structure; hence the bond angle is predicted to be $<109.5°$. In actuality, it is $97°$.

20.37 (a) When we consider formal charges and allow the possibility of expanded octets in S atoms, we can visualize two types of resonance structures that might contribute to the overall structure of SO_2:

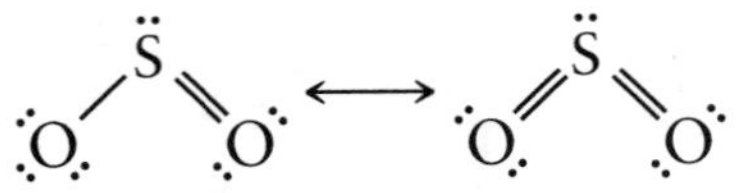

(2 ways)   (1 way)

The completely double-bonded structure has zero formal charge on all atoms and, as a result, may predominate in the resonance hybrid. Both structures have angular geometry.

(b)

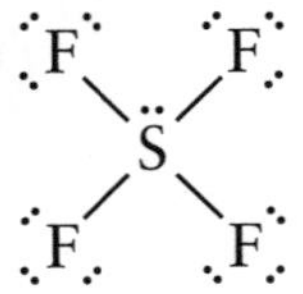

SF_4 is an AX_4E VSEPR structure. Therefore, its shape is seesaw.

(c) When we consider formal charges and the possibility of expanded octets in S atoms, we can visualize three types of resonance structures that might contribute to the overall structure of SO_4^{2-}:

$$:\ddot{O}: \quad \rceil^{2-} \qquad :\ddot{O}: \quad \rceil^{2-} \qquad :\ddot{O}: \quad \rceil^{2-}$$
$$:\ddot{O}-\underset{\underset{:\ddot{O}:}{|}}{\overset{|}{S}}-\ddot{O}: \quad \longleftrightarrow \quad :\ddot{O}-\underset{\underset{:\ddot{O}:}{|}}{\overset{|}{S}}=\ddot{O} \quad \longleftrightarrow \quad \ddot{O}=\underset{\underset{:\ddot{O}:}{|}}{\overset{|}{S}}=\ddot{O}$$

(1 way)   (4 ways)   (6 ways)

The third type of structure, which has smaller average differences in formal charge between the S and O atoms, may be the predominant structure. All three structures have tetrahedral geometry.

20.39 $2H_2O_2(l) \longrightarrow 2H_2O(l) + O_2(g)$

Assume 3% by mass. At 273 K and 1.00 atm, 1 mol O_2 has a volume of 22.4 L.

$$\text{volume of } O_2 = (500 \text{ mL soln}) \times \left(\frac{1.0 \text{ g soln}}{1.0 \text{ mL soln}}\right) \times \left(\frac{0.03 \text{ g } H_2O_2}{1.0 \text{ g soln}}\right)$$

$$\times \left(\frac{1 \text{ mol } H_2O_2}{34.0 \text{ g } H_2O_2}\right) \times \left(\frac{1 \text{ mol } O_2}{2 \text{ mol } H_2O_2}\right) \times \left(\frac{22.4 \text{ L } O_2}{1 \text{ mol } O_2}\right) = 4.\bar{9} \text{ L } O_2 = 5 \text{ L } O_2$$

20.41 $O_2^{2-} + H_2O \rightleftharpoons HO_2^- + OH^-$ essentially complete

$$HO_2^- + H_2O \rightleftharpoons H_2O_2 + OH^- \quad K_b = \frac{K_w}{K_{a1}}$$

$$K_{a1} = 1.8 \times 10^{-12} \quad K_b = \frac{1.00 \times 10^{-14}}{1.8 \times 10^{-12}} = 5.6 \times 10^{-3}$$

Because this K_b is relatively small, we can assume that essentially all the OH^- is formed in the first ionization; hence,

$$[OH^-] = \left(\frac{2.00 \text{ g } Na_2O_2}{0.200 \text{ L}}\right) \times \left(\frac{1 \text{ mol } Na_2O_2}{78.0 \text{ g } Na_2O_2}\right) \times \left(\frac{1 \text{ mol } OH^-}{1 \text{ mol } Na_2O_2}\right) = 0.128 \text{ mol} \cdot L^{-1}$$

$pOH = -\log(0.128) = 0.89$ $pH = 14.00 - 0.89 = 13.11$

If we do not ignore the second ionization, then the additional contribution to $[OH^-]$ can be approximately calculated as follows:

$$K_b = \frac{[H_2O_2][OH^-]}{[HO_2^-]} = \frac{x(0.128 + x)}{(0.128 - x)} = 5.6 \times 10^{-3}$$

To a first approximation, $x = 5.6 \times 10^{-3} \text{ mol} \cdot L^{-1}$

To a second approximation, $x = \dfrac{K_b(0.128 - 0.0056)}{(0.128 + 0.0056)} = 0.005$

Then $[OH^-] = 0.128 + 0.005 = 0.133$; $pOH = -\log(0.133) = 0.88$; and $pH = 13.12$. The difference between calculations is slight.

20.43 See Fig. 9.16 for bond strengths. The weaker the H—X bond, the stronger the acid. H_2Te has the weakest bond; H_2O, the strongest. Therefore, the acid strengths are $H_2Te > H_2Se > H_2S > H_2O$.

20.45 $\frac{3}{2}O_2(g) \longrightarrow O_3(g)$

    (a) $\Delta H_f^{\circ}(O_3, g) = 142.7 \text{ kJ} \cdot \text{mol}^{-1}$

    $\Delta S_f^{\circ}(O_3, g) = 238.93 \text{ J} \cdot \text{K}^{-1} \cdot \text{mol}^{-1} - \frac{3}{2} \times 205.14 \text{ J} \cdot \text{K}^{-1} \cdot \text{mol}^{-1}$

                 $= -68.78 \text{ J} \cdot \text{K}^{-1} \cdot \text{mol}^{-1}$

    (b) $\Delta G_f^{\circ}(O_3, g) \approx \Delta H_f^{\circ}(O_3, g, 25°C) - T\Delta S_f^{\circ}(O_3, g, 25°C)$

Because $\Delta G_f^{\circ}(O_3, g)$ is positive at all temperatures, the reaction is not spontaneous at any temperature. It is less favored at high temperatures.

    (c) Because the reaction entropy is negative, the $-T\Delta S_f^{\circ}$ term is always positive; so the entropy contribution to ΔG_f° is always positive, and the entropy does not favor the spontaneous formation of ozone.

Group 17

20.47 Fluorine comes from the minerals fluorspar, CaF_2; cryolite Na_3AlF_6; and the fluorapatites, $Ca_5F(PO_4)_3$. The free element is prepared from HF and KF by electrolysis, but the HF and the KF needed for the electrolysis are prepared in the laboratory. Chlorine primarily comes from the mineral rock salt, NaCl. The pure element is obtained by electrolysis of liquid NaCl.

20.49 Fluorine: KF acts as an electrolyte for the electrolytic process, but the net reaction is

$$2H^+ + 2F^- \xrightarrow{\text{current}} H_2(g) + F_2(g)$$

Chlorine:

$$2NaCl(l) \xrightarrow{\text{current}} 2Na(s) + Cl_2(g)$$

20.51 (a) HBr(aq), hydrobromic acid

    (b) IBr, iodine bromide

    (c) ClO_2, chlorine dioxide

    (d) $NaIO_3$, sodium iodate

20.53 (a) perchloric acid, $HClO_4(aq)$

    (b) sodium chlorate, $NaClO_3$

    (c) hydroiodic acid, HI(aq)

(d) sodium triiodide, NaI_3

20.55 (a) $HIO(aq)$ $H = +1$, $O = -2$; therefore, $I = +1$
(b) ClO_2 $O = -2$; therefore, $Cl = +4$
(c) Cl_2O_7 $O = -2$; therefore, $Cl = +14/2 = +7$
(d) $NaIO_3$ $Na = +1$, $O = -2$; therefore, $I = +5$

20.57 (a)

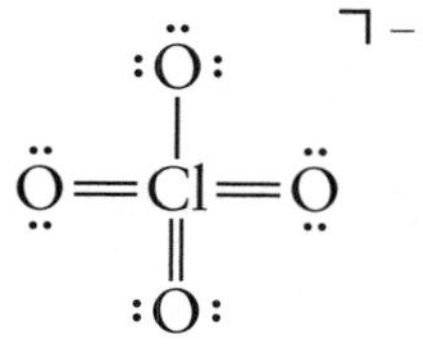

AX_4, tetrahedral electronic arrangement and shape
Note: This structure is the preferred structure based on formal charge considerations; alternative structures with 0, 1, 2, and 4 double bonds could be drawn. All structures have the same geometry, however. See Exercises 20.37 and 20.38 for similar examples in sulfur-containing compounds.

(b)

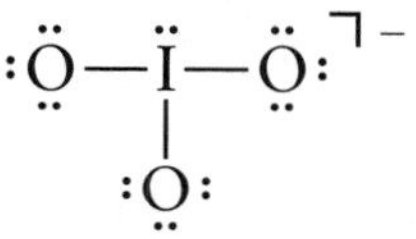

AX_3E, tetrahedral electronic arrangement, trigonal pyramidal shape
Note: Lewis structures with one and two iodine-oxygen double bonds are also possible. All structures have the same geometry. See the note above in part (a).

(c)

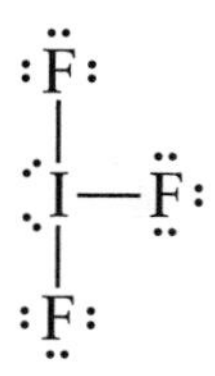

AX_3E_2, trigonal bipyramidal electronic arrangement, T-shaped

20.59 (a) $4KClO_3(l) \xrightarrow{\Delta} 3KClO_4(s) + KCl(s)$
(b) $Br_2(l) + H_2O(l) \longrightarrow HBrO(aq) + HBr(aq)$
(c) $NaCl(s) + H_2SO_4(aq) \longrightarrow NaHSO_4(aq) + HCl(g)$
(d) (a) and (b) are redox reactions. In (a), Cl is both oxidized and reduced. In (b), Br is both oxidized and reduced.
(c) is a Brønsted acid-base reaction; H_2SO_4 is the acid, and Cl^- the base.

309

20.61 (a) $HClO < HClO_2 < HClO_3 < HClO_4$ ($HClO_4$ is strongest; $HClO$, weakest)

(b) The oxidation number of Cl increases from HClO to $HClO_4$. In $HClO_4$, chlorine has its highest oxidation number of $+7$, so $HClO_4$ will be the strongest oxidizing agent.

20.63

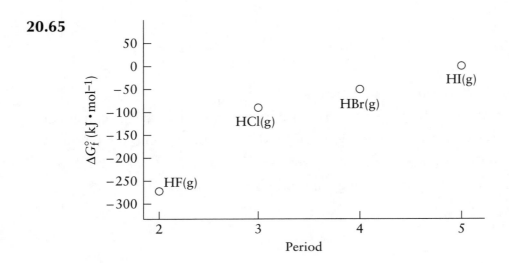

AX_2E_2, angular, slightly less than $109°$

20.65

The thermodynamic stability of the hydrogen halides decreases down the group. The ΔG_f° values of HCl, HBr, and HI fit nicely on a straight line; whereas HF is anomalous. In other properties, HF is also the anomalous member of the group, in particular, its acidity. Also see Exercise 20.66.

20.67 $Cl_2(g) + 2e^- \longrightarrow 2Cl^-(aq)$ $E° = +1.36$ V

$MnO_4^-(aq) + 8H^+(aq) + 5e^- \longrightarrow Mn^{2+}(aq) + 4H_2O(l)$ $E° = +1.51$ V

$E_{cell}° = (1.36 - 1.51)$ V $= -0.15$ V

Because $E_{cell}°$ is negative, $Cl_2(g)$ will not oxidize Mn^{2+} to form the permanganate ion in an acidic solution.

20.69 $\frac{1}{2}H_2(g) + \frac{1}{2}I_2(s) \rightleftharpoons HI(g)$

$\Delta G_r° = \Delta G_f°(HI, g) = 1.70$ kJ $\cdot$ mol^{-1}

$\Delta G_r° = -RT \ln K_p$

$$\ln K_p = \frac{-1.70 \times 10^3 \text{ J} \cdot \text{mol}^{-1}}{8.31 \text{ J} \cdot \text{mol}^{-1} \cdot \text{K}^{-1} \times 298 \text{ K}} = -0.686$$

$$K_p = 0.504$$

20.71 $F^-(aq) + PbCl_2(s) \longrightarrow Cl^-(aq) + PbClF(s)$

$$\text{molarity of } F^- \text{ ions} = \left(\frac{0.765 \text{ g PbClF}}{0.0250 \text{ L}} \right) \times \left(\frac{1 \text{ mol PbClF}}{262 \text{ g PbClF}} \right) \times \left(\frac{1 \text{ mol } F^-}{1 \text{ mol PbClF}} \right)$$

$$= 0.117 \text{ mol} \cdot \text{L}^{-1}$$

Group 18

20.73 Helium occurs as a component of natural gases found under rock formations in certain locations, especially some in Texas. Argon is obtained by distillation of liquid air.

20.75 (a) KrF_2: $F = -1$; therefore, $Kr = +2$
      (b) XeF_6: $F = -1$; therefore, $Xe = +6$
      (c) KrF_4: $F = -1$; therefore, $Kr = +4$
      (d) XeO_4^{2-}: $O = -2$, $N_{ox}(Xe) + 4 \times (-2) = -2$; therefore, $N_{ox}(Xe)$
$$= -2 - (-8) = +6$$

20.77 $XeF_4 + 4H^+ + 4e^- \longrightarrow Xe + 4HF$

20.79 Because H_4XeO_6 has more highly electronegative O atoms bonded to Xe, we predict that H_4XeO_6 is more acidic than H_2XeO_4.

20.81

AX_4E_2, square planar, hence 90°

SUPPLEMENTARY EXERCISES

20.83 Ionization energies increase; electron affinities also increase (in magnitude). Large ionization energies and electron affinities are characteristic of nonmetals. Electronegativities and standard reduction potentials increase as well; large values of these properties are also characteristic of nonmetals.

20.85 (a)

$$NO_2^- \quad \left[:\ddot{O}-\ddot{N}=\ddot{O}\right]^- \longleftrightarrow \left[\ddot{O}=\ddot{N}-\ddot{O}:\right]^-$$

$$NO_3^- \quad \ddot{O}=N\begin{smallmatrix}\nearrow\ddot{O}:\\ \searrow\ddot{O}:\end{smallmatrix}^- \longleftrightarrow :\ddot{O}-N\begin{smallmatrix}\nearrow\ddot{O}:\\ \searrow\ddot{O}:\end{smallmatrix}^- \longleftrightarrow :\ddot{O}-N\begin{smallmatrix}\nearrow\ddot{O}:\\ \searrow\ddot{O}\end{smallmatrix}^-$$

(b) NO_2^-: AX_2E, trigonal planar electron pair arrangement, therefore sp^2 hybridization

NO_3^-: AX_3, trigonal planar electron pair arrangement, therefore sp^2 hybridization

20.87 oxidation: $As_2S_3(s) + 8H_2O(l) \longrightarrow 2AsO_4^{3-}(aq) + 3S^{2-}(aq) + 16H^+(aq) + 4e^-$

reduction: $H_2O_2(aq) + 2H^+(aq) + 2e^- \longrightarrow 2H_2O(l)$

Multiply the reduction reaction by 2, cancel electrons, and add.

overall: $As_2S_3(s) + 2H_2O_2(aq) \longrightarrow 2AsO_4^{3-}(aq) + 3S^{2-}(aq) + 12H^+(aq)$

20.89 This ratio, $\Delta H_{vap}/T_b$, is the entropy of vaporization. See Section 16.11 and Example 16.3. Hydrogen bonding is much stronger in $H_2O(l)$ than in $H_2S(l)$. Thus $H_2O(l)$ has a more ordered arrangement than $H_2S(l)$. Consequently, the change in entropy upon transformation to the gaseous state is greater for H_2O than for H_2S.

20.91 $Ca_3(PO_4)_2(s) + 3H_2SO_4(l) \longrightarrow 2H_3PO_4(l) + 3CaSO_4(s)$

$$\text{volume} = (1000 \text{ kg } H_3PO_4) \times \left(\frac{10^3 \text{ g } H_3PO_4}{1 \text{ kg } H_3PO_4}\right) \times \left(\frac{1 \text{ mol } H_3PO_4}{98.0 \text{ g } H_3PO_4}\right) \times \left(\frac{3 \text{ mol } H_2SO_4}{2 \text{ mol } H_3PO_4}\right)$$

$$\times \left(\frac{98.1 \text{ g } H_2SO_4}{1 \text{ mol } H_2SO_4}\right) \times \left(\frac{1 \text{ mL}}{1.84 \text{ g}}\right) \times \left(\frac{10^{-3} \text{ L}}{1 \text{ mL}}\right) = 8.16 \times 10^2 \text{ L conc. } H_2SO_4$$

20.93 (a) $SO_2(g) + H_2O(l) \longrightarrow H_2SO_3(l)$ This is a Lewis acid-base reaction. SO_2 is the acid and H_2O is the base.

(b) $2F_2(g) + 2NaOH(aq) \longrightarrow OF_2(g) + 2NaF(aq) + H_2O(l)$ This is a redox reaction illustrating the oxidizing ability of F_2 in basic solution and is used for the preparation of $OF_2(g)$. O is oxidized and F is reduced.

(c) $S_2O_3^{2-}(aq) + 4Cl_2(g) + 13H_2O(l) \longrightarrow 2HSO_4^-(aq) + 8H_3O^+(aq) + 8Cl^-(aq)$ This is a redox reaction illustrating the oxidizing power of $Cl_2(g)$ in acidic solution. S is oxidized and Cl is reduced.

(d) $2XeF_6(s) + 16OH^-(aq) \longrightarrow XeO_6^{4-}(aq) + Xe(g) + 12F^-(aq) + 8H_2O(l) + O_2(g)$ This is a redox reaction that is also a disproportionation reaction in that

Xe goes from oxidation number $+6$ to $+8$ and to 0. Xe is both oxidized and reduced.

20.95 Fluorine:

(1) The production of UF_6, which is part of the procedure for separating the isotopes ^{238}U and ^{235}U for use in nuclear processes.

(2) The production of SF_6 for electrical equipment.

(3) The production of fluorinated hydrocarbons, such as Teflon.

Chlorine:

(1) The manufacture of many important chemicals, including plastics, solvents, and many organic chemicals.

(2) As a bleach and a disinfectant.

(3) The production of bromine.

Bromine:

(1) The production of organic bromides, which are incorporated into textiles as fire retardants; others are used as pesticides.

(2) In photography, as AgBr, which is the active part of photographic emulsions.

(3) In the oil industry, in the form of high-density aqueous zinc bromide, which is used to control the escape of oil from deep wells.

(4) Alkali and alkaline earth metal bromides are used as sedatives.

Iodine:

(1) Iodides are used as an additive to table salt to prevent iodine deficiency, which leads to thyroid disorders.

(2) As an antiseptic in alcohol solution.

(3) In photography, as AgI.

20.97 (a) $I_2(s) + 3F_2(g) \longrightarrow 2IF_3(s)$

(b) $I_2(aq) + I^-(aq) \longrightarrow I_3^-(aq)$

(c) $Cl_2(g) + H_2O(l) \longrightarrow HCl(aq) + HOCl(aq)$

But there are competing reactions, such as $Cl_2(g) + H_2O(l) \longrightarrow 2HCl(aq) + \frac{1}{2}O_2(g)$. The predominant reaction is determined by the temperature and pH.

(d) $2F_2(g) + 2H_2O(l) \longrightarrow 4HF(aq) + O_2(g)$

20.99 (a) $CaCl_2(s) + 2H_2SO_4(aq, conc) \longrightarrow Ca(HSO_4)_2(aq) + 2HCl(g)$

(b) $KBr(s) + H_3PO_4(aq) \xrightarrow{\Delta} KH_2PO_4(aq) + HBr(g)$

(c) $KI(s) + H_3PO_4(aq) \xrightarrow{\Delta} KH_2PO_4(aq) + HI(g)$

20.101 (a) +3: N_2O_3, dinitrogen trioxide

HNO_2, nitrous acid

KNO_2, potassium nitrite

+5: N_2O_5, dinitrogen pentoxide

HNO_3, nitric acid

KNO_3, potassium nitrate

(b) +3: P_4O_6, phosphorus(III) oxide

H_3PO_3, phophorous acid

K_2HPO_3, potassium hydrogen phosphite

+5: P_4O_{10}, phosphorous(V) oxide

H_3PO_4, phosphoric acid

$Na_4P_2O_7$, sodium pyrophosphate

20.103 The heads of matches consist of a paste of potassium chlorate ($KClO_3$), antimony sulfide, (Sb_2S_3), sulfur, and powdered glass. The striking strip contains red phosphorus. When the match is struck against the red phosphorus surface, a reaction of the red phosphorus and potassium chlorate causes the match to ignite. The Sb_2S_3 and sulfur are the fuels that are consumed by combustion after the ignition. The powdered glass helps to produce the friction required for ignition.

20.105

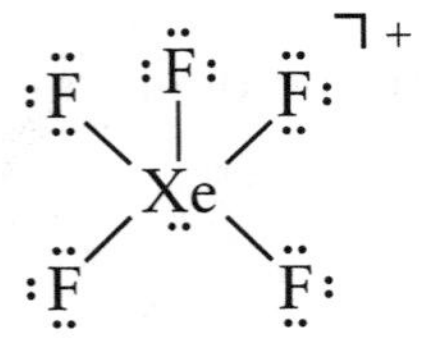

AX_5E, square pyramidal

20.107 Until 1962, when their first compounds were prepared, the closed-shell electron configurations of the noble gases were taken to indicate that these elements were chemically inert. The noble gases all have high ionization energies and low (in magnitude) electron affinities. This combination implies chemical inertness. Thus, compounds were not actively sought. In addition, the noble gases do not form compounds easily; the reagents and apparatus that promote reaction were not available until recent years.

20.109 Proceeding down Group 14, carbon exhibits little metallic character, but Si is already a semimetal or semiconductor. Tin and lead show pronounced metallic character, with low ionization energies and high electrical conductivities. They also form cations of more than one charge type, which is characteristic of metals. Proceeding down Group 15, P, which is the neighbor of Si, shows little metallic character; As shows some, but not as much metallic character as its neighbor Ge. The last member of this group, Bi, shows pronounced metallic character. Proceeding down Group 16, Se and Te show definite metallic character, about the same as As and Sb, but less than Ge and Sn. So there is a big difference in the metallic character of the heavy members of Groups 14 and 15, but only a slight difference between Groups 15 and 16. This pattern is most evident when one compares the ionization energies in Fig. 7.31. Group 14 elements have lower ionization energies than do the elements in Groups 15 and 16, but the ionization energies of the elements in Groups 15 and 16 are about the same.

CHALLENGING EXERCISES

20.111 (a) $[\ddot{N}\!=\!N\!=\!\ddot{N}]^-$

AX_2, linear, $180°$

(b) F^-, 133 pm $\quad N_3^-$, 148 pm $\quad Cl^-$, 181 pm $\quad$ hence, between fluorine and chlorine

(c) HCl, HBr, and HI are all strong acids. For HF, $K_a = 3.5 \times 10^{-4}$, so HF is slightly more acidic than HN_3. The small size of the azide ion suggests that the H—N bond in HN_3 is similar in strength to that of the H—F bond, so it is expected to be a weak acid.

(d) ionic: $\quad NaN_3$, $Pb(N_3)_2$, AgN_3, etc.

covalent: $\quad HN_3$, $B(N_3)_3$, FN_3, etc.

20.113 molar concentration of $ClO^- = (0.02834 \text{ L Na}_2\text{S}_2\text{O}_3) \times \left(\dfrac{0.110 \text{ mol S}_2\text{O}_3^{2-}}{1 \text{ L Na}_2\text{S}_2\text{O}_3} \right)$

$\times \left(\dfrac{1 \text{ mol I}_2}{2 \text{ mol S}_2\text{O}_3^{2-}} \right) \times \left(\dfrac{1 \text{ mol ClO}^-}{1 \text{ mol I}_2} \right) \times \left(\dfrac{1}{0.010\,00 \text{ L ClO}^-} \right) = 0.156 \text{ mol} \cdot \text{L}^{-1}$

20.115 The solubility of the ionic halides is determined by a variety of factors, especially the lattice enthalpy and enthalpy of hydration. There is a delicate balance between the two factors, with the lattice enthalpy usually being the determining one. Lattice enthalpies decrease from chloride to iodide, so water molecules can more readily separate the ions in the latter. Less ionic halides, such as the silver halides, generally have a much lower solubility, and the trend in solubility is the reverse of the more ionic halides. For the less ionic halides, the covalent character of the bond allows the ion pairs to persist in water. The ions are not easily hydrated, making them less soluble. The polarizability of the halide ions, and thus, the covalency of their bonding, increases down the group.

CHAPTER 21
THE *d*-BLOCK:
METALS IN TRANSITION

EXERCISES

The d-Block Elements and Their Electron Configurations

21.1 (a) Rh, rhodium (b) Ag, silver (c) Pd, palladium (d) W, tungsten

21.3 (a) Mn, [Ar] $3d^5 4s^2$
(b) Cd, [Kr] $4d^{10} 5s^2$
(c) Zn, [Ar] $3d^{10} 4s^2$
(d) Zr, [Kr] $4d^2 5s^2$

21.5 (a) Sc, [Ar] $3d^1 4s^2$: one unpaired $3d$-electron
(b) V, [Ar] $3d^3 4s^2$: three unpaired $3d$-electrons
(c) Cu, [Ar] $3d^{10} 4s^1$: one unpaired $4s$-electron
(d) Au, [Xe] $4f^{14} 5d^{10} 6s^1$: one unpaired $6s$-electron

21.7 iron, Fe; cobalt, Co; nickel, Ni

Trends in Properties

21.9 See Figs. 21.2 and 21.4
(a) Sc (b) Au (c) Nb

21.11 See Fig. 7.32 and Appendix 2D.
(a) Ti (b) Cu (c) Zn

21.13 The lanthanide contraction accounts for the failure of the third-row (Period 6) metallic radii to increase as expected relative to the radii of the second row (Period 5). It results from the presence of the *f*-block orbitals. The *f*-electrons present in the lanthanides are even poorer as nuclear shields than *d*-electrons, and a marked decrease in metallic radius occurs along the *f*-block elements as a result of the increased effective nuclear charge, which pulls the electrons inward. When the *d*-block resumes (at lutetium), the metallic radius has "contracted" from 188 to 157 pm. Therefore, all the elements following lutetium have smaller-than-expected radii. Examples of this effect include the high density of the Period 6 elements and lack of reactivity of gold and platinum.

21.15 Hg is much more dense than Cd, because the shrinkage in atomic radius that occurs between $Z = 58$ and $Z = 71$ (the lanthanide contraction) causes the atoms following the rare earths to be smaller than might have been expected for their atomic masses and atomic numbers. Zn and Cd have densities that are not too dissimilar, because the radius of Cd is subject to only a smaller *d*-block contraction.

21.17 Proceeding down a group in the *d*-block (for example, from Cr to Mo to W), there is an increasing probability of finding the elements in higher oxidation states. That is, higher oxidation states become more stable on going down a group.

21.19 In MO_3, M has an oxidation number of $+6$. Of these three elements, the $+6$ oxidation state is most stable for Cr. See Fig. 21.7.

Scandium through Nickel

21.21 (a) $TiO_2(s) + 2C(s) + Cl_2(g) \xrightarrow{1000°C} TiCl_4(g) + 2CO(g)$,

followed by $TiCl_4(g) + 2\,Mg(l) \xrightarrow{700°C} Ti(s) + 2MgCl_2(s)$
(b) $V_2O_5(g) + 5Ca(l) \longrightarrow 5CaO(s) + 2V(s)$

21.23 (a) $Ti(s)$, $MgCl_2(s)$
$TiCl_4(g) + 2Mg(l) \longrightarrow Ti(s) + 2MgCl_2(s)$
(b) $Co^{2+}(aq)$, $HCO_3^-(aq)$, $NO_3^-(aq)$
$CoCO_3(s) + HNO_3(aq) \longrightarrow Co^{2+}(aq) + HCO_3^-(aq) + NO_3^-(aq)$
(c) $V(s)$, $CaO(s)$
$V_2O_5(s) + 5Ca(l) \xrightarrow{\Delta} 2V(s) + 5CaO(s)$

21.25 (a) titanium(IV) oxide, TiO_2
(b) iron(III) oxide, Fe_2O_3
(c) manganese(IV) oxide, MnO_2

21.27 (a) $E°$ ($Cr_2O_7^{2-}/Cr^{3+}$) = +1.33 V, $E°$ (Br_2/Br^-) = +1.09 V

Yes, $Cr_2O_7^{2-}$ is a stronger oxidizing agent than Br_2.

(b) $E°(Ag^{2+}/Ag^+)$ = +1.98 V

No, Ag^{2+} is a stronger oxidizing agent than $Cr_2O_7^{2-}$.

21.29 (a) CO

(b) $Fe_2O_3(s) + 3CO(g) \longrightarrow 2Fe(s) + 3CO_2(g)$ (Zone C)

$Fe_2O_3(s) + CO(g) \longrightarrow 2FeO(s) + CO_2(g)$ (Zone D)

followed by $FeO(s) + CO(g) \longrightarrow Fe(s) + CO_2(g)$ (Zone C)

(c) carbon

21.31 (a) $V^{2+} + 2e^- \longrightarrow V(s)$ $E°$ = -1.19 V

$V^{3+} + e^- \longrightarrow V^{2+}$ $E°$ = -0.26 V

$2H^+ + 2e^- \longrightarrow H_2(g)$ $E°$ = 0.00 V

Therefore, V(s) will be oxidized to V^{3+}. The products are V^{3+}, H_2, and Cl^-.

(b) $Hg_2^{2+} + 2e^- \longrightarrow 2Hg$ $E°$ = +0.79 V

$Hg^{2+} + 2e^- \longrightarrow Hg$ $E°$ = +1.62 V

$2H^+ + 2e^- \longrightarrow H_2(g)$ $E°$ = 0.00 V

Therefore, no reaction.

(c) $Co^{2+} + 2e^- \longrightarrow Co(s)$ $E°$ = -0.28 V

$Co^{3+} + e^- \longrightarrow Co^{2+}$ $E°$ = +1.81 V

$2H^+ + 2e^- \longrightarrow H_2(g)$ $E°$ = 0.00 V

Therefore, Co(s) will be oxidized to Co^{2+}. The products are Co^{2+}, H_2, and Cl^-.
The further oxidation to Co^{3+} is not favorable.

Groups 11 and 12

21.33 All three elements in this group—Cu, Ag, and Au—are chemically rather inert, Ag more so than Cu, and Au more so than Ag. The reduction potentials of their ions are all positive, in the order Au > Ag > Cu, so they are not readily oxidized. They have a common electron configuration, $(n-1)d^{10}ns^1$.

21.35 (a) chalcopyrite, $CuFeS_2$, copper iron sulfide

(b) sphalerite, ZnS, zinc sulfide

(c) cinnabar, HgS, mercury(II) sulfide

21.37 (a) $2ZnS(s) + 3O_2(g) \xrightarrow{\Delta} 2ZnO(s) + 2SO_2(g)$,

followed by $ZnO(s) + C(s) \xrightarrow{\Delta} Zn(l) + CO(g)$

(b) $HgS(s) + O_2(g) \xrightarrow{\Delta} Hg(g) + SO_2(g)$

21.39
$$Cu^+ + e^- \longrightarrow Cu \qquad E° = +0.52 \text{ V}$$
$$\frac{Cu^+ \longrightarrow Cu^{2+} + e^- \qquad E° = +0.15 \text{ V}}{2Cu^+ \longrightarrow Cu^{2+} + Cu \quad E° = +0.37 \text{ V}}$$

$\Delta G_r° = -nFE° = -RT \ln K \quad (n = 1)$

$nFE° = RT \ln K$

$$\ln K = \frac{(1)(9.65 \times 10^4 \text{ C} \cdot \text{mol}^{-1})(0.37 \text{ V})}{(8.31 \text{ J} \cdot \text{mol}^{-1} \cdot \text{K}^{-1})(298 \text{ K})} = 14.\overline{5}$$

$K = \overline{2} \times 10^6$ or 10^6

d-Metal Complexes

21.41 Let x = the oxidation number to be determined.

(a) $x(Fe) + 6 \times (-1) = -4$

$x(Fe) = -4 - (-6) = +2$

(b) $(Co) + 6 \times (0) = +3$

$x(Co) = +3$

(c) $x(Co) + 5 \times (-1) + 1 \times (0) = -2$

$x(Co) = -2 - (-5) = +3$

(d) $x(Co) + 1 \times (-2) + 5 \times (0) = +1$

$x(Co) = +1 - (-2) = +3$

21.43 (a) 4   (b) 2   (c) 6 (en is bidentate)   (d) 6 (EDTA is hexadentate)

21.45 (a) hexacyanoferrate(II) ion

(b) hexaamminecobalt(III) ion

(c) aquapentacyanocobaltate(III) ion

(d) pentaamminesulfatocobalt(III) ion

21.47 (a) $K_3[Cr(CN)_6]$

(b) $[Co(NH_3)_5(SO_4)]Cl$

(c) $[Co(NH_3)_4(H_2O)_2]Br_3$

(d) $Na[Fe(H_2O)_2(C_2O_4)_2]$

Isomerism

21.49 (a) structural isomers, linkage isomers

(b) structural isomers, ionization isomers

(c) structural isomers, linkage isomers

(d) structural isomers, ionization isomers

21.51 $[Co(H_2O)_6]Cl_3$, $[CoCl(H_2O)_5]Cl_2 \cdot H_2O$, $[CoCl_2(H_2O)_4]Cl \cdot 2H_2O$, and $[CoCl_3(H_2O)_3] \cdot 3H_2O$

21.53 $[CoCl(NO_2)(en)_2]Cl$ and $[CoCl(ONO)(en)_2]Cl$

21.55 (a) yes

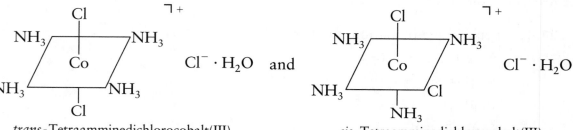

trans-Tetraamminedichlorocobalt(III) chloride monohydrate

cis-Tetraamminedichlorocobalt(III) chloride monohydrate

(b) no

(c) yes

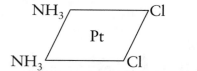 and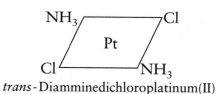

cis-Diamminedichloroplatinum(II)

trans-Diamminedichloroplatinum(II)

21.57 (a) yes, in the form of optical isomerism; see part (c)

(b) no, only 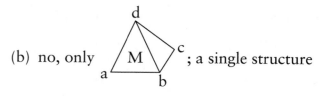 ; a single structure

(c) Yes; if four different ligand groups are bonded to the central atom, then the central atom is chiral and exhibits optical activity.

21.59

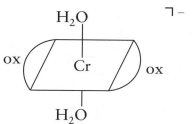

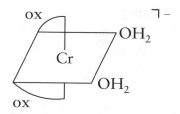

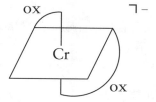

trans-Diaquabis(oxalato)chromate(III) ion   cis-Diaquabis(oxalato)chromate(III) ion

A second cis isomer with the same name exists.

21.61 first complex:

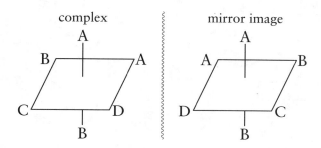

No rotation will make the complex and its mirror image match; hence it is chiral.
second complex:

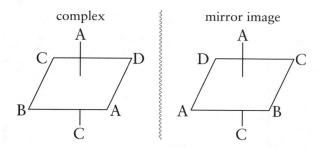

A double rotation shows that the complex and its mirror image are superimposable; hence it is not chiral.

The two complexes are not enantiomers; they are not even isomers.

21.63

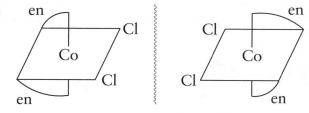

Crystal Field Theory

21.65 (a) d^7 (b) d^8 (c) d^5 (d) d^3

21.67 (a) octahedral: strong-field ligand, $6e^-$

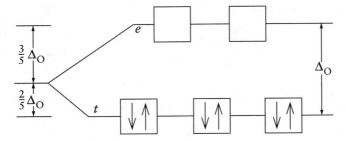

(b) tetrahedral: weak-field ligand, $8e^-$

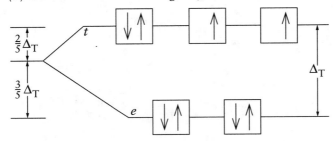

(c) octahedral: weak-field ligand, $5e^-$

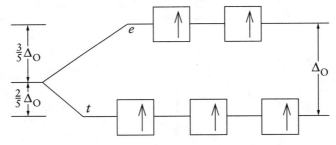

(d) octahedral: strong-field ligand, $5e^-$

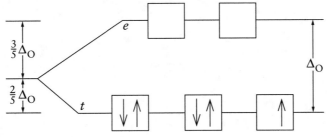

21.69 (a) $[Co(en)_3]^{3+}$ $6e^-$ ↓↑   ↓↑   ↓↑   0 unpaired electrons

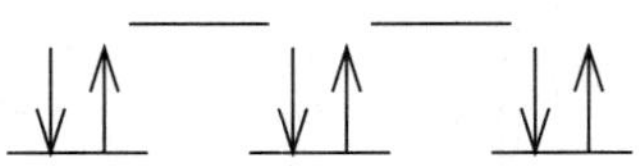

(b) $[Mn(CN)_6]^{3-}$ $4e^-$ ↓↑   ↑   ↑   2 unpaired electrons

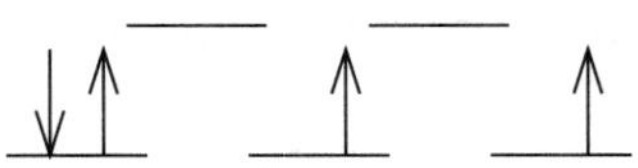

21.71 Weak-field ligands do not interact strongly with the *d*-electrons in the metal ion, so they produce only a small crystal field splitting of the *d*-electron energy states. The opposite is true of strong-field ligands. With weak-field ligands, unpaired electrons remain unpaired if there are unfilled orbitals; hence a weak-field ligand is likely to lead to a high-spin complex. Strong-field ligands cause electrons in excess of three to pair up with electrons in lower energy orbitals. A strong-field ligand is likely to lead to a low-spin complex. Ligands arranged in the spectrochemical series help to distinguish strong-field and weak-field ligands. Measurement of magnetic susceptibility (paramagnetism) can be used to determine the number of unpaired electrons, which in turn establishes whether the associated ligand is weak-field or strong-field in nature.

21.73 (a) $[CoF_6]^{3-}$ $6e^-$ F^- is a weak-field ligand; therefore,

↑   ↑

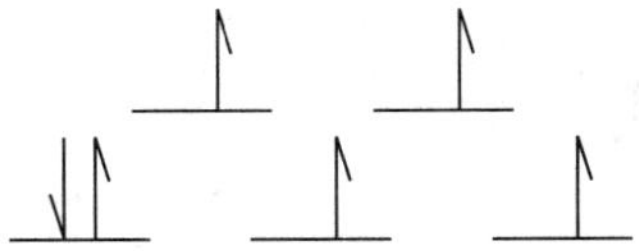

↓↑   ↑   ↑   4 unpaired electrons

(b) $[Co(en)_3]^{3+}$ $6e^-$ en is a strong-field ligand; therefore,

↓↑   ↓↑   ↓↑   0 unpaired electrons

Because F^- is a weak-field ligand and en a strong-field ligand, the splitting between levels is less in (a) than in (b). Therefore, (a) will absorb light of longer wavelength than will (b) and consequently will display a shorter wavelength color. Blue light is shorter in wavelength than yellow light, so (a) $[CoF_6]^{3-}$ is blue and (b) $[Co(en)_3]^{3+}$ is yellow.

21.75 See Fig. 21.41.

(a) 410 nm, yellow

(b) 650 nm, green

(c) 480 nm, orange

(d) 590 nm, blue

21.77 In Zn^{2+}, the $3d$-orbitals are filled (d^{10}). Therefore, there can be no electronic transitions between the t and e levels; hence no visible light is absorbed and the aqueous ion is colorless. The d^{10} configuration has no unpaired electrons, so Zn compounds would not be paramagnetic.

21.79 (a) $\Delta_O = \dfrac{hc}{\lambda} = \dfrac{(6.63 \times 10^{-34}\ J \cdot s^{-1})(3.00 \times 10^8\ m \cdot s^{-1})}{740 \times 10^{-9}\ m} = 2.69 \times 10^{-19}\ J$

(b) $\Delta_O = \dfrac{hc}{\lambda} = \dfrac{(6.63 \times 10^{-34}\ J \cdot s^{-1})(3.00 \times 10^8\ m \cdot s^{-1})}{460 \times 10^{-9}\ m} = 4.32 \times 10^{-19}\ J$

(c) $\Delta_O = \dfrac{hc}{\lambda} = \dfrac{(6.63 \times 10^{-34}\ J \cdot s^{-1})(3.00 \times 10^8\ m \cdot s^{-1})}{575 \times 10^{-9}\ m} = 3.46 \times 10^{-19}\ J$

These numbers can be multiplied by 6.02×10^{23} to obtain $kJ \cdot mol^{-1}$.
(a) $2.69 \times 10^{-19}\ J \times 6.02 \times 10^{23}\ mol^{-1} = 162\ kJ \cdot mol^{-1}$
(b) $4.32 \times 10^{-19}\ J \times 6.02 \times 10^{23}\ mol^{-1} = 260\ kJ \cdot mol^{-1}$
(c) $3.46 \times 10^{-19}\ J \times 6.02 \times 10^{23}\ mol^{-1} = 208\ kJ \cdot mol^{-1}$
$Cl < H_2O < NH_3$ (spectrochemical series)

SUPPLEMENTARY EXERCISES

21.81 (a) A compound with unpaired electrons is paramagnetic and is pulled into a magnetic field. A diamagnetic substance has no unpaired electrons and is weakly pushed out of a magnetic field.
(b) Paramagnetism is a property of any substance with unpaired electrons, whereas ferromagnetism is a property of certain substances that can become permanently magnetized. Ferromagnetism results when a large number of electrons in the metal have parallel spins. This parallel alignment can be retained even in the absence of a magnetic field. In a paramagnetic substance, the alignment is lost when the magnetic field is removed.

21.83 $[Sc(H_2O)_6]^{3+}(aq) + H_2O(l) \longrightarrow [Sc(H_2O)_5OH]^{2+}(aq) + H_3O^+(aq)$ Here the hydrated ion acts as a proton donor, and therefore it is a Brønsted acid.

21.85 (a) bronze, an alloy of copper and tin
(b) green "patina," a compound, basic copper carbonate, $Cu_2(OH)_2CO_3$
(c) 24-carat gold, "native" or pure gold
(d) densest element, osmium

21.87 (a) More than one kind of reduction occurs. In Zone C,

$$Fe_2O_3(s) + 3CO(g) \longrightarrow 2Fe(s) + 3CO_2(g)$$

In Zone D,

$$3Fe_2O_3(s) + CO(g) \longrightarrow 2Fe_3O_4(s) + CO_2(g)$$
$$Fe_3O_4(s) + CO(g) \longrightarrow 3FeO(s) + CO_2(g)$$

These reactions combine to give

$$Fe_2O_3(s) + CO(g) \longrightarrow 2FeO(s) + CO_2(g)$$

In Zone C,

$$FeO(s) + CO(g) \longrightarrow Fe(s) + CO_2(g)$$

(b) $TiCl_4(g) + 2Mg(l) \xrightarrow{\Delta} Ti(s) + 2MgCl_2(s)$

(c) $CaO(s) + SiO_2(s) \xrightarrow{\Delta} CaSiO_3(l)$

21.89 $4FeCr_2O_4(s) + 8Na_2CO_3(s) + 7O_2(g) \longrightarrow 8Na_2CrO_4(s) + 2Fe_2O_3(s) + 8CO_2(g)$

$$\text{mass of } FeCr_2O_4 = (1.00 \text{ kg } Na_2CrO_4) \times \left(\frac{10^3 \text{ g}}{1 \text{ kg}}\right) \times \left(\frac{1 \text{ mol } Na_2CrO_4}{162.0 \text{ g } Na_2CrO_4}\right)$$

$$\times \left(\frac{4 \text{ mol } FeCr_2O_4}{8 \text{ mol } Na_2CrO_4}\right) \times \left(\frac{223.9 \text{ g } FeCr_2O_4}{1 \text{ mol } FeCr_2O_4}\right) \times \left(\frac{1 \text{ kg}}{10^3 \text{ g}}\right) = 0.691 \text{ kg } FeCr_2O_4$$

21.91 (a) Cr^{3+} ions in water form the complex $[Cr(H_2O)_6]^{3+}$(aq), which behaves as a Brønsted acid:

$[Cr(H_2O)_6]^{3+}(aq) + H_2O(l) \rightleftharpoons [Cr(H_2O)_5OH]^{2+}(aq) + H_3O^+(aq)$

(b) The gelatinous precipitate is the hydroxide $Cr(OH)_3$. The precipitate dissolves as the $Cr(OH)_4^-$ complex ion is formed:

$Cr^{3+}(aq) + 3OH^-(aq) \longrightarrow Cr(OH)_3(s)$

$Cr(OH)_3(s) + OH^-(aq) \longrightarrow Cr(OH)_4^-(aq)$

21.93 (a) pentaamminesulfatochromium(III) chloride

(b) tris(ethylenediamine)chromium(III) tris(oxalato)chromate(III)

(c) diamminechloroplatinum(II)

(d) potassium hexanitritocobaltate(III)

21.95 (a) tetrakis(oxalato)zirconate(IV) ion; CN = 8, Zn = +4

(b) diaquatetrachlorocuprate(II) ion; CN = 6, Cu = +2

(c) amminetrichloroplatinate(II) ion; CN = 4, Pt = +2

(d) tetracyanodioxomolybdate(IV) ion; CN = 6, Mo = +4

21.97 [PtBrCl(NH₃)₂]

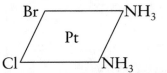
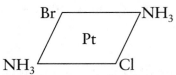

cis-Diamminebromochloroplatinum(II)   *trans*-Diamminebromochloroplatinum(II)

21.99 (a) The first, [Ni(SO₄)(en)₂]Cl₂, will give a precipitate of AgCl when AgNO₃ is added; the second will not.

(b) The second, [NiCl₂(en)₂]I₂, will show free I₂ when mildly oxidized with, for example, Br₂, but the first will not.

21.101 These compounds show ionization isomerization.

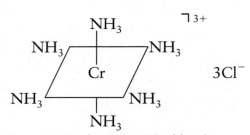

Hexaamminechromium(III) chloride

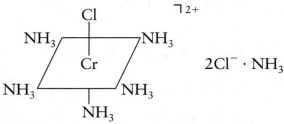

Pentaamminechlorochromium(III) ammine dichloride

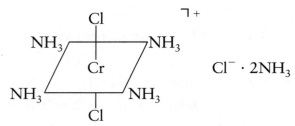

trans-Tetraamminedichlorochromium(III) ammoniate chloride

Geometrical isomers exist for the last compound; the trans isomer is shown.

21.103 (a), (b)

[MnCl₆]⁴⁻   5e⁻   Cl⁻ is a weak-field ligand

5 unpaired e⁻

[Mn(CN)₆]⁴⁻   5e⁻   CN⁻ is a strong-field ligand

1 unpaired e⁻

(c) A weak-field ligand absorbs long-wavelength light; therefore, $[MnCl_6]^{4-}$ transmits shorter wavelengths and $[Mn(CN)_6]^{4-}$ transmits longer wavelengths.

21.105 (a) $\Delta_O = \dfrac{hc}{\lambda} = \dfrac{(6.63 \times 10^{-34} \text{ J} \cdot \text{s})(3.00 \times 10^8 \text{ m} \cdot \text{s}^{-1})}{550 \times 10^{-9} \text{ m}} = 3.62 \times 10^{-19} \text{ J}$

This number can be multiplied by 6.02×10^{23} to obtain $218 \text{ kJ} \cdot \text{mol}^{-1}$.

(b) complementary color is red

CHALLENGING EXERCISES

21.107 Refer to the solution to Exercise 17.123.

$\Delta G_r^{\circ} = -nFE^{\circ}$ for each half-reaction

$$
\begin{array}{llll}
Sn^{4+} + 2e^- \longrightarrow Sn^{2+} & E^{\circ} = +0.15 \text{ V} & \Delta G_r^{\circ} = -28.\overline{9} \text{ kJ} \cdot \text{mol}^{-1} \\
Sn^{2+} + 2e^- \longrightarrow Sn & E^{\circ} = -0.14 \text{ V} & \Delta G_r^{\circ} = +27.\overline{0} \text{ kJ} \cdot \text{mol}^{-1} \\
\hline
Sn^{4+} + 4e^- \longrightarrow Sn & E^{\circ} = ? & \Delta G_r^{\circ} = -1.\overline{9} \text{ kJ} \cdot \text{mol}^{-1}
\end{array}
$$

$E^{\circ}(Sn^{4+}/Sn) = -\dfrac{\Delta G_r^{\circ}}{nF} = -\dfrac{-1.\overline{9} \text{ kJ} \cdot \text{mol}^{-1}}{4 \times 9.65 \times 10^4 \text{ C} \cdot \text{mol}^{-1}} = +0.005 \text{ V}$

21.109 $\Delta G_r^{\circ} = -nFE^{\circ}$

$$
\begin{array}{llll}
Cr^{2+} + 2e^- \longrightarrow Cr & E^{\circ} = -0.91 \text{ V} & \Delta G_r^{\circ} = +175.\overline{6} \text{ kJ} \cdot \text{mol}^{-1} \\
Cr^{3+} + 1e^- \longrightarrow Cr^{2-} & E^{\circ} = -0.41 \text{ V} & \Delta G_r^{\circ} = +39.\overline{6} \text{ kJ} \cdot \text{mol}^{-1} \\
\hline
Cr^{3+} + 3e^- \longrightarrow Cr & E^{\circ} = ? & \Delta G_r^{\circ} = +215.\overline{2} \text{ kJ} \cdot \text{mol}^{-1}
\end{array}
$$

$E^{\circ} = -\dfrac{\Delta G_r^{\circ}}{nF} = -\dfrac{2.1\overline{5} \times 10^5 \text{ J} \cdot \text{mol}^{-1}}{(3) \times 9.65 \times 10^4 \text{ C} \cdot \text{mol}^{-1}} = -0.74 \text{ V}$

21.111

$$
\begin{array}{lr}
[AuCl_4]^-(aq) + 3e^- \longrightarrow Au(s) + 4Cl^-(aq) & E^{\circ} = +1.00 \text{ V} \\
NO(g) + 2H_2O(l) \longrightarrow NO_3^-(aq) + 4H^+(aq) + 3e^- & E^{\circ} = +0.96 \text{ V} \\
\hline
[AuCl_4]^-(aq) + NO(g) + 2H_2O(l) \longrightarrow Au(s) + 4Cl^-(aq) + NO_3^-(aq) + 4H^+(aq) & \\
& E_{cell}^{\circ} = +0.04 \text{ V}
\end{array}
$$

(a) This is the spontaneous reaction under standard conditions.

(b) $E_{cell}^{\circ} = +0.04 \text{ V}$

(c) $E_{cell} = E_{cell}^{\circ} - \left(\dfrac{0.0257 \text{ V}}{n}\right) \ln Q$

$\quad = E_{cell}^{\circ} - \left(\dfrac{0.0257 \text{ V}}{3}\right) \ln \left(\dfrac{[Cl^-]^4[NO_3^-][H^+]^4}{[AuCl_4^-]P_{NO}}\right)$ [assume $P_{NO} = 1$ atm]

$\quad = 0.04 \text{ V} - \left(\dfrac{0.0257 \text{ V}}{3}\right) \ln \left(\dfrac{(6.0)^4(6.0)(6.0)^4}{(1.0 \times 10^{-6})(1.0)}\right) = -0.22 \text{ V}$

(d) When concentrated hydrochloric and nitric acids are present, the direction of the reaction is reversed relative to (a) and Au is oxidized

$$E_{cell} = 0.04 \text{ V} - \left(\frac{0.0257 \text{ V}}{3} \right) \ln \left(\frac{(6.0)^4(6.0)(12.0)^4}{(1.0 \times 10^{-6})(1.0)} \right)$$

21.113 The correct structure for $[Co(NH_3)_6]Cl_3$ consists of four ions, $Co(NH_3)_6^{3+}$ and $3Cl^-$ in aqueous solution. The chloride ions can be easily precipitated as AgCl. This would not be possible if they were bonded to the other (NH_3) ligands. If the structure were $Co(NH_3-NH_3-Cl)_3$, VSEPR theory would predict that the Co^{3+} ion would have a trigonal planar ligand arrangement. The splitting of the d-orbital energies would not be the same as the octahedral arrangement and would lead to different spectroscopic and magnetic properties inconsistent with the experimental evidence. In addition, neither optical nor geometrical isomers would be observed.

CHAPTER 22
NUCLEAR CHEMISTRY

EXERCISES

Nuclear Structure and Radiation

22.1

Type of radiation	Composition	Mass	Charge	Relative penetrating power
α	$^4_2$He nuclei	~4.0 u	2+	low
β	electrons	0.000 55 u	1−	moderate
γ	photons	0 u	0	high

22.3 In each case, the number of protons is the atomic number of the element, the number of nucleons is the mass number (not the molar atomic mass), and the number of neutrons is the difference between the mass number and atomic number.

Nuclide	Protons	Neutrons	Nucleons
(a) ^{2}H	1	1	2
(b) ^{24}Mg	12	12	24
(c) ^{263}Rf	104	159	263
(d) ^{60}Co	27	33	60
(e) ^{238}Pu	94	144	238
(f) ^{258}Md	101	157	258

22.5 In each case, the nuclear symbol is obtained from the chemical symbol for the element, with the mass number placed as a superscript and the atomic number as a subscript, both on the left of the symbol. The atomic number is not always specifically included in the symbol, because the chemical symbol itself identifies the atomic number.

Nuclear symbol	Protons	Neutrons	Nucleons
(a) $^{81}_{35}Br$	35	46	81
(b) $^{90}_{36}Kr$	36	54	90
(c) $^{244}_{96}Cm$	96	148	244
(d) $^{128}_{53}I$	53	75	128
(e) $^{32}_{16}S$	16	16	32
(f) $^{241}_{95}Am$	95	146	241

22.7 $\lambda = \dfrac{c}{\nu}$, $E = N_A h\nu$, $1\ Hz = 1\ s^{-1}$

(a) $\lambda = \dfrac{3.00 \times 10^8\ m \cdot s^{-1}}{9.4 \times 10^{19}\ s^{-1}} = 3.2 \times 10^{-12}\ m$

$E = 6.02 \times 10^{23}\ mol^{-1} \times 6.63 \times 10^{-34}\ J \cdot s \times 9.4 \times 10^{19}\ s^{-1}$
$= 3.8 \times 10^{10}\ J \cdot mol^{-1}$

(b) $\lambda = \dfrac{3.00 \times 10^8\ m \cdot s^{-1}}{5.7 \times 10^{21}\ s^{-1}} = 5.3 \times 10^{-14}\ m$

$E = 6.02 \times 10^{23}\ mol^{-1} \times 6.63 \times 10^{-34}\ J \cdot s \times 5.7 \times 10^{21}\ s^{-1}$
$= 2.3 \times 10^{12}\ J \cdot mol^{-1}$

(c) $\lambda = \dfrac{3.00 \times 10^8\ m \cdot s^{-1}}{3.7 \times 10^{20}\ s^{-1}} = 8.1 \times 10^{-13}\ m$

$E = 6.02 \times 10^{23}\ mol^{-1} \times 6.63 \times 10^{-34}\ J \cdot s \times 3.7 \times 10^{20}\ s^{-1}$
$= 1.5 \times 10^{11}\ J \cdot mol^{-1}$

(d) $\lambda = \dfrac{3.00 \times 10^8\ m \cdot s^{-1}}{7.3 \times 10^{22}\ s^{-1}} = 4.1 \times 10^{-15}\ m$

$E = 6.02 \times 10^{23}\ mol^{-1} \times 6.63 \times 10^{-34}\ J \cdot s \times 7.3 \times 10^{22}\ s^{-1}$
$= 2.9 \times 10^{13}\ J \cdot mol^{-1}$

22.9 We assume that all the change in energy goes into the energy of the γ ray emitted.
Then, in each case,

$$\nu = \frac{\Delta E}{h}, \qquad \lambda = \frac{c}{\nu}$$

energy of 1 MeV $= \left(\dfrac{10^6\ eV}{1\ MeV}\right) \times \left(\dfrac{1.602 \times 10^{-19}\ J}{1\ eV}\right) = 1.602 \times 10^{-13}\ J \cdot MeV^{-1}$

(a) $\Delta E = (1.33\ MeV) \times \left(\dfrac{1.602 \times 10^{-13}\ J}{1\ MeV}\right) = 2.13 \times 10^{-13}\ J$

$\nu = \dfrac{\Delta E}{h} = \dfrac{2.13 \times 10^{-13}\ J}{6.63 \times 10^{-34}\ J \cdot s} = 3.21 \times 10^{20}\ s^{-1} = 3.21 \times 10^{20}\ Hz$

$$\lambda = \frac{c}{\nu} = \frac{3.00 \times 10^8 \text{ m} \cdot \text{s}^{-1}}{3.21 \times 10^{20} \text{ s}^{-1}} = 9.33 \times 10^{-13} \text{ m}$$

(b) $\Delta E = (1.64 \text{ MeV}) \times \left(\frac{1.602 \times 10^{-13} \text{ J}}{1 \text{ MeV}} \right) = 2.62 \times 10^{-13} \text{ J}$

$$\nu = \frac{\Delta E}{h} = \frac{2.62 \times 10^{-13} \text{ J}}{6.63 \times 10^{-34} \text{ J} \cdot \text{s}} = 3.95 \times 10^{20} \text{ s}^{-1} = 3.95 \times 10^{20} \text{ Hz}$$

$$\lambda = \frac{3.00 \times 10^8 \text{ m} \cdot \text{s}^{-1}}{3.95 \times 10^{20} \text{ s}^{-1}} = 7.59 \times 10^{-13} \text{ m}$$

(c) $\Delta E = (1.10 \text{ MeV}) \times \left(\frac{1.602 \times 10^{-13} \text{ J}}{1 \text{ MeV}} \right) = 1.76 \times 10^{-13} \text{ J}$

$$\nu = \frac{\Delta E}{h} = \frac{1.76 \times 10^{-13} \text{ J}}{6.63 \times 10^{-34} \text{ J} \cdot \text{s}} = 2.66 \times 10^{20} \text{ s}^{-1} = 2.66 \times 10^{20} \text{ Hz}$$

$$\lambda = \frac{c}{\nu} = \frac{3.00 \times 10^8 \text{ m} \cdot \text{s}^{-1}}{2.66 \times 10^{20} \text{ s}^{-1}} = 1.13 \times 10^{-12} \text{ m}$$

Radioactive Decay

22.11 (a) $^3_1\text{T} \longrightarrow ^{\ 0}_{-1}\text{e} + ^A_Z\text{E}$ $A = 3 - 0 = 3$, $Z = 1 - (-1) = 2$, E = He
so $^3_1\text{T} \longrightarrow ^{\ 0}_{-1}\text{e} + ^3_2\text{He}$

(b) $^{83}_{39}\text{Y} \longrightarrow ^0_1\text{e} + ^A_Z\text{E}$ $A = 83 - 0 = 83$, $Z = 39 - 1 = 38$, E = Sr
so $^{83}_{39}\text{Y} \longrightarrow ^0_1\text{e} + ^{83}_{38}\text{Sr}$

(c) $^{87}_{36}\text{Kr} \longrightarrow ^{\ 0}_{-1}\text{e} + ^A_Z\text{E}$ $A = 87 - 0 = 87$, $Z = 36 - (-1) = 37$, E = Rb
so $^{87}_{36}\text{Kr} \longrightarrow ^{\ 0}_{-1}\text{e} + ^{87}_{37}\text{Rb}$

(d) $^{225}_{91}\text{Pa} \longrightarrow ^4_2\alpha + ^A_Z\text{E}$ $A = 225 - 4 = 221$, $Z = 91 - 2 = 89$, E = Ac
so $^{225}_{91}\text{Pa} \longrightarrow ^4_2\alpha + ^{221}_{89}\text{Ac}$

22.13 (a) $^8_5\text{B} \longrightarrow ^0_1\text{e} + ^A_Z\text{E}$ $A = 8 - 0 = 8$, $Z = 5 - 1 = 4$, E = Be
so $^8_5\text{B} \longrightarrow ^0_1\text{e} + ^8_4\text{Be}$

(b) $^{63}_{28}\text{Ni} \longrightarrow ^{\ 0}_{-1}\text{e} + ^A_Z\text{E}$ $A = 63 - 0 = 63$, $Z = 28 - (-1) = 29$, E = Cu
so $^{63}_{28}\text{Ni} \longrightarrow ^{\ 0}_{-1}\text{e} + ^{63}_{29}\text{Cu}$

(c) $^{185}_{79}\text{Au} \longrightarrow ^4_2\alpha + ^A_Z\text{E}$ $A = 185 - 4 = 181$, $Z = 79 - 2 = 77$, E = Ir
so $^{185}_{79}\text{Au} \longrightarrow ^4_2\alpha + ^{181}_{77}\text{Ir}$

(d) $^7_4\text{Be} + ^{\ 0}_{-1}\text{e} \longrightarrow ^A_Z\text{E}$ $A = 7 + 0 = 7$, $Z = 4 - 1 = 3$, E = Li
so $^7_4\text{Be} + ^{\ 0}_{-1}\text{e} \longrightarrow ^7_3\text{Li}$

22.15 (a) $^{24}_{11}\text{Na} \longrightarrow ^{24}_{12}\text{Mg} + ^{\ 0}_{-1}\text{e}$; a β particle is emitted.

(b) $^{128}_{50}\text{Sn} \longrightarrow ^{128}_{51}\text{Sb} + ^{\ 0}_{-1}\text{e}$; a β particle is emitted.

(c) $^{140}_{57}\text{La} \longrightarrow ^{140}_{56}\text{Ba} + ^0_1\text{e}$; a positron ($\beta^+$) is emitted.

(d) $^{228}_{90}\text{Th} \longrightarrow ^{224}_{88}\text{Ra} + ^4_2\alpha$; an α particle is emitted.

The Pattern of Nuclear Stability

22.17 Let N = number of neutrons, Z = number of protons, and $A = N + Z$. Then $N = A - Z$. The N/Z ratio is close to 1 for light nuclei, but approaches 1.6 for heavy stable nuclei. Note that Fig. 22.12 shows A as a function of Z, not N as a function of Z. $A/Z = N/Z + 1$ or $N/Z = A/Z - 1$.

(a) α particles are emitted in the decay of nuclei with $Z > 83$. A few other nuclei that have N/Z ratios lying near the band of stability and with $60 < Z < 70$ also emit α particles.

(b) β particles are emitted in the decay of nuclei with N/Z ratios greater than the N/Z ratio of the band of stability. The emission of a β particle is the equivalent of converting a neutron into a proton; thus, the N/Z ratio becomes smaller to fit the values required for stability.

22.19 (a) $A/Z = 68/29 = 2.34 > (A/Z)_{based}$; hence, $^{68}_{29}Cu$ is neutron rich, and β decay is most likely.

$$^{68}_{29}Cu \longrightarrow ^{\ 0}_{-1}e + ^{68}_{30}Zn$$

(b) $A/Z = 103/48 = 2.15 < (A/Z)_{based}$; hence, $^{103}_{48}Cd$ is proton rich, and β^+ decay is most likely.

$$^{103}_{48}Cd \longrightarrow ^{0}_{1}e + ^{103}_{47}Ag$$

(c) $^{243}_{97}Bk$ has $Z > 83$ and is proton rich; therefore, α decay is most likely.

$$^{243}_{97}Bk \longrightarrow ^{4}_{2}\alpha + ^{239}_{95}Am$$

(d) $^{260}_{105}Db$ has $Z > 83$; therefore, α decay is most likely.

$$^{260}_{105}Db \longrightarrow ^{4}_{2}\alpha + ^{256}_{103}Lr$$

22.21

α	$^{235}_{92}U \longrightarrow ^{4}_{2}\alpha + ^{231}_{90}Th$	α	$^{219}_{86}Rn \longrightarrow ^{4}_{2}\alpha + ^{215}_{84}Po$
β	$^{231}_{90}Th \longrightarrow ^{\ 0}_{-1}e + ^{231}_{91}Pa$	β	$^{215}_{84}Po \longrightarrow ^{\ 0}_{-1}e + ^{215}_{85}At$
α	$^{231}_{91}Pa \longrightarrow ^{4}_{2}\alpha + ^{227}_{89}Ac$	α	$^{215}_{85}At \longrightarrow ^{4}_{2}\alpha + ^{211}_{83}Bi$
β	$^{227}_{89}Ac \longrightarrow ^{\ 0}_{-1}e + ^{227}_{90}Th$	β	$^{211}_{83}Bi \longrightarrow ^{\ 0}_{-1}e + ^{211}_{84}Po$
α	$^{227}_{90}Th \longrightarrow ^{4}_{2}\alpha + ^{223}_{88}Ra$	α	$^{211}_{84}Po \longrightarrow ^{4}_{2}\alpha + ^{207}_{82}Pb$
α	$^{223}_{88}Ra \longrightarrow ^{4}_{2}\alpha + ^{219}_{86}Rn$		

Nucleosynthesis

22.23 To determine the charge and mass of the unknown particle, it helps to write ^1_1p and ^1_0n for the proton and neutron, respectively; and $^0_{-1}e$ and ^0_1e for the β particle and positron, respectively.

(a) $^{14}_7N + ^4_2\alpha \longrightarrow ^{17}_8O + ^1_1p$

(b) $^{248}_{96}Cm + ^1_0n \longrightarrow ^{249}_{97}Bk + ^0_{-1}e$

(c) $^{243}_{95}Am + ^1_0n \longrightarrow ^{244}_{96}Cm + ^0_{-1}e + \gamma$

(d) $^{13}_6C + ^1_0n \longrightarrow ^{14}_6C + \gamma$

22.25 (a) $^{20}_{10}Ne + ^4_2\alpha \longrightarrow ^8_4Be + ^{16}_8O$

(b) $^{20}_{10}Ne + ^{20}_{10}Ne \longrightarrow ^{24}_{12}Mg + ^{16}_8O$

(c) $^{44}_{20}Ca + ^4_2\alpha \longrightarrow \gamma + ^{48}_{22}Ti$

(d) $^{27}_{13}Al + ^2_1H \longrightarrow ^1_1p + ^{28}_{13}Al$

22.27 In each case, identify the unknown particle by performing a mass and charge balance as you did in the solutions to Exercises 22.11 and 22.13. Then write the complete nuclear equation.

(a) $^{14}_7N + ^4_2\alpha \longrightarrow ^{17}_8O + ?;$ $? = ^1_1p;$ therefore, $^{14}_7N + ^4_2\alpha \longrightarrow ^{17}_8O + ^1_1p$

(b) $^{239}_{94}Pu + ^1_0n \longrightarrow ^{240}_{95}Am + ?;$ $? = ^0_{-1}e;$ therefore, $^{239}_{94}Pu + ^1_0n \longrightarrow$

$$^{240}_{95}Am + ^0_{-1}e$$

22.29 In each case, solve for the unknown particle by doing a mass and charge balance as you did in the solutions to Exercises 22.11 and 22.13.

(a) $^{244}_{95}Am \longrightarrow ^{134}_{53}I + ^{107}_{42}Mo + 3\,^1_0n$

(b) $^{235}_{92}U + ^1_0n \longrightarrow ^{96}_{40}Zr + ^{138}_{52}Te + 2\,^1_0n$

(c) $^{235}_{92}U + ^1_0n \longrightarrow ^{101}_{42}Mo + ^{132}_{50}Sn + 3\,^1_0n$

Measuring Radioactivity and Its Effects

22.31 activity $= (3.7 \times 10^6 \text{ Bq}) \times \left(\dfrac{1 \text{ Ci}}{3.7 \times 10^{10} \text{ Bq}}\right) = 1.0 \times 10^{-4} \text{ Ci}$

22.33 1 Bq = 1 disintegration per second (dps)

(a) $1.0 \text{ Ci} = 3.7 \times 10^{10} \text{ dps} = 3.7 \times 10^{10} \text{ Bq}$

(b) $(82 \text{ mCi}) \times \left(\dfrac{10^{-3} \text{ Ci}}{1 \text{ mCi}}\right) \times \left(\dfrac{3.7 \times 10^{10} \text{ dps}}{1 \text{ Ci}}\right) = 3.0 \times 10^9 \text{ dps}$

$$= 3.0 \times 10^9 \text{ Bq}$$

(c) $(1.0 \text{ } \mu\text{Ci}) \times \left(\dfrac{10^{-6} \text{ Ci}}{1 \text{ } \mu\text{Ci}}\right) \times \left(\dfrac{3.7 \times 10^{10} \text{ dps}}{1 \text{ Ci}}\right) = 3.7 \times 10^4 \text{ dps}$

$$= 3.7 \times 10^4 \text{ Bq}$$

22.35 dose in rads $= 1.0 \text{ J} \cdot \text{kg}^{-1} \times \left(\dfrac{1 \text{ rad}}{10^{-2} \text{ J} \cdot \text{kg}^{-1}}\right) = 1.0 \times 10^2 \text{ rad}$

dose equivalent in rems $= Q \times$ dose in rads

$$= \left(\dfrac{1 \text{ rem}}{1 \text{ rad}}\right) \times 1.0 \times 10^2 \text{ rad} = 1.0 \times 10^2 \text{ rem}$$

22.37 $1.0 \text{ rad} \cdot \text{day}^{-1} = 1.0 \text{ rad} \times \left(\dfrac{1 \text{ rem}}{1 \text{ rad}}\right) \times \text{day}^{-1} = 1 \text{ rem} \cdot \text{day}^{-1}$

$100 \text{ rem} = 1 \text{ rem} \cdot \text{day}^{-1} \times \text{time}$

$\text{time} = 100 \text{ day}$

Rate of Nuclear Disintegration

22.39 $k = \dfrac{0.693}{t_{1/2}}$

(a) $k = \dfrac{0.693}{12.3 \text{ y}} = 5.63 \times 10^{-2} \text{ y}^{-1}$

(b) $k = \dfrac{0.693}{0.84 \text{ s}} = 0.82 \text{ s}^{-1}$

(c) $k = \dfrac{0.693}{10.0 \text{ min}} = 0.0693 \text{ min}^{-1}$

22.41 In each case, $k = \dfrac{0.693}{t_{1/2}}$, initial activity $\propto N_0$, final activity $\propto N$, and $N = N_0 e^{-kt}$

Therefore, $\dfrac{\text{initial activity}}{\text{final activity}} = \dfrac{N_0}{N} = e^{kt}$ and $\ln\left(\dfrac{N_0}{N}\right) = kt$.

Solving for t, $t = \left(\dfrac{1}{k}\right) \ln\left(\dfrac{N_0}{N}\right) = \left(\dfrac{1}{k}\right) \ln\left(\dfrac{\text{initial activity}}{\text{final activity}}\right)$

(a) $k = \dfrac{0.693}{1.60 \times 10^3 \text{ y}} = 4.33 \times 10^{-4} \text{ y}^{-1}$

$t = \left(\dfrac{1}{4.33 \times 10^{-4} \text{ y}^{-1}}\right) \ln\left(\dfrac{1.0 \text{ Ci}}{0.10 \text{ Ci}}\right) = 5.3 \times 10^3 \text{ y}$

(b) $k = \dfrac{0.693}{1.26 \times 10^9 \text{ y}} = 5.50 \times 10^{-10} \text{ y}^{-1}$

$t = \left(\dfrac{1}{5.50 \times 10^{-10} \text{ y}^{-1}}\right) \ln \left(\dfrac{1.0 \times 10^{-6} \text{ Ci}}{10 \times 10^{-9} \text{ Ci}}\right) = 8.4 \times 10^9 \text{ y}$

(c) $k = \dfrac{0.693}{5.26 \text{ y}} = 0.132 \text{ y}^{-1}$

$t = \left(\dfrac{1}{0.132 \text{ y}^{-1}}\right) \ln \left(\dfrac{10 \text{ Ci}}{8 \text{ Ci}}\right) = 2\text{y}$

22.43 We know that initial activity $\propto N_0$, and final activity $\propto N_0$. Therefore,

$$\frac{\text{final activity}}{\text{initial activity}} = \frac{N}{N_0} = e^{-kt}$$

$k = \dfrac{0.693}{t_{1/2}} = \dfrac{0.693}{5.26 \text{ y}} = 0.132 \text{ y}^{-1}$

final activity $=$ initial activity $\times e^{-kt}$

$\quad = 4.4 \text{ Ci} \times e^{-(0.132 \text{ y}^{-1} \times 50 \text{ y})}$

$\quad = 6.0 \times 10^{-3} \text{ Ci}$

22.45 In each case, $k = \dfrac{0.693}{t_{1/2}}$, $N = N_0 e^{-kt}$, $\dfrac{N}{N_0} = e^{-kt}$, and the percentage remaining $=$ $100\% \times (N/N_0)$.

(a) $k = \dfrac{0.693}{5.73 \times 10^3 \text{ y}} = 1.21 \times 10^{-4} \text{ y}^{-1}$

percentage remaining $= 100\% \times e^{-(1.21 \times 10^{-4} \text{ y}^{-1} \times 1000 \text{ y})} = 88.6\%$

(b) $k = \dfrac{0.693}{12.3 \text{ y}} = 0.0563 \text{ y}^{-1}$

percentage remaining $= 100\% \times e^{-(0.0563 \text{ y}^{-1} \times 20.0 \text{ y})} = 32.4\%$

22.47 (a) $t_{1/2} = 4.5 \times 10^9 \text{ y}$, $k = \dfrac{0.693}{t_{1/2}} = \dfrac{0.693}{4.5 \times 10^9 \text{ y}} = 1.54 \times 10^{-10} \text{ y}^{-1}$

fraction remaining $= \dfrac{N}{N_0} = e^{-kt}$

$\quad = e^{-(1.54 \times 10^{-10} \text{ y}^{-1} \times 9.0 \times 10^9 \text{ y})}$

$\quad = e^{-1.386} = 0.25$

(b) fraction remaining $= \dfrac{N}{N_0} = \dfrac{1}{2}$; hence age $= t_{1/2} = 1.26 \times 10^9 \text{ y}$

22.49 Let dis = disintegrations.

$$\text{activity from "old" sample} = \frac{1500 \text{ dis}/0.250 \text{ g}}{10.0 \text{ h}} = 600 \text{ dis} \cdot \text{g}^{-1} \cdot \text{h}^{-1}$$

$$\text{activity from current sample} = 920 \text{ dis} \cdot \text{g}^{-1} \cdot \text{h}^{-1}$$

$$k = \frac{0.693}{t_{1/2}} = \frac{0.693}{5.73 \times 10^3 \text{ y}} = 1.21 \times 10^{-4} \text{ y}^{-1}$$

"old" activity $\propto N$, current activity $\propto N_0$

$$\frac{\text{"old" activity}}{\text{current activity}} = \frac{N}{N_0} = e^{-kt}, \frac{N_0}{N} = e^{kt}, \ln\left(\frac{N_0}{N}\right) = kt,$$

Solve for t (= age).

$$t = \frac{\ln\left(\dfrac{N_0}{N}\right)}{k} = \frac{\ln\left(\dfrac{920}{600}\right)}{1.21 \times 10^{-4} \text{ y}^{-1}} = 3.53 \times 10^3 \text{ y}$$

22.51 In each case, $k = \dfrac{0.693}{t_{1/2} \text{ (in s)}}$, activity in $Bq = k \times N$

$$\text{activity in Ci} = \frac{\text{activity in } Bq}{3.7 \times 10^{10} \, Bq \cdot Ci^{-1}}$$

Note: Bq (= disintegrating nuclei per second) has the units of nuclei $\cdot$ s^{-1}

(a) $k = \left(\dfrac{0.693}{1.60 \times 10^3 \text{ y}}\right) \times \left(\dfrac{1 \text{ y}}{3.16 \times 10^7 \text{ s}}\right) = 1.37 \times 10^{-11} \text{ s}^{-1}$

$N = (1.0 \times 10^{-3} \text{ g}) \times \left(\dfrac{1 \text{ mol}}{226 \text{ g}}\right) \times \left(\dfrac{6.02 \times 10^{23} \text{ nuclei}}{1 \text{ mol}}\right) = 2.6\overline{6} \times 10^{18} \text{ nuclei}$

activity $= 1.37 \times 10^{-11} \text{ s}^{-1} \times 2.6\overline{6} \times 10^{18} \text{ nuclei} \times \left(\dfrac{1 \text{ Ci}}{3.7 \times 10^{10} \text{ Bq}}\right)$

$\qquad = 9.8 \times 10^{-4} \text{ Ci}$

(b) $k = \left(\dfrac{0.693}{28.1 \text{ y}}\right) \times \left(\dfrac{1 \text{ y}}{3.16 \times 10^7 \text{ s}}\right) = 7.80 \times 10^{-10} \text{ s}^{-1}$

$N = (2.0 \times 10^{-6} \text{ g}) \times \left(\dfrac{1 \text{ mol}}{90 \text{ g}}\right) \times \left(\dfrac{6.02 \times 10^{23} \text{ nuclei}}{1 \text{ mol}}\right) = 1.3\overline{4} \times 10^{16} \text{ nuclei}$

activity $= 7.80 \times 10^{-10} \text{ s}^{-1} \times 1.3\overline{4} \times 10^{16} \text{ nuclei} \times \left(\dfrac{1 \text{ Ci}}{3.7 \times 10^{10} \text{ Bq}}\right)$

$\qquad = 2.8 \times 10^{-4} \text{ Ci}$

(c) $k = \left(\dfrac{0.693}{2.6 \text{ y}}\right) \times \left(\dfrac{1 \text{ y}}{3.16 \times 10^7 \text{ s}}\right) = 8.4\overline{3} \times 10^{-9} \text{ s}^{-1}$

$N = (0.43 \times 10^{-3} \text{ g}) \times \left(\dfrac{1 \text{ mol}}{147 \text{ g}}\right) \times \left(\dfrac{6.02 \times 10^{23} \text{ nuclei}}{1 \text{ mol}}\right) = 1.7\overline{6} \times 10^{18} \text{ nuclei}$

activity $= 8.4\overline{3} \times 10^{-9} \text{ s}^{-1} \times 1.7\overline{6} \times 10^{18} \text{ nuclei} \times \left(\dfrac{1 \text{ Ci}}{3.7 \times 10^{10} \text{ Bq}}\right) = 0.40 \text{ Ci}$

22.53 This term refers to self-sustaining nuclear chain reactions. For a chain reaction to be self-sustaining, each nucleus that splits must provide an average of at least one new neutron that results in the fission of another nucleus. If the mass of the fissionable material is too small, the neutrons will escape before they can produce fission. The critical mass is the smallest mass that can sustain a nuclear chain reaction.

22.55 In each case, first calculate ΔE for the process described. Note whether ΔE is positive or negative, corresponding to energy added or removed from the system. Then calculate the change in mass from the change in energy with use of $\Delta E = (\Delta m)c^2$ or

$$\Delta m = \frac{\Delta E}{c^2}$$

(a) $\Delta E = 250 \text{ g} \times 0.39 \text{ J} \cdot (°\text{C})^{-1} \cdot \text{g}^{-1} \times (250°\text{C} - 35°\text{C}) = 2.1\overline{0} \times 10^4 \text{ J}$

$\Delta m = \dfrac{2.1\overline{0} \times 10^4 \text{ J}}{(3.00 \times 10^8 \text{ m} \cdot \text{s}^{-1})^2} = 2.3 \times 10^{-13} \text{ kg} = 2.3 \times 10^{-10} \text{ g} = \text{mass gained}$

(b) $\Delta E = -\Delta H°_{\text{melt}} \times n$, where $n = $ number of moles

$\Delta E = -6.01 \text{ kJ} \cdot \text{mol}^{-1} \times \left(\dfrac{50.0 \text{ g}}{18.0 \text{ g} \cdot \text{mol}^{-1}}\right) = -16.7 \text{ kJ} = -1.67 \times 10^4 \text{ J}$

$\Delta m = \dfrac{-1.67 \times 10^4 \text{ J}}{(3.00 \times 10^8 \text{ m} \cdot \text{s}^{-1})^2} = -1.86 \times 10^{-13} \text{ kg} = -1.86 \times 10^{-10} \text{ g}$

$= \text{mass lost}$

(c) $\Delta E = 2 \text{ mol} \times \Delta H°_{\text{f}}(\text{PCl}_5, \text{g}) = 2 \text{ mol} \times (-374.9 \text{ kJ} \cdot \text{mol}^{-1}) = -749.8 \text{ kJ}$

$= -7.498 \times 10^5 \text{ J}$

$\Delta m = \dfrac{-7.498 \times 10^5 \text{ J}}{(3.00 \times 10^8 \text{ m} \cdot \text{s}^{-1})^2} = -8.33 \times 10^{-12} \text{ kg} = -8.33 \times 10^{-9} \text{ g} = \text{mass lost}$

22.57 Remember to convert g to kg.

(a) $E = mc^2 = 1.0 \times 10^{-3} \text{ kg} \times (3.00 \times 10^8 \text{ m} \cdot \text{s}^{-1})^2$

$= 9.0 \times 10^{13} \text{ kg} \cdot \text{m}^2 \cdot \text{s}^{-2} = 9.0 \times 10^{13} \text{ J}$

(b) $E = mc^2 = 9.109 \times 10^{-31} \text{ kg} \times (2.997 \times 10^8 \text{ m} \cdot \text{s}^{-1})^2$

$= 8.187 \times 10^{-14} \text{ kg} \cdot \text{m}^2 \cdot \text{s}^{-2} = 8.187 \times 10^{-14} \text{ J}$

22.59 $\Delta m = \dfrac{\Delta E}{c^2} = \dfrac{-3.9 \times 10^{26} \text{ J} \cdot \text{s}^{-1}}{(3.00 \times 10^8 \text{ m} \cdot \text{s}^{-1})^2} = -4.3 \times 10^9 \text{ kg} \cdot \text{s}^{-1}$

22.61 $1 \text{ u} = 1.6605 \times 10^{-27} \text{ kg}$

In each case, calculate the difference in mass between the nucleus and the free particles from which it may be considered to have been formed. Then obtain the binding energy from the relation $E_{bind} = \Delta mc^2$.

(a) $^4_2$He: $2\,^1H + 2n \longrightarrow\,^4_2He$

$\Delta m = 4.0026\ u - (2 \times 1.0078\ u + 2 \times 1.0087\ u) = -0.0304\ u$

$$\Delta m = (-0.0304\ u) \times \left(\frac{1.6605 \times 10^{-27}\ kg}{1\ u}\right) = -5.05 \times 10^{-29}\ kg$$

$$E_{bind} = -5.05 \times 10^{-29}\ kg \times (3.00 \times 10^8\ m \cdot s^{-1})^2$$
$$= -4.55 \times 10^{-12}\ kg \cdot m^2 \cdot s^{-2} = -4.55 \times 10^{-12}\ J$$

$$E_{bind}/nucleon = \frac{-4.55 \times 10^{-12}\ J}{4\ nucleons} = -1.14 \times 10^{-12}\ J \cdot nucleon^{-1}$$

(b) $^{239}_{94}$Pu: $94\,^1H + 145n \longrightarrow\,^{239}_{94}Pu$

$\Delta m = 239.0522\ u - (94 \times 1.0078\ u + 145 \times 1.0087\ u) = -1.9425\ u$

$$\Delta m = -1.9425\ u \times \left(\frac{1.6605 \times 10^{-27}\ kg}{1\ u}\right) = -3.2255 \times 10^{-27}\ kg$$

$$E_{bind} = -3.2255 \times 10^{-27}\ kg \times (2.997 \times 10^8\ m \cdot s^{-1})^2 = -2.897 \times 10^{-10}\ J$$

$$E_{bind}/nucleon = \frac{-2.897 \times 10^{-10}\ J}{239\ nucleons} = -1.213 \times 10^{-12}\ J \cdot nucleon^{-1}$$

(c) $^2_1$H: $^1H + n \longrightarrow\,^2_1H$

$\Delta m = 2.0141\ u - (1.0078\ u + 1.0087\ u) = -0.0024\ u$

$$\Delta m = -0.0024\ u \times \left(\frac{1.6605 \times 10^{-27}\ kg}{1\ u}\right) = -4.0 \times 10^{-30\ kg}$$

$$E_{bind} = -4.0 \times 10^{-30}\ kg \times (3.00 \times 10^8\ m \cdot s^{-1})^2 = -3.6 \times 10^{-13}\ J$$

$$E_{bind}/nucleon = \frac{-3.6 \times 10^{-13}\ J}{2\ nucleons} = -1.8 \times 10^{-13}\ J \cdot nucleon^{-1}$$

(d) $^{56}_{26}$Fe: $26\,^1H + 30n \longrightarrow\,^{56}_{26}Fe$

$\Delta m = 55.9349\ u - (26 \times 1.0078\ u + 30 \times 1.0087\ u) = -0.5289\ u$

$$\Delta m = -0.5289\ u \times \left(\frac{1.661 \times 10^{-27}\ kg}{1\ u}\right) = -8.785 \times 10^{-28}\ kg$$

$$E_{bind} = -8.785 \times 10^{-28}\ kg \times (2.998 \times 10^8\ m \cdot s^{-1})^{-2} = -7.896 \times 10^{-11}\ J$$

$$E_{bind}/nucleon = \frac{-7.896 \times 10^{-11}\ J}{56\ nucleons} = -1.410 \times 10^{-12}\ J \cdot nucleon^{-1}$$

^{56}Fe is the most stable, because it has the largest binding energy per nucleon.

22.63 In each case, we first determine the change in mass, $\Delta m = $ (mass of products) $-$ (mass of reactants). We then calculate the energy released from $\Delta E = (\Delta m)c^2$.

(a) $D + D \longrightarrow\,^3He + n$

$2.0141\ u + 2.0141\ u \longrightarrow 3.0160\ u + 1.0087\ u$

$4.0282\ u \longrightarrow 4.0247\ u$

$$\Delta m = -0.0035 \text{ u}$$

$$\Delta m = (-0.0035 \text{ u}) \times \left(\frac{1.661 \times 10^{-27} \text{ kg}}{1 \text{ u}}\right) = -5.8 \times 10^{-30} \text{ kg}$$

$$\Delta E = \Delta mc^2 = (-5.8 \times 10^{-30} \text{ kg}) \times (3.00 \times 10^8 \text{ m} \cdot \text{s}^{-1})^2 = -5.2 \times 10^{-13} \text{ J}$$

$$\left(\frac{-5.2 \times 10^{-13} \text{ J}}{4.0282 \text{ u}}\right) \times \left(\frac{1 \text{ u}}{1.661 \times 10^{-24} \text{ g}}\right) = -7.8 \times 10^{10} \text{ J} \cdot \text{g}^{-1}$$

(b) $^3\text{He} + \text{D} \longrightarrow {}^4\text{He} + {}^1_1\text{H}$

$3.0160 \text{ u} + 2.0141 \text{ u} \longrightarrow 4.0026 \text{ u} + 1.0078 \text{ u}$

$5.0301 \text{ u} \longrightarrow 5.0104 \text{ u}$

$$\Delta m = -0.0197 \text{ u}$$

$$\Delta m = -0.0197 \text{ u} \times \left(\frac{1.661 \times 10^{-27} \text{ kg}}{1 \text{ u}}\right) = -3.27 \times 10^{-29} \text{ kg}$$

$$\Delta E = \Delta mc^2 = -3.19 \times 10^{-29} \text{ kg} \times (3.00 \times 10^8 \text{ m} \cdot \text{s}^{-1})^2 = -2.94 \times 10^{-12} \text{ J}$$

$$\left(\frac{-2.94 \times 10^{-12} \text{ J}}{5.0301 \text{ u}}\right) \times \left(\frac{1 \text{ u}}{1.661 \times 10^{-24} \text{ g}}\right) = -3.52 \times 10^{11} \text{ J} \cdot \text{g}^{-1}$$

(c) $^7\text{Li} + {}^1_1\text{H} \longrightarrow 2\,{}^4\text{He}$

$7.0160 \text{ u} + 1.0078 \text{ u} \longrightarrow 2(4.0026 \text{ u})$

$8.0238 \text{ u} \longrightarrow 8.0052 \text{ u}$

$$\Delta m = -0.0186 \text{ u}$$

$$\Delta m = (-0.0186 \text{ u}) \times \left(\frac{1.661 \times 10^{-27} \text{ kg}}{1 \text{ u}}\right) = -3.09 \times 10^{-29} \text{ kg}$$

$$\Delta E = \Delta mc^2 = (-3.09 \times 10^{-29} \text{ kg}) \times (3.00 \times 10^8 \text{ m} \cdot \text{s}^{-1})^2 = -2.78 \times 10^{-12} \text{ J}$$

$$\left(\frac{-2.78 \times 10^{-12} \text{ J}}{8.0238 \text{ u}}\right) \times \left(\frac{1 \text{ u}}{1.661 \times 10^{-24} \text{ g}}\right) = -2.09 \times 10^{11} \text{ J} \cdot \text{g}^{-1}$$

(d) $\text{D} + \text{T} \longrightarrow {}^4\text{He} + {}^1_1\text{H}$

$2.0141 \text{ u} + 3.0160 \text{ u} \longrightarrow 4.0026 \text{ u} + 1.0078 \text{ u}$

$5.0301 \text{ u} \longrightarrow 5.00104 \text{ u}$

$$\Delta m = -0.0197 \text{ u}$$

$$\Delta m = (-0.0197 \text{ u}) \times \left(\frac{1.661 \times 10^{-27} \text{ kg}}{1 \text{ u}}\right) = -3.27 \times 10^{-29} \text{ kg}$$

$$\Delta E = \Delta mc^2 = (-3.27 \times 10^{-29} \text{ kg}) \times (3.00 \times 10^8 \text{ m} \cdot \text{s}^{-1})^2 = -2.94 \times 10^{-12} \text{ J}$$

$$\left(\frac{-2.94 \times 10^{-12} \text{ J}}{5.0301 \text{ u}}\right) \times \left(\frac{1 \text{ u}}{1.661 \times 10^{-24} \text{ g}}\right) = -3.52 \times 10^{11} \text{ J} \cdot \text{g}^{-1}$$

22.65 Uranium tetrafluoride, which is obtained in the refining of uranium ores, is oxidized to the hexafluoride:

$$\text{UF}_4(s) + \text{F}_2(g) \xrightarrow{450°\text{C}} \text{UF}_6(s)$$

The hexafluoride is vaporized and then used in the enrichment process, which makes use of the different effusion rates of gaseous $^{235}UF_6$ (349 amu) and $^{238}UF_6$ (352 amu). According to Graham's law (Section 5.15), the relative rates of effusion are

$$\frac{\text{Rate of effusion of } ^{235}UF_6}{\text{Rate of effusion of } ^{238}UF_6} = \sqrt{\frac{352}{349}} = 1.004$$

Because this ratio is so close to 1, the uranium hexafluoride vapor must be allowed to effuse repeatedly through porous barriers designed for the purpose. These are screens with large numbers of minute holes. In practice, it is allowed to do so thousands of times. An alternative enrichment procedure utilizes a centrifuge that rotates samples of uranium hexafluoride vapor at very high speed. This process causes the heavier $^{238}UF_6$ molecules to be thrown outward and collected as a solid on the outer parts of the rotor, thereby leaving a higher proportion of $^{235}UF_6$ closer to the axis of the rotor, from where it can be removed.

SUPPLEMENTARY EXERCISES

22.67 The order of penetrating power is

$$\gamma > \beta > \alpha$$

γ rays are uncharged, high-energy photons that can pass right through objects like the body with little retardation. β particles are fast electrons that can penetrate flesh to a depth of about 1 cm before they are stopped by electrostatic interactions. α particles are the least penetrating because of their charge and relatively large mass. Although they do not penetrate deeply, they are very damaging because of their high energy, which is proportional to their large mass. Consequently, they can dislodge atoms from molecules, thereby altering the structure of the molecule, which in turn alters the ability of the molecule to function properly. If the molecule is DNA, a necessary enzyme, or another essential molecule in a living system, the result may be cancer.

22.69 The stabilities of nuclei vary and the greatest stabilities are associated with certain numbers of nucleons. These numbers are referred to as magic numbers; they are

$$2, 8, 20, 50, 82, 126$$

The existence of this series of numbers reminds us of the magic numbers of electrons in the electronic configurations of the noble gases:

$$2, 10, 18, 36, 54, 86$$

Because this series of numbers corresponds to a shell model for electrons in atoms, the analogous series of numbers for nucleons suggests a nuclear shell model.

22.71 The basic difference between polyester fabrics and fabrics such as wool, silk, and nylon is that the latter group are all polyamides. The presence of the amide functional group, $-\overset{\parallel}{\underset{O}{C}}-\overset{\mid}{\underset{H}{N}}-$, allows for extensive cross-linking between polymer chains by hydrogen bonding with the amine, $-N-H$, group on one chain and the carbonyl, $>C=O$, group on another. Intermolecular attractions are thus greater between polyamide molecules than between polyester molecules. The less polar polyester molecules can more readily accept radon atoms among their chains.

22.73 (a) $^{11}_{5}B + ^{4}_{2}\alpha \longrightarrow ^{13}_{7}N + 2^{1}_{0}n$

(b) $^{35}_{17}Cl + ^{2}_{1}D \longrightarrow ^{36}_{18}Ar + ^{1}_{0}n$

(c) $^{96}_{42}Mo + ^{2}_{1}D \longrightarrow ^{97}_{43}Tc + ^{1}_{0}n$

(d) $^{45}_{21}Se + ^{1}_{0}n \longrightarrow ^{42}_{19}K + ^{4}_{2}\alpha$

22.75 (a) $1\ Ci = 3.7 \times 10^{10}$ decays per second (dps)

decays per minute (dpm) for 4 pCi $= 4 \times 10^{-12}\ Ci \times 3.7 \times 10^{10}\ dps \times \left(\dfrac{60\ s}{1\ min}\right)$

$$= 9\ dpm$$

(b) volume(L) $= (2 \times 3 \times 2.5)\ m^3 \times \left(\dfrac{10^3\ L}{1\ m^3}\right) = 1.\overline{5} \times 10^4\ L$

number of decays $= (1.\overline{5} \times 10^4\ L) \times \left(\dfrac{4\ pCi}{1\ L}\right) \times \left(\dfrac{9\ decays \cdot min^{-1}}{4\ pCi}\right)$

$$\times (5.0\ min) = 7 \times 10^5\ decays$$

22.77 $N_0 =$ number of ^{222}Rn atoms $= 1.0 \times 10^{-5}\ mol \times 6.0 \times 10^{23}\ atoms \cdot mol^{-1}$

$$= 6.0 \times 10^{18}\ atoms$$

$k = \dfrac{\ln 2}{t_{1/2}} = \dfrac{0.693}{3.82d} = 0.181\ d^{-1}$

(a) rate of decay $= k \times N = \left(\dfrac{0.181}{d}\right) \times \left(\dfrac{1\ d}{8.64 \times 10^4\ s}\right) \times 6.0 \times 10^{18}\ atoms$

$$= 1.26 \times 10^{13}\ atoms \cdot s^{-1}\ (dps\ or\ Bq)$$

initial activity (pCi $\cdot$ L^{-1}) $= 1.26 \times 10^{13}\ Bq \times \left(\dfrac{1\ Ci}{3.7 \times 10^{10}\ Bq}\right) \times \left(\dfrac{1\ pCi}{10^{-12}\ Ci}\right)$

$$\times \left(\dfrac{1}{2000\ m^3}\right) \times \left(\dfrac{1\ m^3}{10^3\ L}\right) = 1.7 \times 10^8\ pCi \cdot L^{-1}$$

(b) $N = N_0 e^{-kt} = 6.0 \times 10^{18}$ atoms $\times\ e^{-0.181\ d^{-1} \times 1\ d} = 5.0 \times 10^{18}$ atoms

(c) $\ln\left(\dfrac{\text{activity}}{\text{initial activity}}\right) = -kt$

$t = -\left(\dfrac{1}{k}\right) \ln\left(\dfrac{\text{activity}}{\text{initial activity}}\right) = -\left(\dfrac{1}{0.181\ d^{-1}}\right) \ln\left(\dfrac{4}{1.70 \times 10^8}\right)$

$\quad = 9\overline{7}$ days or 1×10^2 days

22.79 $k = \dfrac{0.693}{t_{1/2}} = \dfrac{0.693}{8.05\ d} = 0.0861\ d^{-1}$

$N = N_0\ e^{-kt}$ and $\dfrac{N}{N_0} = e^{-kt}$

Taking the natural log of both sides gives

$$\ln\left(\frac{N}{N_0}\right) = -kt$$

Because activity is proportional to N (Eq. 1), we can write

$$\ln\left(\frac{\text{final activity}}{\text{initial activity}}\right) = -kt$$

Solving for t gives

$$t = -\left(\frac{1}{k}\right) \ln\left(\frac{\text{final activity}}{\text{initial activity}}\right) = -\left(\frac{1}{0.0861\ d^{-1}}\right) \ln\left(\frac{10}{500}\right) = 45\ d$$

22.81 (a) activity $\propto N$; and, because $\ln\left(\dfrac{N}{N_0}\right) = -kt$

$\ln\left(\dfrac{\text{final activity}}{\text{initial activity}}\right) = -kt$

$\ln\left(\dfrac{32}{58}\right) = -k \times 12.3\ d$

$k = 0.048\overline{4}\ d^{-1}$

$t_{1/2} = \dfrac{0.693}{k} = \dfrac{0.693}{0.048\overline{4}\ d^{-1}} = 14.\overline{3}\ d$

(b) $\ln\left(\dfrac{N}{N_0}\right) = -0.048\overline{4}\ d^{-1} \times 30\ d = -1.4\overline{5}$

$\dfrac{N}{N_0} = \text{fraction remaining} = 0.23$

22.83

$$10.0 \text{ Ci} = 10.0 \times 3.7 \times 10^{10} \text{ nuclei} \cdot \text{s}^{-1} \times \frac{8.64 \times 10^4 \text{ s}}{1 \text{ d}}$$

$$= 3.2\overline{0} \times 10^{16} \text{ nuclei} \cdot \text{d}^{-1}$$

$$k = \frac{0.693}{t_{1/2}} = \frac{0.693}{88 \text{ d}} = 7.8\overline{75} \times 10^{-3} \text{ d}^{-1}$$

activity = rate = $3.2\overline{0} \times 10^{16} \text{ nuclei} \cdot \text{d}^{-1} = 7.8\overline{75} \times 10^{-3} \text{ d}^{-1} \times \text{N}$

$$N = \frac{3.2\overline{0} \times 10^{16} \text{ nuclei} \cdot \text{d}^{-1}}{7.8\overline{75} \times 10^{-3} \text{ s}^{-1}} = 4.0\overline{6} \times 10^{18} \text{ nuclei}$$

$$\text{mass of } {}^{35}\text{S} = (35 \text{ u}) \times \left(\frac{1.661 \times 10^{-24} \text{ g}}{1 \text{ u}} \right) \times (4.0\overline{6} \times 10^{18} \text{ nuclei}) = 2.4 \times 10^{-4} \text{ g}$$

22.85 $\quad {}^{24}_{11}\text{Na} \longrightarrow {}^{24}_{12}\text{Mg} + {}^{0}_{-1}\text{e}$

mass $({}^{24}_{11}\text{Na}) = 23.990\ 96 \text{ u}$

mass $({}^{24}_{12}\text{Mg}) = 23.985\ 04 \text{ u}$

The mass of the electron does not need to be explicitly included in the calculation as it is already included in the mass of Mg.

$\Delta m = $ mass $({}^{24}_{12}\text{Mg}) - $ mass $({}^{24}_{11}\text{Na}) = 23.985\ 04 \text{ u} - 23.990\ 96 \text{ u} = -5.92 \times 10^{-3} \text{ u}$

Δm (in kg) $= -5.92 \times 10^{-3} \text{ u} \times 1.6605 \times 10^{-27} \text{ kg u}^{-1} = -9.83 \times 10^{-30} \text{ kg}$

It is convenient to work part (b) first.

(b) $\Delta E = \Delta mc^2 = -9.83 \times 10^{-30} \text{ kg} \times (3.00 \times 10^8 \text{ m} \cdot \text{s}^{-1}) = -8.85 \times 10^{-13} \text{ J}$

(a) ΔE (per nucleon) $= \dfrac{-8.85 \times 10^{-13} \text{ J}}{24 \text{ nucleons}} = -3.69 \times 10^{-14} \text{ J} \cdot \text{nucleon}$

CHALLENGING EXERCISES

22.87 (a) At first thought, it might seem that a fusion bomb would be more suitable for excavation work, because the fusion process itself does not generate harmful radioactive waste products. However, in practice, fusion cannot be initiated in a bomb in the absence of the high temperatures that can only be generated by a fission bomb. So there is no environmental advantage to the use of a fusion bomb. The fission bomb has the advantage that its destructive power can be more carefully controlled. It is possible to make small fission bombs whose destructive effect can be contained within a small area.

(b) The principal argument for the use of bombs in excavation is speed, and hence cost-effectiveness, of the process. The principal argument against their use is environmental damage.

22.89 $\quad k = \dfrac{0.693}{4.5 \times 10^9 \text{ y}} = 1.5\overline{4} \times 10^{-10} \text{ y}^{-1}$

$$t(=\text{age}) = -\left(\frac{1}{k}\right)\ln\left(\frac{N}{N_0}\right) \quad \text{[Example 22.2]}$$

$$\frac{N}{N_0} = \frac{\text{mass of }^{238}\text{U}}{\text{initial mass of }^{238}\text{U}} = \frac{1}{1 + \dfrac{\text{mass of }^{206}\text{Pb}}{\text{mass of }^{238}\text{U}}}$$

(a) $\dfrac{N}{N_0} = \dfrac{1}{1 + 1.00} = \dfrac{1}{2.00}$, hence age $= t_{1/2} = 4.5 \times 10^9$ y

(b) $\dfrac{N}{N_0} = \dfrac{1}{1 + \dfrac{1}{1.25}} = 0.556$

$$t(=\text{age}) = -\left(\frac{1}{1.5\overline{4} \times 10^{-10}\text{ y}^{-1}}\right)\ln(0.556) = 3.8 \times 10^9 \text{ y}$$

22.91 (a) activity $= (17.3 \text{ Ci}) \times \left(\dfrac{3.7 \times 10^{10}\text{ Bq}}{1 \text{ Ci}}\right)$

$$= 6.4 \times 10^{11} \text{ Bq} = 6.4 \times 10^{11} \text{ nuclei} \cdot \text{s}^{-1}$$

$$N = (2.0 \times 10^{-6} \text{ g}) \times \left(\frac{1 \text{ u}}{1.661 \times 10^{-24} \text{ g}}\right) \times \left(\frac{1 \text{ nucleus}}{24 \text{ u}}\right) = 5.0 \times 10^{16} \text{ nuclei}$$

$$k = \frac{\text{activity}}{N} = \frac{6.4 \times 10^{11} \text{ nuclei} \cdot \text{s}^{-1}}{5.0 \times 10^{16} \text{ nuclei}} = 1.2\overline{8} \times 10^{-5} \text{ s}^{-1} = 1.11 \text{ d}^{-1}$$

$$t_{1/2} = \frac{0.693}{k} = \frac{0.693}{1.2\overline{8} \times 10^{-5} \text{ s}^{-1}} = 5.4 \times 10^4 \text{ s} = 15 \text{ h} = 0.63 \text{ d}$$

(b) $m = m_0 e^{-kt} = 2.0 \text{ μg} \times e^{-1.11 \text{ d}^{-1} \times 2.0 \text{ d}} = 0.22 \text{ μg}$

ANSWERS TO ODD-NUMBERED CASE STUDY QUESTIONS

CHAPTER 1

1. This statement is not justified. A proper statement might be, "No conclusive evidence found for life on Mars."

3. If Mars were to support a human population, farming the Martian soil would seem to be a necessity. Thus experiments would have to be performed to see whether the growth of plants needed by humans could be achieved with Martian soil. These farming experiments could probably be performed on a small scale inside the lander of a spacecraft. Because water and oxygen are scarce on the surface, sources would have to be found, perhaps underground. Metal ores would also be sought for use as building materials.

CHAPTER 2

1. (a) average molar mass = $(0.999\ 85 \times 1.007\ 825\ 031\ 6$ u $+ 0.000\ 15$
$$\times\ 2.014\ 101\ 779 \text{u}) = 1.007\ 976 \text{ u}$$

To convert to molar mass in $g \cdot mol^{-1}$, we need the mass of the atomic mass unit in grams. This mass is given as $1.660\ 54 \times 10^{-24}$ g, which is only six significant figures. It is, however, known to more figures:

$$1 \text{ u} = 1.660\ 540\ 2 \times 10^{-24} \text{ g}$$

Thus,
average molar mass $= 1.007\ 976$ u $\times 1.660\ 540\ 2 \times 10^{-24}$ g $\cdot$ u^{-1}
$$\times\ 6.022\ 14 \times 10^{23} \text{ mol}^{-1} = 1.007\ 976 \text{ g} \cdot \text{mol}^{-1}$$
(b) to five significant figures; that is, 1.0080 g $\cdot$ mol^{-1}

3. The mass standard needs to be ultrapure because the standard serves as a reference to determine the masses of other elements. If the mass of the standard is not accurately measured, then data for other materials will not be accurate. The standard material should be a solid for ease in handling.

CHAPTER 3

1. (a) Physical processes | (b) Chemical processes
    |

aeration (replacement of unwanted gases)

oxidation ($Fe^{2+} \longrightarrow Fe^{3+} + 1e^-$)

settling (separation of ppt from soln)

precipitation (hydroxide and carbonate formation)

filtration (through sand)

coagulation (pptn with alum)

adsorption (organics onto activated charcoal)

acid/base (controlling pptn, forming HClO, killing bacteria)

ion exchange

reverse osmosis

3. complete equations:

$$Pb^{2+}(aq) + Ca(OH)_2(aq) \longrightarrow Pb(OH)_2(s) + Ca^{2+}(aq)$$
$$2Fe^{3+}(aq) + 3Ca(OH)_2(aq) \longrightarrow 2Fe(OH)_3(s) + 3Ca^{2+}(aq)$$

net ionic equations:

$$Pb^{2+}(aq) + 2OH^-(aq) \longrightarrow Pb(OH)_2(s)$$
$$Fe^{3+}(aq) + 3OH^-(aq) \longrightarrow Fe(OH)_3(s)$$

Note: $Ca(OH)_2$ is only sparingly soluble in water, but, to the extent that it does dissolve, it exists in the ionic form.

CHAPTER 4

1. combustion of methanol:

$$2CH_3OH(l) + 3O_2(g) \longrightarrow 2CO_2(g) + 4H_2O(l)$$

combustion of octane:

$$2C_8H_{18}(l) + 25O_2(g) \longrightarrow 16CO_2(g) + 18H_2O(l)$$

$$\text{mass of } CO_2 \text{ from } \atop 1.00 \text{ L methanol} = 1.00 \text{ L} \times \left(\frac{10^3 \text{ cm}^3}{1 \text{ L}}\right) \times \left(\frac{0.791 \text{ g}}{1 \text{ cm}^3}\right) \times \left(\frac{1 \text{ mol } CH_3OH}{32.04 \text{ g}}\right)$$

$$\times \left(\frac{2 \text{ mol } CO_2}{2 \text{ mol } CH_3OH}\right) \times \left(\frac{44.01 \text{ g } CO_2}{1 \text{ mol } CO_2}\right) \times \left(\frac{1 \text{ kg } CO_2}{10^3 \text{ g } CO_2}\right) = 1.09 \text{ kg } CO_2$$

This is the theoretical yield of CO_2 from 1.00 L of methanol.

$$\text{mass of } CO_2 \text{ from } \atop 1.00 \text{ L octane} = 2.16 \times 10^3 \text{ g} \times \left(\frac{1 \text{ mol octane}}{114.23 \text{ g octane}}\right) \times \left(\frac{16 \text{ mol } CO_2}{2 \text{ mol octane}}\right)$$

$$\times \left(\frac{44.01 \text{ g } CO_2}{1 \text{ mol } CO_2}\right) \times \left(\frac{1 \text{ kg } CO_2}{10^3 \text{ g } CO_2}\right) = 6.66 \text{ kg } CO_2$$

This is the theoretical yield of CO_2 from 1.00 L of octane. Clearly, octane contributes more CO_2 per liter to the atmosphere.

An important factor that must be taken into account is the amount of energy released by the combustion. The method of determining this factor is taken up in Chapter 6. We will find that octane releases more energy per liter (and per kilogram) than methanol does. Another important factor is engine performance. It is more difficult to determine conclusively which fuel is superior in this regard.

Another factor is cost.

3. Assuming that the figure given is 1.74 ppm by mass, then mass of methane =
$1.74 \times 10^{-6} \times 5.1 \times 10^{21}$ g $= 8.9 \times 10^{15}$ g

8.9×10^{15} g $\times \left(\dfrac{1 \text{ kg}}{10^3 \text{ g}} \right) \times \left(\dfrac{1 \text{ metric ton}}{10^3 \text{ kg}} \right) = 8.9 \times 10^9$ metric ton

CHAPTER 5

1. Equation 6 of Section 5.16 demonstrates that

$$v \propto \frac{1}{\sqrt{M}}$$

where v = average speed and M = molar mass. Therefore, the smaller the molar mass, the greater the average speed.

$M_{NO} = 30.01$ g $\cdot$ mol^{-1},   therefore fastest
$M_{O_2} = 32.00$ g $\cdot$ mol^{-1}
$M_{NO_2} = 46.01$ g $\cdot$ mol^{-1}
$M_{O_3} = 48.00$ g $\cdot$ mol^{-1},   therefore slowest
So, $O_3 < NO_2 < O_2 < NO$ (fastest).

3. The density of a gas is proportional to the molar mass of the gas. Therefore, under the same conditions of temperature and pressure, the most dense gas is the one with the greatest molar mass. In this case, O_2 would be the most dense gas.

CHAPTER 6

1. specific enthalpy of cheese $= 17.0$ kJ $\cdot$ g^{-1} (Table in Case)

mass in grams $= 2$ oz $\times \left(\dfrac{28.35 \text{ g}}{1 \text{ oz}} \right) = 56.7$ g

energy (= enthalpy change) $= 56.7$ g $\times 17.0$ kJ $\cdot$ g$^{-1} = 963.9$ kJ

time spent $= \dfrac{963.9 \text{ kJ}}{30 \text{ kJ} \cdot \text{min}^{-1}} = 32$ min

3. Fats are only very slightly oxidized hydrocarbons, thus most of their fuel value is still intact. Carbohydrates, on the other hand, are already oxidized to a considerable extent. Typically they contain almost equal numbers of carbon and oxygen atoms; thus most of the fuel value of the carbon and hydrogen atoms has already been spent.

CHAPTER 7

1. We need to establish the relationship between the absorbance and percentage transmittance. Then from the absorbance, we may find the concentration through the relation

$$A = \text{constant} \times (\text{molar concentration}) \times (\text{sample thickness}) = C \times M \times l$$

and

$$A = \log\left(\frac{I_0}{I}\right) = \log\left(\frac{100}{\%T}\right)$$

Then

$$\frac{A_2}{A_1} = \frac{M_2}{M_1} = \frac{\log\left(\dfrac{100}{\%T_2}\right)}{\log\left(\dfrac{100}{\%T_1}\right)}$$

and

$$M_2 = M_1 \left[\frac{\log\left(\dfrac{100}{\%T_2}\right)}{\log\left(\dfrac{100}{\%T_1}\right)}\right] = 0.10 \text{ M} \left[\frac{\log\left(\dfrac{100}{40}\right)}{\log\left(\dfrac{100}{65}\right)}\right] = 0.21 \text{ M}$$

CHAPTER 8

1. (a) $:\!\dot{N}\!=\!\ddot{\ddot{O}}$ (b) $:\!\ddot{\ddot{O}}\!-\!H$ (c)

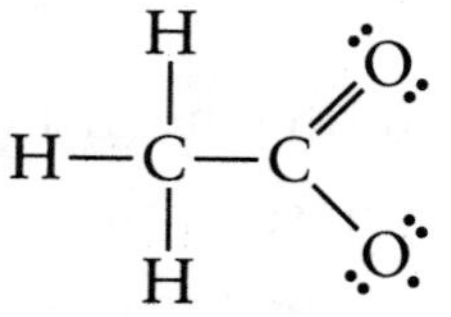

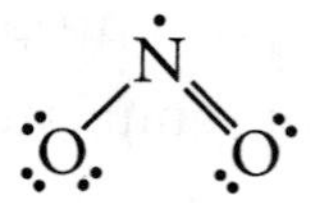

2 resonance forms

(d)

2 resonance forms

3. $CH_3CH_3 + \cdot\ddot{\ddot{O}}\!-\!H \longrightarrow \cdot CH_2CH_3 + H_2O$

CHAPTER 9

1. (a) The carbon atoms in C_{60} are the A atoms of a distorted planar AX_3 VSEPR structure; therefore, we expect approximately sp^2 hybridization.

(b) Because carbon nanotubes have basically the same bonding structure as graphite, the hybridization is sp^2.

3. Those species that are polar will be attracted to the polar ends of these self-assembling layers. Therefore, (a) nitric oxide, (c) ethanol, and (d) glycine will be attracted to the polar ends of molecules.

CHAPTER 10

1. (a) anisotropic   (b) isotropic   (c) anisotropic   (d) anisotropic   (e) anisotropic

3. Polar groups aid in the alignment of the molecules, the positive end of one molecule adhering to the negative end of another, and vice versa. That is, the dipoles align antiparallel to one another. Curiously, the presence of an —OH group in the molecule, which leads to hydrogen bonding, as in cholesterol itself, can sometimes hinder liquid crystal formation. Thus cholesterol does not form a cholesteric liquid crystal.

CHAPTER 11

1. (a) The Lewis structure of ethyne is H—C≡C—H. See Fig. 9.34 for its valence bond structure and the figure below. The top portion of the figure shows the σ-bond framework and the bottom portion the overlapping of atomic p-orbitals that result in the two π-bonds.

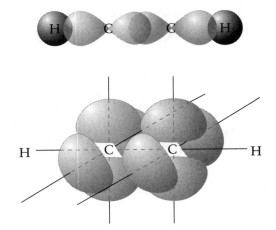

The carbon atoms are sp hybrids, as shown in the top part of the figure.

(b)

$$-\overset{\scriptstyle|}{\underset{\scriptstyle H}{C}}=\overset{\scriptstyle|}{\underset{\scriptstyle H}{C}}-\overset{\scriptstyle|}{\underset{\scriptstyle H}{C}}= \longleftrightarrow =\overset{\scriptstyle|}{\underset{\scriptstyle H}{C}}-\overset{\scriptstyle|}{\underset{\scriptstyle H}{C}}=\overset{\scriptstyle|}{\underset{\scriptstyle H}{C}}-$$

(*Note:* The second structure has the same number of C—H units, but the single and double bonds have exchanged places.)

(c) All carbon σ orbitals are sp^2 hybrids.

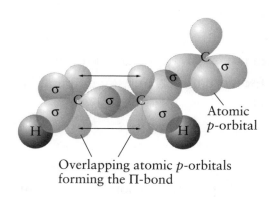

Overlapping atomic p-orbitals
forming the Π-bond

Because of resonance, every carbon-carbon bond in polyacetylene has considerable double-bond character. Free rotation cannot occur about double bonds; and even though these bonds are only partially double, we expect polyacetylenes to be fairly stiff.

3.

CHAPTER 12

1. (a) both a sol and an emulsion (b) foam (c) sol

3. (a) hydrophilic colloid; so hydrogen bonds
(b) hydrophilic colloid; so hydrogen bonds
(c) hydrogen bonds, dipole-dipole forces, and London forces

CHAPTER 13

1. (a) step 1 $K_{c1} = \dfrac{[BrO_2]^2}{[H^+]^2[BrO_2^-][BrO_3^-]}$

step 2 $K_{c2} = \dfrac{[Ce^{4+}]^2[BrO_2^-]^2}{[Ce^{3+}]^2[BrO_2]^2}$

step 3 $K_{c3} = \dfrac{[BrO_3^-][BrO^-]}{[BrO_2^-]^2}$

(b) One possibility is $2H^+ + BrO_2^- + 2Ce^{3+} \rightleftharpoons BrO^- + 2Ce^{4+} + H_2O$.

$K_c = \dfrac{[BrO^-][Ce^{4+}]^2}{[H^+]^2[BrO_2^-][Ce^{3+}]^2}$

(c) $K_c = K_{c1}K_{c2}K_{c3}$

3. step 1 BrO_2^- is oxidized, BrO_3^- is reduced.

step 2 Ce^{3+} is oxidized, BrO_2 is reduced.

step 3 BrO_2^- is oxidized, BrO_2^- is also reduced.

CHAPTER 14

1. When $CO_2(g)$ dissolves in water, the following reaction takes place:

$$CO_2(g) + H_2O(l) \longrightarrow H_2CO_3(aq)$$

and

Concentration	$H_2CO_3(aq)$	$+ H_2O(l) \rightleftharpoons$	$H_3O^+(aq)$	$+ HCO_3^-(aq)$
initial	$[H_2CO_3]_0$	—	0	0
change	$-x$	—	$+x$	$+x$
equilibrium	$[H_2CO_3]_0 - x$	—	x	x

We can justifiably ignore the second ionization of H_2CO_3, because $K_{a2} \ll K_{a1}$. The initial concentration of H_2CO_3 can be calculated from the Henry's law constant for CO_2; thus,

$[H_2CO_3]_0 = [CO_2] = 2.3 \times 10^{-2}$ mol $\cdot$ L$^{-1} \cdot$ atm$^{-1} \times 3.04 \times 10^{-4}$ atm

$\qquad = 6.9\overline{9} \times 10^{-6}$ mol $\cdot$ L^{-1}

$K_{a1} = 10^{-pK_a}$ mol $\cdot$ L$^{-1} = 10^{-6.37}$ mol $\cdot$ L$^{-1} = 4.2\overline{7} \times 10^{-7}$ mol $\cdot$ L^{-1}

$K_{a1} = 4.2\overline{7} \times 10^{-7} = \dfrac{[H_3O^+][HCO_3^-]}{[H_2CO_3]} = \dfrac{x^2}{[H_2CO_3]_0 - x} = \dfrac{x^2}{6.99 \times 10^{-6} - x}$

Because $[H_2CO_3]_0$ is so small, we cannot neglect x relative to it. This leads to the quadratic:

$$x^2 + 4.2\overline{7} \times 10^{-7}x - 2.9\overline{85} \times 10^{-12} = 0$$

which has the solution:

$$x = [H_3O^+] = 1.5\overline{3} \times 10^{-6} \text{ mol} \cdot \text{L}^{-1}$$

and

$$pH = -\log[H_3O^+] = -\log(1.5\overline{3} \times 10^{-6}) = 5.82,$$

which is close to 5.7.

There are two possible explanations for this small but not negligible difference. The first is that we have not included in the calculation the contribution to $[H_3O^+]$ from the autoprotolysis of water. However, when we do so, the pH changes by only 0.03 to 5.79 ($\sim$5.8). (See the solution to Exercise 14.83 for the method used in calculating this contribution.) The remaining difference, assuming it is real (namely, outside of experimental error), could be accounted for by the fact that the Henry's law constant is sensitive to temperature changes. An average temperature for rain, for all seasons and at all elevations, may not correspond to the temperature (20°C) of the Henry's law constant given in the case.

3. In Question 2(b), we calculated that $82\overline{0}$ mol of SO_2 was produced. Because we assumed in 2(c) that all SO_2 was converted to SO_3, which then reacted with water to form H_2SO_4, the amount of H_2SO_4 formed would also be $82\overline{0}$ mol. Half of this amount, namely, $41\overline{0}$ mol, is then assumed to react with the Ca^{2+} ions in the soil.

$$H_2SO_4(aq) + Ca^{2+}(clay) \longrightarrow CaSO_4(s) + 2H^+(clay)$$

$$\text{mass Ca} = 41\overline{0} \text{ mol } H_2SO_4 \times \left(\frac{1 \text{ mol Ca}^{2+}}{1 \text{ mol } H_2SO_4}\right) \times \left(\frac{40.08g}{1 \text{ mol Ca}^{2+}}\right)$$

$$= 1.6 \times 10^4 \text{ g Ca}^{2+} = 16 \text{ kg Ca}^{2+}$$

CHAPTER 15

1. The equilibria involved are

$$CO_2(g) + H_2O(l) \rightleftharpoons H_2CO_3(aq)$$
$$H_2CO_3(aq) + H_2O(l) \rightleftharpoons H_3O^+(aq) + HCO_3^-(aq)$$

Hyperventilation decreases the amount of $CO_2(g)$, thus driving the first equilibrium to the left, which in turn drives the second equilibrium to the left. Therefore, both $[HCO_3^-]$ and $[H_2CO_3]$ are diminished, but it is not immediately apparent how their ratio is affected. We can analyze the effect on the ratio through the use of the Henderson-Hasselbalch equation:

$$pH = -\log[H_3O^+] = pK_{a1} + \log\left(\frac{[HCO_3^-]}{[H_2CO_3]}\right)$$

With loss of CO_2 during hyperventilation, there is a decrease in $[H_3O^+]$, which corresponds to an increased pH, which in turn corresponds to an increased $[HCO_3^-]/[H_2CO_3]$ ratio, or a decreased $[H_2CO_3]/[HCO_3^-]$ ratio.

3. From the Henderson-Hasselbalch equation, the effective buffer range in water is $pH = pK_a, \pm \log 10 = 6.1 \pm 1.00$
The $20:1$ $[HCO_3^-]/[H_2CO_3]$ ratio in blood places this buffer slightly beyond its most effective pH range, but blood is a more complex liquid than pure water and other buffer systems play a role.

CHAPTER 16

1. $C_6H_{12}O_6(s) + 6O_2(g) \longrightarrow 6CO_2(g) + 6H_2O(l)$
Data from Appendix 2A:

$$\Delta H_r^\circ = 6 \times \Delta H_f^\circ(CO_2, g) + 6 \times \Delta H_f^\circ(H_2O, l) - \Delta H_f^\circ(C_6H_{12}O_6, s)$$
$$= [6 \times (-393.51) + 6 \times (-285.83) - (-1268)] \, kJ \cdot mol^{-1}$$
$$= -2808 \, kJ \cdot mol^{-1}$$
$$\Delta S_r^\circ = 6 \times S_m^\circ(CO_2, g) + 6 \times S_m^\circ(H_2O, l) - 1 \times S_m^\circ(C_6H_{12}O_6, s) - 6 \times S_m^\circ(O_2, g)$$
$$= (6 \times 213.74 + 6 \times 69.91 - 212 - 6 \times 205.14) \, J \cdot K^{-1} \cdot mol^{-1}$$
$$= 259 \, J \cdot K^{-1} \cdot mol^{-1} = 0.259 \, kJ \cdot K^{-1} \cdot mol^{-1}$$
$$\Delta G_r^\circ = \Delta H_r^\circ - T\Delta S_r^\circ = -2808 \, kJ \cdot mol^{-1} - 298 \, K \times 0.259 \, kJ \cdot K^{-1} \cdot mol^{-1}$$
$$= -2885 \, kJ \cdot mol^{-1}$$

As the temperature is raised, ΔG_r° becomes more negative, and more energy becomes available to do work, $\Delta G_r^\circ = w_{max}$. Because ΔS_r° is positive, the reaction becomes more spontaneous as the temperature is raised.

3. ΔG_r° for the photosynthetic synthesis of glucose is the negative of the value for the combustion of glucose calculated in the answer to Question 1.

$$\Delta G_r^\circ = +2885 \, kJ \cdot mol^{-1}$$

For ATP $\longrightarrow$ ADP, $\Delta G_r^\circ = -30.5 \, kJ \cdot mol^{-1}$; therefore, to provide $-2885 \, kJ$, the number of moles required is

$$n = \frac{-2885 \, kJ}{-30.5 \, kJ \cdot mol^{-1}} = 94.6 \, mol \, ATP$$

CHAPTER 17

1. The overall reaction is

$$6CO_2(g) + 6H_2O(l) \longrightarrow C_6H_{12}O_6(s) + 6O_2(g)$$

This is not a spontaneous process.
$$\Delta G_r^\circ = \Delta G_f^\circ(C_6H_{12}O_6, s) - 6 \times \Delta G_f^\circ(CO_2, g) - 6 \times \Delta G_f^\circ(H_2O, l)$$
$$= (-910 \, kJ \cdot mol^{-1}) - 6 \times (-394.36 \, kJ \cdot mol^{-1}) - 6 \times (-237.13 \, kJ \cdot mol^{-1})$$
$$= 2879 \, kJ \cdot mol^{-1}$$

If this reaction were to occur electrochemically, the minimum potential that would have to be supplied to this electrolytic process can be calculated from

$$\Delta G_r^\circ = -nFE^\circ$$

In this process, for each O_2 molecule produced, there is a transfer of $4e^-$, or $6 \times 4e^- = 24e^-$ for $6O_2$. Thus $n = 24$, and

$$E^\circ = \frac{\Delta G_r^\circ}{-nF} = \frac{2879 \times 10^3 \, J \cdot mol^{-1}}{-24 \times 9.6485 \times 10^4 \, C \cdot mol^{-1}}$$
$$= -1.24 \, V$$

Therefore, the photoelectrochemical cell would have to supply $E > 1.24$ V. This value is slightly larger than the 1.23 V needed for H_2 and O_2 evolution from water, so one might initially guess that H_2 and O_2 would preferentially form. But the overvoltage for H_2 and O_2 formation is about 0.6 V; consequently, because about 1.8 V are needed for the evolution of these gases from water, glucose would preferentially form.

3. If the sulfide ions in CdS(s) are not oxidized in a saturated H_2S(aq) solution, then the net reaction is H_2S(aq) $\longrightarrow H_2$(g) + S(s). The half-reactions are

$$(1) \quad 2H^+ + 2e^- \longrightarrow H_2(g) \quad E°\text{(cathode)} = 0.00 \text{ V}$$
$$(2) \quad S(s) + 2e^- \longrightarrow S^{2-}(aq) \quad E°\text{(anode)} = -0.48 \text{ V}$$

Reversing (2) gives

$$S^{2-}(aq) \longrightarrow S(s) + 2e^-$$

and adding gives the net overall reaction:

$$E°_{cell} = E°\text{(cathode)} - E°\text{(anode)} = +0.48 \text{ V}$$

But this is the potential generated by the cell.

CHAPTER 18

1. At high concentrations of substrate, the plot of rate against substrate concentration levels off to a constant rate. Therefore,

$$\text{rate} \propto [S]^a = \text{constant}$$

implies that $a = 0$ and $[S]^0 = 1 = \text{constant}$. So the reaction is zero order in substrate at high substrate concentrations.

3. There are many types of inhibitors. Suppose, for example, that the inhibitor functions by competing with the substrate to form an EI complex; then the slope of the curve will be reduced, and the rate of product formation for a given substrate concentration will also be less.

CHAPTER 19

1. Several reactions occur, depending on the silica to alkali ratio:
(1) $SiO_2(s) + OH^-(aq) \longrightarrow HSiO_3^-(aq)$
(2) $SiO_2(s) + 2OH^-(aq) \longrightarrow H_2O(l) + SiO_3^{2-}(aq)$ (metasilicate ion)
(3) $SiO_2(s) + 4OH^-(aq) \longrightarrow 2H_2O(l) + SiO_4^{4-}(aq)$ (orthosilicate ion)
(4) $2SiO_2(s) + 6OH^-(aq) \longrightarrow 3H_2O(l) + Si_2O_7^{6-}(aq)$ (pyrosilicate ion)

3. Glasses form from materials in which inhibited recrystallization occurs. Such materials are likely to be covalently bonded materials involving extensive network structures and materials with large complex molecules. On the basis of these principles, we predict that, of the substances listed, the following would probably solidify as a glass: (a) tar; (c) molten granite; (e) low-density polyethylene; and (f) a highly branched polymer. Any substance can form a glass if cooled rapidly enough, but (b) sodium chloride and (d) water would normally form crystalline solids.

CHAPTER 20

1. The suggested reaction is

$$3NH_4ClO_4(s) + 3Al(s) \xrightarrow{Fe_2O_3} Al_2O_3(s) + AlCl_3(s) + 6H_2O(g) + 3NO(g)$$

Chlorine is reduced: $Cl(+7) \longrightarrow Cl(-1)$

Aluminium is oxidized: $Al(0) \longrightarrow Al(+3)$

Nitrogen is oxidized: $N(-3) \longrightarrow N(+2)$

The half-reactions are

$$3Al + 3H_2O \longrightarrow Al^{3+} + Al_2O_3 + 6H^+ + 9e^-$$
$$NH_4^+ + H_2O \longrightarrow NO + 6H^+ + 5e^-$$
$$ClO_4^- + 8H^+ + 8e^- \longrightarrow Cl^- + 4H_2O^-$$

Multiply the last two equations by 3 and add all the half-reactions together to get the overall equation above.

3. (a) $3NH_4ClO_4(s) + 3Al(s) \longrightarrow Al_2O_3(s) + AlCl_3(s) + 6H_2O(g) + 3NO(g)$

$\Delta H_r^\circ = 1 \times \Delta H_f^\circ(Al_2O_3, s) + 1 \times \Delta H_f^\circ(AlCl_3, s) + 6 \times \Delta H_f^\circ(H_2O, g) + 3$
$$\times \Delta H_f^\circ(NO, g) - 3 \times \Delta H_f^\circ(NH_4ClO_4, s)$$

$= [-1675.7 - 704.2 + 6 \times (-241.82) + 3 \times 90.25 - 3 \times (-295)] \text{ kJ} \cdot \text{mol}^{-1}$

$= -2675 \text{ kJ} \cdot \text{mol}^{-1}$

(b) specific enthalpy $= \dfrac{2675 \text{ kJ} \cdot \text{mol}^{-1}}{3 \times 26.98 \text{ g} \cdot \text{mol}^{-1}} = +33.05 \text{ kJ} \cdot \text{g}^{-1} \text{ Al}$

Note: The specific enthalpy for the fuel mixture of aluminum and ammonium perchlorate would be less.

5. (a) $2H_2(l) + O_2(l) \longrightarrow 2H_2O(g)$

specific enthalpy $= \dfrac{475 \text{ kJ} \cdot \text{mol}^{-1}}{4 \times 1.008 \text{ g} \cdot \text{mol}^{-1}} = 118 \text{ kJ} \cdot \text{g}^{-1}$

(b) The specific enthalpy is largest for $H_2(l)$ ($118 \text{ kJ} \cdot \text{g}^{-1}$), then Al ($32.83 \text{ kJ} \cdot \text{g}^{-1}$), and smallest for CH_3NHNH_2 ($25.70 \text{ kJ} \cdot \text{g}^{-1}$).

(c) For $2H_2(g) + O_2(g) \longrightarrow 2H_2O(g)$, $\Delta H° = 2 \times (-241.82 \text{ kJ}) = -483.64$. The specific enthalpy of liquid hydrogen is less than that for gaseous hydrogen. This can be seen by comparing the enthalpy of combustion of $H_2(g)$ ($\Delta H_r = -483.64 \text{ kJ} \cdot \text{mol}^{-1}$) to that of $H_2(l)$ ($\Delta H_r = -475 \text{ kJ} \cdot \text{mol}^{-1}$). The difference is due to the enthalpy required to vaporize the liquids.

CHAPTER 21

1. "Fixing," that is, removing undeveloped HgI, was not a part of the process of producing a daguerrotype. Consequently, on further exposure to light, reduction of some of the remaining Ag^+ ions continued and caused a darkening or fading of the image.

In photochromic sunglasses, the darkening of the glass is a result of the reversible redox reaction

$$Ag^+(s) + Cu^+(s) \xrightarrow{\text{light}} Ag(s) + Cu^{2+}(s)$$

This reaction is driven to the right in the presence of light, and the formation of Ag(s) causes a darkening of the lens. When the light is removed, Ag(s) is oxidized by $Cu^{2+}(s)$ back to Ag^+.

The images on photographic film are permanent because further reduction of Ag^+ is prevented by "fixing," that is, removing undeveloped AgBr with sodium hyposulfite $(Na_2S_2O_3 \cdot 5H_2O)$:

$$AgBr(s) + 2S_2O_3^{2-}(aq) \longrightarrow Ag(S_2O_3)_2^{3-}(aq) + Br^-(aq)$$

The water-soluble ions are then washed away.

3. The standard reduction potential for $Ag^+ + e^- \longrightarrow Ag(s)$ is +0.80 V. Metal ion/metal couples with similar positive reduction potentials might be likely candidates. Referring to Appendix 2B, we see that mercury, gold, platinum, and copper seem to be theoretically possible; but there would be no price advantage with gold or platinum. These elements also share a common ability to form complex ions, which would aid in the fixing of the film. The solubility of the metal halides of mercury, gold, platinum, and copper should also be considered; more soluble salts would be washed away in the developing process.

CHAPTER 22

1. Positron emission results in a lowering of positive charge in the nucleus; that is, Z is decreased, and A/Z is increased. Consequently, isotopes that are below the band of stability are likely candidates for positron emission, because such emissions will move them in the direction of the band.

(a) $^{18}_{8}O$, $\dfrac{A}{Z} = 2.25 > \left(\dfrac{A}{Z}\right)_{band}$; therefore, not suitable

(b) $^{13}_{7}N$, $\dfrac{A}{Z} = 1.86 < \left(\dfrac{A}{Z}\right)_{band}$;

therefore, might be suitable: $^{13}_{7}N \longrightarrow {}^{0}_{1}e + {}^{13}_{6}C$

(c) $^{11}_{6}C$, $\dfrac{A}{Z} = 1.83 < \left(\dfrac{A}{Z}\right)_{band}$;

therefore, might be suitable: $^{11}_{6}C \longrightarrow {}^{0}_{1}e + {}^{11}_{5}B$

(d) $^{20}_{9}F$, $\dfrac{A}{Z} = 2.22 > \left(\dfrac{A}{Z}\right)_{band}$; therefore, not suitable

(e) $^{15}_{8}O$, $\dfrac{A}{Z} = 1.88 < \left(\dfrac{A}{Z}\right)_{band}$;

therefore, might be suitable: $^{15}_{8}O \longrightarrow {}^{0}_{1}e + {}^{15}_{7}N$

3. $^{98}_{42}Mo + {}^{1}_{0}n \longrightarrow {}^{99}_{42}Mo \longrightarrow {}^{99}_{43}Tc + {}^{0}_{-1}e$